Mathematics National 5

Curriculum for Excellence

Lifeskills

Written by the TeeJay Writing Group

This book forms the basis of a one or two-year course following the outcomes for National 5 Lifeskills as outlined by Education Scotland and the SQA.

- The assumption is that pupils embarking on this course will have been successful at National 4 or may have completed the National 4 Lifeskills course.
- The book covers the three Units, Numeracy, Geometry/Measure and Finance/Statistics in that order.
- Each Unit ends with a Specimen Unit Assessment.
- The book contains Revision Chapters A, B and C*, one before each of the three Units, which primarily revise all the relevant strands from National 4 Lifeskills as covered in our National 4 Lifeskills book.
- Each chapter has an Assessment exercise as a summary.
- There are no A and B exercises. The book covers the entire National 5 Lifeskills Course without the teacher having to pick and choose which questions to leave out and which exercises are important. They all are!
- Pupils who cope well with the contents of this National 5 Lifeskills book should be able to be assessed at various stages throughout the course and be ready to sit an end-of-unit or end-of-course assessment or examination.
- There is an End-of-Course Added Value Assessment Paper 1 and Paper 2.

Note 1* These 3 Revision Chapters are optional, but do provide a list of topics assumed to have been covered in National 4 or National 4 Lifeskills. Each topic is also met in the Review Exercises that precede each chapter.

Note 2 Use of calculators throughout the book has been left as discretionary, but certain exercises are specifically designated as "calculator free", particularly for those pupils being presented for the Added Value Assessment.

Acknowledgements

Every effort has been made to trace all copyright holders, but if any have been inadvertently overlooked, the Publishers will be pleased to make the necessary arrangements at the first opportunity.

Although every effort has been made to ensure that website addresses are correct at time of going to press, Hodder Gibson cannot be held responsible for the content of any website mentioned in this book. It is sometimes possible to find a relocated web page by typing in the address of the home page for a website in the URL window of your browser.

Hachette UK's policy is to use papers that are natural, renewable and recyclable products and made from wood grown in well-managed forests and other controlled sources. The logging and manufacturing processes are expected to conform to the environmental regulations of the country of origin.

Orders

Please contact Bookpoint Ltd, 130 Park Drive, Milton Park, Abingdon, Oxon OX14 4SE. Telephone: (44) 01235 827827. Fax: (44) 01235 400401.

Email education@bookpoint.co.uk

Lines are open from 9 a.m. to 5 p.m., Monday to Friday, with a 24-hour message answering service. You can also order through our website:

www.hoddergibson.co.uk

If you have queries or questions that aren't about an order you can contact us at hoddergibson@hodder.co.uk

The legal bit

First published in 2019 by
TeeJay Publishers, an imprint of Hodder Gibson, which is part of the Hodder Education Group.
An Hachette UK Company
211 St Vincent Street
Glasgow, G2 5QY

www.hoddergibson.co.uk

Impression number 10 9 8 7 6 5 4 3
Year 2023 2022 2021 2020

Cover design Fraser McKie
Printed in Spain

A catalogue record for this title is available from the British Library.

ISBN: 978 1 9077 8965 6

Index

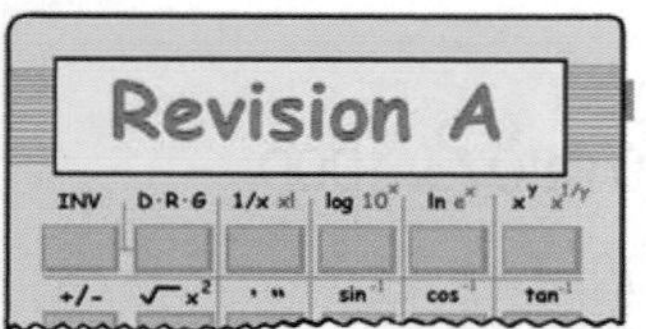

Numeracy Revision

(The following was covered in Nat 4 Lifeskills and should be known, though much of it will be revised later).

Whole Numbers

1. Round to the nearest whole number :- a 46·45 b 83·505.
2. Round to the nearest 10 :- a 145 b 974·8
3. Round to the nearest 100 :- a 1272 b 3990.
4. Round to the nearest 1000 :- a 18 469 b 125 512.
5. Round to 1 significant figure :- a 8594 b 99 999.
6. By rounding each number to 1 significant figure, find an **estimate** to :-

   a 187×42 b $18\,459 \div 38$ c 79×97.

7. Write down the answer to :-

   a 150×10 b 100×4040 c 6002×1000.

8. Find :-

   a 27×40 b 502×300 c 210×5000.

9. Find :-

   a $6900 \div 30$ b $45\,000 \div 200$ c $624\,000 \div 4000$.

10. During the month of June, 18 600 people crossed a stone bridge.

    How many people is that on average per day ?

Decimals

11. Round these numbers to **1 decimal place** :-

    a 3·56 b 39·93 c 20·75 d 0·749.

12. Round these numbers to **2 decimal places** :-

    a 6·384 b 23·397 c 0·865 d 0·0981.

13. Copy and work out the following :-

    a $2{\cdot}83 + 3{\cdot}56$ b $29{\cdot}73 - 8{\cdot}85$ c $0{\cdot}76 + 11{\cdot}4$ d $30 - 6{\cdot}09$.

14. Copy and find the answers to the following :-

    a $6{\cdot}7 \times 9$ b $7\overline{)52{\cdot}5}$ c $0{\cdot}98 \times 9$ d $6\overline{)9{\cdot}54}$.

15. Write down the answers to the following :-

a $6{\cdot}7 \times 10$ b $100 \times 0{\cdot}205$ c $0{\cdot}0807 \times 1000$

d $69{\cdot}1 \div 10$ e $100 \overline{)8{\cdot}35}$ f $\frac{1030}{1000}$.

16. To what number is the arrow pointing ?

17. Change :-

a 187 mm to cm b 13 cm to metres c 60 450 metres to km.

18. 10 copies of a book cost £70·50

a What will it cost for 1 copy ?

b What would 100 copies cost ?

Percentages

19. Write 67% as :- a a fraction b a decimal.

20. Write each of the following as a fraction and simplify as much as possible :-

a 80% b 35% c 24%.

21. Use your calculator to change each to a :- (i) decimal (ii) percentage :-

a $\frac{7}{20}$ b $\frac{19}{25}$ c $\frac{35}{40}$.

22. Derek scored in 34 out of 40 games last year. Write this as a percentage.

23. Work out the following :-

a 11% of £300 b 6% of £70 c 35% of £80 d $2\frac{1}{2}$% of £8000.

24. I decided to wait till January to buy a new £480 TV.

a How much could be saved in the January sale ?

b How much will a TV set cost in the sale ?

25. A farmer began to plough his 64 acres of farmland.

At the end of the first day, he had managed to plough 15% of his land.

a How many acres had he ploughed ?

b How many had he still to plough ?

26. 

Last October, our family holiday to Tenerife cost £3200.

This year, we found it has risen by 4%.

How much will it cost us this year ?

27. The *Federal Building Society* is offering interest of 1·5% per year.

If I invest £2400 in a savings account with *Federal* and leave it there for 1 year, how much interest will I be due, and how much will I have altogether in my savings account after a year ?

Fractions

28. Write down two fractions equivalent to the fraction $\frac{3}{5}$.

29. Simplify the following fractions :-

a $\frac{10}{15}$ b $\frac{28}{35}$ c $\frac{14}{98}$.

30. Find :- a $\frac{1}{3}$ of 108 g b $\frac{1}{5}$ of £3·50.

31. Find :- a $\frac{5}{6}$ of 2040 mm b $\frac{7}{8}$ of 144 kg.

32. 40 new lambs were born last year on McEwe's farm.

$\frac{5}{8}$ of them were sold at a market.

How many were left on the farm ?

33. What **fraction**, in its simplest form, is equivalent to :-

a 25% b 60% c 15% ?

34. Attempt the following without using a calculator :-

a 50% of £52 b 25% of £30 c 10% of £9·60

d $33\frac{1}{3}$% of 75p e 20% of £65 f 5% of £2400.

Time, Distance, Speed

35. A mill wheel rotates at a speed of 6 revolutions per minute.

How many times will it turn in one and a half hours ?

36.

A hot air balloon travels 15 miles from its take off point to where it lands.

It flew this distance in $1\frac{1}{4}$ hours.

What was the **average speed** of the balloon ?

37. A light Cessna plane flew for 275 miles at an average speed of 110 mph.

How long did it take, in hours and minutes ?

38. The ferry from Dover to Calais covers the 36 kilometres at an average speed of 24 km/hr.

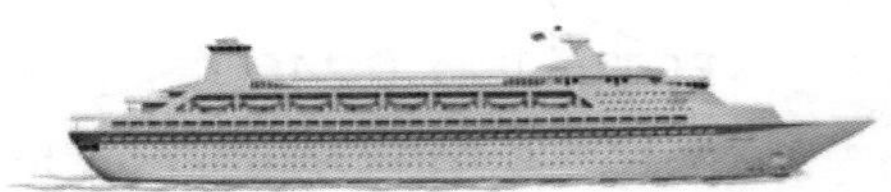

At what time (*local*) should the 1645 ferry reach Calais ?
(*Remember - Calais is 1 hour ahead of Britain*).

Area & Perimeter

39. Write down the area of this shape, in cm^2.

(*Each square is 1 cm by 1 cm*).

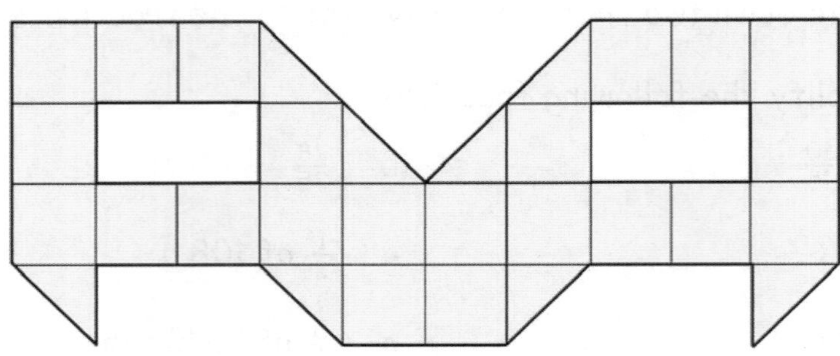

40. Calculate the area of each rectangle :-
(*Use the formula and show your working*).

a

9 cm

22 cm

b

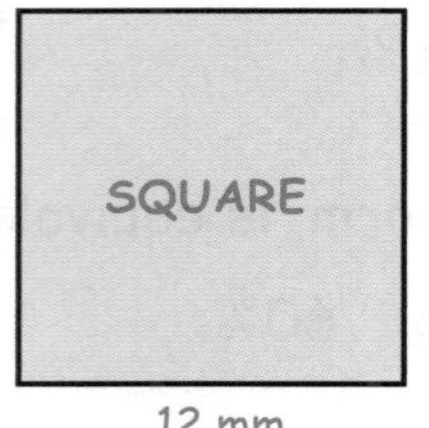

c

2·5 m

60 cm

41. Calculate the perimeter of these three shapes :-

a

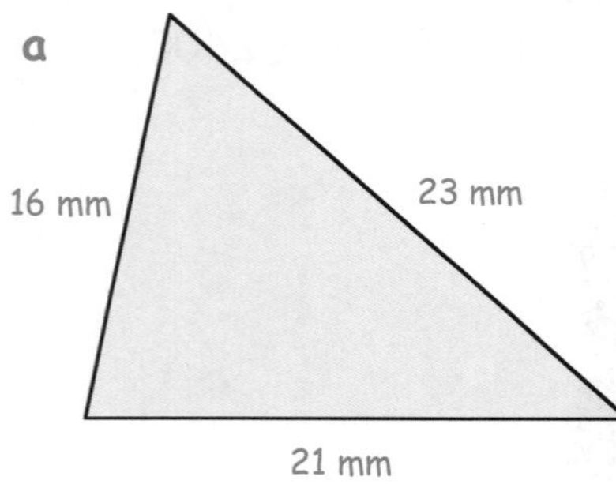

b

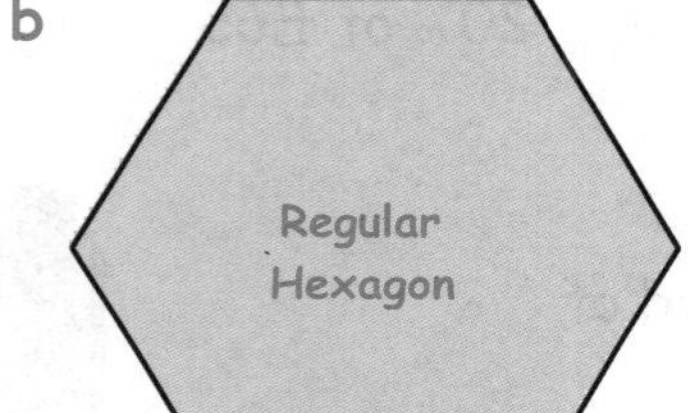

c

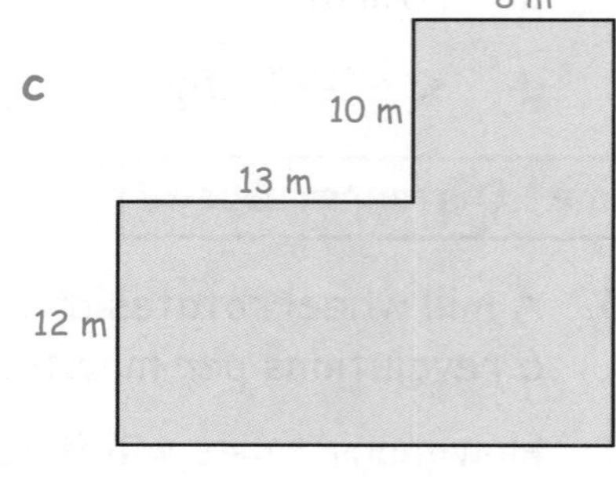

Integers

42. Write down the temperature shown on each thermometer, in °C :-

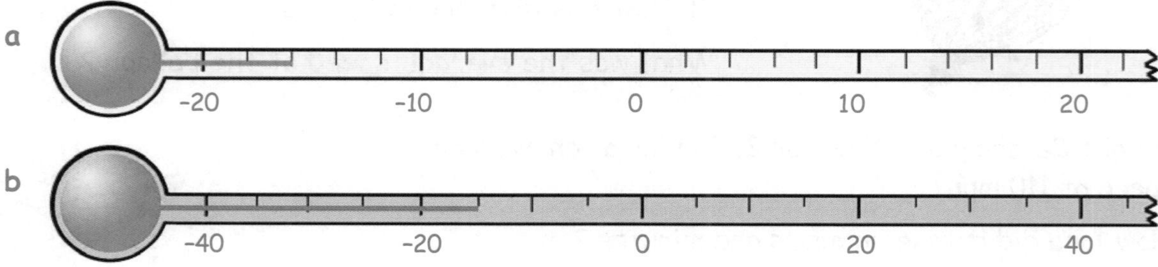

43. a Jak had an overdraft of £180 in his account, then his salary of £1350 was paid in.

What was Jak's new balance ?

b Near the end of the month, Tina's account read +£35·40.

She deposited a cheque for £96·80, then bought a pair of boots for £69·99, using her bank card.

What will Tina's bank balance read now ?

44. What is the temperature that is :-

a 10°C up from -7°C b 13°C down from -14°C c 35°C below 18°C ?

45. The temperature on the Moon varies from -233 Celsius on the dark side, to +123 Celsius in sunlight.

By how many degrees does it heat up going from dark to light ?

46. Find the following :-

a	6 - 11	b	(-2) + 8	c	(-12) + (-8)	d	9 - 20
e	(-6) - 7	f	(-53) - 47	g	(-90) + 75	h	(-65) + (-95).

47. Find :- a $9 + (-5) - 7$ b $(-35) + (-145) - 120$.

Ration & Proportion

48. In a golf bag, there are 3 woods and 9 irons.

Write down the ratio of woods to irons and simplify this ratio as far as possible.

49. Simplify the following ratios as far as possible :-

a	12 : 16	b	25 : 45	c	16 : 48	d	36 : 18
e	120 : 200	f	88 : 99	g	360 : 240	h	$1\frac{1}{2} : 6$.

50. In an estate, the ratio of houses with a conservatory to those without is 2 : 9.

There are 44 houses on the estate. How many of them have a conservatory ?

51. 

Mobiles 4 U only sell iPhones and Samsungs.

The ratio of Samsungs sold : iPhones sold is 5 : 4.

If in fact *Mobiles 4U* sold 20 iPhones one Saturday, how many phones must they have sold altogether ?

52. 

At *Glebe's the Bakers*, Joe bought 4 sausage rolls for £3·40.

His mate Billy bought 5 sausage rolls.

How much would Billy have paid ?

53. Beth played the "*Beastie Boys*" new single 3 times right through last night and it lasted 8 minutes and 30 seconds altogether.

How long will it take her tonight to listen to the single 5 times ?

Volume

54. Calculate the **volume** of this cuboid, in cm^3 :-

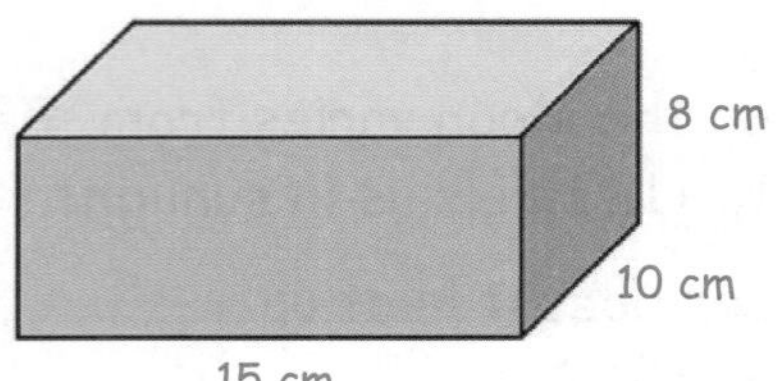

55. 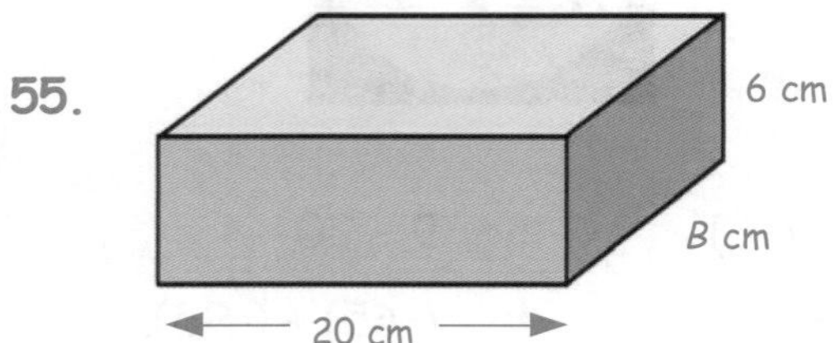

The volume of this cuboid is 960 cm^3.

Calculate its **breadth**.

56. Change to litres :- a 5500 ml b 950 ml c 40 ml.

57. Change to millilitres :- a 5·8 litres b 0·065 litres c $3\frac{1}{4}$ litres.

58. a Calculate the **volume** of water in this tank, in cm^3.

b How many millilitres of water can it hold ?

c How many litres is this ?

d When the tap is opened fully, water flows out of the tank at a rate of 3·5 litres per minute.

How long will it take for the tank to empty ?

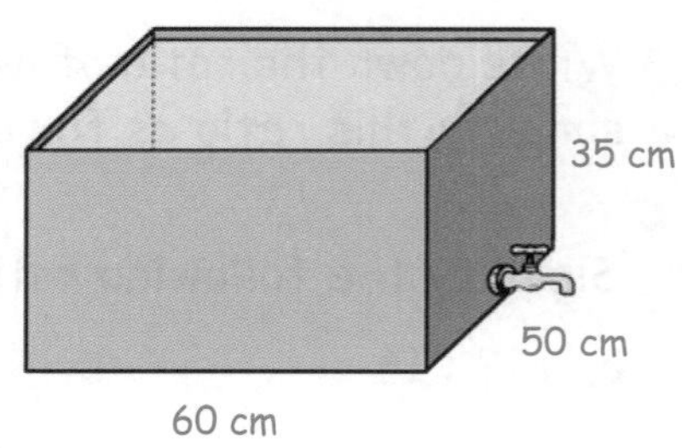

Probability

59. This 12-sided dice with faces numbered 1 to 12, is rolled.

What is the probability it will end up showing :-

a the number 7 b an even number

c **not** the number 12 d a number greater than 5 ?

60. A group of people was asked to say who their mobile phone contract was with. See opposite.

If I pick one person at random from the group, what is the probability the person :-

a is with S-Mobile

b is with FF or P3

c is **not** with Dovaphone ?

61. A jewellery box holds 4 platinum rings, 3 gold rings and 5 silver rings.

a If a lady chooses one at random, what is the probability it will be gold ?

b If it is gold, and she slips it on, what is the probability the next ring she chooses is also gold ?

Graphs, Charts & Tables

62. This bar graph shows the number of pairs of trainers sold in a large Edinburgh sports shop in 2015.

a How many Hike were sold ?

b How many Ted Berry were sold ?

c How many **more** BeeBok than Abibas were sold ?

d What **fraction** of the trainers sold were made by Lakissed ?

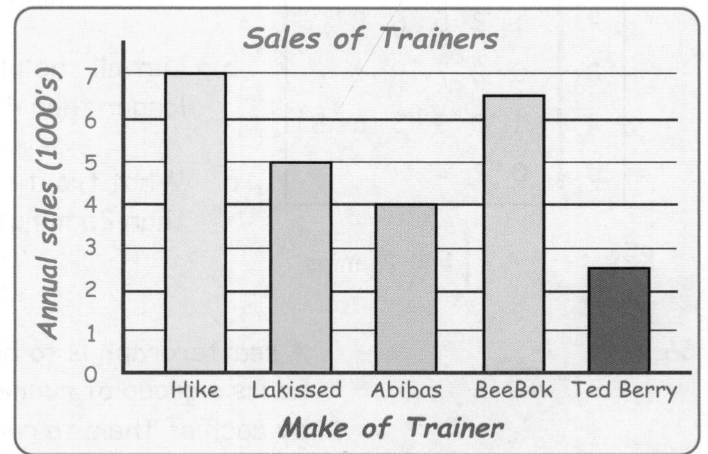

63. The line graph shows the altitude of an aircraft on its flight back from Tenerife to Glasgow.

a At what time did it take off ?

b How long did the flight take ?

c What was the plane's height at

(i) 1730 (ii) 2030 ?

d To avoid turbulence, the pilot took the plane up by 10 000 feet.

At what time did he do this ?

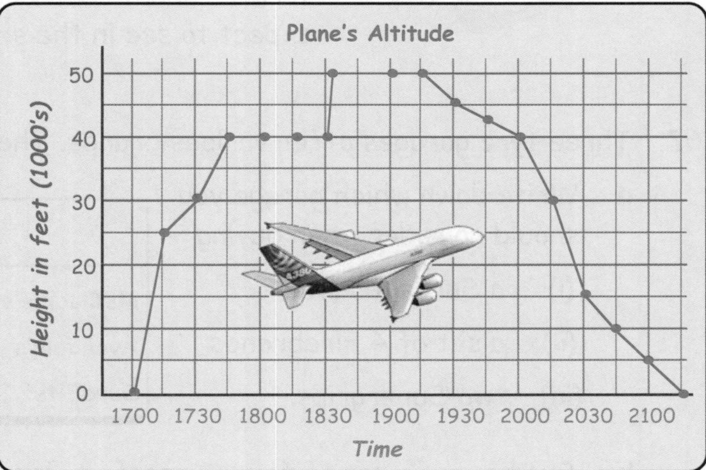

e Between which 2 times did the plane make its steepest descent ?

f The seatbelt sign came on 30 minutes before the plane landed. When was this ?

64. The pie chart shows how much time Navid, a professional gardener, spent gardening in an average week in summertime.

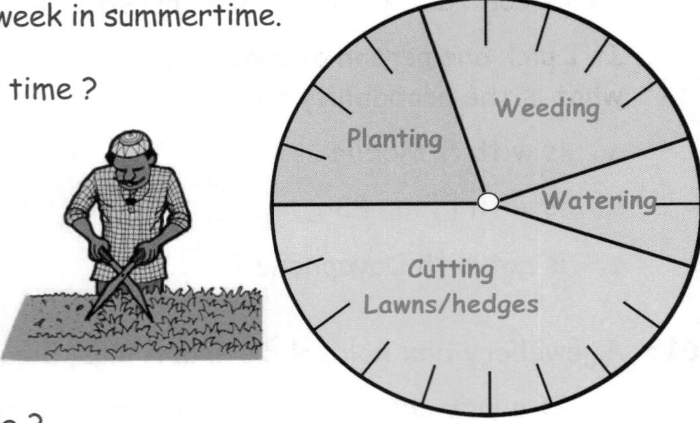

a What task takes up most of Navid's time ?

b What fraction of Navid's time is spent weeding gardens ?

c Navid worked 160 hours in total during the month of June.

How many hours did he spend :-

(i) Watering (ii) Planting ?

65.

Length of call (*minutes*)	
0	8
1	3 6
2	1 2 5 6 8
3	0 2 7 9
4	1 3 3 3 6 8
5	0 2

Key :- 2 | 1 = 21 mins

Lucy Jane checked her mobile phone to see how long each of her last 20 telephone calls had lasted, (*in minutes*).

a How many of Lucy Jane's calls lasted :-

(i) 50 minutes (ii) 43 minutes ?

b List all the phone calls that lasted longer than 45 minutes.

c What fraction of them lasted less than 25 minutes ?

66.

A scattergraph is to be constructed by plotting the number of hours a group of runners spend training, against the times taken by each of them to run in a 10 K charity race.

Write a short sentence explaining what connection you would expect to see in the scattergraph.

67. Three tyre garages offer various brands. The prices in the table include fitting.

a Write down which garage you should consider when buying :-

(i) a Suresafe tyre

(ii) a set of 4 Firebrands

(iii) two Supergrips.

	Firebrand	Supergrip	Suresafe
McCluchie's	£45·75	£52·25	£74·50
Avondale's	£48·00	£55·50	£69·75
SureFits	£39·75	£58·50	£72·00

b Sue bought a set of four Suresafe tyres from McClutchie's.

How much could she have saved altogether if she had shopped around these 3 suppliers for her set of Suresafe tyres ?

Number Work

Revision of Number Work

1. Round to the nearest whole number :-

   a 3·8 b 6·6 c 21·1 d 62·5
   e 17·49 f 102·51 g 245·199 h 207·508.

2. Round to the nearest 10 :-

   a 54 b 73 c 8 d 205
   e 319 f 995 g 8014 h 1005.

3. Round to the nearest 100 :-

   a 109 b 545 c 92 d 750
   e 4739 f 6250 g 1449 h 9975.

4. Round to the nearest 1000 :-

   a 2300 b 7900 c 6490 d 12 500
   e 82 199 f 110 700 g 225 497 h 109 999.

5. Round to 1 significant figure :-

   a 193 b 2199 c 19 500 d 250 001.

6. By rounding each number to 1 significant figure, find an estimate to :-

   a 19 x 21 b 13 x 69 c 196 x 98
   d 91 ÷ 29 e 307 ÷ 21 f 8943 ÷ 32.

7. Write down the answer to :-

   a 73 x 10 b 100 x 16 c 21 x 1000
   d 10 x 125 e 300 x 100 f 1000 x 450
   g 1101 x 10 h 100 x 801 i 610 x 1000.

8. Write down the answer to :-

   a 40 ÷ 10 b 800 ÷ 100 c 6000 ÷ 1000
   d 570 ÷ 10 e 6200 ÷ 100 f 35 000 ÷ 1000
   g 75 000 ÷ 10 h 39 800 ÷ 100 i 120 000 ÷ 1000.

9. Do the following, using the "two-step" method shown :-

a 28 x 20 (*Find 28 x 10 = 280 and then find 280 x 2*).

b	24 x 20	c	18 x 30	d	45 x 50
e	72 x 80	f	150 x 90	g	4120 x 40

h 15 x 300 (*Find 15 x 100 = 1500 and then find 1500 x 3*).

i	14 x 200	j	16 x 300	k	25 x 400
l	500 x 18	m	2000 x 35	n	15 x 5000.

10. Do the following divisions, using the "two-step" method shown :-

a 420 ÷ 20 (*Find 420 ÷ 10 = 42 and then find 42 ÷ 2*).

b	160 ÷ 20	c	270 ÷ 30	d	4500 ÷ 50
e	17 200 ÷ 40	f	23 100 ÷ 70	g	54 900 ÷ 90

h 13 200 ÷ 300 (*Find 13 200 ÷ 100 = 132 and then find 132 ÷ 3*).

i	6600 ÷ 200	j	3200 ÷ 400	k	21 500 ÷ 500
l	15 400 ÷ 200	m	56 700 ÷ 700	n	416 000 ÷ 800.

11. There are 1500 paper clips in one box.

If I ordered 20 boxes of them, how many paper clips would I have ?

12. The *Tea Shop* bought in 45 packs of tea bags.

Each pack contained 300 tea bags.

a How many tea bags had the shop bought ?

b Round your answer to the nearest thousand.

13. 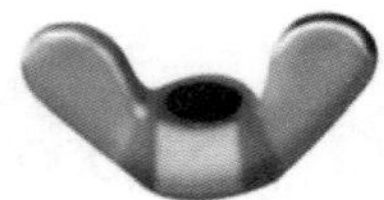

A factory turns out 13 200 wing nuts over a period of 60 hours.

How many nuts per hour does that work out at ?

14. Over a period of 30 days, *Ryanjet Airlines* carried 29 550 passengers.

How many passengers did that average out at per day ?

15. One of *Ryanjet's* pilots clocked up 138 000 miles over 400 hours flying time.

a How many miles did he fly per hour ?

b Round your answer to the nearest ten miles.

Number Work

Add, Subtract, Multiply & Divide

In the following exercise, you have to decide which mathematical operation to use - either +, −, x or ÷. Once you have decided, set down the working and calculate the answer.

A number that you may not be too familiar with is one billion .... **1 billion = 1000 million**

Discussion :- How many **zeros** in a :- (i) billion (ii) trillion (iii) quadrillion ?

Exercise 1

1. In a prize draw, for matching 5 numbers and a bonus ball, the prize money was £406 929.

   The prize money for matching 6 balls was four times that.

   a What was the prize money for matching six balls ?

   b Three people shared the prize for having 5 numbers and the bonus ball.

   How much did they each win ?

2. The voting in a council election went as follows :-

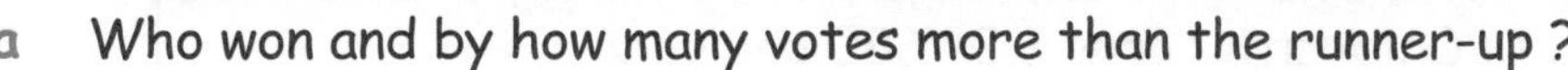
Jones - 26 497, Davis - 13 628, Murray - 6287, Wills - 28 103.

   a Who won and by how many votes more than the runner-up ?

   b It was noted that 18 485 people who were eligible to vote did not turn up to vote.

   How many people in total were registered to vote in that council ?

3. The number of supporters at Rovers' home games during this season was 751 120.

   Last season, the average attendance was 40 000 for each of the twenty games at home.

   By how much is this season's total attendance lower than last season ?

4. Mr Swallow is an editor of a newspaper. He gets an annual salary of £38 417.

   Miss Sims, the managing director of a wholesale firm, is paid treble that amount.

   What is her annual salary ?

5. Mr Baker lives in a house, valued at £200 000.

   To insure his house, he pays a premium of 85 pence for every £1000 his house is worth.

   How much, in pounds, does his house insurance cost him ?

6. For 2015-2016, NHS Scotland had an operational budget of £11·9 billion.

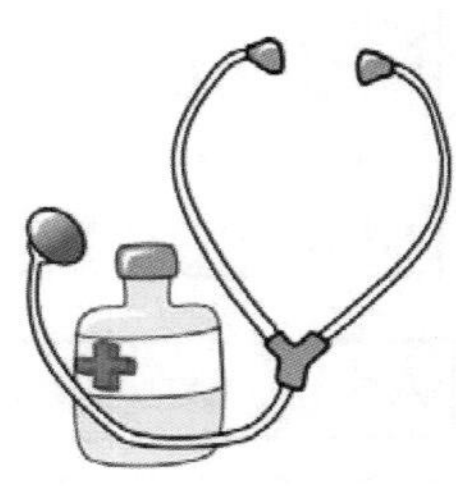

 a Write this amount out in millions of pounds.

 b This represented an increase of £0·55 billion from 2014-2015.

 What was the operational budget (in £million) in 2014-2015 ?

7. The UK National Debt grows at a rate of £5170 **per second**.

 How much would that be over a 1 hour period ?

8. In 2013-2014, the total amount of Council Tax billed in Scotland was £2·04 billion.

 Of this total, £1·942 billion was collected by the due date, 31st March 2014.

 How much tax had still to be collected ?

9. 

 The number of overseas visitors to Scotland in 2007 was 2·8 million.

 In 2013, the figure had dropped to 2·45 million.

 By how many thousands had the figure fallen ?

10. China's population was 1 355 692 576 in 2014.

 In the same year, the population of Pakistan was a seventh of that.

 What was the population of Pakistan ?

11. Miss Galbraith earns £24 680 per year.

 She is allowed £10 600 tax free, but pays one fifth of the remainder on income tax.

 How much is she left with after paying her tax ?

12. The table shows the average monthly exchange rates for British pounds to euros between Oct. 2014 and Mar. 2015.

 How many fewer euros would I have received if I had exchanged £500 when the exchange rate was at its lowest rather than its highest ?

£1 = ...

Oct. 2014	€1·277
Nov. 2014	€1·251
Dec. 2014	€1·266
Jan. 2015	€1·282
Feb. 2015	€1·346
Mar. 2015	€1·402

13. Calculate the following :- (*Remember :- **Bomdas***):-

 a 200 + 2 × 20 b 500 – 80 ÷ 4 c 5800 + 210 × 5

 d 6500 – 500 ÷ 5 e 400 + 30 × 4 – 75 f $\frac{1}{9}$ of 8910 + 110

 g 3460 – $\frac{1}{6}$ of 20 754 h 250 – $\frac{1}{3}$ of 180 + 190 i 8000 × 9 – 300 ÷ 4 + 1.

Integers - Focusing on Negative Numbers

Integers are made up of positive and negative whole numbers, and zero.

Negative numbers are commonly used in :-

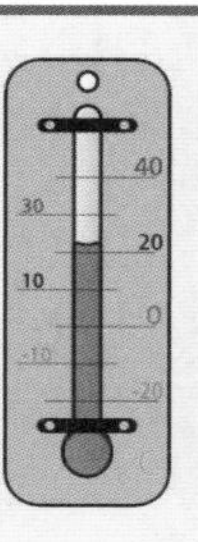

- Temperature - -6°C is 8 degrees below 2°C.
- Banking - A balance of –£50 means you are £50 overdrawn.
- Addition/Subtraction - -4 + 9 = 5 and (-6) - 5 + (-9) = -20.

Exercise 2

1. Write down the temperature shown on each thermometer :-

a 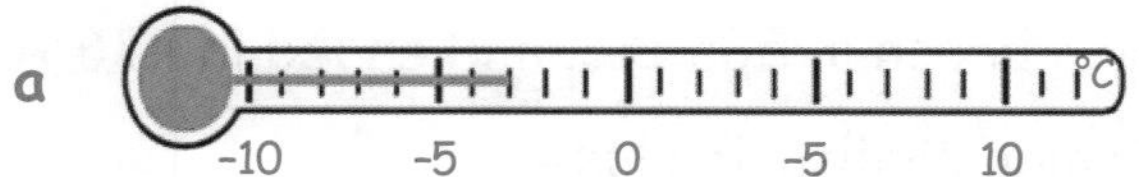

b 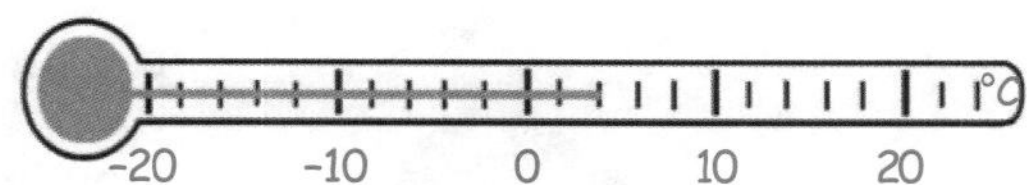

c 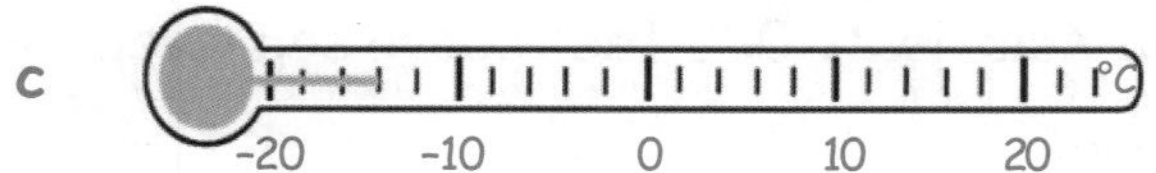

d 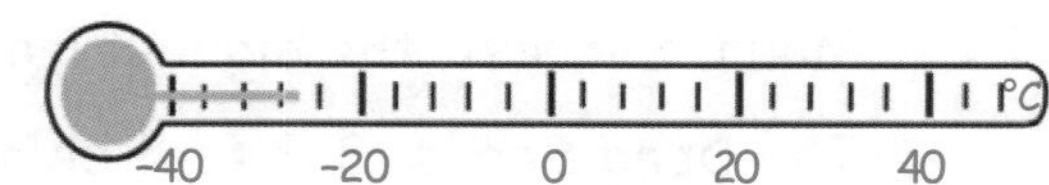

2. a Thomas had £60 in his bank account and withdrew £80.

   What was his new balance ?

   b Anna's bank account read as –£280.

   She deposited £310 and then paid a £150 gas bill.

   What will her bank balance read now ?

3. On 30th April, Joe's bank balance read –£340.

   a Describe "a balance of -£340" another way.

   His monthly salary of £1235 was paid in the next day and Joe then used his debit card to pay £112 for his monthly rail card.

   b Write down Joe's new bank balance.

4. What is the temperature that is :-

   a 12°C up from 2°C
   b 9°C up from –3°C
   c 4°C down from –6°C
   d 15°C down from 18°C
   e 20°C above –14°C
   f 20°C below –5°C
   g 7°C above –26°C
   h 16°C below –16°C ?

5. a In London, the temperature was -4°C.

In Aberdeen, it was 17° colder.

What was the temperature in Aberdeen ?

b 

On holiday in Canada, the temperature at noon was 19°C.

By midnight, the temperature had dropped by 31°C.

What was the temperature at midnight ?

c A submarine was situated 800 feet below sea level.

Its engines started up and it climbed 290 feet.

What was its new position ?

d 

Roman civilisation began in 509 B.C. and ended in 476 A.D..

How long did Roman civilisation last ?

e Mount Everest, the highest mountain in Asia, is 29 028 feet above sea level.

The Dead Sea is 1312 feet below sea level.

What is the difference between these two elevations ?

f 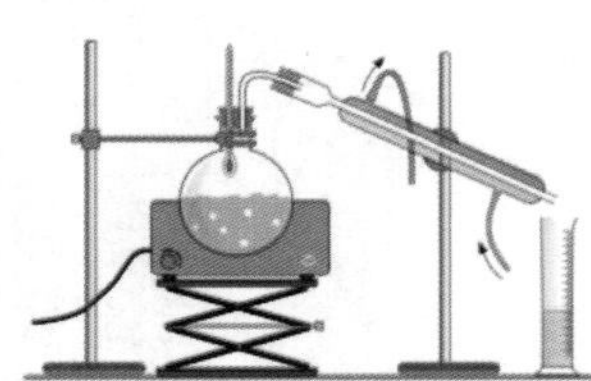

Metal mercury at room temperature is a liquid.

Its melting point is -39°C.

The freezing point of alcohol is -114°C.

How much warmer is the melting point of mercury than the freezing point of alcohol ?

6. Work out the following :-

a	3 - 7	b	1 + (-5)	c	12 - 18	d	(-6) + 9
e	-5 + (-5)	f	-11 - 3	g	(-7) - 7	h	(-15) + (-15)
i	-45 + 45	j	0 - 210	k	0 + (-77)	l	(-18) + (-13)
m	85 + (-80)	n	(-180) + 70	o	(-222) + 22	p	(-6) - 32
q	120 + (-90)	r	(-1000) + 2500	s	(-1000) - 250	t	155 - 196.

7. Find :-

a	2 + (-1) + 5	b	5 + (-3) + 7	c	7 + (-2) - 5
d	10 + (-5) - 7	e	(-4) + (-8) + 12	f	(-3) + (-5) - 2
g	(-9) + 11 - 3	h	(-9) + (-11) + 3	i	85 + (-91) + (-94).

Number Work

Numeracy Assessment 1

1. Mr Wilson wrote a cheque for £910 for his new dining room suite.

   This included a discount from the company he bought it from.

   The table was priced £385 and the 6 chairs were priced at £185 per pair.

   How much of a discount did he receive ?

2. In a local election, Harris, with 14 789 votes was beaten into second place by Williams, who polled 1467 votes more.

   Jackson came third, 4728 votes behind Williams.

   How many people voted for Jackson ?

3. The table shows the average monthly exchange rates for British pounds to U.S. dollars between October 2014 and March 2015.

   How many more dollars would I have received if I had exchanged £3000 when the exchange rate was at its highest rather than at its lowest ?

Dollars to £1.

Oct. 2014	1·595
Nov. 2014	1·597
Dec. 2014	1·556
Jan. 2015	1·507
Feb. 2015	1·495
Mar. 2015	1·488

4. The net expenditure on education in 2013-2014 was £4·60 billion.

   £1·77 billion went on primary education, £1·87 billion on secondary education with the remainder being spent on nursery, special and community education.

   Write out that remaining amount in millions of pounds.

5. The UK spends £1·7 billion on health care every 5 days.

   How much is that per day, to the nearest £1000 ?

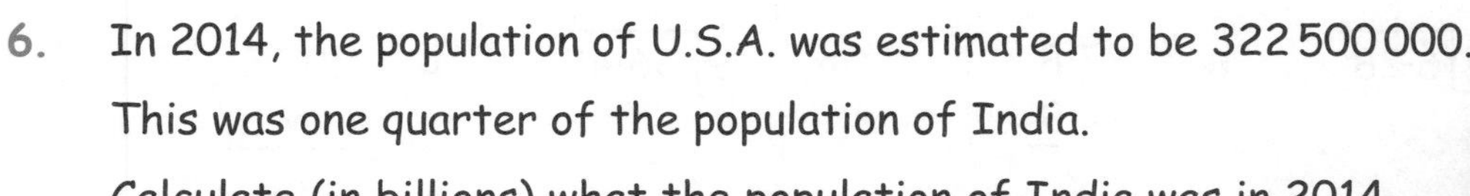

6. In 2014, the population of U.S.A. was estimated to be 322 500 000.

   This was one quarter of the population of India.

   Calculate (in billions) what the population of India was in 2014.

7. Calculate :-

a	2700 + 280 × 5	b	8293 – 744 ÷ 8	c	700 + 25 × 7 – 175
d	$\frac{1}{4}$ of 25 160 + 1710	e	10 000 – $\frac{1}{3}$ of 22 425	f	$\frac{1}{5}$ of (8972 – 3247)
g	–110 + (–90)	h	–475 + 325	i	324 – 387
j	(–19) + 21 – 13	k	(–45) + (–27) + 63	l	185 + (–191) + (–194).

Decimals

Revision of Decimals

1. This stands for 1

What number does this stand for ?

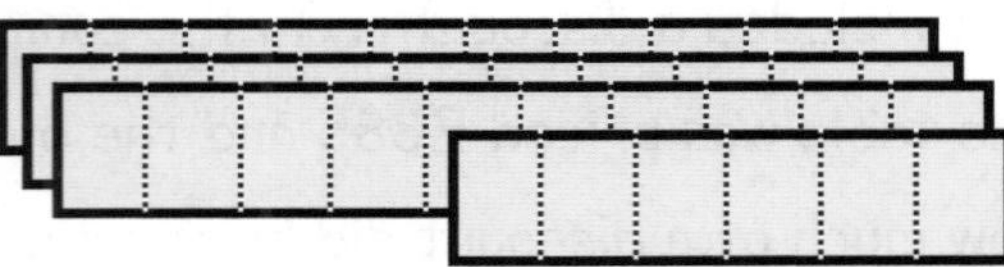

2. Round these numbers to 1 decimal place :-

a 8·17	b 9·93	c 32·05	d 0·84
e 158·91	f 62·71	g 70·19	h 99·99.

3. Round these numbers to 2 decimal places :-

a 7·183	b 11·706	c 0·876	d 9·927
e 0·0874	f 16·555	g 0·1007	h 99·999.

4. Copy and work out the following :-

a 5·14 + 2·63

b 13·78 + 1·56

c 49·14 − 7·02

d 137·67 − 86·79

e 0·93 + 9·2

f 31 − 8·06

g 137·88 + 5·7

h 234·7 − 23·712.

i 8·3 × 6

j $6 \overline{)31{\cdot}8}$

k 0·89 × 8

l $7 \overline{)11{\cdot}06}$

m $100 \overline{)6{\cdot}28}$

n 37·8 × 9

o $9 \overline{)36{\cdot}45}$

p 107·5 × 8

5. Write down the answers to the following :-

a 8·91 × 10	b 100 × 6·114	c 0·0234 × 1000
d 731·1 ÷ 10	e 71·09 ÷ 100	f $\frac{63}{100}$
g 14·014 × 100	h $\frac{729}{1000}$	i 0·007 ÷ 1000.

6. What numbers are the arrows pointing to ?

a

b

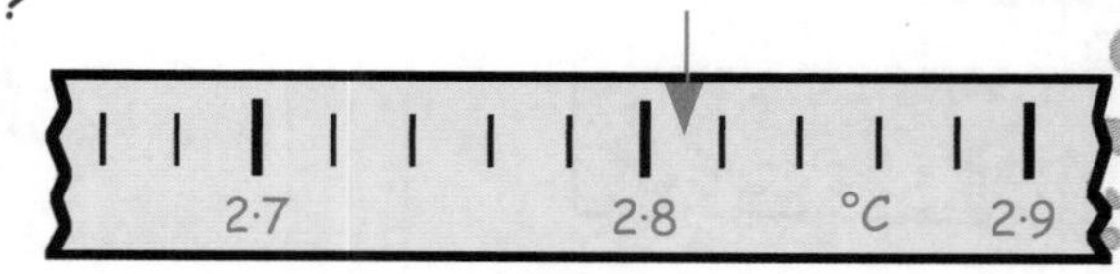

c

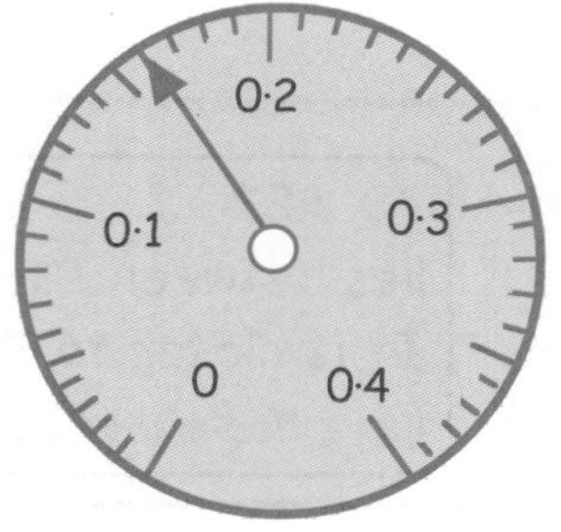

d

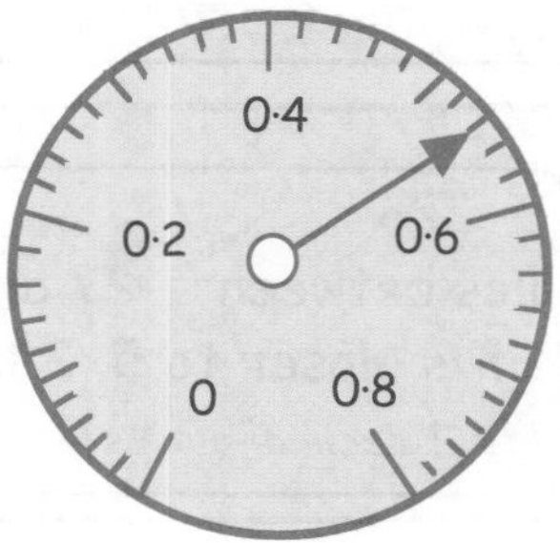

7. Change :-

a	75 mm to cm	b	82 cm to metres	c	5800 metres to km
d	4 km to cm	e	18 m to mm	f	1 km to mm.

8. a Four parcels weighing 6·7 kg, 8·21 kg, 9·08 kg and 11·75 kg are placed on a scale.

What will the reading be on the scale ?

b Three packages on a scale read 112·72 kg.

One package is removed and the scale reads 84·09 kg.

What was the weight of the package that was removed ?

9. a

The total weight of a set of six chairs is 116·4 kg.

What is the weight of each chair ?

b Nine marble tables, each weighing 272 kg, are to be transported in a van from the depot to a warehouse.

If the van can carry a maximum of one tonne, how many trips will the van have to make ?

10. A sheet of tracing paper weighs 0·04 g.

- There are 100 sheets in a packet, which weighs 4 grams.
- There are 100 packets in a box, which weighs 150 grams.
- There are 100 boxes in a crate.
- An empty crate weighs 0·01 tonnes.

What is the total weight of a crate full of tracing paper :-

a	in grams	b	in kilograms	c	in tonnes ?

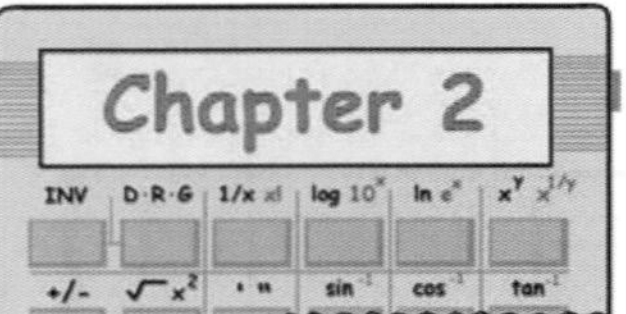

Decimals

Rounding to 1, 2 or 3 Decimal Places

Example 1 :- 5·276
lies between 5·27 and 5·28
It is closer to 5·28,
(*to 2 decimal places*).

Example 2 :- 73·482
lies between 73·48 and 73·49
It is closer to 73·48,
(*to 2 decimal places*).

Exercise 1

1. Copy and complete these statements :-

   a 7·287 lies between 7·28 and 7·2 ... It is closer to ... to 2 decimal places

   b 14·548 lies between ... and ... It is closer to ... to 2 decimal places

   c 20·184 lies between ... and ... It is closer to ... to 2 decimal places.

2. Which of the two numbers in the brackets gives the correct answer when the number is rounded to 2 decimal places :-

   a 6·341 (6·34 or 6·35) b 36·047 (36·04 or 36·05)

   c 10·296 (10·29 or 10·30) d 1·006 (1·00 or 1·01) ?

To round "longer" numbers like <u>4·76243</u> to <u>3</u> decimal places :-

Step 1 – note that it lies between 4·762 and 4·763

Step 2 – say which number it is closer to —> 4·762.

3. Round these numbers to 3 decimal places, using this method :-

   a 1·28512 —> 1·2... b 2·97254 —> c 5·32865 —>

   d 6·18633 —> e 9·92166 —> f 8·04034 —>

4. 6·998 rounded to 1 decimal place is 7. Explain what is wrong with this.

5. Round each number to the number of decimal places shown in the bracket :-

   a 6·8765 (2) b 10·99999 (1) c 5·9876 (3)

   d 12·65465 (2) e 11·000099 (2) f 9·991111 (2)

   g 0·0555 (2) h 317·1455 (3) i 1·999999 (4).

Rounding using Significant Figures

In mathematics, a figure or digit in a number is "**significant**" if it gives some sense of **Quantity & Accuracy**.

Examples :-

8361 rounded to 1 significant figure	=>	8000
13 342 rounded to 3 significant figures	=>	13 300
4·5568 rounded to 3 significant figures	=>	4·56
0·007 7912 rounded to 2 significant figures	=>	0·0078

Exercise 2

1. Round each number to 1 significant figure :-

a	67	b	742	c	6118	d	56 297
e	4298	f	3467	g	7·54	h	0·046
i	0·456	j	0·0099	k	0·000 642	l	39·21.

2. Round each number to 2 significant figures :-

a	607	b	5124	c	30 701	d	653 761
e	46·68	f	36·54	g	9·276	h	0·123
i	0·587	j	0·006 647	k	0·044 55	l	99·512.

3. Round each number to 3 significant figures :-

a	7654	b	55 066	c	99 754	d	345 199
e	8·234	f	77·934	g	0·534 456	h	0·876 534
i	0·001 541	j	0·010 67	k	0·055 66	l	0·099 999.

4. a Find the weight of 56 books if each book weighs 0·85 kilograms. (*Give your answer to 2 significant figures*).

   b What is the total volume, in millilitres, of 37 bottles of juice each containing 1·25 litres ? (*Give your answer to 3 sig. figs*).

5. a A doll weighs 1·63 kg. Find the weight of 45 dolls, to 2 significant figures.

   b A chemist's beaker holds 180·7 millilitres of liquid.

   Find to one significant figure, how many millilitres 24 beakers would hold.

Using the 4 Operators (+ - x ÷) with Decimals

Add and Subtract Decimal Numbers

Example 1 :- To find 18·74 + 5·68

=> 18·74
 + 5·68
 = 24·42

line up

Make sure the decimal points are always beneath each other.

Example 2 :- To find 45·6 - 22·33

=> 45·60
 - 22·33
 = 23·27

note (Adding 0's often helps).

line up

Exercise 3

1. Set these down and find the answers :-

a	21·65 + 7·99	b	56·7 + 29·37	c	67·64 - 18·37
d	19·27 - 6·58	e	73·01 - 48·02	f	92·52 + 62·3
g	35·1 - 0·27	h	62 - 32·93	i	100 - 87·738.

Multiplying and Dividing Decimals Numbers

Example 3 :- To find 7·38 x 9

 7·38
 x 9
 66·42

remember the point

It helps to copy the decimal point straight down from where it is.

Example 4 :- To find :- 25·76 ÷ 7

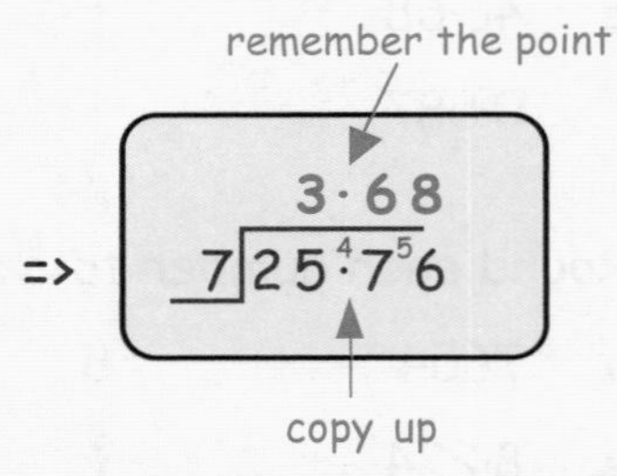

2. Set these down and find the answers :-

a	21·74 x 4	b	10·87 x 7	c	8 x 11·98
d	2 ⟌ 14·86	e	5 ⟌ 29·35	f	7 ⟌ 37·94
g	11·75 ÷ 5	h	50·47 ÷ 7	i	123·004 ÷ 4
j	161·81 x 9	k	1·76 x 3 x 4	l	0·708 x 7 x 8
m	15 ÷ 2	n	30 ÷ 8	o	$\frac{51}{4}$.

Multiplying & Dividing Decimals by 10, 100, 1000

Example 1 :- To find $2 \cdot 79 \times 10$

=>

```
  2·79
   x10
 27·9
```

move all the figures
1 place left

Example 2 :- To find $25 \cdot 9 \div 10$

=>

```
      2·59
 10 | 25·9
```

move all the figures
1 place to the right

RULES for multiplying decimals

× 10	move all figures 1 place **left**
× 100	move all figures 2 places **left**
× 1000	move all figures 3 places **left**

RULES for dividing decimals

÷ 10	move all figures 1 place **right**
÷ 100	move all figures 2 places **right**
÷ 1000	move all figures 3 places **right**

Exercise 4

1. Copy these down and find the following :-

   a $8{\cdot}41 \times 10$ b $3{\cdot}129 \times 100$ c $0{\cdot}851 \times 1000$ d $0{\cdot}79 \times 1000$

   e $4{\cdot}1 \times 10$ f $31{\cdot}801 \times 100$ g $0{\cdot}87 \times 100$ h $1{\cdot}01 \times 1000$.

2. Copy and find the following :-

   a 10 ⟌ 5·8 b 100 ⟌ 42·1 c 100 ⟌ 357 d 1000 ⟌ 357

   e $47{\cdot}1 \div 10$ f $3{\cdot}001 \div 100$ g $18{\cdot}1 \div 1000$ h $3 \div 1000$.

3. A bottle holds 1·15 litres of apple juice.
   How many litres are there in :- a 10 bottles b 1000 bottles ?

4. One thousand pencils are laid end to end and have a total length of 140 metres.
   Find the length of each pencil in :- a metres b millimetres.

Multiplying & Dividing Decimals by Multiples of 10, 100, 1000

Example 1 :-

To multiply 7·64 x 20

Step 1 Find 7·64 x 10 = 76·4

Step 2 Now find 76·4 x 2 = 152·8

Example 2 :-

To multiply 1·182 x 400

Step 1 Find 1·182 x 100 = 118·2

Step 2 Now find 118·2 x 4 = 472·8

Example 3 :-

To divide 1·95 ÷ 30

Step 1 Divide by 10 first = 0·195

Step 2 Now divide by 3 $\frac{0 \cdot 195}{3}$

$$3 \overline{)0 \cdot 1^{1}9^{1}5} = 0 \cdot 065$$

Exercise 5

1. Calculate each of these, using the same method shown above :-

   a 4·23 x 20 (*Find 10 x 4·23 first = 42·3 and then find 42·3 x 2*).

   b 1·97 x 30 c 12·1 x 500 d 0·308 x 600

   e 4·005 x 8000 f 1·24 x 500 g 0·135 x 4000

   h 0·076 x 9000 i 700 x 1·002 j 0·00095 x 3000.

2. Divide the following :-

   a 182·4 ÷ 20 (Find *182·4 ÷ 10 = 18·24 and then divide 18·24 by 2*).

   b 21·9 ÷ 30 c 16·8 ÷ 400 d 3200 ÷ 2000

   e 16·84 ÷ 400 f 2·4 ÷ 5000 g 181·8 ÷ 900

   h 246·804 ÷ 400 i 500·05 ÷ 5000 j 72 ÷ 8000.

3. Each box in a truck weighs 4·21 kg.

   What would be the weight of :-

   a 200 boxes b 6000 boxes ?

4. 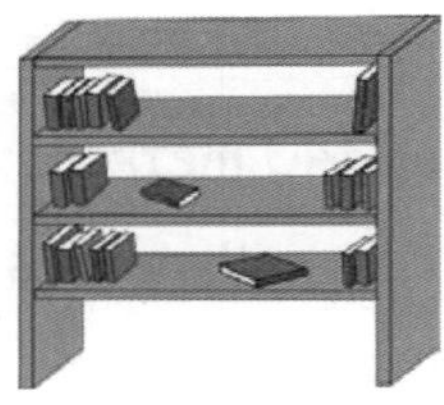

   The width of 400 books on a shelf is 5·32 metres.

   What is the average width of 1 book :-

   a in metres b in millimetres ?

Exercise 6 *Problem Solving*

1. Jessica ran three marathons last year.

   Her times were 4·75 hours, 5·2 hours and 4·36 hours.

   a What was her combined time for all 3 races ?
   (*Give your answer to one decimal place*).

   b What was her average time ?
   (*Give your answer to two significant figures*).

2. In a four by 100 metre relay race, the four runners ran the following times :-

   12·625 secs, 13·07 secs, 12·066 secs, 11·872 secs.

   a What was their total running time for the team ?
   (*Give your answer to two decimal places*).

   b What was the difference between the fastest and slowest runner in the team ?
   (*Give your answer to two significant figures.*).

3. 

   Charlie does 20 laps of a karting track.

   His average lap time is 34·76 secs.

   a What was his total time for the 20 laps ?
   (*Give your answer to one significant figure*).

   b Jake's total time for 20 laps is 704·84 seconds.

   Who has the better time, and by how much ?
   (*Give your answer to one decimal place*).

4. In a 1600 m race, Team GB timed 4:03·62. This reads as 4 minutes and 3·62 seconds.

   Other teams recorded the following times :-

   Germany - 4:01·7 Italy - 4:10·35

   Kenya - 3:57·04 USA - 3:39·17.

   a Who won and by how many seconds did they beat second place ?
   (*Give your answer to one decimal place*).

   b By how many seconds was the winner in front of last place.
   (*Give your answer to two significant figures*).

5. A particle in the *Hadron Collider* covers the 27 km round trip in 0·0000909 seconds.

   a How long will it take to go round one million times ?

   b ***Difficult - you will need a calculator.***
   How many times (*to 2 significant figures*) will it go round in one second ?

Decimals

Numeracy Assessment 2

1. Round each number to the number of decimal places shown in the bracket :-

a	5·8146	(2)	b	9·99999	(1)	c	0·45678	(3)
d	10·13465	(2)	e	11·099	(2)	f	9·995555	(4).

2. Round 3·65455 to :-

a	1 significant figure	b	2 significant figures	c	3 sig. figs.

3. Find :-

a	37·84 x 7	b	31·6 ÷ 4	c	10·8765 x 1000
d	0·13 ÷ 100	e	15·565 ÷ 50	f	0·762 x 700.

4. Alice has a party punch bowl that can hold 11 litres of liquid.

She fills the bowl with 4·15 litres of apple juice, 3·1 litres of strawberry juice, 2·65 litres of lemonade and some ginger beer.

How much ginger beer can she put into the bowl ?

5. 

At a javelin competition, Jason tripped and only threw 4·65 metres.

Sara threw 8 times this distance.

Jack threw a third of Sara's length.

What was Jack's recorded throw ?

6. The *Hubble Telescope* records three new planets.

- *Planet A* is 4·7036 light years away from Earth.
- *Planet B* is 300 times this distance from Earth.
- *Planet C* is a fortieth of the distance of Planet B.

How far is Planet C from Earth ?
(*Give your answer to 4 significant figures*).

7. Three runners' race times were recorded, in minutes and seconds, as :-

Briggs - 1 : 14·73, Huntly - 1 : 21·98, Martin - 0 : 58·8.

What was the time difference between the fastest and the slowest times ?

Percentages

Revision of Percentages

1. Write 47% as :- a a fraction b a decimal.

2. Write 9% as :- a a fraction b a decimal.

3. Write each of the following as a fraction and simplify as far as possible :-

a	15%	b	26%	c	84%
d	25%	e	8%	f	70%.

4. Use your calculator to change each of the following fractions to a :-

(i) decimal (ii) percentage :-

a	$\frac{9}{20}$	b	$\frac{1}{25}$	c	$\frac{12}{100}$
d	$\frac{7}{8}$	e	$\frac{13}{40}$	f	$\frac{13}{16}$.

5. Michael scored 58 out of 80 in a Science Test.
Write his score as a percentage.

6. Cheryl went on holiday to the Isle of Skye for 15 days.
It rained on six days out of the fifteen.
What percentage of her holiday did she get dry weather ?

7. Work out the following :-

a	12% of £40	b	5% of £10
c	33% of £70	d	45% of £120
e	58% of £300	f	14% of £500
g	92% of £1000	h	75% of £6
i	25% of £3·20	j	4% of £1200
k	$12\frac{1}{2}$% of £80	l	$2\frac{1}{2}$% of £500
m	$7\frac{1}{2}$% of £2400	n	2% of £4500.

8. Of the 380 pupils in Rose Street Primary, 45% are boys.

a How many boys are there ?

b How many girls are there ?

9. 

Games consoles normally cost £390 at *CheapGame*.

a How much could be saved in the Autumn sale ?

b How much will a console cost in the sale ?

10. A video game usually costs £45 at *CheapGame*.

What will the Autumn sale price of a video game be ?

11. A weekend in Rome was priced at £450. It has risen by 8%.

What is the new cost of the holiday ?

12. This *Apple* computer was priced at £990 last December.

Six months later, its value had fallen by 35%.

What was the new cost ?

13. Charlie managed a top speed of 20 miles per hour on his old bike.

On his new bike, he has upped his top speed by 15%.

What is his new top speed ?

14. 

This pair of trainers usually costs £85.

The price dropped by 45% in an online sale.

What was their new price ?

15. 12·8 centimetres of snow fell one night.

By lunchtime the following day, 25% of it had melted.

What was the depth of the remaining snow ?

16. *Clydeside Bank* is offering interest at $\frac{1}{2}$% per year. *Forth Bank's* rate is 0·85%.

Frank puts £1500 in the *Clydeside Bank* and Sandra puts £900 in the *Forth Bank*.

How much more interest will Sandra receive than Frank when they both close their accounts at the end of the year ?

Percentages

Percentages, Decimals & Fractions

By now, you should be able to find a percentage of a quantity using a calculator :-

Example :-

19% of £400 = $\frac{19}{100}$ x 400

= (19 ÷ 100) x 400 = £76

You should also be able to work out certain percentage calculations **MENTALLY**.

Examples :-

50% of 98p means a half of 98p (=> ÷ 2)

$33\frac{1}{3}$% of 240 mm means a third of 240 mm (=> ÷ 3)

75% of £12 means three quarters of £12 (=> ÷ 4 then x 3)

40% of 30 grams means two fifths of 30 grams (=> ÷ 5 then x 2)

Exercise 1

1. Copy and complete both tables :-

Percentage	50	25	75	$33\frac{1}{3}$	$66\frac{2}{3}$
Fraction	$\frac{1}{2}$				

Percentage	20	40	60	80	10	30	70	90
Fraction	$\frac{1}{5}$						$\frac{7}{10}$	

2. Find the following, **without** using a calculator :-

a 10% of £42
b 70% of £430
c 20% of £2·60
d 80% of 70p
e 25% of £612
f $33\frac{1}{3}$% of £63
g 75% of £18
h 1% of £3240
i 30% of £6000
j 50% of £42 700
k 40% of £910
l 10% of 20p
m $66\frac{2}{3}$% of £150
n 90% of 60p
o 2·5% of £80.

3. 60% of the dentists' patients are attending today for a check up.
If 180 appointments have been made altogether for the day, how many are **not** there for a check up ?

4. $33\frac{1}{3}$% of the birds in an aviary are cockateels, 25% are budgies and the rest of them are finches.

If there are 72 birds in the aviary, how many are :-

a cockateels b budgies c finches ?

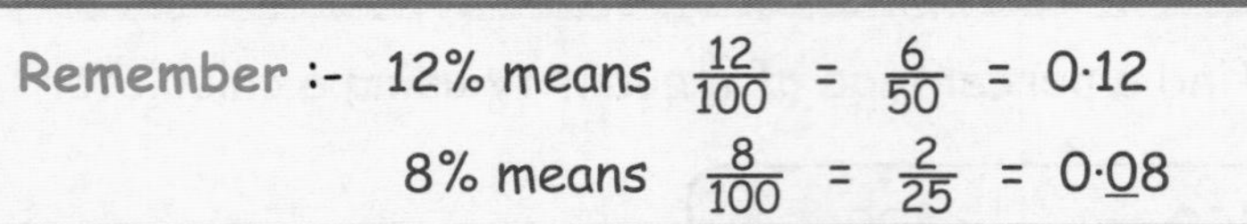

Remember :- 12% means $\frac{12}{100} = \frac{6}{50} = 0{\cdot}12$

8% means $\frac{8}{100} = \frac{2}{25} = 0{\cdot}\underline{0}8$

5. Write each of the following as a simplified fraction and as a decimal :-

a 36% b 65% c 21% d 74%

e 88% f 6% g 12·5% h 2·5%.

6. Use your calculator to find the following :-

a 9% of £50 = (9 ÷ 100) x 50 = £......

b 12% of £70 c 38% of £50 d 54% of £180

e 76% of £24 f 83% of £2000 g 95% of £8

h 7% of £34 i 3% of £9 j $4\frac{1}{2}$% of £500.

7. During a storm, the level of rain that ran into a barrel outside my back door was 120 mm.

Even when the heavy rain eased, the water level rose by another 15%.

What was the total level of rain water in the barrel ?

8. Abonshire Council decided to increase council tax by 1·5% this year.

The Frame family who live in that county, paid council tax totalling £1600 last year.

What should they expect to be paying this year ?

9. 

A jacket, normally £250, is reduced by 12% in a sale.

What will the sale price of the jacket be ?

10. The *Scotia Bank* is offering 2·2% interest per year on a savings bond.

Jenny puts £2400 into the bond.

a How much interest is Jenny due if she leaves her savings there for 6 months ?

b How much will her bond be worth after 6 months ?

Expressing One Number as a Percentage of Another

In many instances, you will be asked to express one number as a percentage of another one.

The process is quite simple and can be done using 3 steps as follows :-

Example :- Joe scored 23 out of 25 in his numeracy test.

=> To find what 23 is, as a percentage of 25 :-

- write 23 as a fraction of 25 => $\frac{23}{25}$
- now do the "division" => 23 ÷ 25 = 0·92
- finally, multiply this decimal by 100 => 0·92 x 100 = 92%

These 3 steps are used to show how to express one number as a percentage of another.

Exercise 2

1. Copy the following and use your calculator to change each fraction to a percentage :-

a $\frac{3}{50}$ = 3 ÷ 50 = 0·..... = (0·.... x 100%) = ... %

b $\frac{2}{5}$ = 2 ÷ 5 = 0·..... = (0·.... x 100%) = ...%

c $\frac{14}{50}$ d $\frac{18}{25}$ e $\frac{7}{20}$ f $\frac{19}{20}$ g $\frac{21}{25}$ h $\frac{3}{8}$

i $\frac{6}{25}$ j $\frac{7}{8}$ k $\frac{50}{80}$ l $\frac{30}{40}$ m $\frac{12}{48}$ n $\frac{38}{76}$.

2. Change each of these marks to percentages :-

a Josh scored 36 out of 40 ($\frac{36}{40}$) => 36 ÷ 40 = 0· ..... x 100% = ... %.

b Mary scored 19 out of 50

c Rob scored 50 out of 80

d Charles scored 3 out of 20

e Paula scored 42 out of 56.

3. Of the 145 pupils in 5th year, 87 of them are doing a Lifeskills course.

a What percentage are doing Lifeskills ?

b What percentage are not ?

4. 

4 potatoes, out of a bag containing 18 had rotted within 3 days.

What percentage of the potatoes had rotted ? (*Answer correct to 1 decimal place*).

5. Determine the following marks as percentages, giving each correct to 1 decimal place :-

a Daisy scored 27 out of 35 in Maths.

b Norris scored 40 out of 41 in Chemistry.

c James scored 7 out of 80 in English.

6. Jenny recorded her monthly test scores :-

Aug - $\frac{15}{30}$	Sep - $\frac{48}{80}$	Oct - $\frac{54}{60}$
Nov - $\frac{30}{50}$	Dec - $\frac{23}{46}$	Jan - $\frac{46}{46}$
Feb - $\frac{26}{40}$	Mar - $\frac{34}{40}$	Apr - $\frac{83}{100}$
May - $\frac{19}{25}$		

a Calculate Jenny's percentage scores over the ten month school period.

b Draw a neat line graph to show her progress.

c What was Jenny's average (**mean**) percentage mark ?

d Describe how her marks change throughout the year.

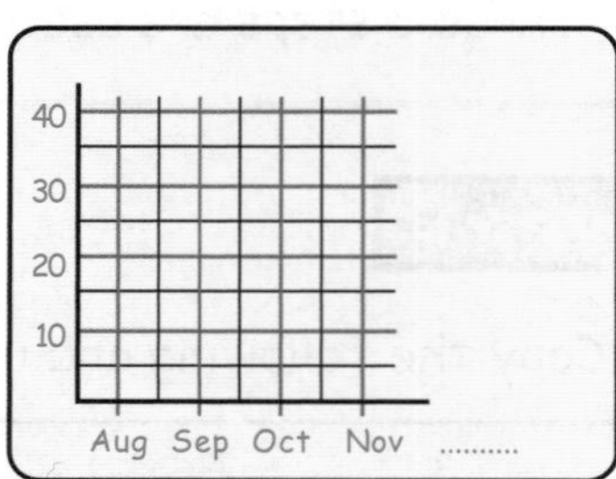

7.

Nick sat a test out of a maximum of 70.

He scored 71%, (*rounded to 1 decimal place*).

What must his score have been ?

8. Alec bought a set of books for £150, and two years later, he sold them for £180.

a How much profit did Alec make ?

b He worked out his percentage profit by dividing the profit (answer to **a**) by what he bought the book for, (£150), and multiplying his answer by 100.

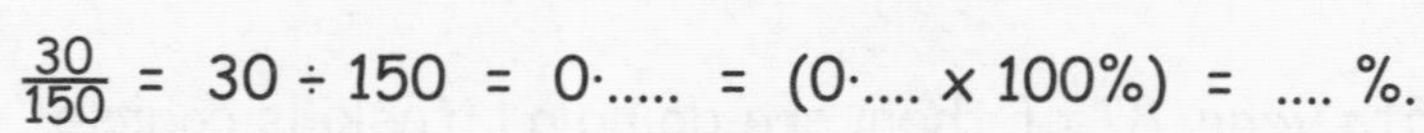

$\frac{30}{150}$ = 30 ÷ 150 = 0·..... = (0·.... x 100%) = ... %.

Work out Alec's % profit.

9. Jessie paid out £12 for ingredients, then baked a cake.

She then sold the cake to a shop for £16.

a How much profit did Jessie make ?

b Work out her percentage profit.

Compound Interest

When money is left in a bank for up to one year, it may gain **interest**.

This is referred to as **Simple Interest** and is found by using percentages.

If you leave money in the bank for several years :-

- the interest is found for the **first year**
- this is then **added** to the **previous balance**
- the new interest for the next year is calculated on the **new balance**
- this is then added on again to the previous balance
- ... and so on until all the interest has been calculated.

This is referred to as **COMPOUND INTEREST**.

Example :- Albert invests £800 in the *Clydeport Bank*. Their **annual** rate is 2%.

Calculate the **compound interest** that builds up over 3 years.

First Year Balance		£800·00
1st Year Interest = 2% of £800·00	=	£16·00
Second Year Balance = £800·00 + £16·00	=	£816·00
2nd Year Interest = 2% of £816·00	=	£16·32
Third Year Balance = £816·00 + £16·32	=	£832·32
3rd Year Interest = 2% of £832·32	=	£16·65*
=> Final Balance = £832·32 + £16·65	=	**£848·97**
=> **Total Interest** = £848·97 − £800·00	=	**£48·97**

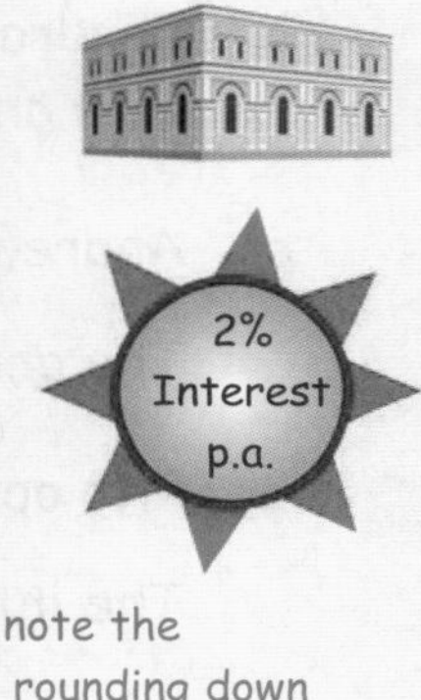

*note the rounding down

Exercise 3

1. Joseph leaves £2000 in his bank for 3 years.

   The annual rate of interest is 3%.

   Calculate how much interest Joseph is due at the end of three years ....

   Copy and complete the statement.

1st Year Balance	£2000·00
1st Year Int = 3% of £2000·00	£........·....
2nd Year Balance = £2000 + ...	£........·....
2nd Year Int = 3% of £.....·...	£........·....
3rd Year Balance = £....... + ...	£........·....
3rd Year Int = 3% of £.....·...	£........·....
Final Balance =	£........·....
Total Interest =	£........·....

2. Tom and Irene Eckford invested £500 in their building society account and left it there for two years. The annual interest rate was 3·5%.

   Calculate the compound interest that built up in their account over the 2 years.

3. Noreen left her £25 000 Premium Bond winnings in a special savings account for 3 years.

   The annual rate of interest was 4·5%.

   How much were her savings then worth ?

4. 

   Peter was told that if he left his savings of £5000 in the *Callaway Bank* for 5 years he would get a special annual rate of 5·4%.

   How much would his £5000 be worth at the end of the 5 year period ?

5. Calculate the total compound interest due when the following investments are made :-

   a Jason deposited £720 in the bank for 3 years with an annual interest rate of 2·5%.

   b Sandra put by £3000 in the bank for 2 years with an annual interest rate of 3·2%.

   c Andrew paid in £400 to his bank and left it for 2 years.

   The annual interest rate was $3\frac{1}{2}$%.

   d Rita opened a two year fixed rate bond with £10 000.

   The interest rate was $1\frac{1}{4}$% p.a. (*per annum*).

6. An internet bank offered a tremendous interest rate of 6% per year on savings.

   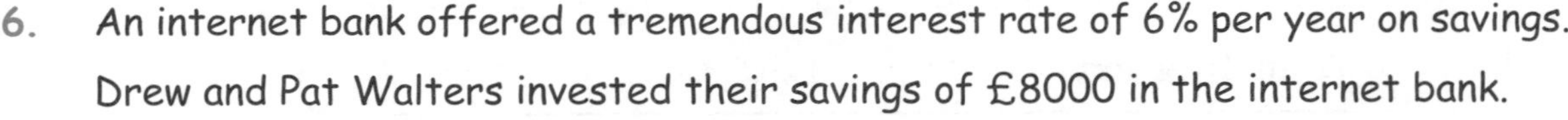

   Drew and Pat Walters invested their savings of £8000 in the internet bank.

   a How much were their savings worth after :- (i) 1 year (ii) 2 years ?

   b How many years would it take before their investment reached over £10 000 ?

7. Danielle was advised to invest her £40 000 life savings in a special Higher Interest Savings account, but she had to agree not to touch it for 4 years.

   The interest rates for the 4 year period were 2·5%, 3%, 3·2% and 4·5% respectively.

   a Calculate the value of her savings at the end of each year.

   b What was the total interest that had accrued on her account ?

   c Express this as a percentage of her original investment.

8. Which of the following would give a better return on investing £5000 for 3 years :-

   Option A :- A fixed interest rate of 4% for each of the 3 years.

   Option B :- A rate of 3% in 1st year, 4% in second year and 5% in third year ?

Depreciation and Appreciation

Most things we buy generally tend to drop or DEPRECIATE in value with time.

Example 1 :- A car, bought for £14 000, depreciated by :-

- 25% during its 1st year,
- 20% in its 2nd year.
- 15% during its 3rd year.

What was its actual value after 3 years ?

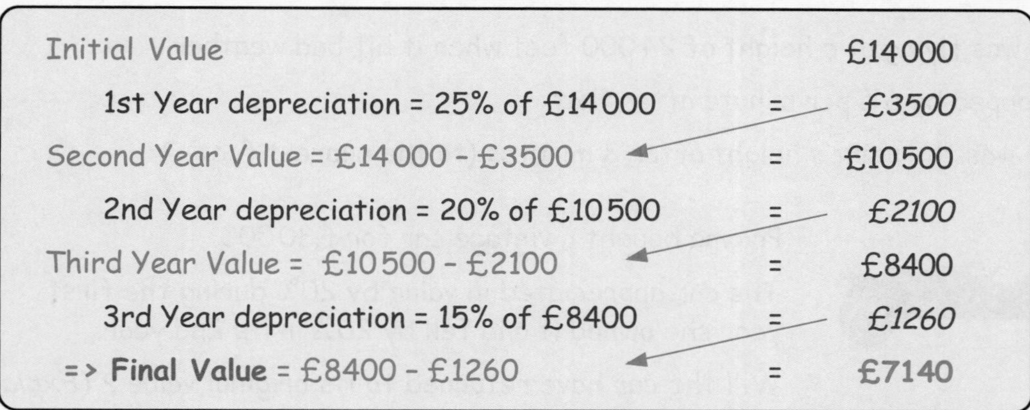

Initial Value		£14 000
1st Year depreciation = 25% of £14 000	=	*£3500*
Second Year Value = £14 000 - £3500	=	£10 500
2nd Year depreciation = 20% of £10 500	=	*£2100*
Third Year Value = £10 500 - £2100	=	£8400
3rd Year depreciation = 15% of £8400	=	*£1260*
=> **Final Value** = £8400 - £1260	=	**£7140**

Some valuables, e.g. paintings, diamond rings and vintage cars tend to rise or APPRECIATE.

Example 2 :- A diamond necklace, bought for £8000, appreciated by :-

- 50% during its 1st year.
- 75% during its 2nd year.

What was the necklace worth after 2 years ?

Initial Value		£8000
1st Year appreciation = 50% of £8000	=	*£4000*
Second Year Value = £8000 + £4000	=	£12 000
2nd Year appreciation = 75% of £12 000	=	*£9000*
=> **Final Value** = £12 000 + £9000	=	**£21 000**

Exercise 4

1. Mo bought a freezer for £500.
   Its value depreciated by 20% in year 1 and by 35% in year 2.
   Copy and complete to find its value then :-

Initial Value		£500
1st Year Dep. = 20% of £500	=	£.........
Second Year Value = £500 - £.......	=	£.........
2nd Year Dep. = 35% of £........	=	£.........
=> **Final Value** = £....... - £.......	=	£.........

2. Alistair bought a new bicycle at the start of 2012 for £450.

It depreciated in value by 25% every year he owned it.

What was the bike worth at the beginning of :- a 2013 b 2014 c 2015 ?

3. 

The Arnolds paid £150 000 for their house 3 years ago.

Due to falling house prices, they found that the house's value had dropped by 5% in the first year, 10% in the second and a further 20% in the third year.

How much was their house then worth ?

4. A jet was flying at a height of 24 000 feet when it hit bad weather.

It dropped by 6% per minute after that.

What was the plane's height after 3 minutes (to the nearest foot) ?

5. 

Paloma bought a vintage car for £30 000.

The car appreciated in value by 20% during the first year she owned it and fell by 20% in its 2nd year.

Will the car have returned to its original value ? (*Explain*)

6. The cost of doing the average weekly shop in a supermarket generally rises each year.

The Reynolds family spent about £180 per week in *Ascos* in 2015.

If the cost of living is expected to rise by 1·5% per year, what will they pay for their weekly shop in :-

a 2016 b 2017 c 2020 ?

7. The graph shows the *cost of living* annual rise during each year 2010 to 2015.

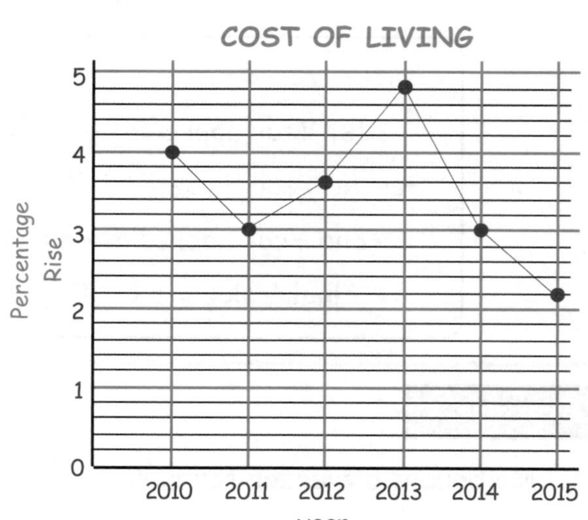

a What was the cost of living rise in :-

(i) 2011 (ii) 2012 ?

b A meal out for 4 costs on average £90 at the beginning of 2013.

What would a similar meal cost by the end of 2013 ?

c Molly and Bill paid £160 000 for their cottage at the beginning of 2010.

Estimate the cottage's value at the end of :-

(i) 2010 (ii) 2012 (iii) 2015, based on the above cost of living indexes ?

Percentages

Numeracy Assessment 3

1. 85% of the cartons of milk on a supermarket shelf had to be removed because they were past their sell-by date.

   Of the 240 cartons initially on display, how many remained ?

2. NUK-EM, a new greenfly spray, kills 8% of the greenfly after each spray application.

   A batch of plants has 720 greenfly to begin with and the gardener sprays them with NUK-EM once each day for 3 days.

   How many of the 720 greenfly will remain after he has completed the treatment ?

3. In 2013, my car insurance premium was £240.

   In 2014, the premium was increased by 5% and there was a further increase of 2·5% in 2015.

   How much was my car insurance in 2015 ?

4. A supermarket bought in a crate of 50 Christmas turkeys for £600.

   All the turkeys were sold within hours at a price of £16 each.

   Work out the supermarket's profit on the turkeys, and express this as a percentage of what it paid for them.

5. A money lender charges a very high 15% per month compound interest rate.

   If you were to borrow £800 from him and agree to pay it back at the end of 3 months, how much would you have to pay ?

6. Miss Simm bought a new car for £18 500 in September 2011.

   Its value depreciated by 20% in the first year, 25% in the second and 40% in the third year.

   By how much had its initial price fallen by September 2014 ?

7. *Edco Electronics* made a pre-tax profit of £254 000 in 2013.

   In 2014, their profits fell by a quarter.

   In 2015, the profits rose by 18% of the 2014 figure.

   a Calculate the pre-tax profits for 2015.

   b What was *Edco's* net profit in 2015, if their profits are taxed at 40%.

Fractions

Revision of Fractions

1. What fraction of each of these shapes is coloured ?

a 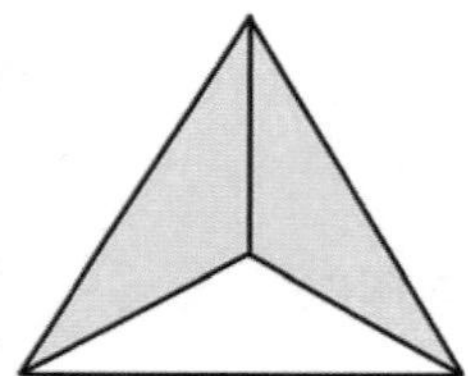 b 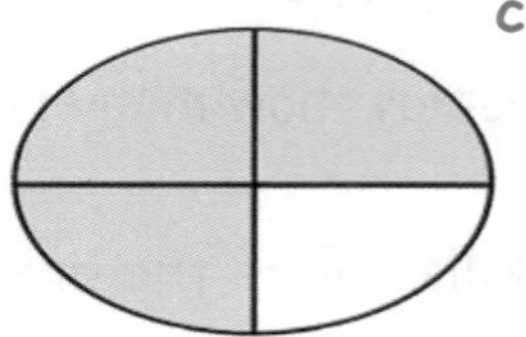 c 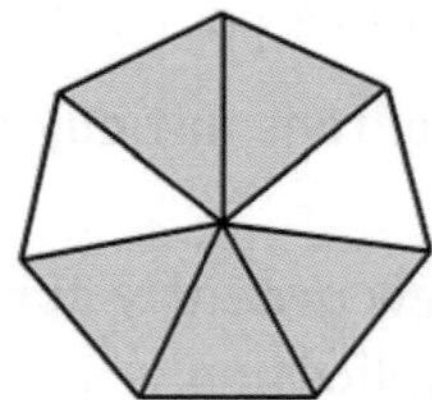 d 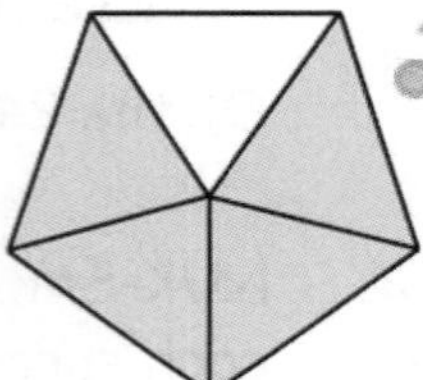

e 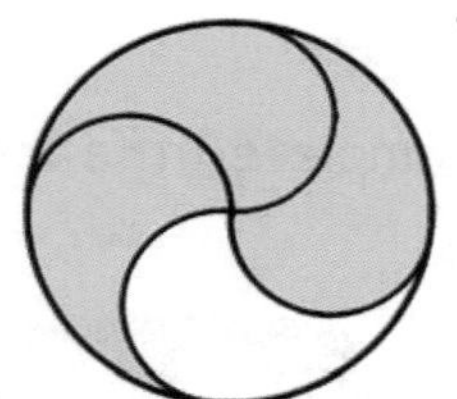 f 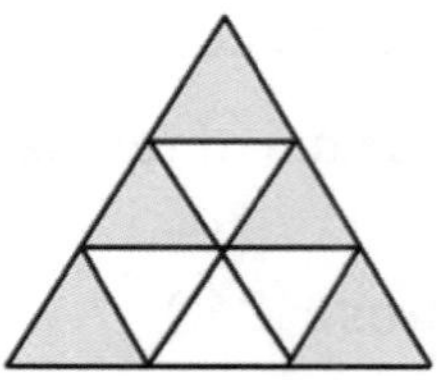 g 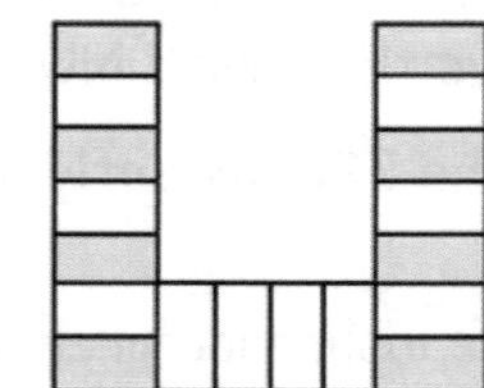 h 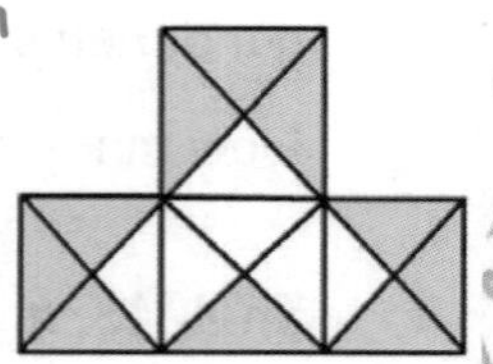

2. Write down the fraction of each shape in question 1 that is not coloured.

3. Write down two other fractions equivalent to :-

a $\frac{1}{3}$ b $\frac{2}{5}$ c $\frac{7}{11}$ d $\frac{5}{3}$.

4. Simplify the following fractions fully :-

a $\frac{8}{10}$ b $\frac{9}{12}$ c $\frac{16}{24}$ d $\frac{13}{39}$

e $\frac{28}{35}$ f $\frac{36}{72}$ g $\frac{17}{51}$ h $\frac{70}{105}$.

5. Find :-

a $\frac{1}{2}$ of 70 m b $\frac{1}{4}$ of 64 kg c $\frac{1}{9}$ of 1809 mm d $\frac{2}{3}$ of 42 kg

e $\frac{3}{5}$ of 255 litres f $\frac{5}{6}$ of 4026 cm g $\frac{7}{12}$ of £6000 h $\frac{19}{20}$ of 640 m.

6. a Two hundred people work in an office.
Two fifths of them have their own computer.
How many of them do not have their own computer ?

6. b William decides to share his pay bonus of £2000.

He gives half to his mum and a fifth of what he had left to his brother George.

How much will he then have left ?

c 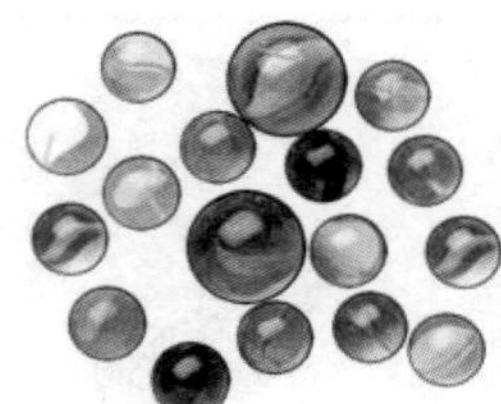

Harry decides to share 300 marbles.

He will get half, Sam will get a third and Jake will get a quarter of the marbles.

What is wrong with Harry's calculations ?

7. What **fraction**, in its simplest form, is equivalent to :-

a	1%	b	25%	c	10%
d	75%	e	40%	f	$12\frac{1}{2}$% ?

8. Attempt the following **without** using a calculator :-

a	50% of £174	b	10% of £4	c	25% of 64 kg
d	$33\frac{1}{3}$% of 336 mm	e	20% of £75	f	1% of £50
g	5% of £160	h	75% of £1·60	i	2% of £200
j	$33\frac{1}{3}$% of £10·08	k	$66\frac{2}{3}$% of £10·08	l	200% of £200.

9. Re-write the following list of numbers, but this time in order, ***smallest first*** :-

$\frac{1}{3}$, 0·3, 13%, $\frac{1}{5}$, 0·098, $\frac{25}{200}$.

10. a Sara buys a coat marked £120.

She receives a discount of 15%.

How much will she pay for the coat ?

b She also buys shoes at £45·20, and receives a 25% discount.

How much will she pay for the shoes ?

11. 

Four women win a million pounds in the lottery.

Jill is to get a quarter of the winnings, Jane is to get 0·3, June gets 10% and Janet gets the rest.

a What percentage of the money will Janet get ?

b List how much each of the women will receive.

Chapter 4 Fractions

Top Heavy and Mixed Fractions

A fraction like $\frac{19}{6}$, where the **numerator** is bigger than the **denominator**, is called a "**top-heavy**" fraction.

A number like $7\frac{3}{4}$, consisting of "whole" part and a "fraction" part, is called a "**mixed**" fraction.

Examples :- Changing a top-heavy fraction to a mixed fraction :-

1. $\frac{19}{6}$ really means $19 \div 6$ => $6\overline{)19}$ with quotient 3 (remainder 1) => $3\frac{1}{6}$ — note :- the 1 is divided by the 6

2. $\frac{33}{7}$ really means $33 \div 7$ => $7\overline{)33}$ with quotient 4 (remainder 5) => $4\frac{5}{7}$ — note :- the 5 is divided by the 7

Exercise 1

1. Copy and complete the following :-

   a $\frac{25}{3}$ really means $25 \div 3$ => $3\overline{)25}$ ... (remainder ....) => $8\frac{...}{3}$.

   b $\frac{37}{8}$ really means $37 \div ...$ => $...\overline{)37}$ ... (remainder ....) => $...\frac{...}{8}$.

   c $\frac{17}{6}$ really means .... ÷ .... => $6\overline{)...}$ ... (remainder ....) => ....

2. In a similar way, change the following top heavy fractions to mixed numbers :-

a	$\frac{17}{3}$	b	$\frac{31}{4}$	c	$\frac{36}{5}$	d	$\frac{91}{9}$
e	$\frac{62}{7}$	f	$\frac{65}{8}$	g	$\frac{69}{8}$	h	$\frac{73}{10}$
i	$\frac{21}{6}$	j	$\frac{90}{11}$	k	$\frac{69}{6}$	l	$\frac{146}{12}$.

3. a 47 litres of apple juice is poured equally into 7 jugs.
   How much apple juice is in each jug, (*as a mixed number*) ?

   b Six girls decide to share 13 metres of ribbon evenly.
   What will each girl receive (*as a mixed number*) ?

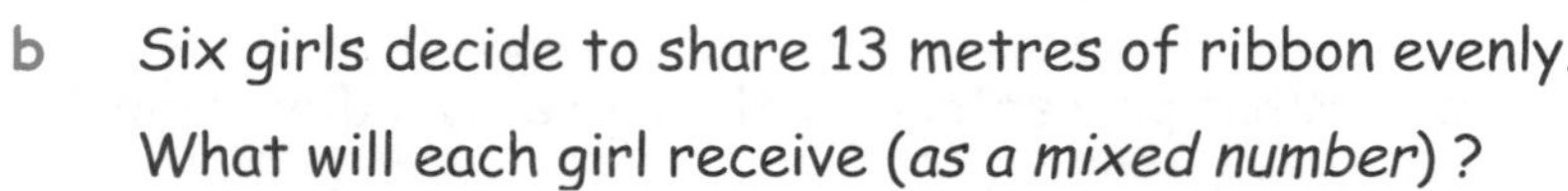

3. c A fish farm tank holds quarter of a million litres of water.

It is emptied in equal amounts into 7 large aquariums.
How much water will be in each aquarium ?

d An oil drum holds 7450 litres of oil.
9 trucks use an equal amount of oil.
How much oil will each truck use from a full oil drum ?

e An electrician needs 1372 metres of wire for 5 identical jobs.
He also needs 794 metres of cable.

(i) How much wire is needed for each job ?

(ii) How much cable will he use for each job ?

4. Copy and complete :- $\frac{75}{10} = 75 \div 10 = 7\frac{5}{10} = 7\frac{\dots}{2}$ (<— simplified).

5. Change each of the following to mixed numbers and **simplify** where possible :-

a $\frac{64}{10}$ b $\frac{86}{4}$ c $\frac{36}{8}$ d $\frac{40}{6}$

e $\frac{146}{100}$ f $\frac{68}{8}$ g $\frac{75}{30}$ h $\frac{69}{6}$.

6. This diagram represents $4\frac{2}{3}$ pizzas.

a How many "$\frac{1}{3}$" pizza slices do you get from 1 pie ?

b How many "$\frac{1}{3}$" pizza slices do you get from 4 pies ?

c How many "$\frac{1}{3}$" pizza slices do you get from $\frac{2}{3}$ of a pie ?

d How many "$\frac{1}{3}$" pizza slices is this altogether from the $4\frac{2}{3}$ pizzas ?

e Write this as $4\frac{2}{3} = \frac{\dots}{3}$.

7. Five "pizzas" have been cut into "quarters".

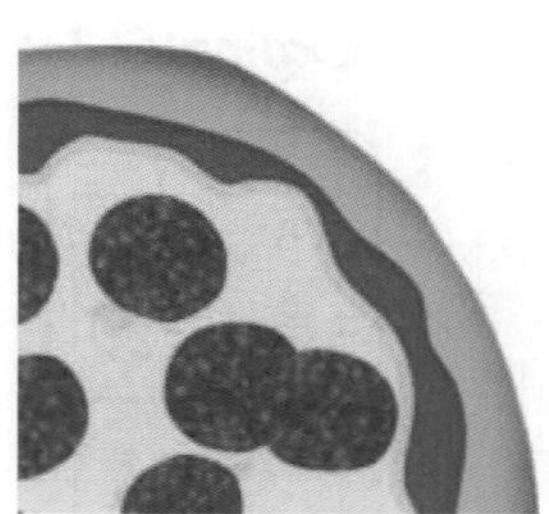

a From the 5 whole pizzas, you get ..... quarters ?

b From the $\frac{3}{4}$ pizza, you get ..... quarters ?

c How many quarters is this altogether ?

d Write this as $5\frac{3}{4} = \frac{\dots}{4}$.

Changing a mixed fraction to a top-heavy fraction :-

Example 1 :- To change $8\frac{2}{3}$ to "thirds"

Step 1 - multiply the 8 by the 3 - (8 becomes 24 "thirds")

Step 2 - add on the 2 (thirds) - (24 + 2 = 26 "thirds").

$8\frac{2}{3}$ = ((8 x 3) + 2) thirds = 26 "thirds" = $\frac{26}{3}$

Example 2 :- Change $4\frac{5}{8}$ to eighths. $4\frac{5}{8}$ = ((4 x 8) + 5) eighths = 37 "eighths" = $\frac{37}{8}$

8. Copy and complete :-

a $9\frac{3}{10}$ = ((9 x 10) + 3) "tenths" = 93 "tenths" = $\frac{...}{10}$.

b $2\frac{5}{8}$ = ((2 x ...) + ...) "eighths" = ... "eighths" = $\frac{...}{...}$.

c $11\frac{1}{9}$ = ((... x ...) + ...) "ninths" = ... "ninths" = $\frac{...}{...}$.

9. Copy and complete :-

a $7\frac{1}{5} = \frac{......}{5}$ b $12\frac{2}{3}$ = ... c $15\frac{2}{5}$ = ... d $40\frac{7}{10}$ = ...

10. Change each of the following mixed numbers to top heavy fractions :-

a $2\frac{1}{2}$ b $3\frac{1}{5}$ c $10\frac{2}{3}$ d $17\frac{2}{5}$

e $1\frac{3}{7}$ f $9\frac{8}{9}$ g $100\frac{9}{10}$ h $60\frac{19}{20}$.

11. How many $\frac{1}{2}$ pizza slices can I get from :-

a 1 pizza b 6 pizzas c $5\frac{1}{2}$ pizzas ?

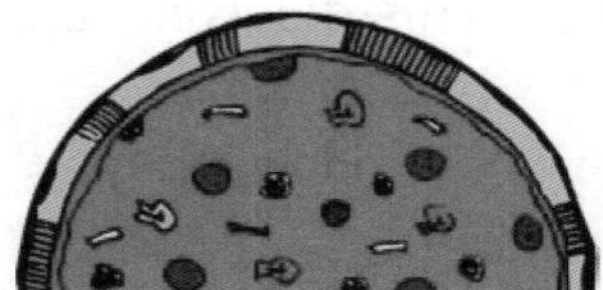

12. How many $\frac{1}{5}$ litre cups can be filled from :-

a 1 litre b $1\frac{1}{5}$ litres c $3\frac{2}{5}$ litres d $7\frac{4}{5}$ litres ?

Adding and Subtracting (basic) Fractions

Simple Rule :- You can only add (or subtract) two fractions if

THEY HAVE THE SAME DENOMINATOR.

Example 1 :-

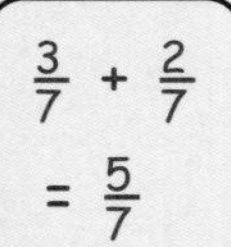

$\frac{3}{7} + \frac{2}{7}$

$= \frac{5}{7}$

Example 2 :-

$\frac{7}{8} - \frac{1}{8}$

$= \frac{6}{8}$ $(= \frac{3}{4})$

Example 3 :-

$2\frac{3}{5} + 1\frac{4}{5}$

$= 3\frac{7}{5}$

$= 4\frac{2}{5}$

Example 4 :-

$5\frac{5}{6} - 1\frac{1}{6}$

$= 4\frac{4}{6}$

$= 4\frac{2}{3}$

$\frac{7}{8}$ - $\frac{1}{8}$

= $\frac{6}{8}$

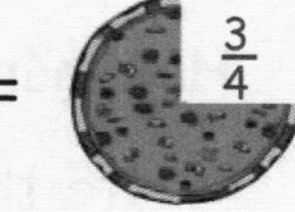

= $\frac{3}{4}$

Exercise 2

1. Copy and complete the following :-

a $\frac{2}{5} + \frac{1}{5}$ $= \frac{...}{5}$

b $\frac{7}{9} - \frac{2}{9}$ $= \frac{...}{9}$

c $\frac{9}{10} - \frac{3}{10}$ $= \frac{...}{10} = \frac{...}{5}$

d $\frac{3}{8} + \frac{3}{8}$ $= \frac{...}{8} = \frac{...}{4}$

2. Copy the following and **simplify** where possible :-

a	$\frac{2}{7} + \frac{1}{7}$	b	$\frac{2}{9} + \frac{3}{9}$	c	$\frac{5}{9} - \frac{1}{9}$	d	$\frac{3}{4} + \frac{3}{4}$
e	$\frac{7}{12} - \frac{5}{12}$	f	$\frac{11}{12} + \frac{11}{12}$	g	$\frac{8}{15} + \frac{7}{15}$	h	$\frac{15}{16} - \frac{7}{16}$.

3. Copy the following and **simplify** where possible :-

a $2\frac{1}{3} + 1\frac{1}{3}$ b $4\frac{3}{5} - 1\frac{2}{5}$ c $5\frac{1}{7} + 1\frac{1}{7}$ d $7\frac{1}{2} + 2\frac{1}{2}$.

4. a John mixes $\frac{3}{5}$ kg flour with $\frac{4}{5}$ kg of butter.
What is the total weight of the mixture ?

b A piece of string was $\frac{3}{5}$ metre long. A piece measuring $\frac{2}{5}$ metre was cut off.
What length of string remained ?

c A fifth of a litre of water evaporates from a bowl containing 3 litres of water.
How much water is now left in the bowl ?

Adding and Subtracting (harder) Fractions

Remember the Rule :- The denominators **MUST** be the same if you wish to add or subtract.

Question :- What do we do if the denominators are **not** the same ?

Answer :- Change each fraction so that they **do have the same** denominator.

Example 1 :- Find $\frac{2}{3} + \frac{1}{2}$. [they do **not** add to give $\frac{3}{5}$ X]

- the denominators **3** and **2** are **not** the same.
- what is the **l.c.m.** (lowest common multiple) of 3 and 2 —> 6.
- we must change $\frac{2}{3}$ and $\frac{1}{2}$ to $\frac{1}{6}$'s.

($\frac{2}{3} = \frac{?}{6}$) note => ? = 4

$\frac{2}{3} + \frac{1}{2}$

$\frac{4}{6} + \frac{3}{6}$

$= \frac{7}{6} = 1\frac{1}{6}$

note ($\frac{1}{2} = \frac{?}{6}$) => ? = 3

Example 2 :-

(8 and 5 go into 40)

$\frac{5}{8} - \frac{1}{5}$

$\frac{?}{40} - \frac{?}{40}$

$= \frac{25}{40} - \frac{8}{40}$

$= \frac{17}{40}$

Exercise 3

1. Copy each of the following and complete :-

a
$$\frac{3}{4} + \frac{1}{3}$$
$$= \frac{?}{12} + \frac{?}{12}$$
$$= \frac{?}{12} = 1\frac{?}{12}$$

b
$$\frac{4}{5} - \frac{2}{3}$$
$$= \frac{?}{15} - \frac{?}{15}$$
$$= \frac{?}{15}$$

c
$$\frac{7}{8} - \frac{3}{4}$$
$$= \frac{?}{8} - \frac{?}{8}$$
$$= \frac{?}{8}$$

d
$$\frac{6}{7} + \frac{2}{3}$$
$$= \frac{?}{21} + \frac{?}{21}$$
$$= \frac{?}{21}$$

2. Show how to simplify the following :-

a $\frac{2}{3} + \frac{1}{5}$ b $\frac{3}{4} - \frac{1}{2}$ c $\frac{5}{8} + \frac{2}{3}$ d $\frac{4}{5} + \frac{1}{2}$

e $\frac{5}{6} - \frac{1}{3}$ f $\frac{3}{4} - \frac{2}{3}$ g $\frac{1}{2} + \frac{1}{3} + \frac{1}{4}$ h $\frac{5}{6} - \frac{1}{2} - \frac{1}{3}$.

Multiplying Basic Fractions

Basic Rule :- **To multiply 2 (or more) fractions, simply multiply all the numerators and multiply all the denominators - then simplify where possible.**

Example 1 :-
$$\frac{1}{3} \times \frac{1}{2}$$
$$= \frac{1 \times 1}{3 \times 2}$$
$$= \frac{1}{6}$$

Example 2 :-
$$\frac{2}{5} \times \frac{3}{7}$$
$$= \frac{2 \times 3}{5 \times 7}$$
$$= \frac{6}{35}$$

Example 3 :-
$$\frac{2}{3} \times \frac{3}{4} \times \frac{5}{6}$$
$$= \frac{2 \times 3 \times 5}{3 \times 4 \times 6}$$
$$= \frac{30}{72} = \frac{5}{12}$$

Exercise 4

1. Copy each of the following and complete :-

a
$$\frac{1}{5} \times \frac{1}{3}$$
$$= \frac{1 \times \dots}{\dots \times 3}$$
$$= \frac{\dots}{15}$$

b
$$\frac{2}{3} \times \frac{1}{3}$$
$$= \frac{2 \times \dots}{\dots \times 3}$$
$$= \frac{\dots}{\dots}$$

c
$$\frac{7}{8} \times \frac{2}{3}$$
$$= \frac{7 \times \dots}{\dots \times 3}$$
$$= \frac{\dots}{24} = \frac{\dots}{12}$$

d
$$\frac{1}{4} \times \frac{2}{5} \times \frac{5}{8}$$
$$= \frac{1 \times \dots \times \dots}{4 \times \dots \times \dots}$$
$$= \frac{\dots}{160} = \frac{\dots}{\dots}$$

2. Multiply each of the following and simplify where possible :-

a $\frac{1}{2} \times \frac{1}{4}$ b $\frac{1}{5} \times \frac{1}{8}$ c $\frac{1}{3} \times \frac{2}{5}$ d $\frac{3}{7} \times \frac{5}{6}$

e $\frac{3}{4} \times \frac{6}{7}$ f $\frac{1}{3} \times \frac{9}{10} \times \frac{5}{8}$ g $\frac{7}{10} \times \frac{4}{5} \times \frac{5}{7}$ h $\frac{1}{2} \times \frac{2}{3} \times \frac{3}{4} \times \frac{4}{5}$.

Fractions

Numeracy Assessment 4

1. Change each of the following to a mixed number :-

   a $\frac{25}{3}$ b $\frac{13}{7}$ c $\frac{63}{8}$ d $\frac{171}{12}$.

2. Change each of the following to a top heavy fraction :-

   a $3\frac{1}{2}$ b $7\frac{3}{4}$ c $11\frac{2}{3}$ d $8\frac{5}{8}$.

3. Simplify fully :-

   a $\frac{5}{9}+\frac{2}{9}$ b $\frac{1}{2}+\frac{1}{4}$ c $\frac{4}{5}-\frac{1}{2}$ d $5\frac{2}{7}+2\frac{3}{7}$.

4. Multiply these fractions and simplify where possible :-

   a $\frac{1}{5}\times\frac{3}{4}$ b $\frac{3}{4}\times\frac{10}{11}$ c $\frac{9}{10}\times\frac{5}{6}$ d $\frac{6}{7}\times\frac{2}{3}\times\frac{5}{8}$.

5. a Chef Colin mixes $\frac{7}{9}$ kg of butter and $\frac{4}{9}$ kg of flour.

   What is the total weight of the mixture ?
   (*Give your answer as a mixed number*).

   b Colin has a bowl with $\frac{7}{8}$ kg of sugar.

   He uses half the sugar in his recipe.

   How much sugar is left in the bowl ?

6. 

   Andi uses $\frac{3}{7}$ of her phone allowance.

   Josh uses $\frac{4}{9}$ of his allowance.

   Who has used up more of their allowance ?

7. Peter has £50, Sally has £32.

   Peter buys a pair of trainers, using *three fifths* of his money.

   Sally buys make-up and is left with *five eighths* of her money.

   Who has more money now ? (*Show all working*).

8. *Greyfriers Bank* offers two types of fixed rate savings bonds.

   - An annual interest rate of $1\frac{5}{8}$% on deposits up to £5000.
   - An annual interest rate of $2\frac{1}{4}$% on deposits over £5000.

   What is the fractional percentage difference between these two rates ?

Time-Distance-Speed

Revision of Time/Dist/Speed

1. Shown is part of the train timetable from Polock to Grenwick.

	Polock →	Nisthill →	Kilmont →	Punton →	Grenwick
Early Train	7.30 am	8.35 am	10.45 am	12.25 pm	2.20 pm
Late Train	2.45 pm	3.50 pm			9.35 pm

a How long does the early train take to travel from :-

(i) Polock to Nisthill ?

(ii) Kilmont to Punton ?

(iii) Polock to Grenwick ?

b Assuming that the late train travels at the same speed as the early train, when would it be expected to arrive at :-

(i) Kilmont ? (ii) Punton ?

2. 

A Teejay delivery van left Barrhead and travelled for 3 hours at an average speed of 35 mph.

How far did the van travel ?

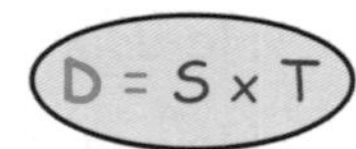

3. A coach left Perth and travelled the 102 kilometres to Glasgow at an average speed of 51 km/hr.

How long did the journey take ?

$T = \frac{D}{S}$

4. 

A flying saucer seemingly travelled 3440 miles over a period of 4 hours.

What was its average speed ?

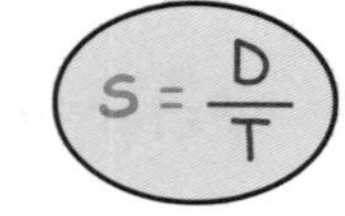

5. 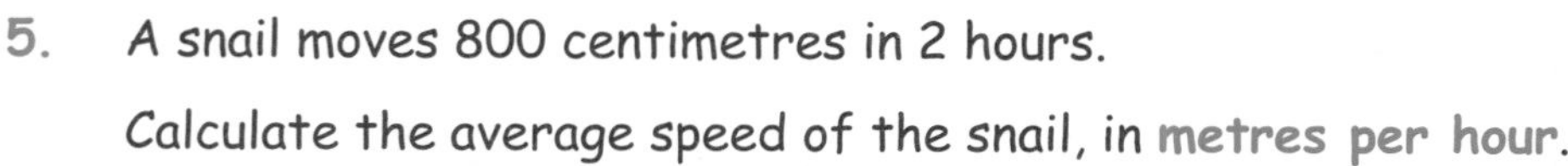

A snail moves 800 centimetres in 2 hours.

Calculate the average speed of the snail, in **metres per hour**.

6. 

Ron only managed to average a speed of 12 mph to travel the 30 miles home from work in the rush hour.

How long did it take him ?

7. A fire engine sped to a fire 34 kilometres from the fire station.

   The journey took 30 minutes.

   What was the fire engine's average speed ?

8. 

   A bulldozer, going at a steady speed of 18 mph, took $1\frac{1}{2}$ hours to travel from its base to the motorway construction site.

   How far did it travel ?

9. A tractor travels at a speed of 5 mph when ploughing a field.

   How long will it take to plough a field, with a total furrow length of $6\frac{1}{4}$ miles ? (*Answer in hours and minutes*).

10. 

    A communications satellite orbits a planet at an average speed of 6200 km/hr.

    It takes $2\frac{1}{2}$ hours to complete its orbit.

    Calculate the length of the orbit.

11. Sandy and Janet leave their home at the same time.

    Sandy has 60 miles to travel and drives at 40 mph.

    Janet has 105 miles to travel and drives at 60 mph.

    a How long does Sandy's journey take ?

    b How many minutes longer than Sandy does it take Janet ?

12. 

    Harrison flew 245 miles in his plane at an average speed of 140 mph.

    If he set off at 1845, at what time did he reach his destination ?

13. A tortoise, travelling at a speed of 50 centimetres per minute, took half an hour to cross a garden path.

    How many metres wide was the path ?

14. 

    A long distance runner took 1 hour 15 minutes to run a distance of 18 kilometres.

    Calculate her average speed, in **metres per second**.

Time-Distance-Speed

More on Time, Distance and Speed

If you used Teejay's National 4 (Lifeskills) textbook you will already be familiar with TDS problems.

In case you didn't, or you need reminding, here are examples of how the 3 formulae are used.

D = S x T

Try to memorise this diagram

$S = \frac{D}{T}$ $T = \frac{D}{S}$

Example 1 :- A train travels at an average speed of 140 km/hr for 5 hours.

How far will the train travel ?

D = S x T
= 140 x 5 = 700 km

Example 2 :- A car travels 270 miles in 4 hours 30 minutes.

What is its average speed ?

S = D / T
S = 270 ÷ 4·5
S = 60 mph

Example 3 :- A woman jogged for 7·5 miles at an average speed of 5 mph.

How long did it take her ?

T = D / S
T = 7·5 ÷ 5
T = 1·5 hrs
= 1 hr 30 mins

Exercise 1

1. Calculate the missing quantity :-

a

Distance	Speed	Time
300 km	?	5 hours

b

Distance	Speed	Time
120 miles	60 mph	?

c

Distance	Speed	Time
?	35 mph	4 hours

d

Distance	Speed	Time
150 km	?	$2\frac{1}{2}$ hrs

e

Distance	Speed	Time
?	40 m/sec	$4\frac{1}{2}$ sec

f

Distance	Speed	Time
275 miles	100 mph	?

2. A train travelled at 150 mph for 2 hours.

What distance did it cover ?

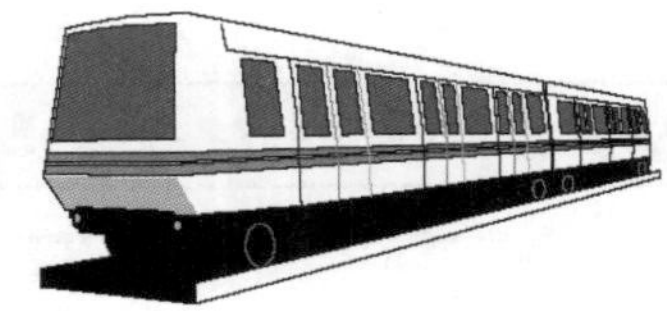

3. 

A marathon runner ran 18 km in $1\frac{1}{2}$ hours.

What was his average speed ?

4. How long did it take a coach to travel from Edinburgh to Manchester, a distance of 260 miles, coasting at an average speed of 65 mph ?

5. 

Sadie and Paul towed their caravan at an average speed of 36 km/hr.

Their first stop for a break was after 2 hours and 30 minutes.

How far had they travelled by then ?

6. A fish van left Arbroath at 1415 and arrived at its destination at 1745.

If the van had travelled 140 miles what speed had it been averaging ?

7. 

A plane flew 1530 miles at an average speed of 360 mph.

What time did the flight take ?

8. A jogger is passing through a valley at an average speed of 6 km/hr.

The valley is 16·5 km long.

How long will it take him ?

9. 

A satellite orbits the moon of a planet at a speed of 4200 mph.

It takes $1\frac{1}{4}$ hours to do this.

What is the length of the orbit ?

10. Old Mr Wilson goes to the Post Office each Thursday to collect his pension.

If he walks the $1\frac{1}{2}$ miles overall distance, it takes him 45 minutes.

If he uses his new electric wheelchair, he can do it in 15 minutes.

a Calculate Mr Wilson's walking speed.

b How many miles per hour faster does he travel in the wheelchair ?

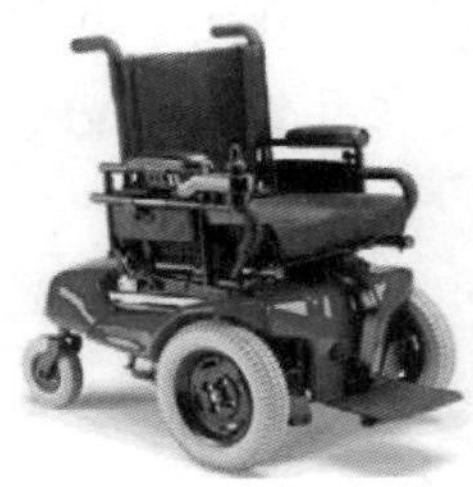

Changing Hours and Minutes to Decimal Times

You already know that :- $\frac{1}{2}$ hour = 0·5 hr, $\frac{1}{4}$ hour = 0·25 hr and $\frac{3}{4}$ hour = 0·75 hr.

How would we enter **27 minutes** into our calculator as a decimal ?

Minutes => Decimals => 27 minutes is $\frac{27}{60}$ of an hour = 27 ÷ 60 = **0·45 hr.**

36 minutes is $\frac{36}{60}$ of an hour = 36 ÷ 60 = **0·6 hr.**

1 hr 40 mins is $1 + \frac{40}{60}$ = 1 + (40 ÷ 60) = **1·6666... hr.**

Simple rule :- "To change minutes to a decimal of an hour => **divide by 60**".

Exercise 2

1. Use a calculator to change the following number of minutes to decimals of an hour :-

   a 18 minutes = $\frac{18}{60}$ of an hour = 18 ÷ 60 = 0·... hr.

   b 6 minutes c 48 minutes

   d 24 minutes e 54 minutes

   f 21 minutes g 39 minutes.

2. Use a calculator to change these times to decimal form (*to 2 decimal places*) :-

   a 10 minutes b 20 minutes c 17 minutes

   d 52 minutes e 50 minutes f 70 minutes.

3. With your calculator, change the following times to decimal form :-

   a 1 hour 48 minutes b 2 hours 36 minutes c 3 hours 51 minutes

   d 4 hours 57 minutes e 6 hours 12 minutes f 5 hours 6 minutes.

4. A hot air balloon travelled at a speed of 80 mph for 24 minutes.

   What distance did it cover ?

   Copy and complete :-

   $D = S \times T \Rightarrow D = 80 \times (\frac{24}{60})$

   $\Rightarrow D = 80 \times 0{\cdot}4$

   $D = ...$ miles

5. Calculate the distances travelled here :-

a A cruise ship sailing at 15 mph for 36 minutes.

b A coach travelling at 40 km/hr for 12 minutes.

c A caravan pulled along at 50 mph for 21 minutes.

d A jet plane flying at 600 km/hr for 20 minutes.

e A scooter travelling at 24 mph for 10 minutes.

6. 

Pat and Drew set off at the same time.

- Pat drives at 42 km/hr for 20 mins.
- Drew drives at 50 km/hr for 12 mins.

Who travels further, and by how much ?

7. A train travels at 200 mph for 1 hour 48 mins.

How far will it have travelled ?

Copy and complete the working in the blue box :-

$D = S \times T = 200 \times (1 + \frac{48}{60})$

$D = 200 \times (1{\cdot}8)$

$D = \dots$ miles

8. Calculate the distance travelled each time :-

a A helicopter flies at 140 mph for 1 hour 36 minutes.

b A bulldozer is driven at 20 km/hr for 2 hours 18 minutes.

9. A train travels a distance of 70 miles in 42 minutes.

Calculate its speed in mph.

Set down your working as shown :-

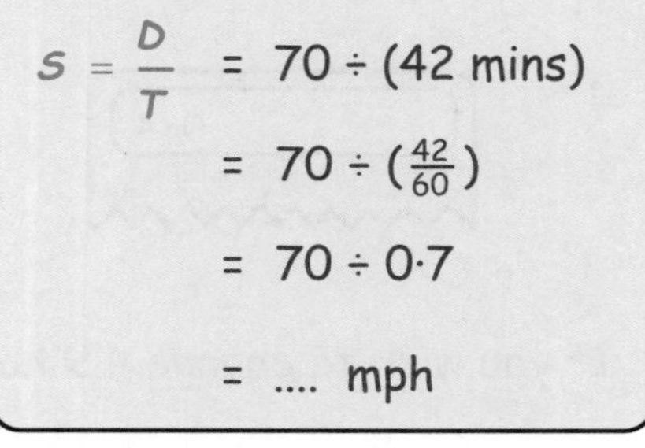

$S = \frac{D}{T} = 70 \div (42 \text{ mins})$

$= 70 \div (\frac{42}{60})$

$= 70 \div 0{\cdot}7$

$= \dots$ mph

10. Find the average speed each time here :-

(*Give answers, in mph or km/hr each time*).

a A police car travels 13 miles in 12 minutes.

b A jet covers 345 miles in 45 minutes.

c A submarine travels 48 km in 1 hour 20 minutes.

d A delivery van covers 56 miles in 48 minutes.

e A space ship flies 3895 miles in 4 hours 6 minutes.

Changing Decimal Times back to Hours and Minutes

In Exercise 2, you learned a simple rule for changing hours and minutes to decimal form.

Rule 1 :- "To change minutes to a decimal fraction => **divide by 60**".

If you have been using a calculator to find the time taken (in hours) for a journey, it might appear as a decimal, such as 0·35 hrs. Here is a way of changing this to minutes :-

Rule 2 :- "To change decimal hours back to minutes => **multiply by 60**".

Examples :- Decimals to Minutes =>

0·6 hr	= (0·6 x 60) mins	=	**36 minutes**
0·35 hr	= (0·35 x 60) mins	=	**21 minutes**
4·3 hrs	= 4 + (0·3 x 60) mins	=	**4 hrs 18 mins**

Exercise 3

1. The following calculator display times are given in decimal form (of an hour).
   Change each of them to minutes :-

   a 

   b 

   c 

   d 

   e 

   f 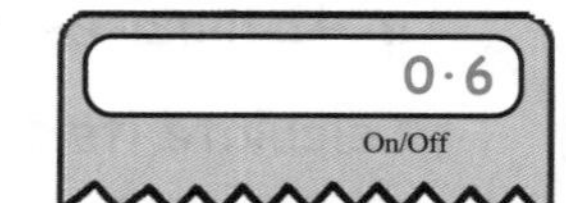

2. If you wish to change **4·9** hours to hours and minutes :-
   - Leave the hours as they are (**4** hours)
   - Multiply the 0·**9** by 60 => (... minutes).

3. Use the same technique to change the following times to hours and minutes :-

   a 6·2 hours = 6 hours + (0·2 x 60) mins = 6 hours ..... minutes.

   b 1·5 hours c 3·65 hours d 4·8 hours

   e 2·85 hours f 7·7 hours g 2·66666.. hours

   h 1·8333333 hours i 2·58333333 hours j 3·91666666 hours.

4. Write the following calculator (decimal) times in hours and minutes :-

a 2·75 On/Off

b 4·6 On/Off

c 

5. A cargo ship covers 33 miles at 10 mph.

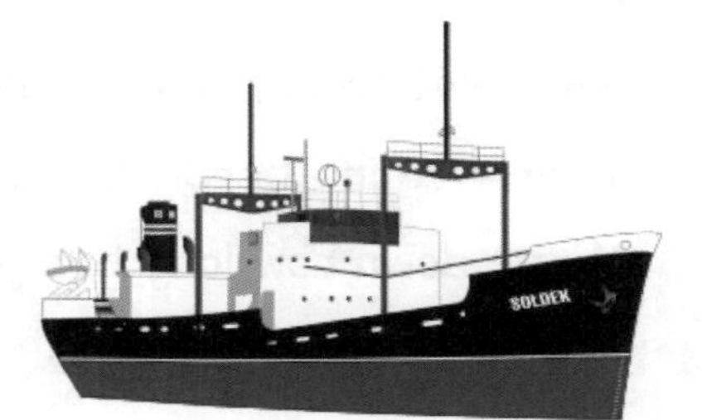

a Calculate the time taken, in hours.

$(T = \frac{D}{S})$ (*Answer as a decimal*).

b Change your answer to hours and mins.

6. Sally travels 14·4 kilometres per day doing her paper round at an average speed of 12 km/hr.

a Calculate how long she takes, in hours, (*as a decimal*).

b How long does she take in hours and minutes ?

7. Calculate the time taken (*as a decimal*) for each of the following, and then give your answer in hours and minutes :-

a A camel crosses 96·9 miles of desert at an average speed of 3 mph.

b A light aircraft flies 36 kilometres at an average speed of 108 km/hr.

c A racing car covers 35 miles at an average speed of 100 mph.

d A hill walker travels 4·5 miles at an average speed of 4 mph.

8. This map shows the 3 stages of an orienteering course.

The average speed as Bob covered the course, was 3 mph.

How long, in hours and minutes, did Bob take to walk between the :-

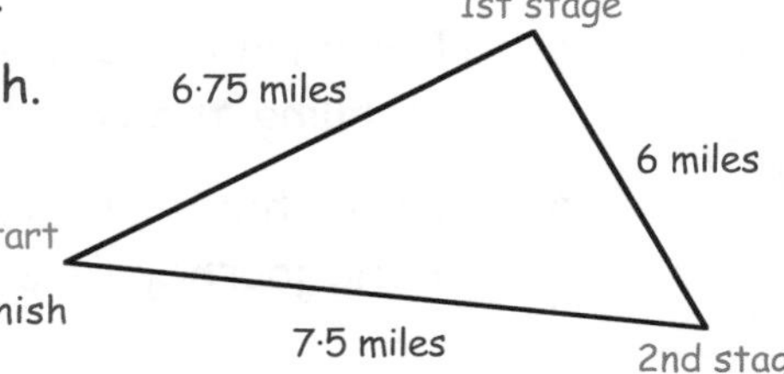

a start and 1st stage ?

b 1st and 2nd stages ?

c start and finish ?

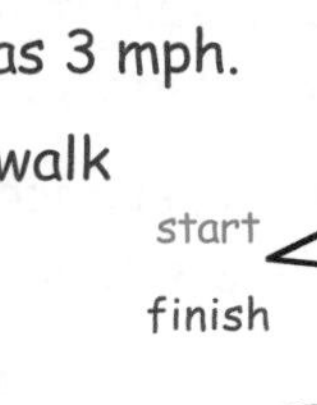

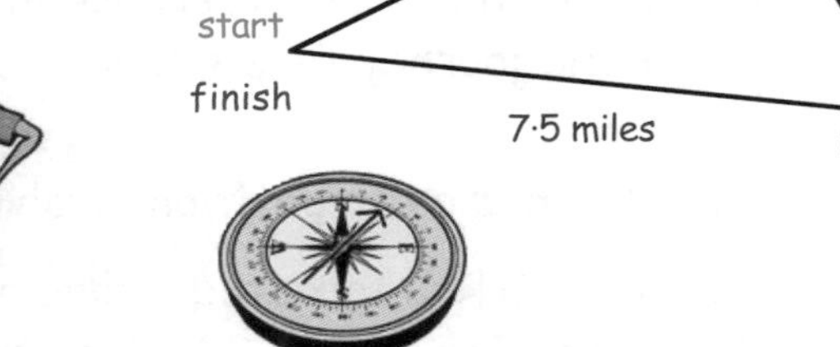

9. Sam ran 560 metres in 80 seconds.

a Work out his speed in metres per second, metres per minute and metres per hour.

b Now calculate his speed in kilometres per hour.

Time-Distance-Speed

Numeracy Assessment 5

1. The 0941 train from Glasgow to Aberdeen left Queen Street Station on time.

   It arrived in Aberdeen at 1235.

   Write down how long this journey took in :-

   a hours and minutes   b hours, as a decimal number.

2. I left one of the service stations on the M6 motorway at 10·20 pm.

   My next stop for petrol was at 3·05 am.

   If I had averaged a speed of 60 mph, how far had I travelled between the two service stations ?

3. Mr McSween left his garage at 0755 and travelled in his van for 2 hours and 48 minutes before stopping for breakfast.

   He had travelled exactly 134·4 kilometres.

   What speed had he averaged on his journey so far ?

4. Jill ran 720 metres in 120 seconds.

   a Work out her speed in metres per second, metres per minute and metres per hour.

   b Now calculate her speed in kilometres per hour.

5. The distance from Edinburgh to London by car is 407 miles.

   By air, it is 336 miles.

   a How much longer would it take a car to go from Edinburgh to London travelling at an average speed of 55 mph rather than a plane doing 252 mph ?

   b Write this time difference in minutes, and express it as a percentage of the journey time taken by car, to the nearest whole number.

6. A triathlon is a competition involving swimming, cycling and running.

   Athlete Seb Roe targeted a time of 11 minutes for swimming 800 metres, 32 minutes for cycling 20 kilometres and 17 minutes for running 5 kilometres.

   a What is the total distance (in km) he will cover during his triathlon ?

   b If he manages to complete the competition exactly on his target time, what will be his average speed, in metres per minute ?

Area and Perimeter

Revision of Area & Perimeter

1. Calculate the area of each rectangle and square :-
(*Use the formula and show your working*).

a
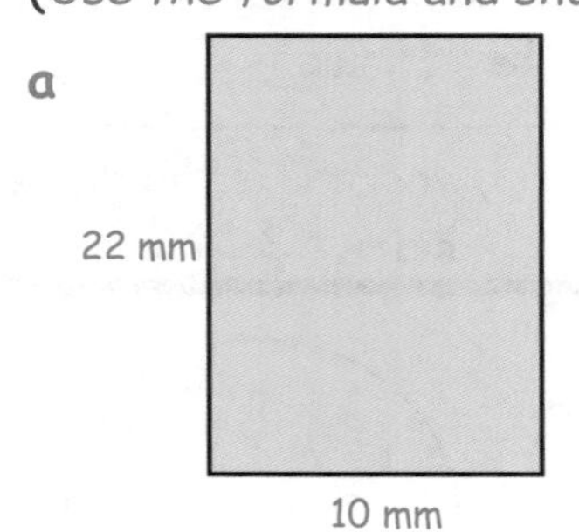

b
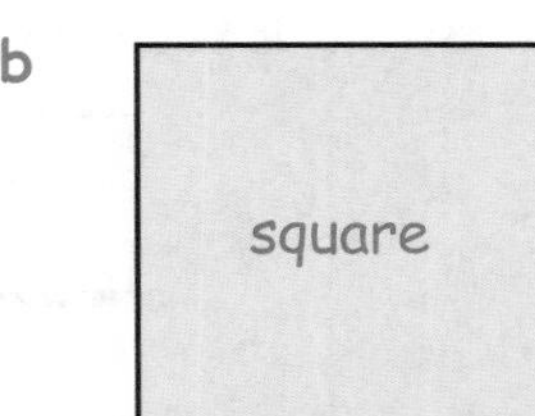

c
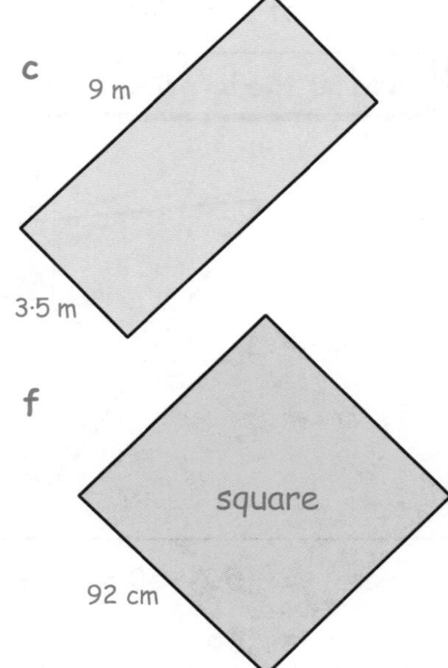

d
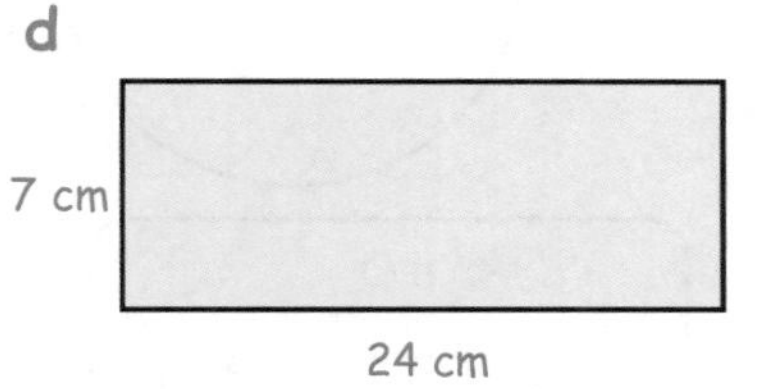

e
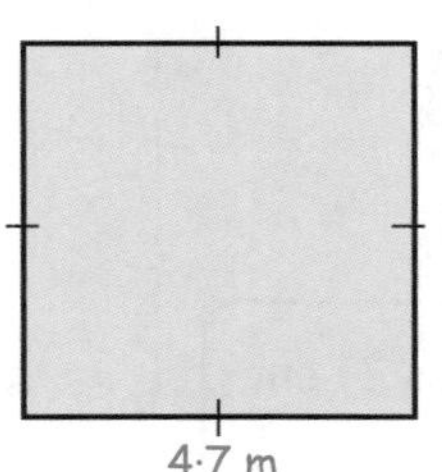

f

2. Find the perimeter of each of the above six shapes.

3. Find the area of a rectangle with length 10 cm and breadth 6·2 cm.

4. This rectangle has an area of 135 cm^2.
Calculate its length.

5. A rectangle has a perimeter of 32·6 cm.
Its length is 9·8 cm. Calculate the breadth of the rectangle.

6. Calculate the area of each triangle :-
(*Use appropriate formula and show your working*).

a
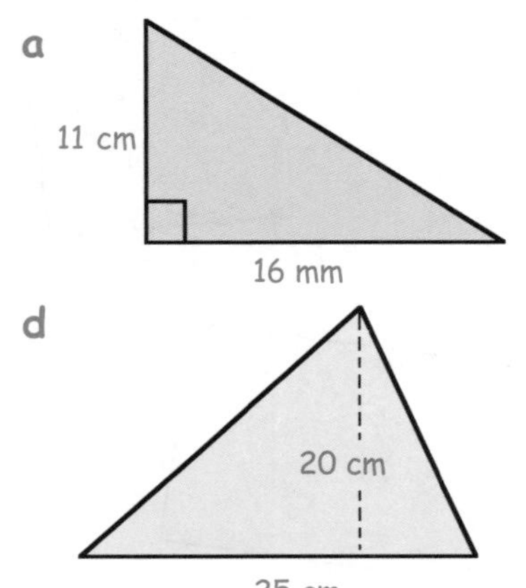

b
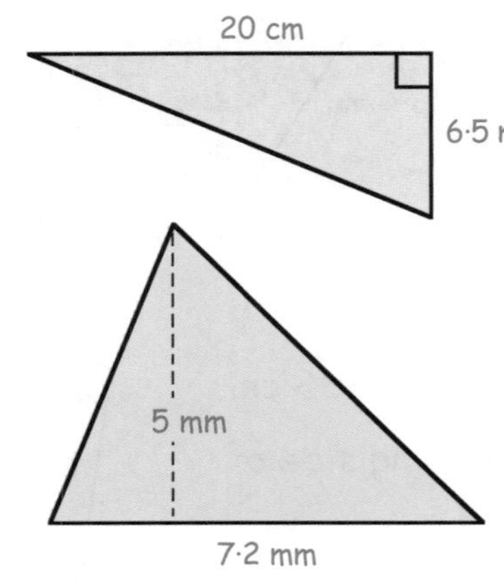

c
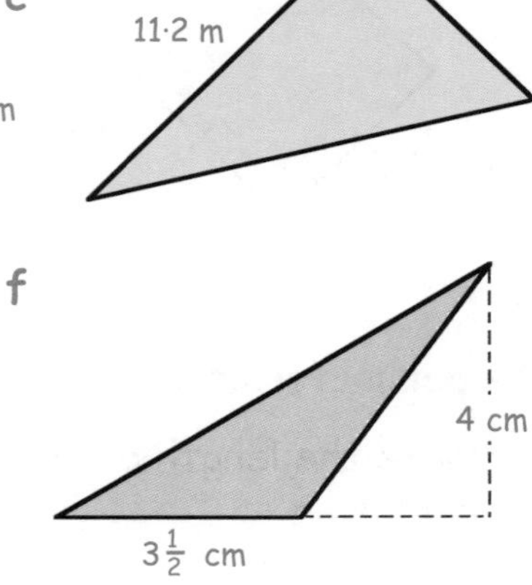

d

e

f

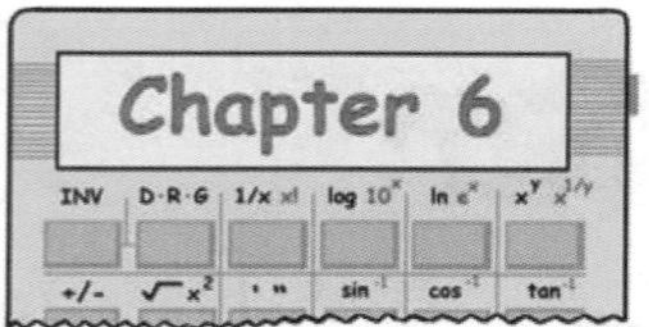

Area & Perimeter

Perimeter of a Rectilinear Shape and a Circle

The perimeter of a rectilinear shape is found by :-

"adding the lengths of its sides".

Example 1 :-

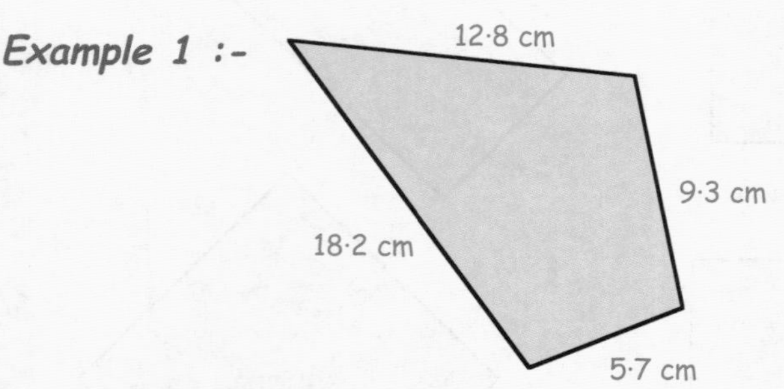

Perimeter = (5·7 + 9·3 + 12·8 + 18·2) cm
= **46 cm**

The perimeter (circumference) of a circle is found by using the formula :-

"$C = \pi \times D$", where D is the diameter and π = 3·14.....

Example 2 :-

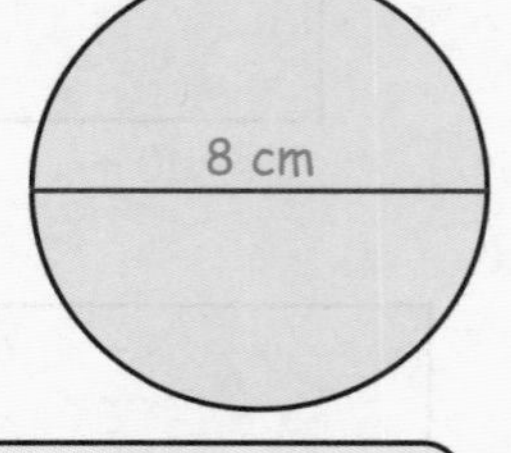

$C = \pi D$
=> $C = 3{\cdot}14 \times 8$ cm
=> C = **25·12 cm**

Exercise 1

1. Calculate the perimeter of each of the following shapes :-

a

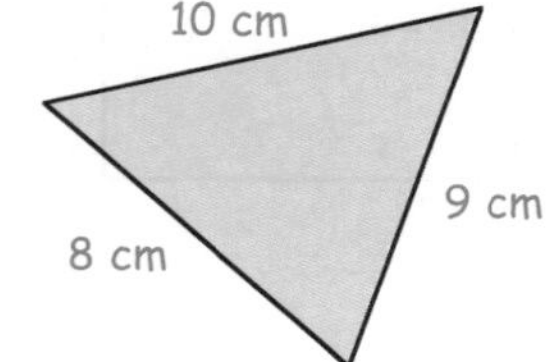

b

c

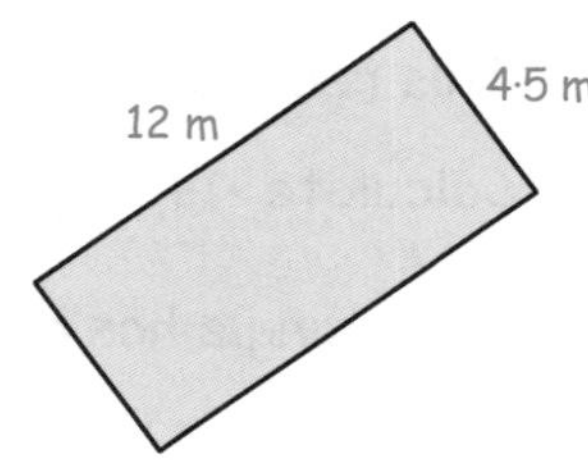

d

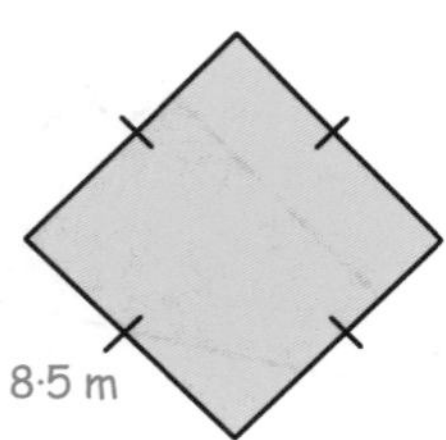

e

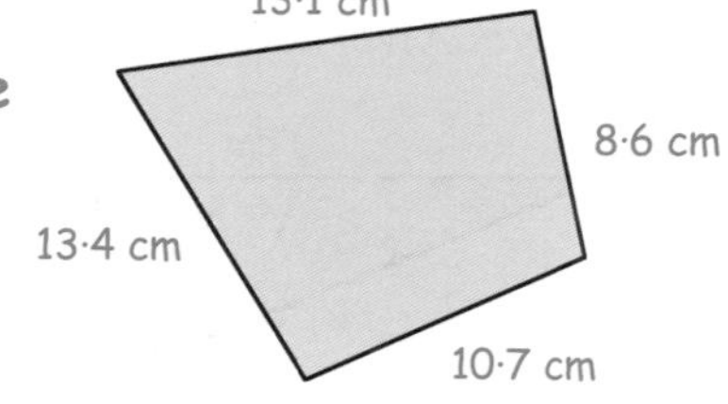

f

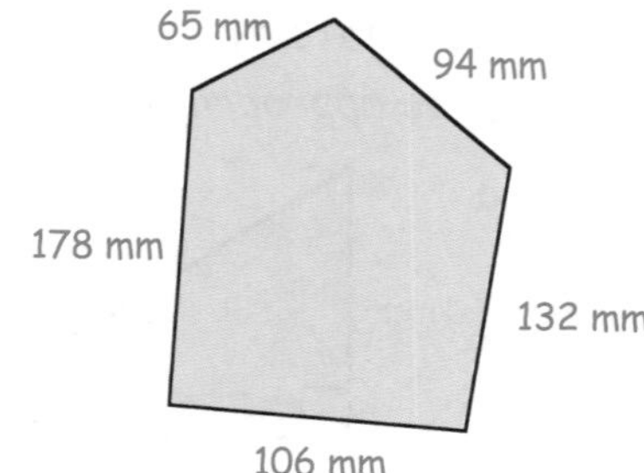

2. The perimeter of this rectangle is 136 cm.

Calculate the length of the missing side of the rectangle.

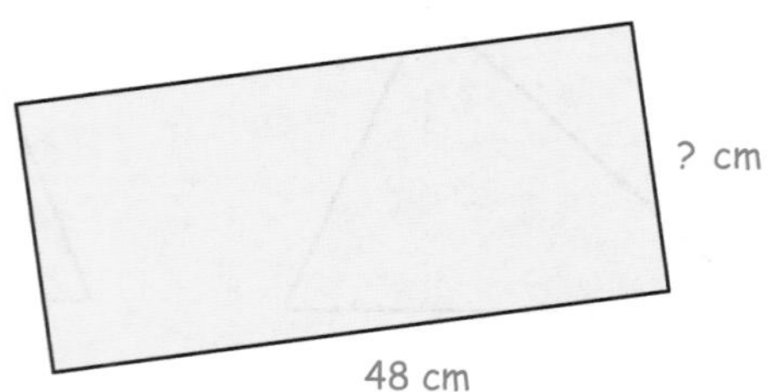

3. The diagram shows Mr Tait's dining room floor.

   a Calculate the perimeter of the floor.

   b How much will it cost to surround it with new skirting board costing £4·50 per metre ?

   (The door is 0·80 metre wide).

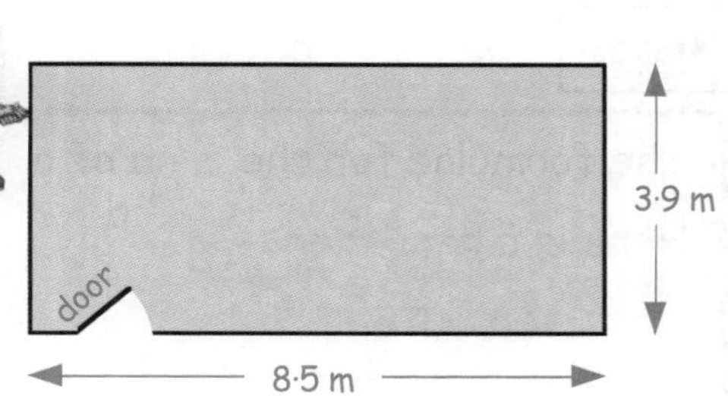

4. Calculate the circumference of a circle with diameter 9 centimetres.

   Copy and complete :-

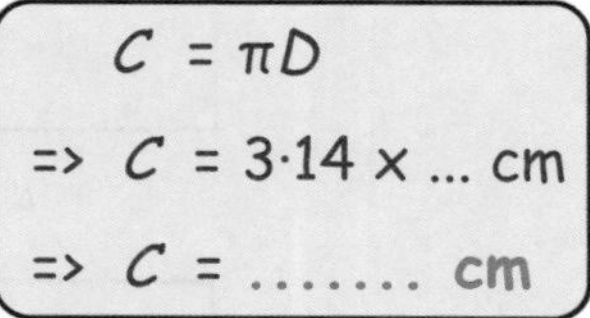

$C = \pi D$

=> C = 3·14 x ... cm

=> C = ... cm

5. Calculate the circumference of each of these circles :-

a 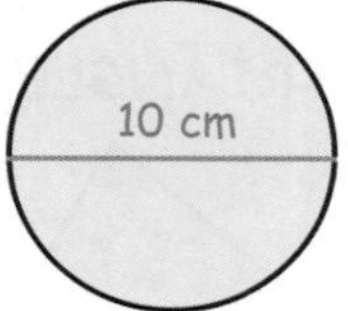

b 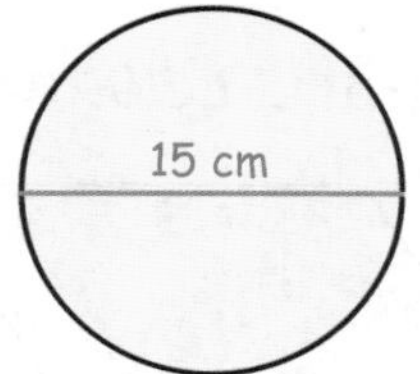

c 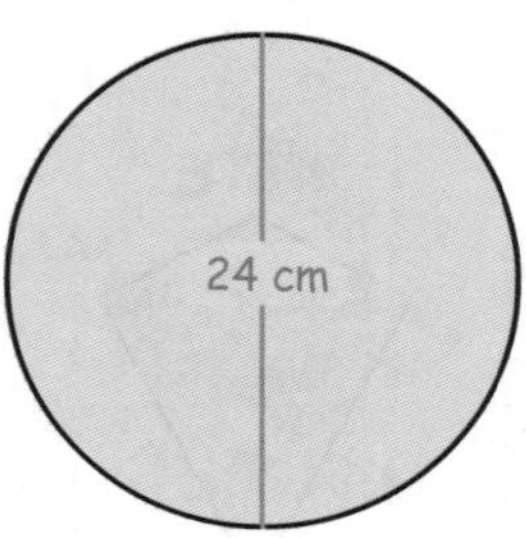

6. Work out the circumference of each object :-

a 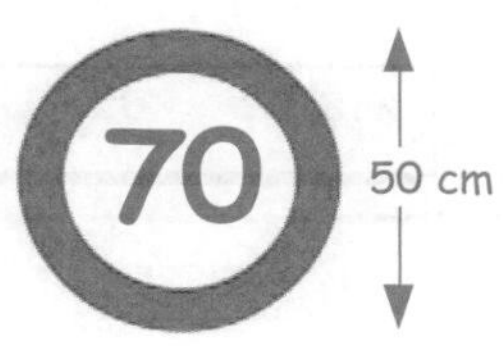

b 

diameter 26 mm

c 

48 cm

Remember :- If you are given the radius, you need to double it to get the diameter.

7. Calculate the circumference of a circle with radius 7 centimetres.

   Copy and complete :-

Radius = 7 cm	$C = \pi D$
Diameter = 14 cm	=> C = 3·14 x ... cm
	=> C = ... cm

8. Find the circumference of these two objects :-

a 

10 cm

b 

radius 2·5 m

9. A semi-circular garden has a radius of 2·1 metres.

   a Write down the length of its diameter.

   b Calculate the length of the semi-circle.

   c Find the perimeter of the garden.

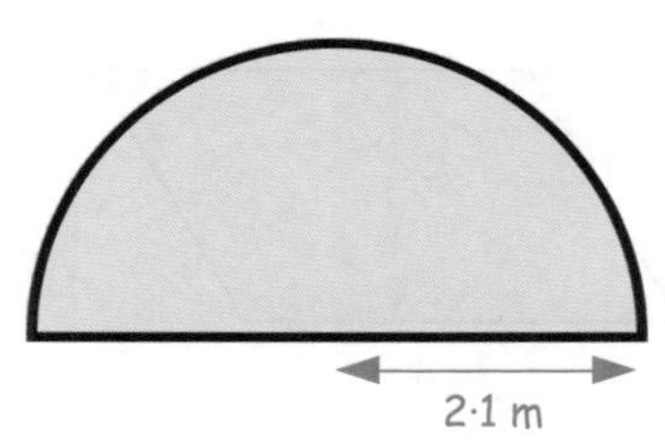

Areas

The formulae for the **area** of a triangle, quadrilateral and circle should now be known.

Here is a **reminder** :-

SQUARE

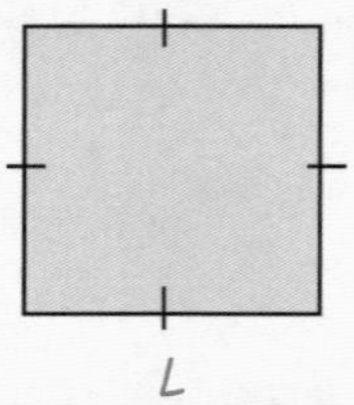

L

Area = L^2

RECTANGLE

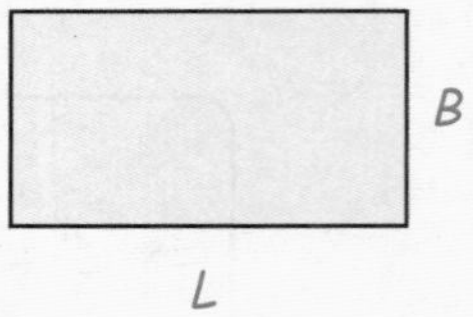

B

L

Area = $L \times B$

RHOMBUS

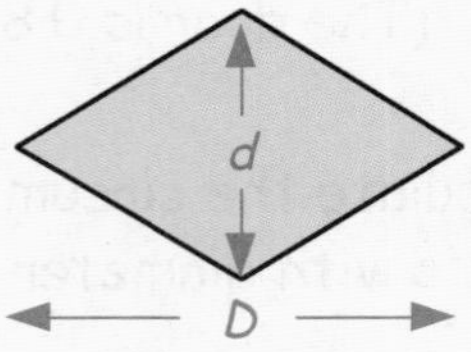

d

D

Area = $\frac{1}{2} D \times d$

KITE

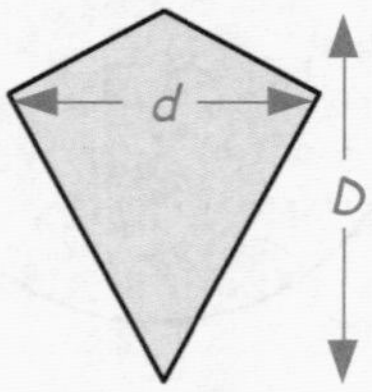

d

D

Area = $\frac{1}{2} D \times d$

PARALLELOGRAM

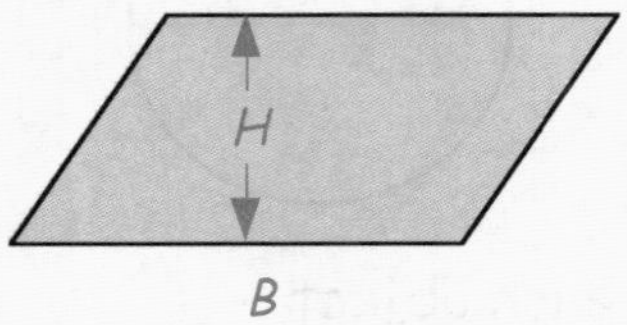

H

B

Area = $B \times H$

TRIANGLE

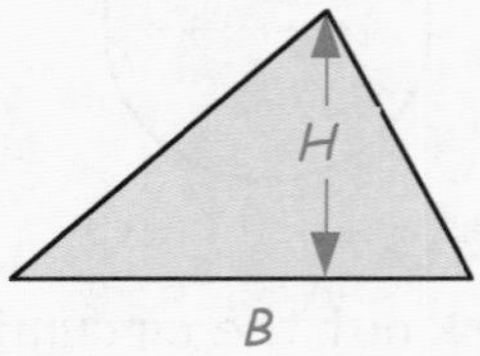

H

B

Area = $\frac{1}{2} B \times H$

Exercise 2

1. Use the correct formula to calculate these areas :-

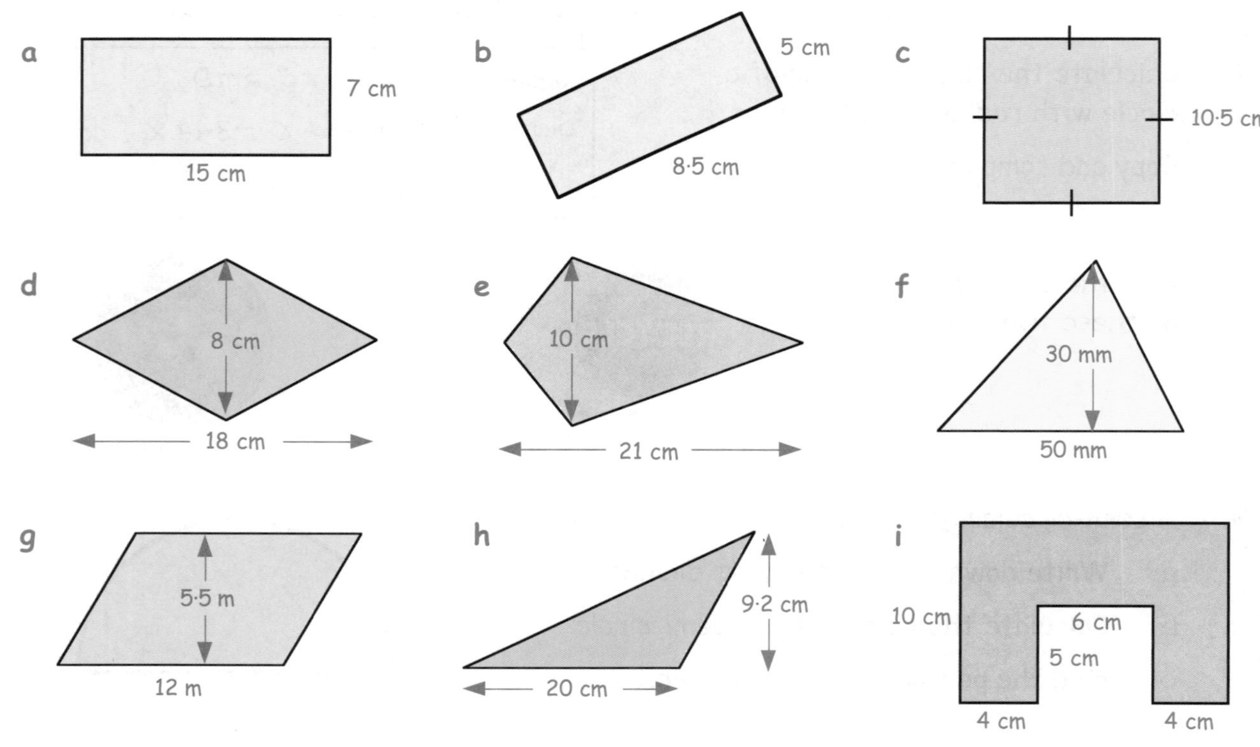

The Area of a Circle

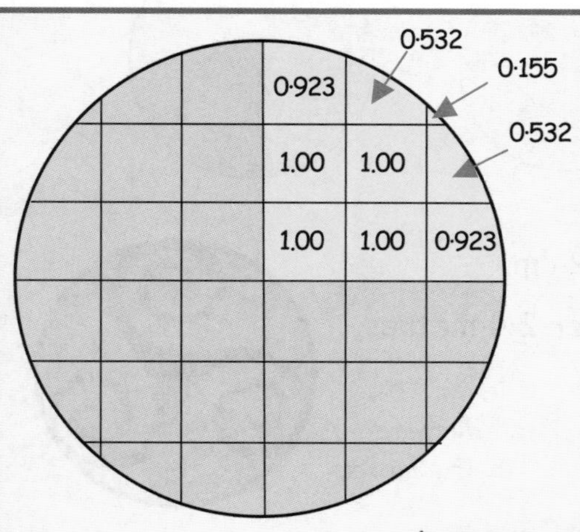

The **blue** area (quarter circle) has been placed in a square centimetre grid and the area for each part has been measured and is given in the diagram.

The total **blue** area (*quarter circle*) is $7 \cdot 065 \text{ cm}^2$.

This means the total area of the circle is :-

$$7{\cdot}065 \times 4 \;=\; 28 \cdot 26 \text{ cm}^2.$$

There is a formula (or rule) we can use to calculate the area of a circle as long as you know its radius.

Area generally uses two measurements (... cm x ... cm).

We find that if we calculate $r \times r$ (or r^2), and multiply it by π, we also get an answer of $28 \cdot 26 \text{ cm}^2$,

which is the same value as we found by measuring !

To find the area of a circle we can use :- $\pi \times r \times r$ or $A = \pi r^2$

Example :- Calculate the area of a circle with radius 30 cm.

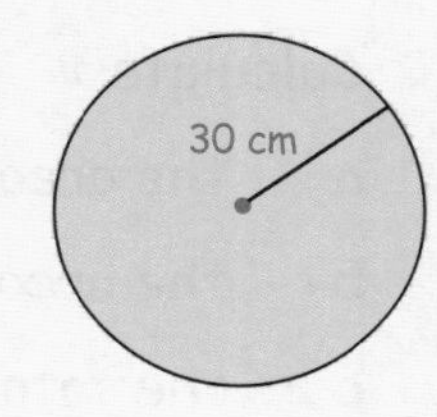

$A = \pi r^2$

=> $A = 3{\cdot}14 \times 30 \times 30$

=> $A = 2826 \text{ cm}^2$ (square centimetres)

Exercise 3 *Give each answer correct to 2 decimal places, where necessary.*

1. Find the **area** of a circle with radius 3 cm.

   Copy and complete :-

   $A = \pi r^2$

   => $A = 3{\cdot}14 \times 3 \times 3$

   => $A = \ldots\ldots \text{ cm}^2$

2. Using 3 lines of working, calculate the **area** of each circle :-

a

b

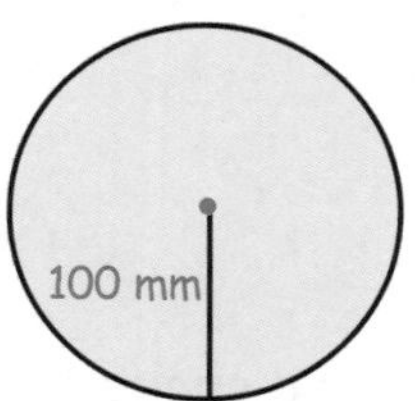

c

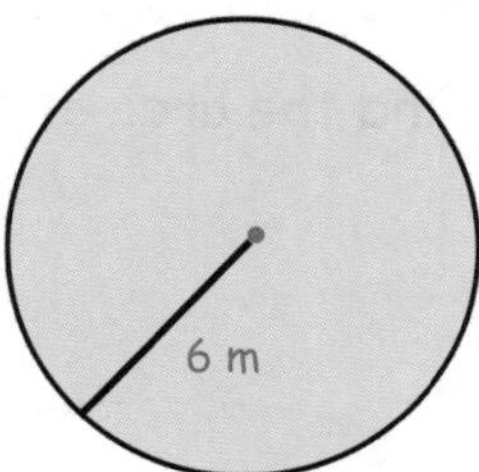

3. 

   Find the radius of this circular place mat and then calculate its **area**.

4. Calculate the area of each circle :-

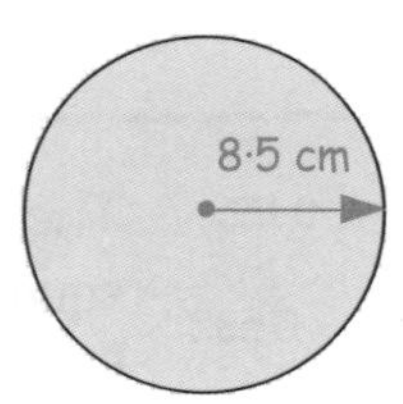

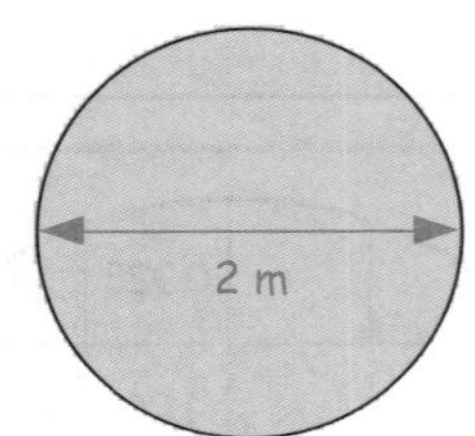

5. a Find the area of a circular poster with radius 32 cm.

   b Work out the area of a circular rug with diameter 2·4 metres.

   c A circular shield has a diameter of half a metre.

   Find the area of the shield.

diameter half a metre

   d 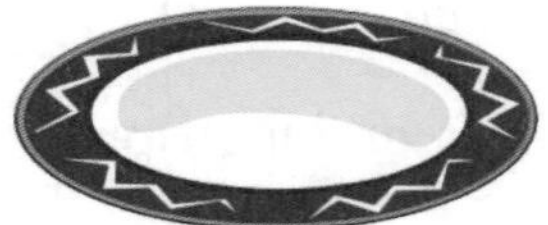

   A circular dessert plate has a radius of 14 cm.

   Calculate the area of the plate.

6. A circle is cut from a square piece of wood with sides 38 centimetres, as shown.

   Calculate :-

   a the area of the original wooden square.

   b the area of the circular piece.

   c the total area of wood that remains.

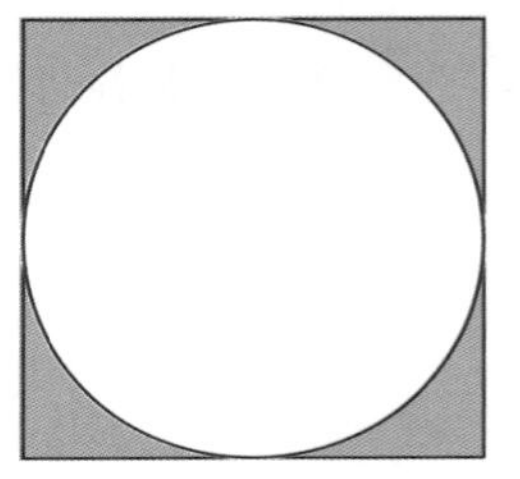

38 cm

7. 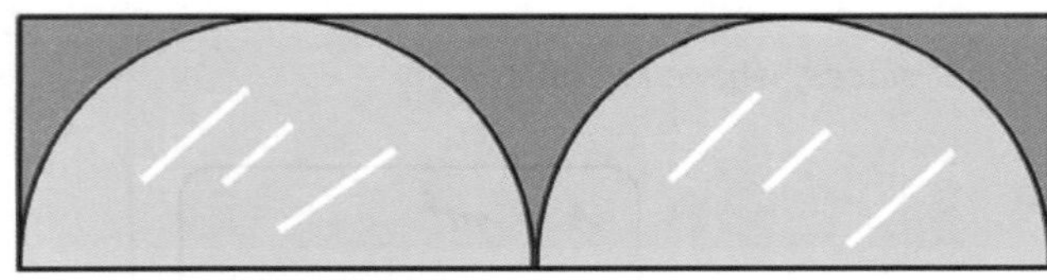

   Two semi-circular mirrors of radius 50 centimetres are placed side by side on a purple frame as shown.

   * to find the area of a semi-circle - find the area of the whole circle first and then halve the answer.

   Find the area of purple frame **not** covered by the mirrors.

8. A garden pond is in the shape of a semi-circle.

   Find the area of the pond.

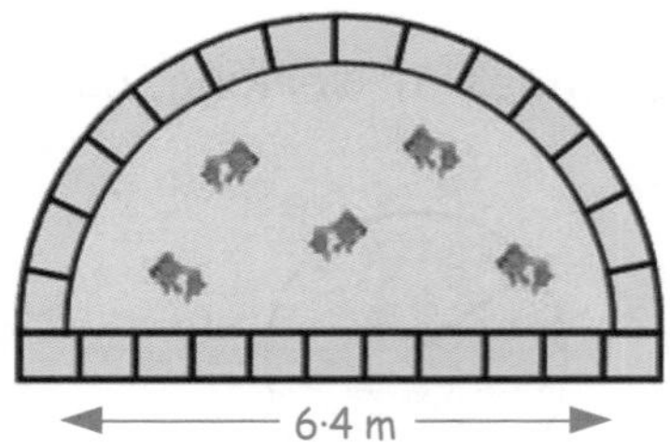

9. 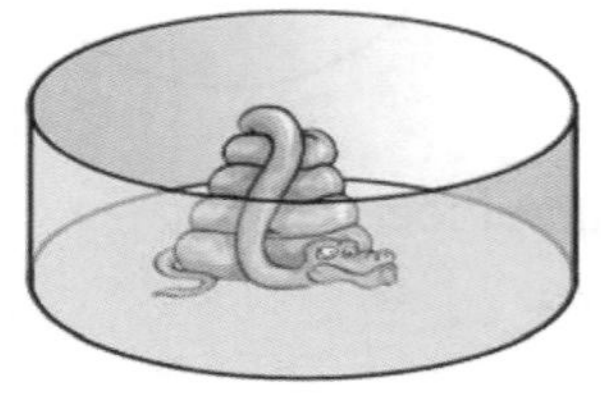

   A cylindrical snake tank has a base with radius 37·5 centimetres.

   The circular base has to be treated with a special paint which costs 0·5 pence per square centimetre.

   Find the cost of painting the base of the tank.

Composite Areas

If a shape is made up of 2 (or more) rectangles, to find its area :-

Step 1 Calculate the area of each rectangle.

Step 2 Add the areas together.

Example 1 :-

=> Area (of A) = $L \times B = 5 \times 14 = 70 \text{ cm}^2$

=> Area (of B) = $L \times B = 20 \times 13 = 260 \text{ cm}^2$

=> **Total Area** = $70 + 260 = \mathbf{330 \text{ cm}^2}$

Example 2 :-

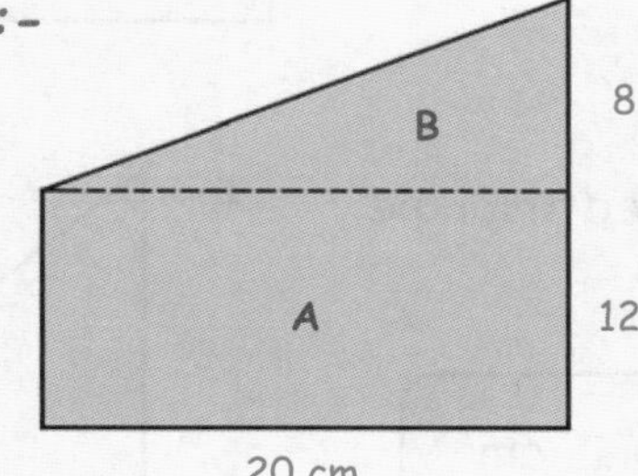

If the shape consists of a triangle and a rectangle, to find its area :-

Step 1 Find the area of the rectangle.

Step 2 Find the area of the triangle.

Step 3 Add the areas together.

Area of rectangle A = $L \times B = 20 \times 12 = 240 \text{ cm}^2$

Area of triangle B = $\frac{1}{2}(B \times H) = \frac{1}{2}$ of $20 \times 8 = 80 \text{ cm}^2$

=> **Total Area** = $240 + 80 = \mathbf{320 \text{ cm}^2}$

Exercise 4

1. a Calculate the area of the big rectangle.
   b Calculate the area of the small rectangle.
   c Calculate the **total** area of the shape.

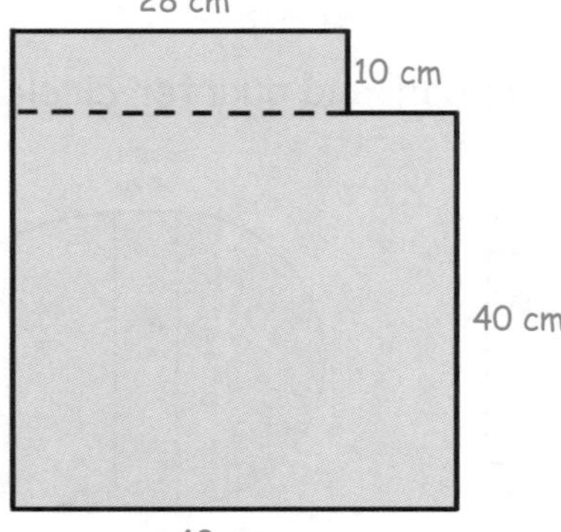

2. a Calculate the area of the square.
   b Calculate the area of the rectangle.
   c Calculate the **total** area of the shape.

3. For each of these shapes :- (i) calculate the area of each part (*show working*)

(ii) calculate the area of the whole shape.

a

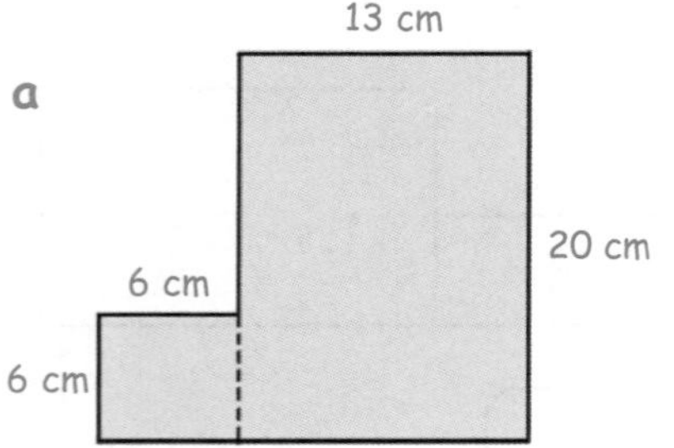

Area of square	$= L \times B$	$= 6 \times ....$	$= .... \text{ cm}^2$
Area of rectangle	$= L \times B$	$= 13 \times ....$	$= .... \text{ cm}^2$
=> **Total Area** =	....	+	$= .... \text{ cm}^2$

b

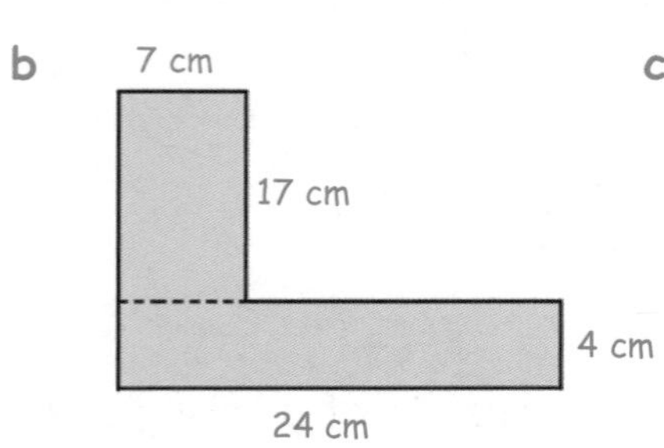

c

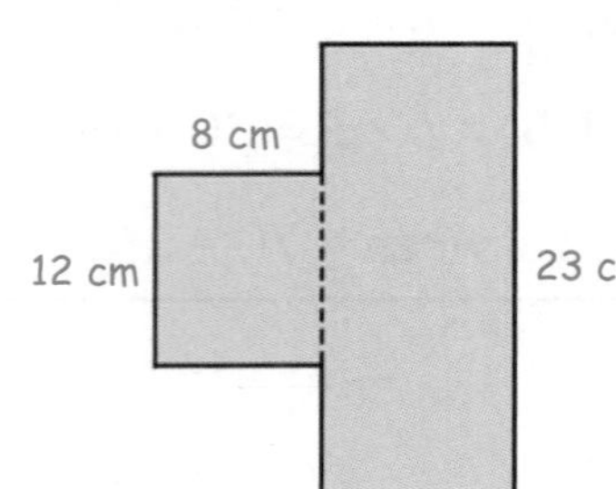

d

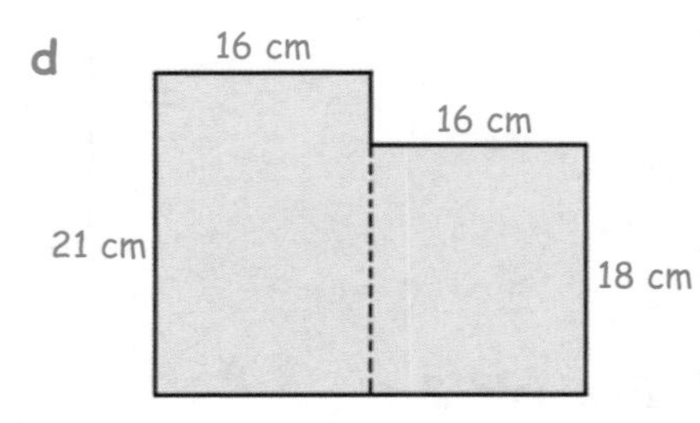

4. This shape consists of a rectangle and a right angled triangle.

Copy the working and complete it :-

Area of rectangle A	$= L \times B$	$= 14 \times ....$	$= .... \text{ cm}^2$
Area of triangle B	$= \frac{1}{2}(B \times H)$	$= \frac{1}{2} \text{ of } 14 \times ....$	$= .... \text{ cm}^2$
=> **Total Area** =	.....	+	$= ... \text{ cm}^2.$

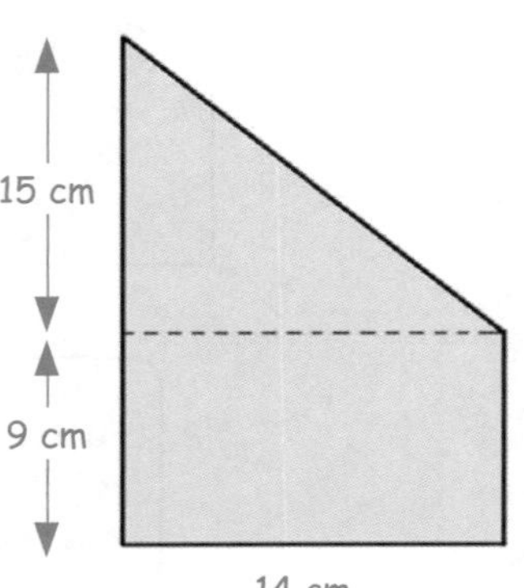

5. Calculate the area of each of the following shapes :-

a

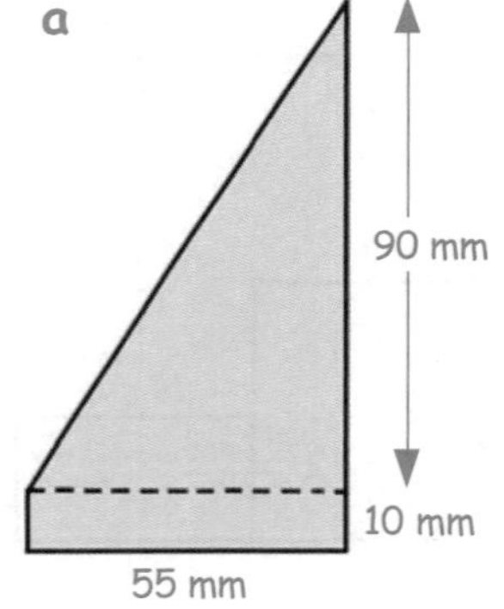

b

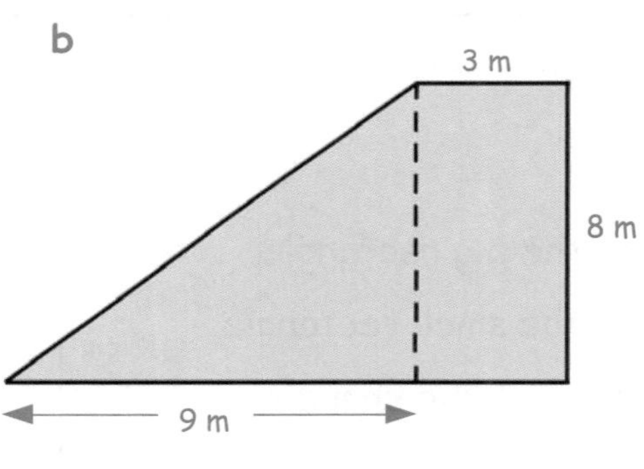

c

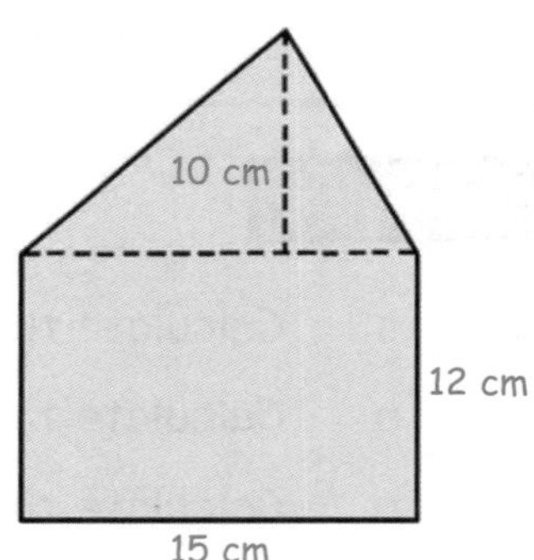

6. Calculate the area of each of the shapes below involving half and quarter circles :-

a

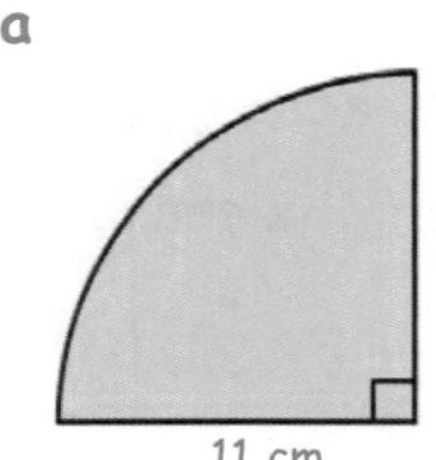

b

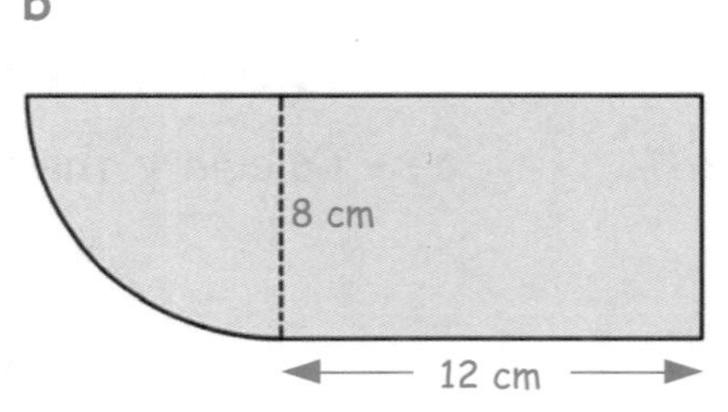

c

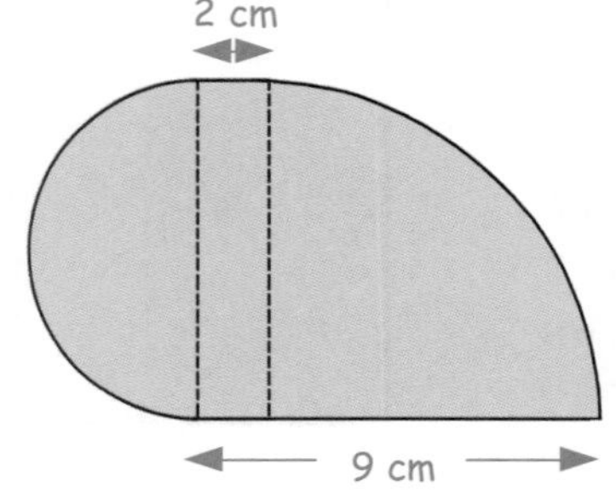

Area & Perimeter

Numeracy Assessment 6

1. Joe uses a circular piece of wood to make a trundle wheel.

   The wheel has radius 15 centimetres.

   What distance is covered by 20 complete rotations of the wheel ?

2. 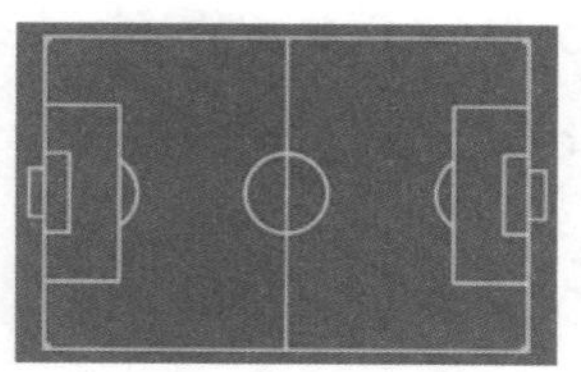

   A football pitch is 75 metres wide.

   It has an area of 8250 square metres.

   Calculate the perimeter of the football pitch.

3. A semi-circular window in a church door is made from three identical pieces of glass.

   One pane of glass was broken during a stormy night.

   The semi-circle has a radius of 40 centimetres.

   Work out the area of the damaged pane of glass.

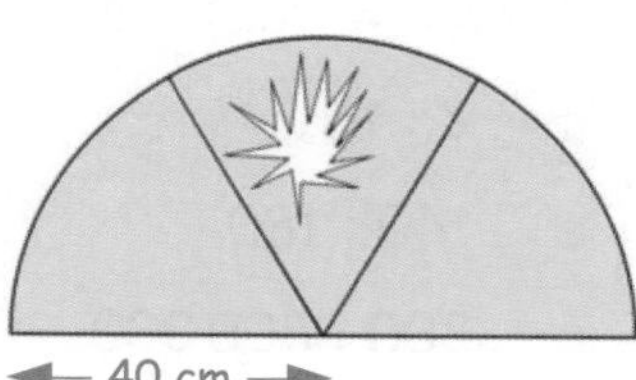

4. 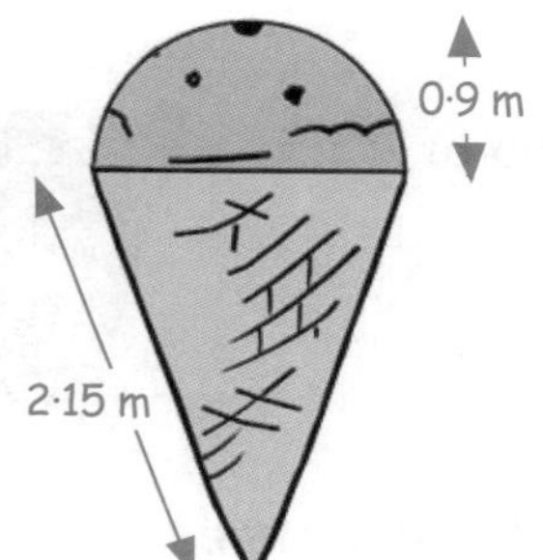

   Shown is the sign outside an ice cream shop.

   It has two equal straight edges and a semi-circular edge.

   Each straight edge is 2·15 metres long and the radius of the semi-circle is 0·9 metres.

   Work out the perimeter of the sign.

5. The top of Lisa Turner's computer table is in the shape of a quarter-circle.

   0·85 m

   a Calculate the area of her table.

   b Lisa asks her father to varnish the table.

      The tin of varnish Mr Turner buys covers 2 square metres.

      Will he be able to give the table 4 coats of varnish ? *Explain.*

6. A golden pendant is designed in the form of a rhombus with a circular hole of diameter 4 cm cut from its centre.

   Calculate the area of gold needed to make the pendant.

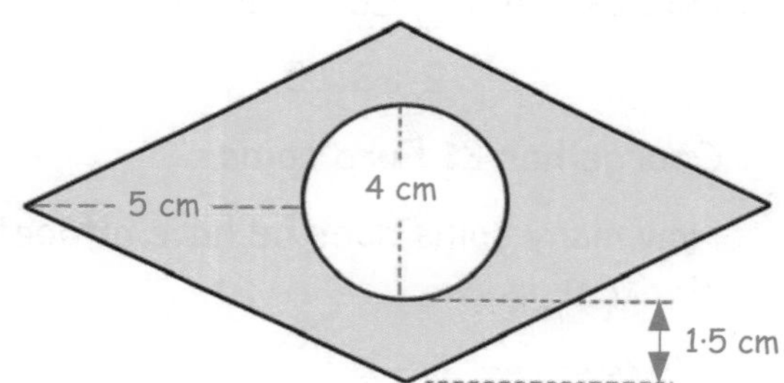

Ratio & Proportion

Revision of Ratio & Proportion

1. In a jar there are 24 plastic buttons and 18 brass buttons.
   - a Write down the ratio of plastic : brass buttons.
   - b Simplify this ratio as far as possible.

2. On a shop shelf there are 160 cans and 72 bottles of cola.
   - a Write down the ratio of bottles to cans on the shelf.
   - b Write this ratio in its simplest form.

3. Simplify the following ratios fully where possible :-

a	2 : 16	b	25 : 5	c	18 : 48	d	72 : 18
e	140 : 180	f	17 : 53	g	333 : 444	h	81 : 108
i	200 : 800 000	j	66 : 88	k	720 : 240	l	1313 : 13
m	1·5 : 5	n	1·6 : 6·4	o	1·7 : 51	p	$3\frac{1}{2}$: 14.

4. A phone shop sells iPhones and Samsung phones in a ratio of 7 : 5.
   Last week the shop sold 42 iPhones.
   How many Samsung phones did it sell ?

5. A shoe shop sells dress shoes and casual shoes.
   The ratio of dress to casual shoes is 2 : 11.
   If there were 40 dress shoes sold :-
   - a how many casual shoes were sold ?
   - b how many shoes were sold altogether ?

6. George has collected lots of foreign coins from his holidays.
   He has Dollars, Euros and Baht in a ratio of :-

   2 : 3 : 5.

   George has 21 Euro coins.
   How many coins does he have altogether ?
   Show all working.

7. Calculate the cost of one item for each of the following :-

a Eight pens costing 96p

b Seven cakes costing £42

c Twenty DVD's for £140

d 3 shirts for £120

e Nine headphones for £459

f One hundred books for £570

g Seven pies for £8·40

h Four tyres for £207·32.

8. Calculate the weight/length of three of each of these items :-

a two identical boxes weighing 64 kg

b 6 planks with total length 8·4 m

c six filing cabinets weighing 81 kg

d Five carpet rolls with total length 175 metres.

9. 

Five large Hawaiian pizzas cost £45·50.

a What is the cost of 1 Hawaiian pizza ?

b How much would it cost for four ?

10. a It took a go-kart 130 seconds to complete 5 laps.

How long would the go-kart take to go round twice ?

b The go-kart uses 12 litres of petrol in a day.

In a day, the go-kart would be used for 6 one hour sessions.

How much petrol would be used in 5 sessions ?

11. Sam needs a 10 kg bag of sand to cover his lawn which is 10 m by 8 m.

Bob next door has a lawn which is 12 m by 5 m.

What weight of sand should Bob need ?

12. Jill needs four 1 litre tins of paint to paint her 8 m by 3 m wall.

How many litres of paint will she need for a 12 m by 2·5 m wall ?

13. 

Gary runs 24 kilometres in 3 hours.

Gareth runs for 2 hours and covers 18 kilometres.

Gio runs at an average speed of 8·5 km /hr.

Who is running fastest ?

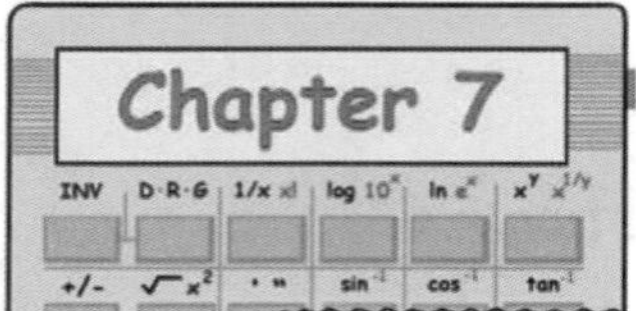

Ratio & Proportion

Ratio Calculations Revision

Ratios can be used in a variety of real life problems.

Example :- To obtain a particular shade of **purple** paint, *Q & B* have to mix red and blue paint in the ratio, red : blue = 4 : 7.

For a large order, *Q & B* use 20 tins of red paint. How many blue tins are required ?

Set down like this :-

	red	blue	
× 5	4	7	× 5
	20	35	

Since 20 = **5** × **4**

then blue = **5** × **7** = 35.

=> Needs 35 blue tins.

Exercise 1

1. A different shade of **purple** can be made by using red : blue = 5 : 6.

   a If *Q & B* used 15 tins of red paint, how many tins of blue are needed ?

   Start with this :-

	red	blue	
× ?	5	6	× ?
	15	...	

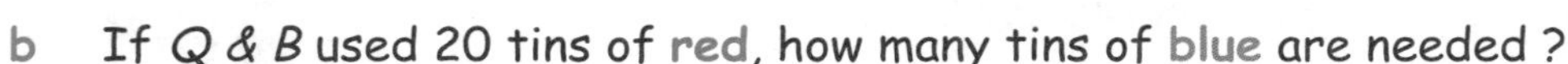

   b If *Q & B* used 20 tins of red, how many tins of blue are needed ?

   c If, this time, *Q & B* used 42 tins of blue, how much red is needed ?

2. 

Rabbits	Mice
7	10
21	...

In a pet shop, the ratio of rabbits to mice is 7 : 10.

   a If there are 21 rabbits, how many mice must there be ?

   b If in fact, there are 90 mice, how many rabbits are there ?

3. A warehouse stores tables and chairs in a ratio of 1 : 6.

   a How many chairs are stored if there are 15 tables ?

   b How many tables are stored if there are 72 chairs ?

   c How many items are there if there are 186 chairs stored ?

4. 

Ben and Jerry compared their weekly wages.

The **ratio** of their pay was :- Ben : Jerry = 5 : 8.

a If Ben earned £250, how much must Jerry have earned ?

b If Jerry earned £328, how much must Ben have earned ?

c Their Christmas bonus was also in the same ratio. Ben got a £480 bonus. How much did Jerry get for his bonus ?

5. Look at this chart for making **purple** paint.

Which **shade** of **purple** will I get if I mix :-

a 1200 ml of **red** with 200 ml of **blue**

b 140 ml of **red** with 210 ml of **blue**

c 18 tins of **red** with 12 tins of **blue**

d 3600 ml of **red** with 800 ml of **blue**

e 4 litres of **red** with 16 litres of **blue** ?

	Mix in the Ratio		
Colour	***Red***	**:**	***Blue***
Very dark purple	6	:	1
Dark purple	9	:	2
Mid purple	3	:	2
Light purple	2	:	3
Very light purple	1	:	4

6. The ratio of pens : pencils : markers in a teacher's cupboard is 4 : 5 : 1.

a How many pencils are there if there are 32 pens ?

b How many pens are there if there are 20 markers ?

c How many pencils and markers are there if there are 24 pens ?

7. Ed has a large pile of 5p, 10p and 20p coins in the ratio of 8 : 11 : 13.

a How many 20p coins does he have if he has sixteen 5p coins ?

b He knows he has thirty nine 20p coins. How much money does he have in total ?

8. The ratio of hens : sheep : cows on a large farm is 11 : 6 : 5.

a How many cows are there if there are 18 sheep ?

b How many hens are there if there are 40 cows ?

c How many animals are there if there are 30 cows ?

d If there are 220 animals, how many cows are there ?

9. The ratio of tins : boxes : packets on a store shelf is 17 : 8 : 15.

How many items are on the shelf in total if there are 75 packets ?

Proportional Division - Sharing in a Given Ratio

Example :-

Rosie and Jim share a prize of £2700 in a ratio of 5 : 4.
How much money will each get ?

Step 1 :-	Since the ratio is 5 : 4, there are (5 + 4) = 9 shares
Step 2 :-	Each share is worth (£2700 ÷ 9) = £300
Step 3 :-	Rosie gets 5 shares (5 x £300) = £1500
	Jim gets 4 shares (4 x £300) = £1200
	(Check that the total for Rosie and Jim is £2700).

Exercise 2

1. Share £350 between Lennie and Jean in the ratio 2 : 5.

   Copy and complete :-

Total number of shares		=	2 + 5 = ...
Each share =	£350 ÷	=	£........
Lennie has 2 shares	= 2 x £.....	=	£......
Jean has 5 shares	= 5 x £.....	=	£......

   check your total is £350

2. Show similar working for each of the following and work out :-
   - a Share £10 000 between Ken and Kath in the ratio 1 : 4.
   - b Share £120 between Dan and Dean in the ratio 3 : 5.
   - c Share £880 between Fred and Jess in the ratio 5 : 6.
   - d Share £4000 between Will and Anne in the ratio 11 : 9.
   - e Share £50 between Pete and Pat in the ratio 13 : 12.
   - f Share £250 between Bushra and Mo in the ratio 23 : 27.
   - g Share £3000 in a 1 : 3 : 2 ratio.
   - h Share £1 million in the ratio 2 : 3 : 5.

3. Joe (aged 6) and Lesley (aged 9) are left £300 000 in their Papa's will.

   The money is to be shared between them in the ratio of their ages.

   How much will Joe get ?

4. A fish stall was set up in a market. The ratio of haddock : cod : salmon was 8 : 5 : 2.

   If there were 200 cod, how many fish in total were on sale ?

Direct Proportion

Two quantities, (for example, the **number** of DVDs sold and their **total** cost), are said to be in **direct proportion**, if : -

"... when you double the number of DVDs you double the cost."

Example :-

The cost of 6 DVDs is £75.

Find the cost of 11 of these DVD's.

DVDS		*Cost*
6	—>	£75
1	—>	£75 ÷ 6 = £12·50
11	—>	11 × £12·50
		= **£137·50**

(Note :- Always find the cost or value of 1 item first.)

Exercise 3

1. The cost of 8 calculators is £37·60.
   - a Find the cost of one calculator.
   - b What do 5 of these calculators cost ?

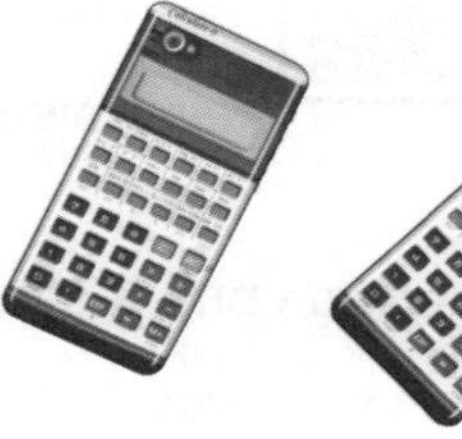

2. 

   Nine identical metal cases weigh 81 kg.
   - a Find the weight of one case.
   - b What is the weight of seven cases ?

3. Before going on holiday, I changed £380 to euros, receiving 425·60 euros for my money.

   My friend, Beth changed her £75 spending money into Euros at the same exchange rate.

   How many euros did she get ?

4. 

   A man can tile an area of 3600 cm^2 in 4 minutes.

   He works for 10 minutes tiling.

   What area does he tile ?

5. a A machine for making board tacks can produce 560 tacks every 7 seconds.

   How many board tacks will it make in one minute ?

5. b A potato picker can pick 12 potatoes in 20 seconds.
Working at the same rate, how many potatoes can he pick in an hour ?

6. a Nine pastries cost £8·01. What will ten cost ?
   b Seven tyres weigh 42 kg. What will six weigh ?
   c A dozen cakes cost £60. How much will five cost ?
   d Twenty sweets cost £3. How much will it cost for 5 sweets ?

7. Tony gets paid £420 for working twenty hours.
How much should he get for 8 hours work ?

8. 

The heights of two multi-storey car parks are in direct proportion to the number of floors in each.
One car park has 5 levels and is 27 metres high.
The other car park has 7 levels.
How high is this car park ?

9. Miss Parker can buy 4 copies of a book for £34·00.
How much extra would it cost her for 3 more copies ?

10. On an eight hour flight, a plane travels 4320 miles.
At the same speed, how far would it fly in 5 hours ?

11. Which of the following shows that the two quantities are in **direct proportion** ?
   a 5 doughnuts cost £1·90. Six cost £2·28.
   b 9 pens cost 72p. Five cost 35p.
   c 3 DVD's for £34·20. 4 DVDs for £45·20.
   d A box of 20 vitamin tablets for £0·50. A box of 30 tablets for 75p.

12. a A box of 500 pencils is on sale for £10. How much is it for 300 ?
   b 200 litres of oil cost £60. Find the cost of 150 litres.
   c 80 metres of fencing cost £128. How much would it cost for 130 metres ?

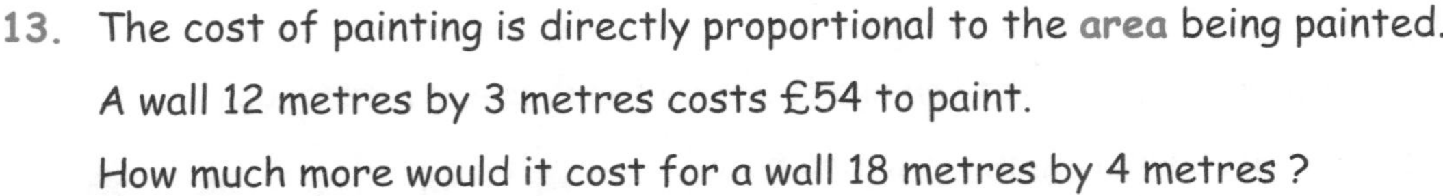

13. The cost of painting is directly proportional to the **area** being painted.
A wall 12 metres by 3 metres costs £54 to paint.
How much more would it cost for a wall 18 metres by 4 metres ?

Indirect (Inverse) Proportion

Direct Proportion means - the **more** of a quantity you buy, the **more** it will cost.

Indirect Proportion - again two quantities, but this time ....
as one quantity **increases** the other **decreases**.

Example :- The **faster** you travel in a car, the **less** time it takes for the journey.

Example :- It takes 8 hours for 3 men to paint a fence.

How long will it take 4 men to paint it if they worked at the same pace ?

Obviously less time !

More men working on the job take less time, as expected !

MEN		*HOURS*
3	–>	8
1	–>	3 x 8 = 24 *(man hours)*
4	–>	24 ÷ 4
		= **6 hours**

(note)

Exercise 4

1. It takes 5 men 12 hours to clean a fleet of buses.

   If 4 men were to do the job, how long would it take ?

MEN		*HOURS*
5	–>	12
1	–>	5 x ... = ... *(man hours)*
4	–>	.... ÷ 4
		= .... **hours**

2. It took 6 women 8 hours to decorate their store for Christmas.

   If only 5 women had been doing this, how long would it have taken ?

3. A train takes 7 hours for a journey at an average speed of 90 km/hr.

   At what speed would the train have to travel to cover the same journey in 5 hours ?

4. A group of five mountaineers take enough food to last a 12 day trip.

   Another seven climbers join the group, but they do not bring food.

   How many days will the food now last this larger group ?

5. 

   Jade has enough bugs to feed her 10 pet spiders for 3 weeks.

   She loses 4 of the spiders.

   How much longer will the food now last ?

6. A town's planning department reckoned that it would take 60 men 2 years to erect a new library building.

   If the building has to be ready in 18 months, how many **more** men will have to be employed ?

7. 

   A truck takes 4 hours to complete a journey, travelling at an average speed of 30 km/hr.

   At what speed will the truck have to travel, on average, if it is to cover the journey in 3 hours ?

8. Which of the following are examples of indirect proportion ? (*Write yes or no*).

   a The distance jogged, (at a fixed speed), and the time taken.

   b Company sales and the amount spent on advertising.

   c The number of seconds after you've been running and your pulse rate.

   d The number of turnstiles open at a football stadium and the time taken to fill the stadium with supporters.

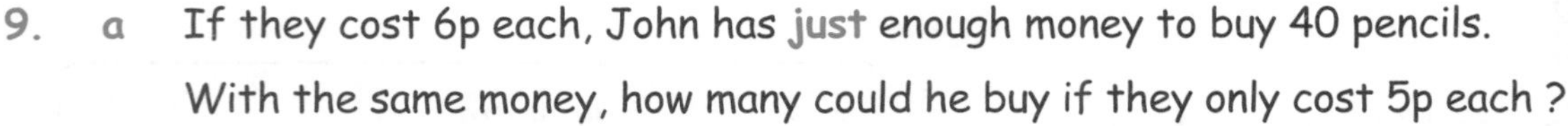

9. a If they cost 6p each, John has **just** enough money to buy 40 pencils.

   With the same money, how many could he buy if they only cost 5p each ?

   b It took 6 pupils 40 minutes to stock the school library.

   If 8 pupils had done the job, how much **quicker** would it have taken ?

10. Thirty hens have enough feed to last 6 days.

    If 10 hens escape, how much **longer** will the feed last those remaining ?

11. 

    It takes 6 men 80 minutes to move a tonne of soil using wheelbarrows.

    What is the fewest number of men needed to move the tonne of soil in **less** than 50 minutes ?

12. The wait time in a Superstore is *inversely proportional* to the number of tills open.

    There is a six minute wait when 3 tills are open.

    What is the wait time if 4 tills are openned ?

13. The more people you have, the less time a job will take.

    Can you think of a real life example where this is not true ?

Ratio & Proportion

Numeracy Assessment 7

1. Simplify the following ratios **fully** :-

   a 12 : 3 b 400 : 160 c 810 : 1080 d 34 : 51.

2. A rectangle has length 6 cm and breadth 5 cm.

   Find the ratio, in its simplest form, of **area : perimeter**. (*Forget units*).

3. A summer punch is made from apple and strawberry juice in a 3 : 2 ratio.

   Sally has 9 litres of apple juice.

   a How many litres of strawberry juice does she need ?

   b How many litres of punch can she make ?

4. A cake recipe requires self raising and plain flour in a ratio of 5 : 2.

   a The cake needs 200 g of self raising flour.

   How much plain flour is needed ?

   b Jake wants to make as many cakes as possible for a fete.

   He has 820 g of self raising flour and 300 g of plain flour.

   How many cakes can he make at most ?

5. a Mr Doyle bought 8 boxes of chocolates for £36.

   How much would he have paid for nine ?

   b Robert runs 3 km in 13 minutes.

   How long, in minutes and seconds, will it take to run 5 km at the same speed ?

6. The cost of painting is directly proportional to the area being painted.

   A wall 10 metres by 2·5 metres costs £12·50 to paint.

   How much will it cost to paint a wall 12 metres by 4 metres ?

7. It took 5 men 12 hours to dig a drainage ditch.

   How many hours less would it have taken 8 men to dig the same ditch ?

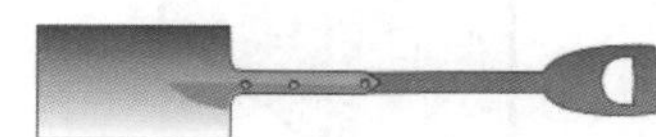

Volume 1

Revision of Volume

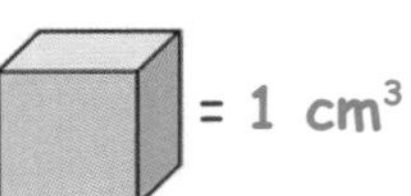

1. Write down the **volume** of each of these shapes, in cm^3 :-

a

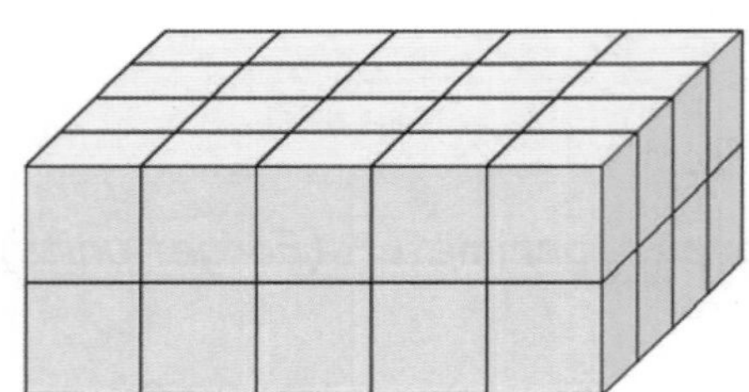

b

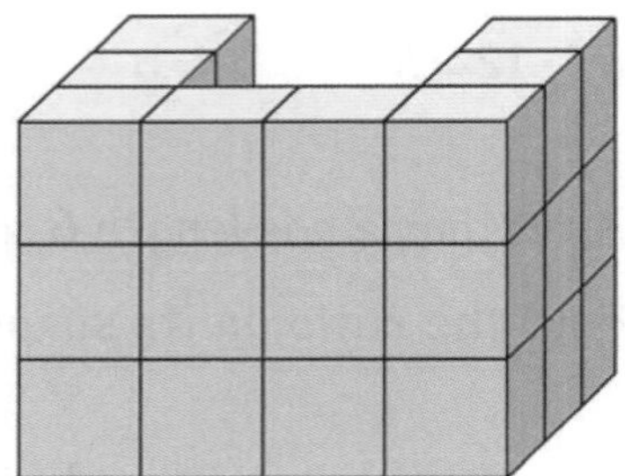

c

d

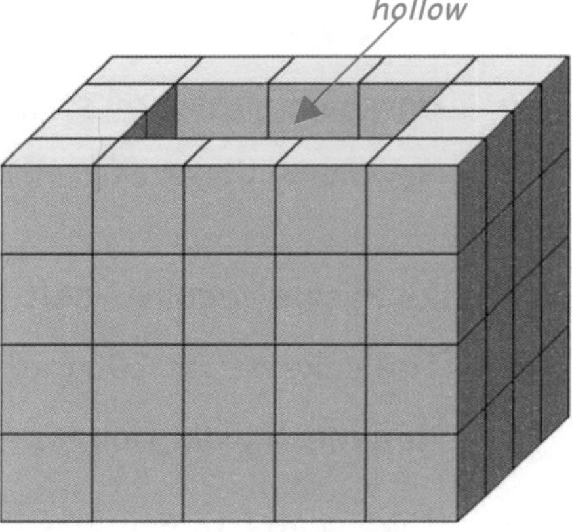

2. Use the formula :- $V = L \times B \times H$, to calculate the **volume** of each cuboid :-

a

2 cm

10 cm

8 cm

b

8·5 cm

12 cm

20 cm

c

d

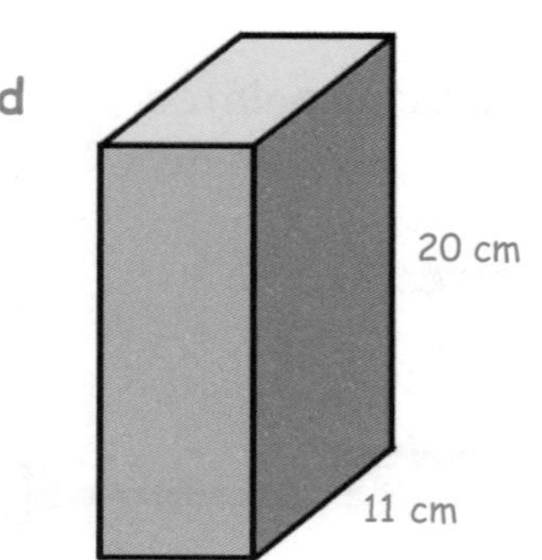

e

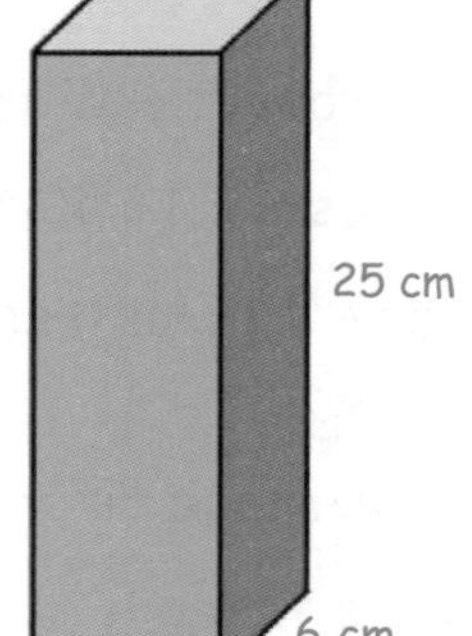

f

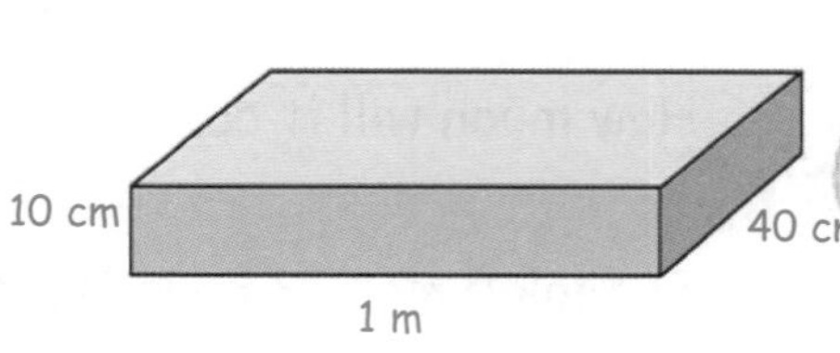

3. The volume of this tissue box is 1500 cm^3. Calculate its **height**.

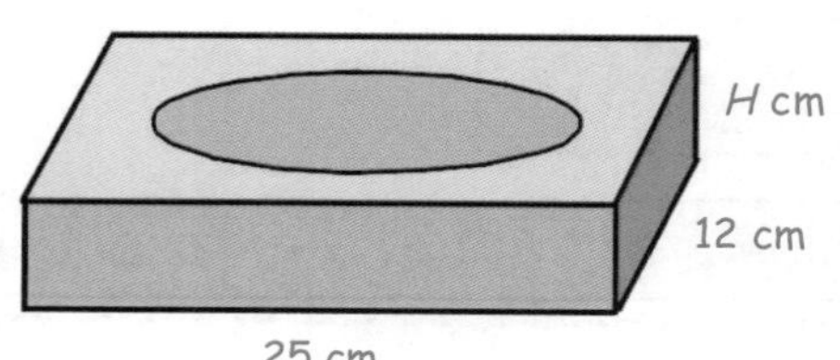

4. Find the missing dimension in each shape :-

a

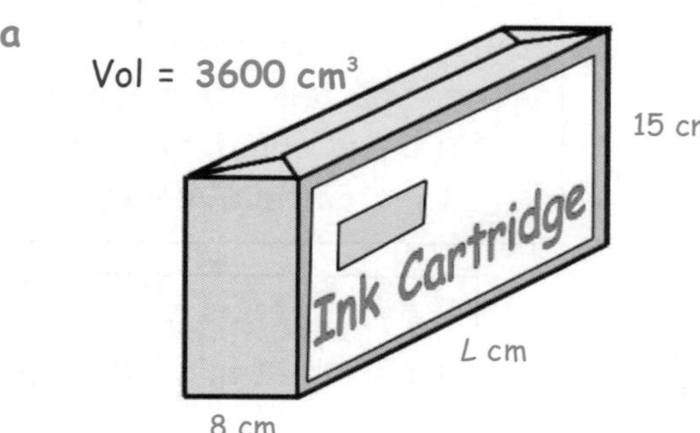

b

5. Change to litres :- (*Remember :- 1 litre = 1000 ml*).

a	4000 ml	b	90 000 ml	c	100 ml
d	750 ml	e	8 ml	f	0·1 ml.

6. Change to millilitres :-

a	5 litres	b	4·1 litres	c	100 litres
d	0·8 litres	e	0·007 litres	f	0·0015 litres.

7. 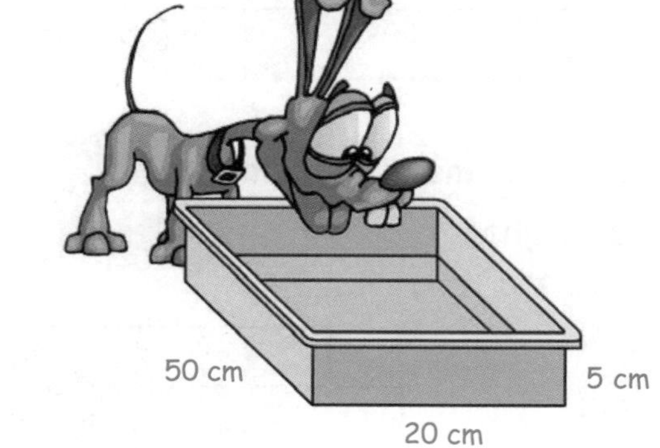

A dog's water tray is in the shape of a cuboid with dimensions as shown.

How many litres of water do you need to half fill this tray ?

8. a Calculate the volume of water in this tank, in cm^3.

b How many millilitres of water can it hold ?

c Change your answer to litres.

d When the tap is opened fully, water flows out of the tank at a rate of 5 litres per minute.

How long will it take for a full tank to empty ?

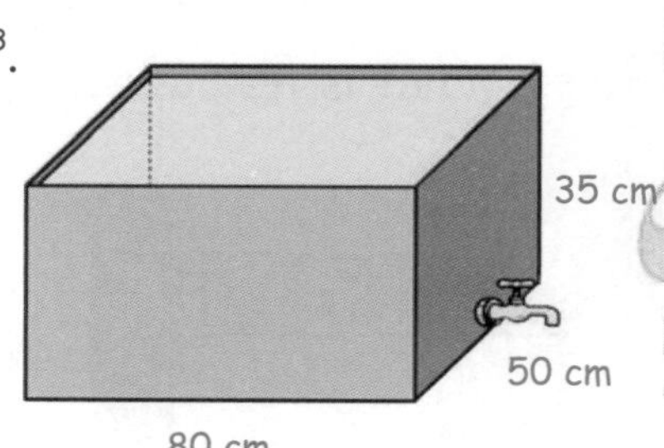

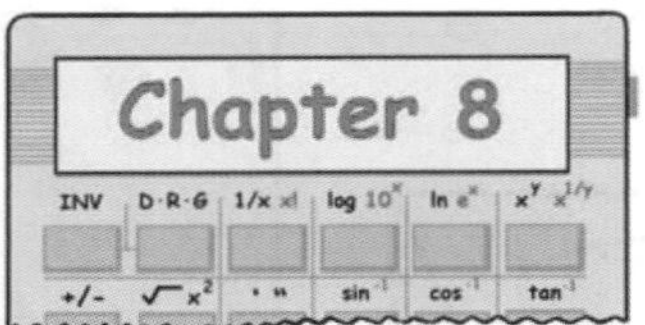

Volume 1

The Volume of a Cube and a Cuboid

The formulae for calculating the volume of a cube and cuboid should already be known.

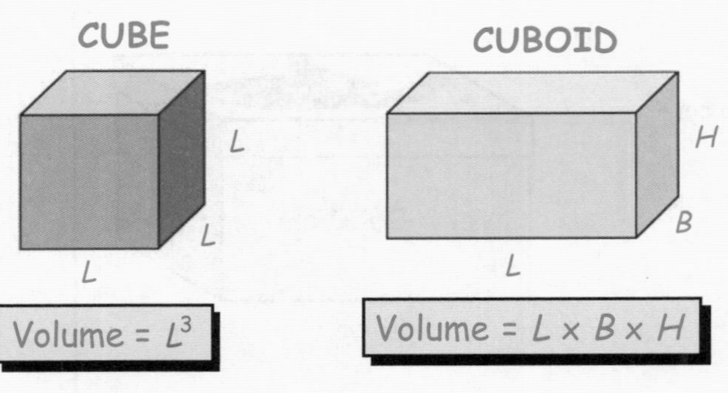

CAPACITY
When you talk about the volume of a liquid quantity, you refer to it as its CAPACITY.

NOTE

$1\ cm^3$ = 1 millilitre (ml)

1000 ml = 1 litre

Exercise 1 Revision

1. Copy and complete the working to help calculate the volume of this cuboid, in cubic cm, (cm^3).

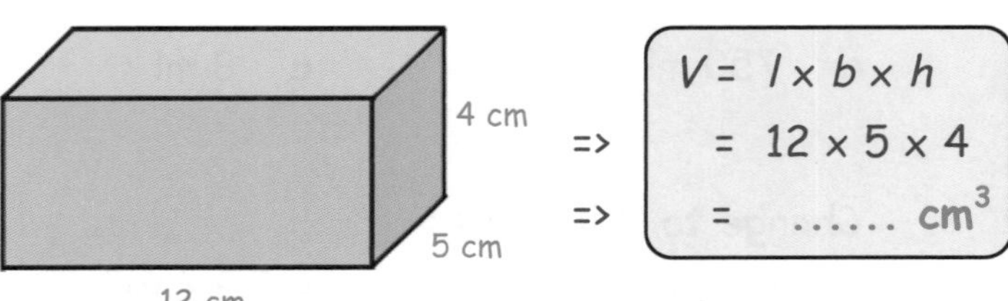

2. Work out the volume of this shallow block.

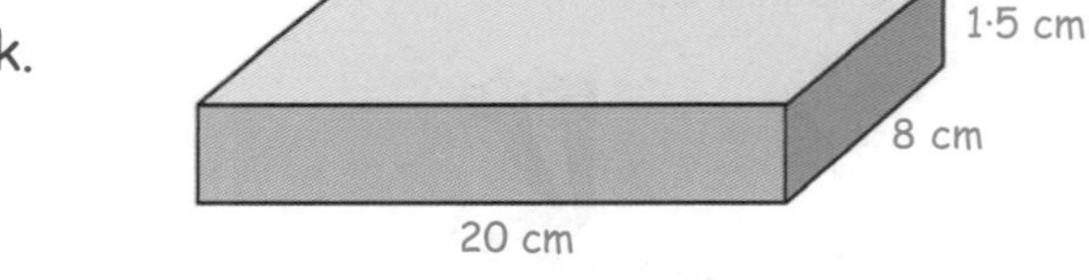

3.

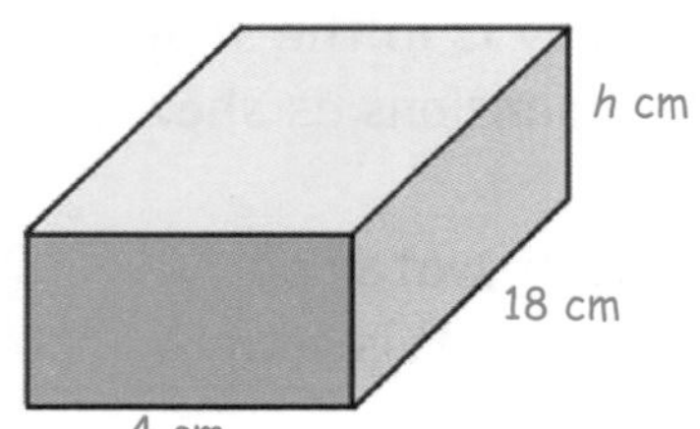

This block has a volume of $216\ cm^3$.
Calculate its height.

4. a Calculate the volume of this tin box, in cm^3.
   b How many millilitres of liquid will it hold ?
   c What is its capacity, in litres ?

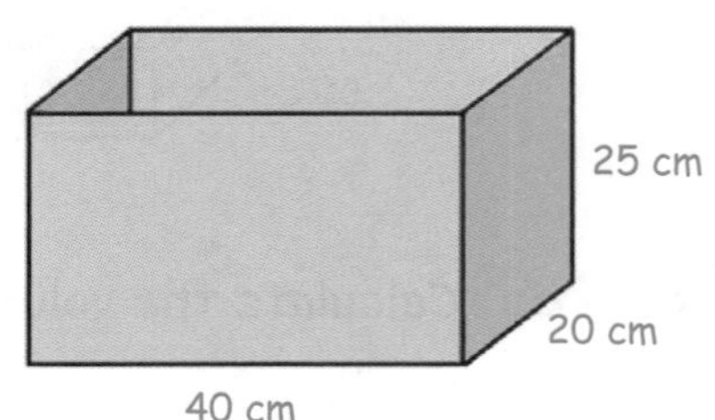

5.

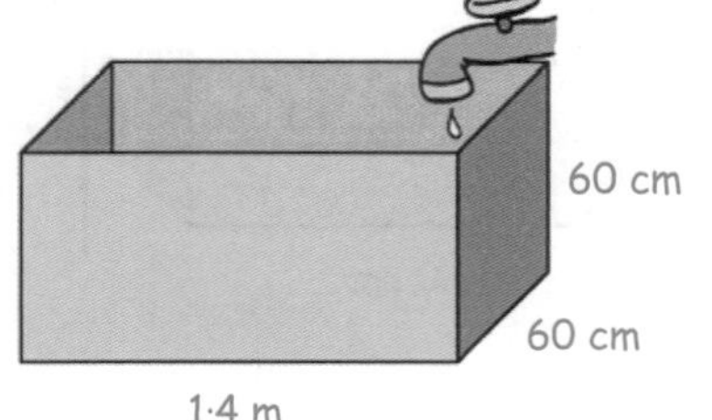

   a Calculate the volume of the tank, in cm^3.
   b When the tap is opened fully, water flows in at the rate of 7 litres per minute.
   How long until the tank is completely full ?

The Volume of a Prism

A **PRISM** is a 3-D shape with two parallel **congruent** faces, usually in the shape of polygons.

Examples :-

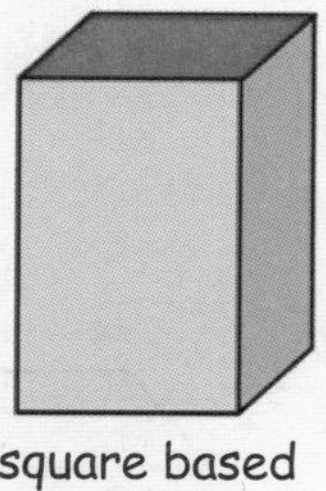
square based prism

triangular prism

hexagonal based prism

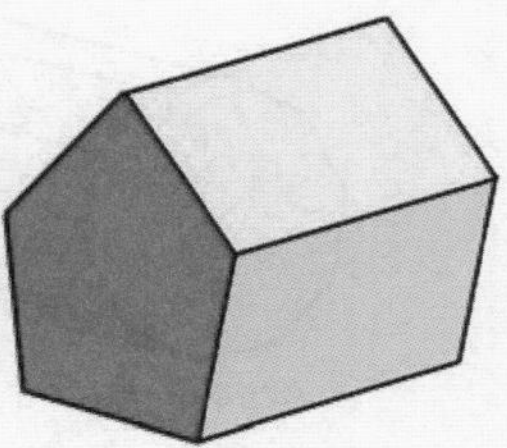
pentagonal prism

The **RED** face is the one that runs right through the shape, (top to bottom, left to right or front to back).

Volume of a Prism

It is fairly easy to calculate the volume of a prism, as long as you know the **area** of the **congruent** face.

Volume (prism) = **Area** (of end face) × **length**

or

Volume (prism) = **Area** (of base) × **height**

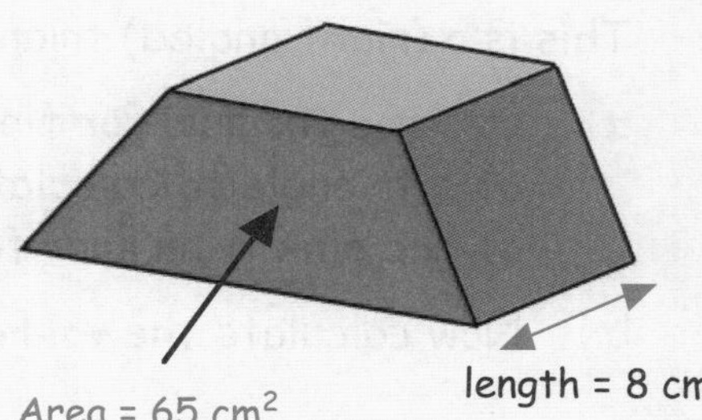

For this trapezoidal prism :-

Volume = Area × length

= $65 \text{ cm}^2 \times 8 \text{ cm}$

= **520 cm^3**

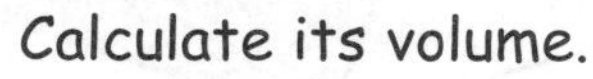
* The usual formula is :- $V = A \times h$

Exercise 2

1. The area of the top of this square based prism is 25 cm^2.

   Its height is 8 cm.

   Calculate its volume.

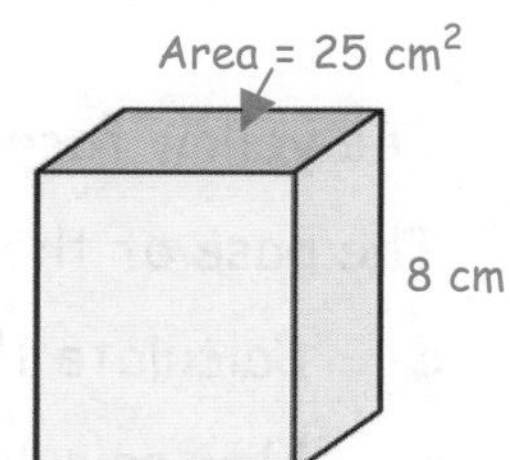

2. Calculate the volume of this triangular prism.

3. Calculate the volume of the hexagonal based prism shown.

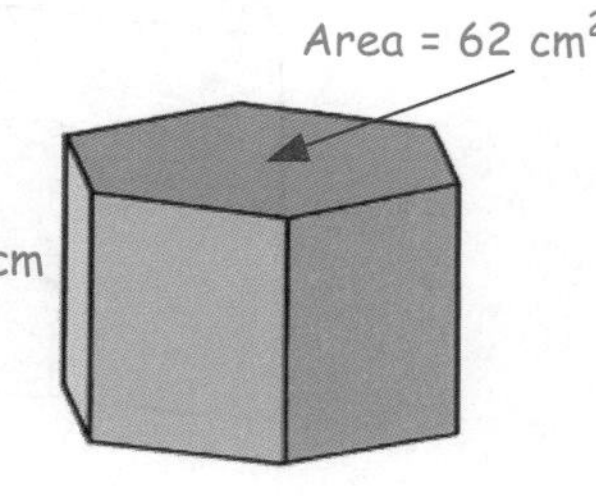

4. The volume of this prism is 210 cm^3.

Calculate its height.

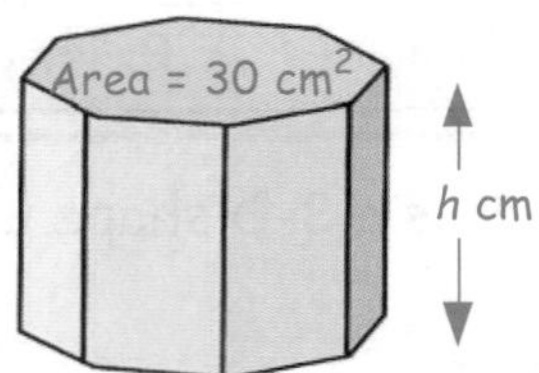

5. 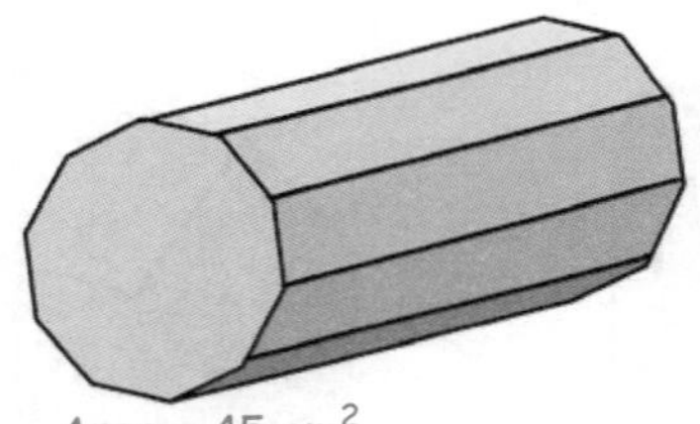

The volume of this prism is 675 cm^3.

Calculate its length.

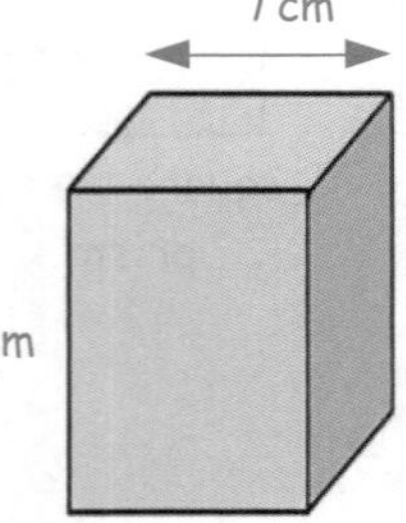

6. The volume of this cuboid with a square top is 250 cm^3.

Calculate the length of one of the sides of the square.

7. This is a (right angled) triangular prism.

a Use the formula for finding the area of a triangle to calculate the **area** of the pink triangular face.

b Now calculate the **volume** of the prism.

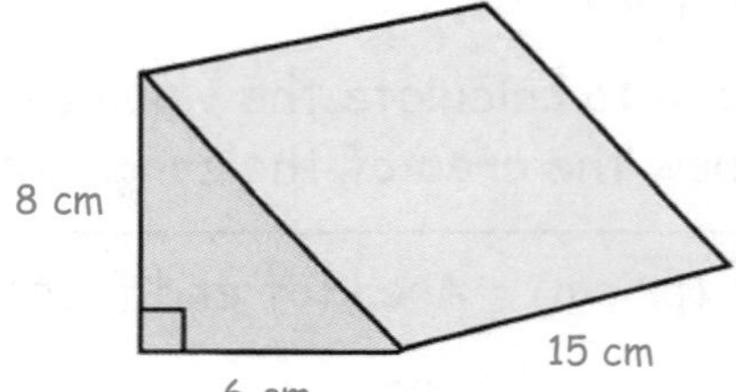

8. 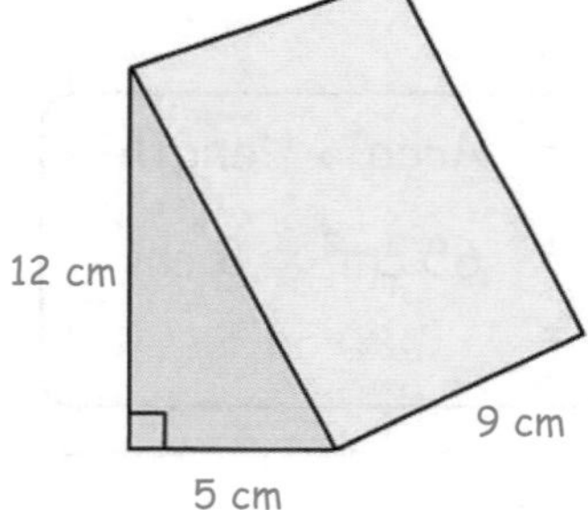

Calculate the volume of this prism in a similar way.

9. The yellow face of this prism is an isosceles triangle.

The base of the triangle is 8 cm and its height is 10 cm.

a Calculate the area of the yellow triangular face.

b Now calculate the volume of the prism.

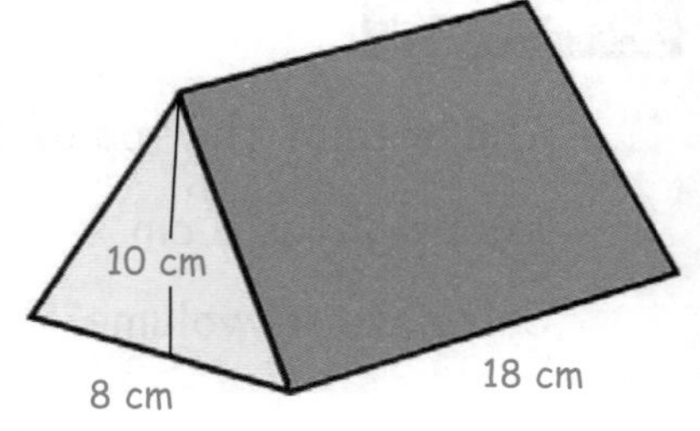

10. 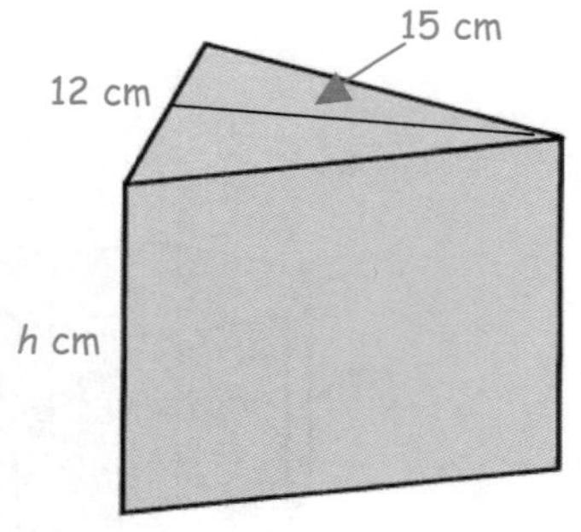

The volume of this prism is 765 cm^3.

The isosceles triangle on top has base 12 cm and height 15 cm.

Calculate the height of the prism.

The Volume of a Cylinder

A Special Prism - The Cylinder

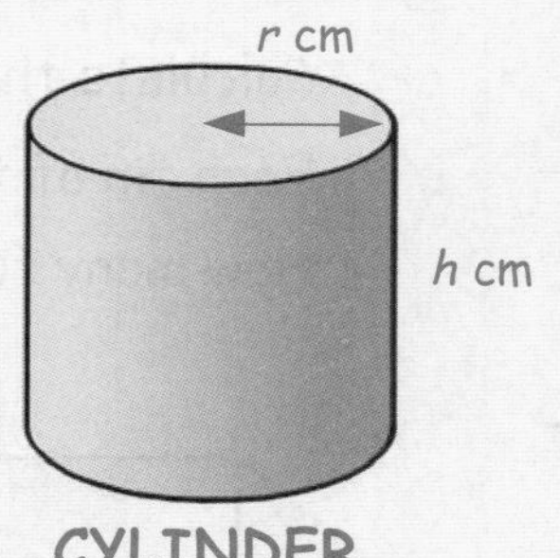

If the common face of a prism is a circle, then the prism is called a CYLINDER, and there is a special formula for calculating its volume.

Volume = Area (of base) × height => $V = \pi r^2 h$
(πr^2) (h)

Example :- Calculate the volume of this cylindrical tin can.

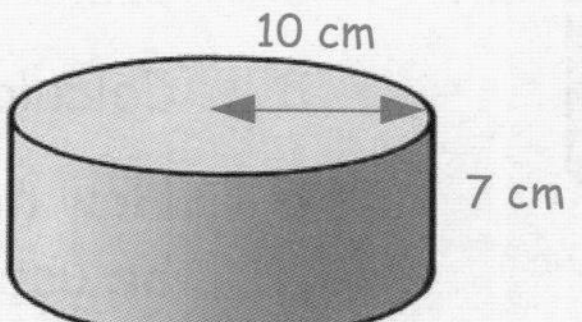

$V = \pi r^2 h$

$V = 3{\cdot}14 \times 10 \times 10 \times 7$

$V = 2198 \text{ cm}^3$

Exercise 3 *Give each answer correct to 2 decimal places, where necessary.*

1. Calculate the volume of this cylinder which has a base with radius 6 cm and a height of 10 cm.

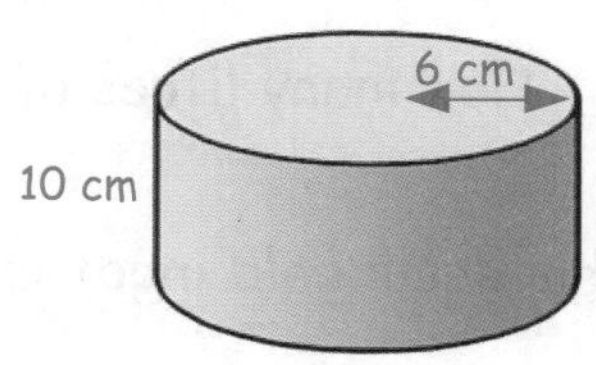

2. 

The diameter of the base of this tin of soup is 8 cm.

a Write down its radius.

b Work out the volume of the tin.

3. Which tin should contain more beans ?

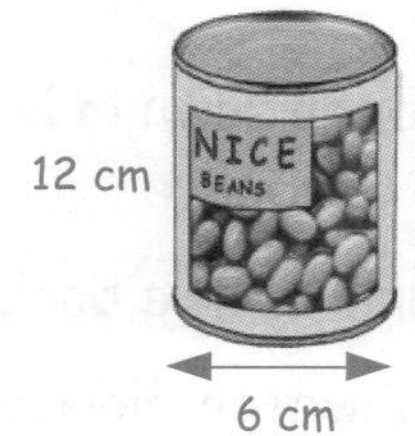

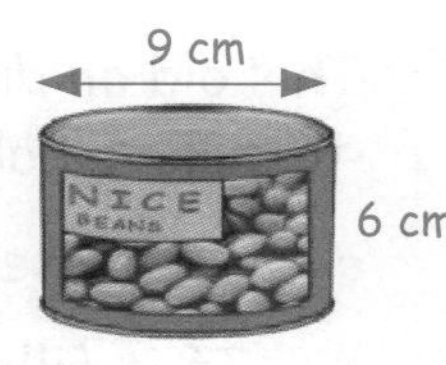

4. 

This oil barrel has base diameter 60 cm.

It is 1·5 metres in height.

a Find its volume, in cubic centimetres.

b How many litres of oil will it hold when it is full.

5. Without using a calculator, calculate the volume of this cylinder, giving your answer in terms of π.

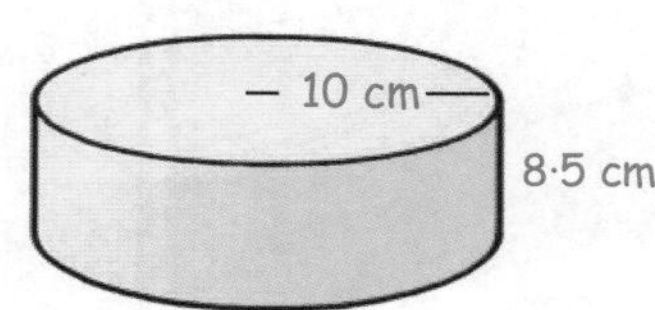

6. Harley cook their Tomato Soup in a large cylindrical pot.

   a Calculate the volume of a full pot of soup.

   b Each tin of tomato soup holds $\frac{1}{2}$ litre.
   How many full tins can be filled from 1 pot ?

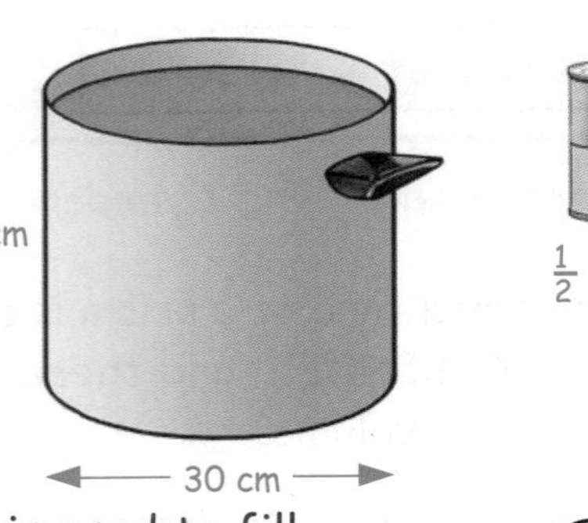

7. A cylindrical bucket is used to fill a rectangular tank with hot water.

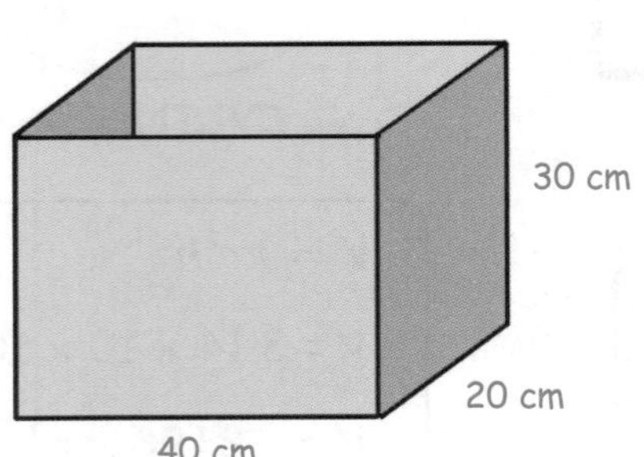

   a Work out the volume of the tank.

   b Calculate the volume of the bucket.

   c How many times will the bucket have to be used to completely fill the tank ?

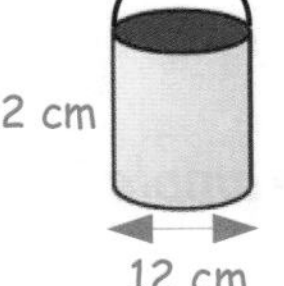

8. Shown is a section of a drainage pipe with diameter 8 cm.

   a Calculate the volume of the pipe.

   b How many litres of water can it hold ?

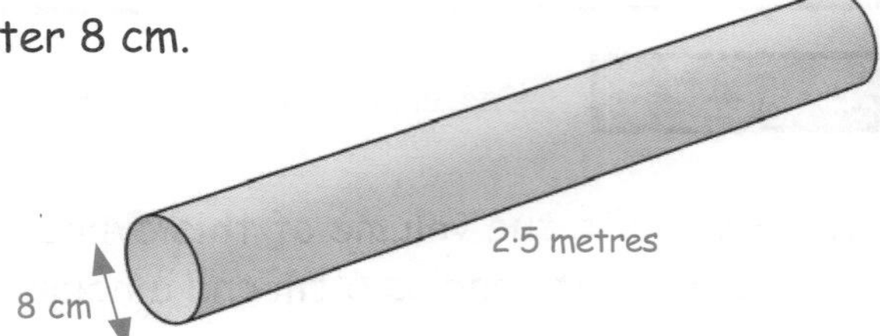

9. This small gold ingot is cylindrical.

   a Calculate its volume, in cm^3, to 2 decimal places.

   b 1 cm^3 of gold weighs about 20 grams.
   Calculate the approximate weight of this ingot.

   c If gold is valued at £25 per gram, how much is the ingot worth ?

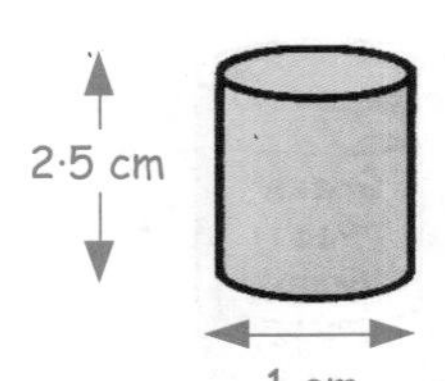

10. This old oil drum has been sawn in half to make a half-barrel barbecue.

   a Calculate the volume of the barbecue.

   b If it fills with rainwater, how many litres will it hold ?

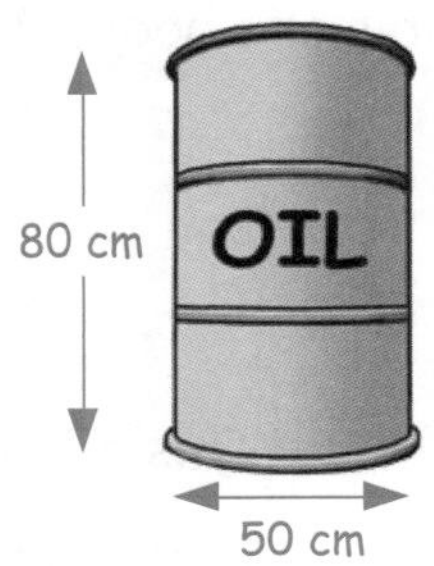

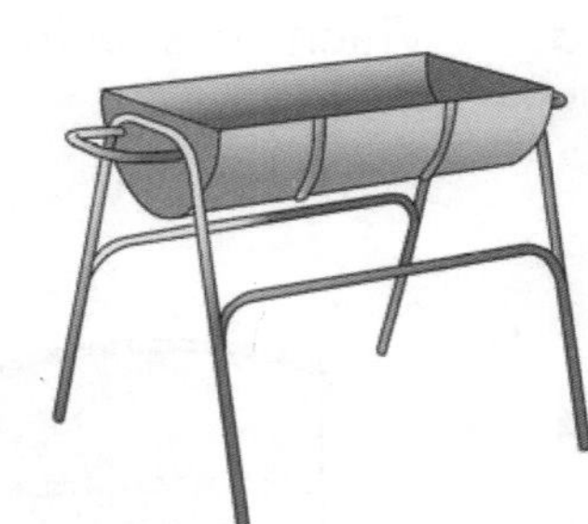

11. The green and yellow awning over the shop windows is in the shape of a quarter cylinder.

The awning is 3·5 metres long and the radius of the quarter circle end is 60 centimetres.

Calculate the volume of air in the the awning, in cubic metres.

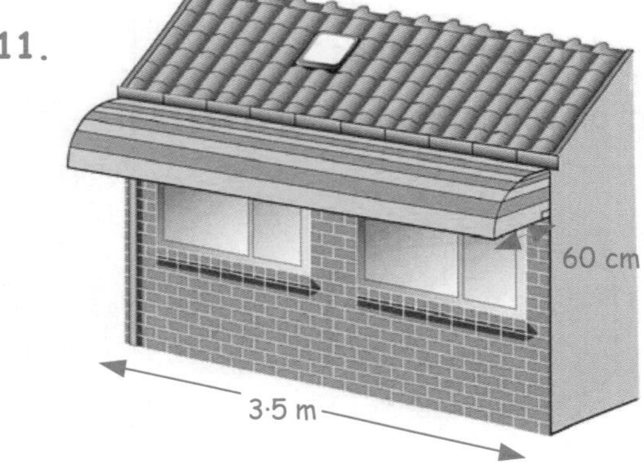

12. This trough is used to feed cattle with grain.

It is in the shape of a half-cylinder, 120 cm long.

Calculate the volume of grain the trough can hold when full, rounded to 2 significant figures,

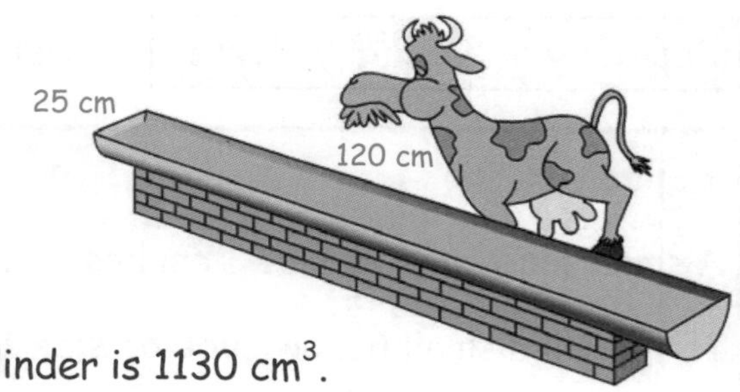

13.

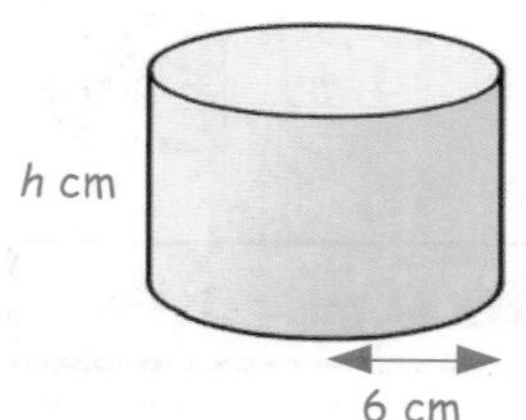

The volume of this cylinder is 1130 cm^3.

The radius of the base is 6 cm.

Calculate the height of the cylinder.

14. **(Harder)** The volume of this cylinder is 15 072 cm^3.

Calculate the radius of its circular top.

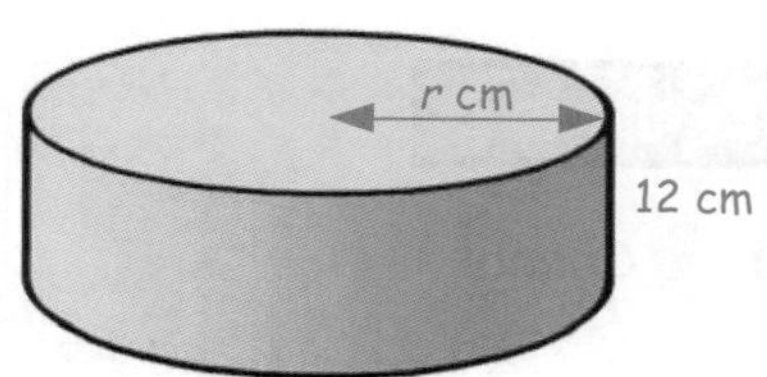

15. This large jelly pan holds 31·4 litres when full.

a How many millilitres is this ?

b If the pan is 25 centimetres tall, calculate the size of its base diameter.

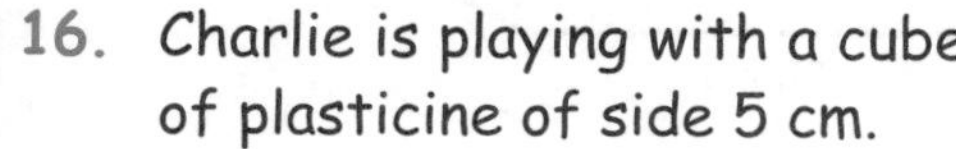

16. Charlie is playing with a cube of plasticine of side 5 cm.

He flattens it, then rolls it into a cylinder with a height of 3 cm, as shown.

Calculate, to 1 decimal place, the **radius** (r cm) of the cylinder formed.

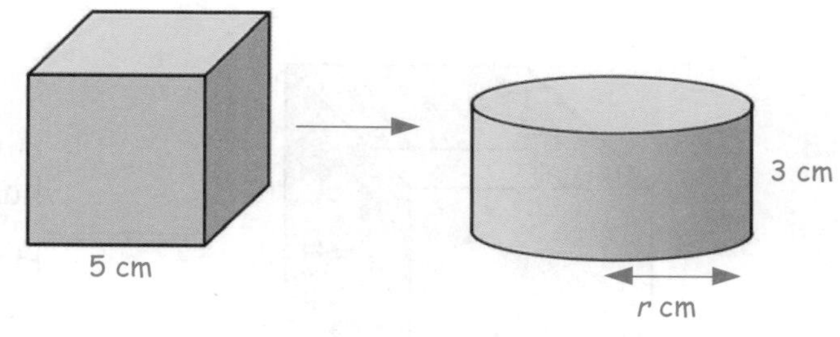

17. A swimming pool, 25 metres long by 10 metres wide, has a sloping floor.

The "shallow" end is 1·2 metres deep.

The "deep" end is 1·6 metres deep.

a By calculating the area of the grey side wall, determine the volume of the pool when full, in cubic metres.

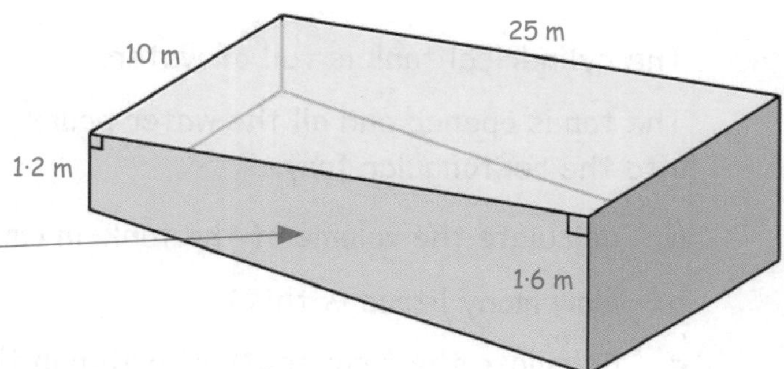

b When the pool is being drained for cleaning purposes, it empties at a rate of 50 000 litres per hour.

How long will the pool take to empty ?

(*1 m^3 = 1000 litres*)

Capacity - Liquid Volume — Revision

Capacity

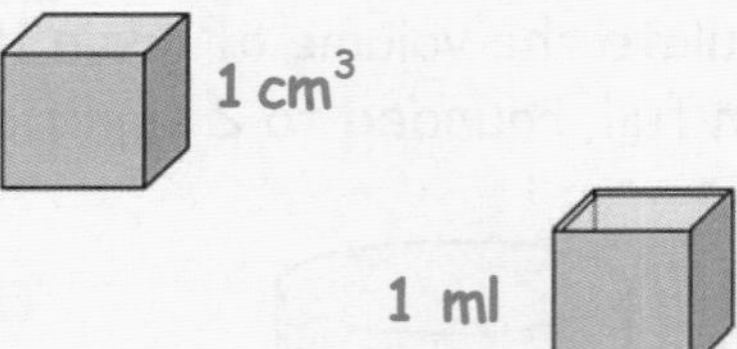

A small solid cube of side 1 cm has a volume of 1 cm^3.

If you fill a small hollow cube of side 1 cm with water, we say it has a capacity of 1 millilitre, or (1 ml).

1000 cm^3 = 1000 ml = 1 litre

Exercise 4

1. Change :-

a	4 litres to ml	b	15 000 ml to litres	c	70 litres to ml
d	900 ml to litres	e	4000 ml to litres	f	2·5 litres to ml
g	0·07 litres to ml	h	25 ml to litres	i	$4\frac{1}{4}$ litres to ml.

2. a Calculate the volume of this box, in cm^3.

   b How many litres of sand can the box hold when full ?

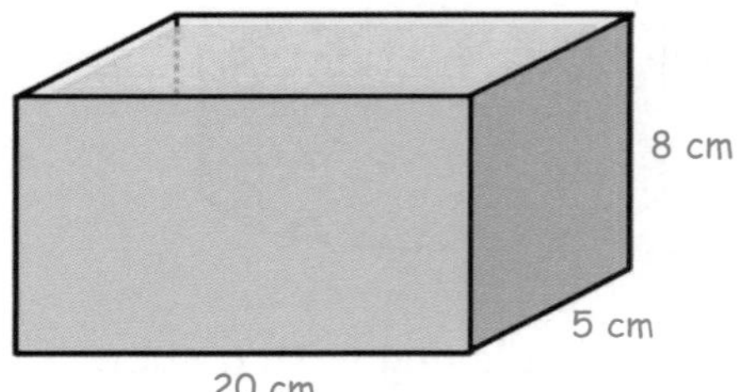

3. 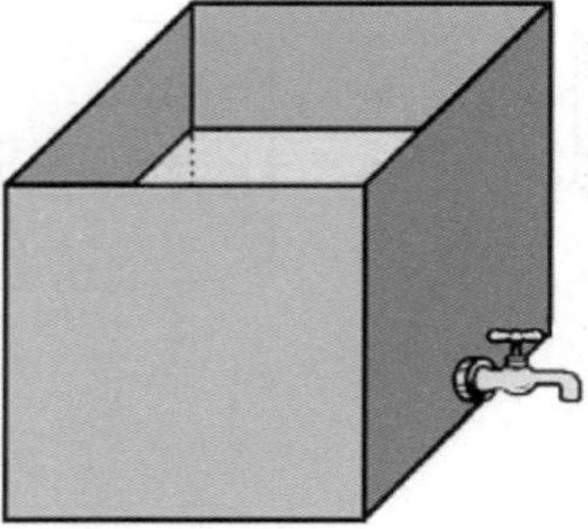

   A metal tank in the shape of a cube has all its sides of length 40 cm.

   How many litres of liquid will it hold when it is three quarters full ?

4. The cylindrical tank is full of water.

   The tap is opened and all the water pours into the rectangular tray.

   a Calculate the volume of the tank, in cm^3.

   b How many litres is this ?

   c Calculate the final depth of water in the tray.

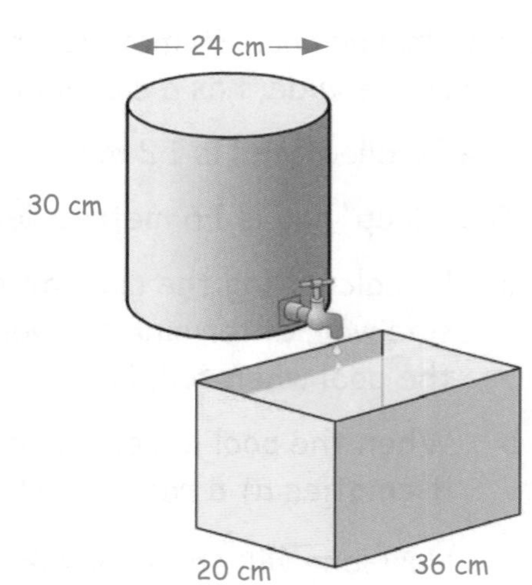

Volume 1

Numeracy Assessment 8

1. How many litres will this metal tank hold when full ?

20 cm
60 cm
1·2 metres

2. A milk carton is in the shape of a prism.

   The width of the container is 10 cm.

   The uniform cross section of the container consists of a rectangle and a triangle.

   Could the container hold 2 litres of milk when full ?

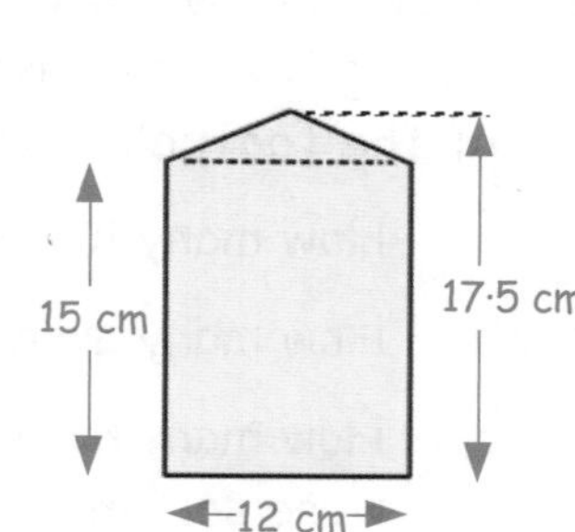

3. Raspberry is poured from a 2 litre bottle into glasses.

   Each glass is in the shape of a cylinder of radius 2·5 cm and height 12 cm.

   How many full glasses can be poured from the bottle ?

4. A mug is in the shape of a cylinder with diameter 8 centimetres and height 12 centimetres.

   a Calculate the volume of the mug.

   b 500 millilitres of tea are poured into the mug.

   Calculate the depth of tea now in the mug.

5. a A block of gold is 18 centimetres long.

   The area of its cross section is 30 cm^2.

   Calculate the volume of the gold block.

30 cm^2
18 cm

   b The block is melted down and a cylindrical golden bar is made.

   The length of the bar is 40 cm.

   Calculate its radius, correct to the nearest centimetre.

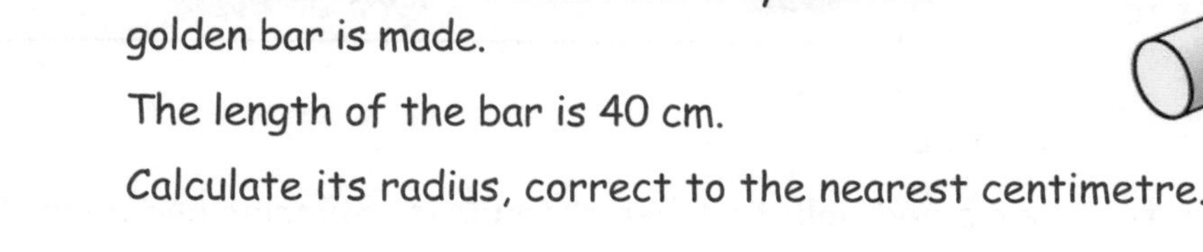

40 cm

6. A section of beading was bought to be attached to a skirting board along a wall 4 metres long.

   The cross sectional end of the beading is in the shape of a quarter circle with radius 15 millimetres.

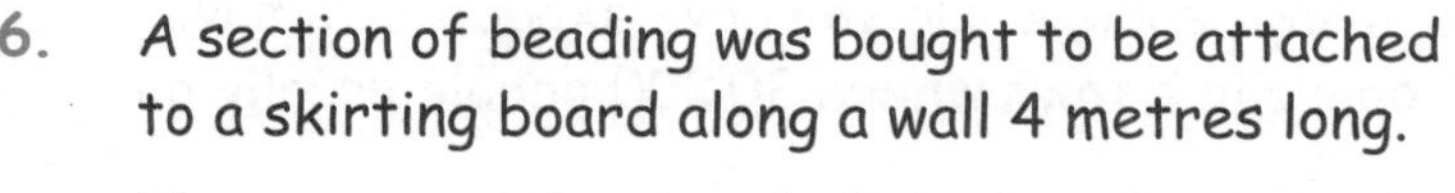

   Work out the volume of the beading, in cubic centimetres.

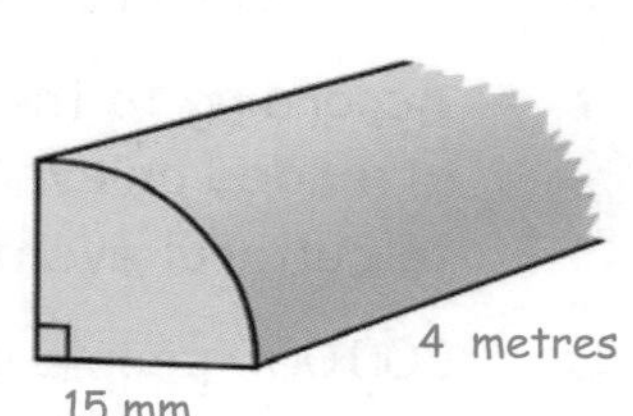

Graphs, Charts & Tables

Revision of Graphs, Charts and Tables

1. This pictograph shows the number of United's home football tops (red) and the number of their away tops (blue) that were sold by a sports shop during the first five months of the football season.

Month
Aug
Sept
Oct
Nov
Dec

a How many home tops were sold in August ?

b How many away tops were sold in December ?

c How many more home tops than away tops were sold in September ?

d How many more away tops than home tops were sold in November ?

e Which colour of top sold better overall and by how many ?

f How many United football tops did the shop sell over the period ?

2. This bar graph shows the percentage of the British population who attended different types of cultural events during 2014.

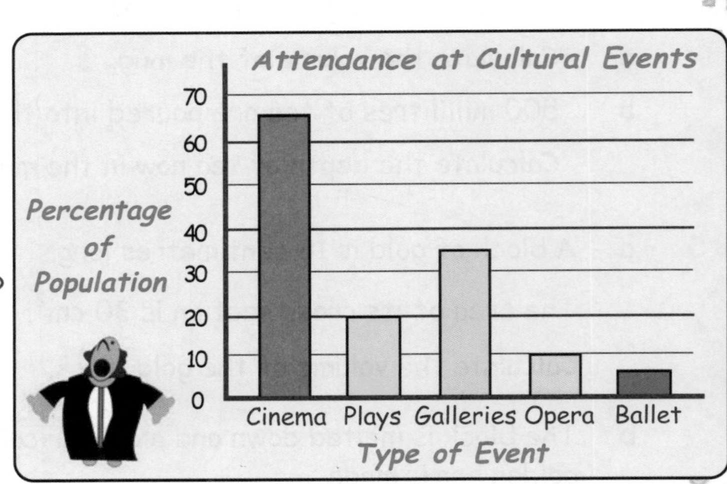

a What % attended plays ?

b What % went to the opera ?

c What was the difference in % between those who went to the cinema and those who went to galleries ?

d What % preferred plays to ballet ?

e How many more for cinema and ballet rather than plays, galleries and opera ?

f According to the graph, how many people would you have expected to have attended an evening at the opera in a town where 30 000 people usually go to cultural events ?

g 200 000 people in Scotland are said to have been included in this survey.

How many of them would you have expected to enjoy ballet ?

3. The line graph opposite shows the number of vacuum cleaners sold at *Karry's Electrical* during the first 7 months of 2015.

a How many vacuums were sold in :-

(i) March (ii) June ?

b How many times did sales fall ?

c (i) When were sales highest ?

(ii) How many was that ?

d (i) Which month had the lowest sales ? (ii) How many was that ?

e Between which two month period did sales drop the most ?

4. The pie chart shows the Johnston's main household expenditure, in categories.

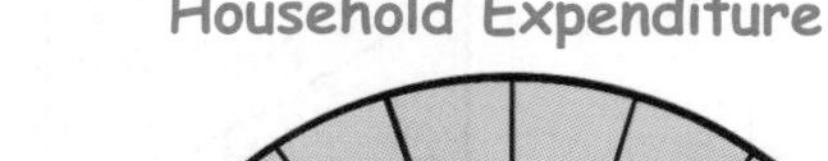

Household Expenditure

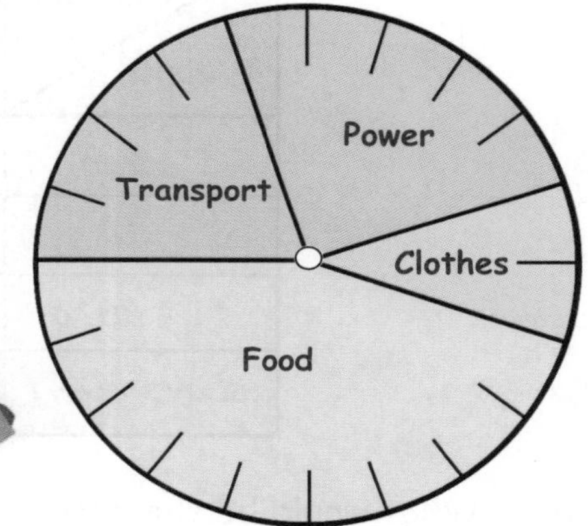

a List the items in order, starting with the most expensive.

b What fraction of their expenditure is spent on gas and electricity ?

c If £30 per week is spent on clothes, how much goes on transport ?

d How much is spent on food ?

e What is their total expenditure for these four items ?

5. The scattergraph shows a connection between the number of hours sleep you need per day and your age.

Amount of Sleep Needed

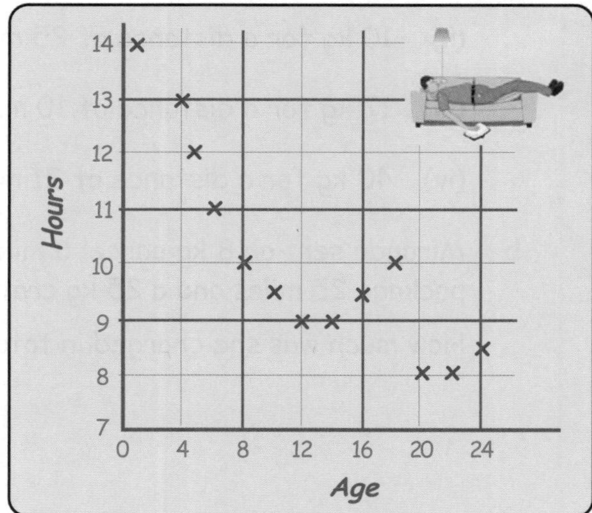

a Suggest in words a general connection between the hours of sleep you need and your age.

b Estimate how many hours sleep a 2 year old needs.

c What ages of children should get nine and a half hours sleep ?

d Which group needs 14 hours sleep ?

e If the graph was to continue to highlight those aged over 24, what do you think it would look like ?

6.

Speed (mph)	
0	8
1	3 6
2	1 1 6 8 9
3	0 3 5 9 9
4	0 1 6 8 8 8
5	3

Key :- 3 | 5 = 35 mph

The stem-and-leaf diagram shows the speeds of vehicles in miles per hour, travelling along a country road.

a How many vehicles were doing :-

(i) 29 mph (ii) 39 mph (iii) 48 mph ?

b How many were going at a speed more than 40 mph ?

c How many vehicles were noted ?

d What was the slowest speed recorded ?

Suggest a reason for this speed.

7. *FasTrack Services'* delivery charges are shown in the table below.

Weight \ Distance	under 10 miles	between 10-20 miles	over 20 miles
1 - 5 kg	£7·50	£9·00	£10·50
6 - 10 kg	£9·50	£12·50	£13·50
11 - 20 kg	£11·50	£14·00	£16·50
above 20 kg	£12·50	£15·00	£18·00

a What would be the charge for delivering a package weighing :-

(i) 3 kg for a distance of 7 miles

(ii) 10 kg for a distance of 25 miles

(iii) 17 kg for a distance of 10 miles

(iv) 40 kg for a distance of 21 miles ?

b Miranda sent an 8 kg parcel 6 miles, a 14 kg package 25 miles and a 25 kg crate 2 miles.

How much was she charged in total ?

Graphs, Charts & Tables

Bar Graphs, Line Graphs and Stem-and-Leaf Diagrams

Statistics is the branch of mathematics that deals with the collection, organisation, and interpretation of numerical data, especially the analysis of population characteristics.

Later, we shall look at the numerical aspect of statistics like averages and spreads, but here, we will concentrate on interpreting and drawing slightly more complicated graphs such as **composite** bar graphs, line and stem-and-leaf graphs and pie charts.

Composite :- In many cases, we wish to compare two or more sets of data, and a composite graph is the ideal way of doing this. There are various ways of drawing these graphs.

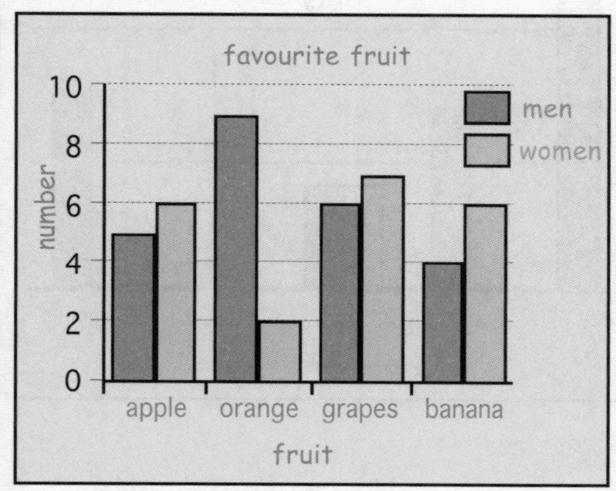

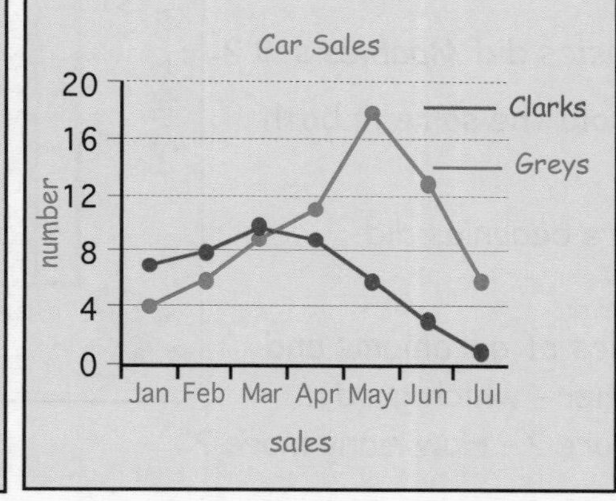

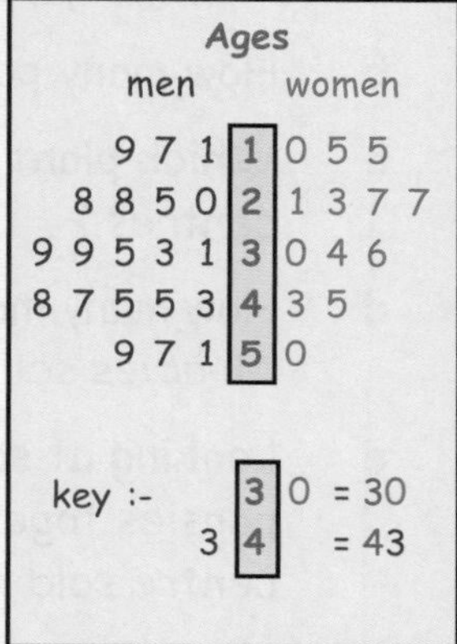

Exercise 1

1. A survey was conducted into what people's favourite fruit was.

   This is shown in the composite bar graph opposite.

   a What is the most popular fruit :-

   (i) for men (ii) for women ?

   b How many more men than women prefer an orange ?

   c How many women did not choose grapes as their favourite ?

   d How many fewer women took part in the survey than men ?

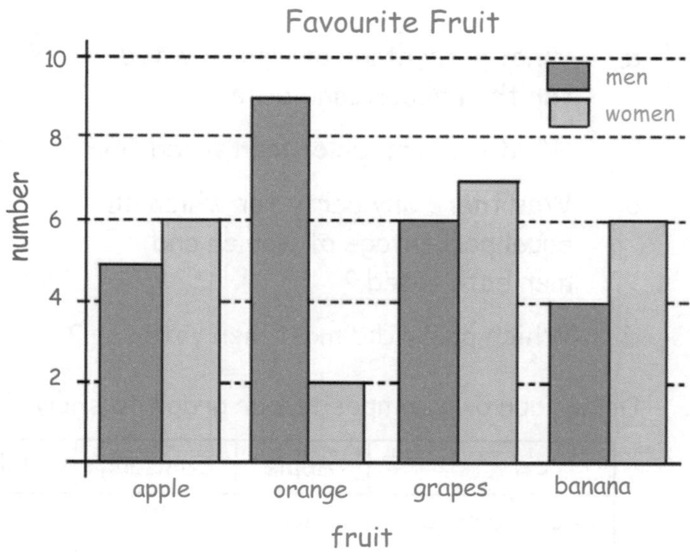

2. The **Comparative Bar Graph** opposite shows the gender of three 4th year classes. (*red - girls, blue - boys*).

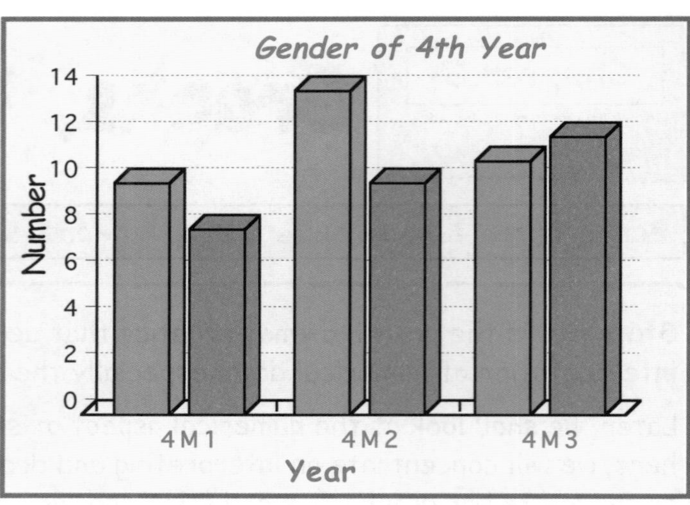

a How many boys are there in 4M1 ?

b How many girls are there in 4M2 ?

c How many pupils are there in 4M3 ?

d How many **more** girls than boys are there in total in all three classes ?

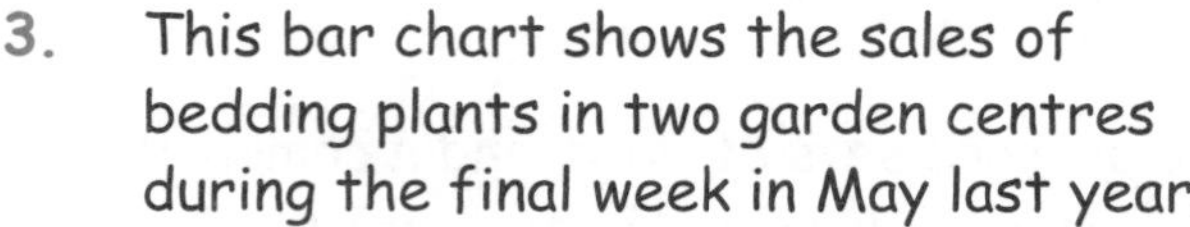

3. This bar chart shows the sales of bedding plants in two garden centres during the final week in May last year.

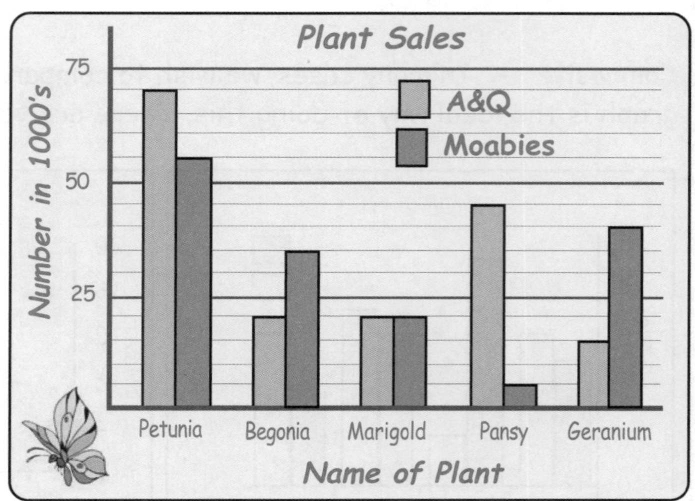

a How many petunias did *A&Q* sell ?

b How many pansies did *Moabies* sell ?

c Which plant sold the same in both centres ?

d How many more begonias did *Moabies* sell ?

e Looking at sales of geraniums and pansies together - which garden centre sold more ? - How many more ?

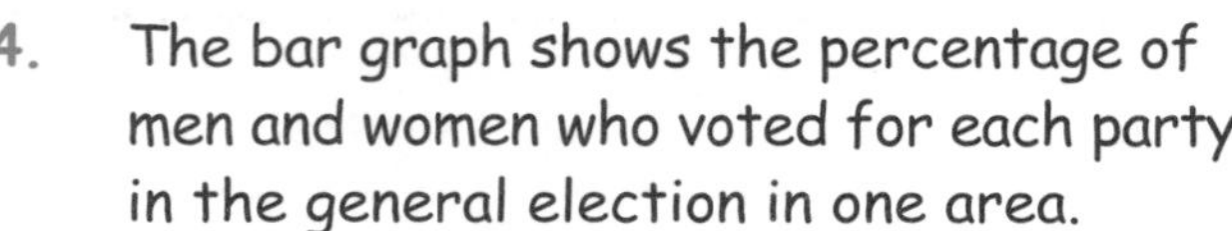

4. The bar graph shows the percentage of men and women who voted for each party in the general election in one area.

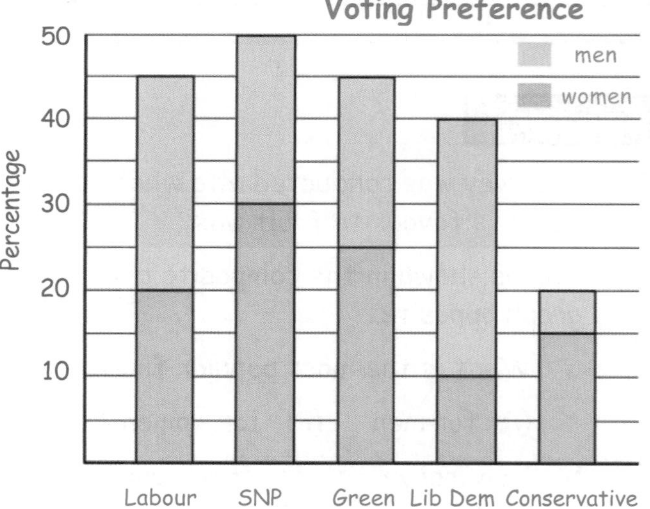

a What percentage of women voted for the Labour candidate ?

b What percentage of men voted SNP ?

c Was there any party for which an equal percentage of women and men both voted ?

d Which party did most men vote for ?

5. Draw your own composite bar graph to show the following sales data for one weekend :-

	Apple	Samsung	Nokia	Blackberry	Sony	Vodaphone
The 4 Store	12	10	3	6	2	5
Fones 4 U	6	11	5	3	2	8

6. A comparison is made between the monthly car sales of two small car showrooms.

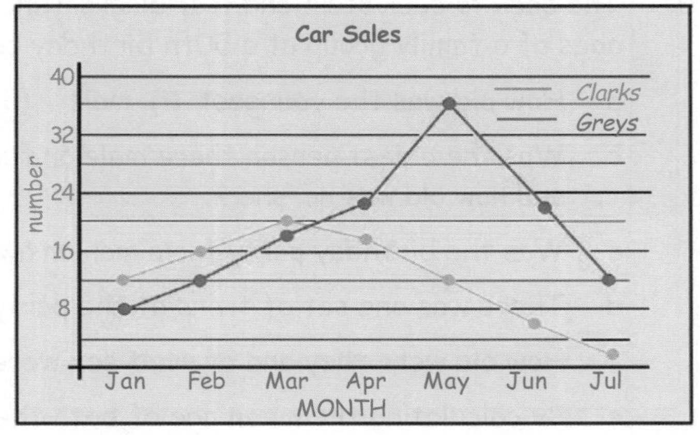

a How many cars did *Clarks* manage to sell in March ?

b How many fewer cars did *Clarks* sell in May than *Greys* ?

c *Greys* stated that over the 7 month period, they sold more than twice the cars sold by *Clarks*. Is this true ?

7. The comparative line graph shows the price of petrol and diesel at *Bridge Garage* over several weeks.

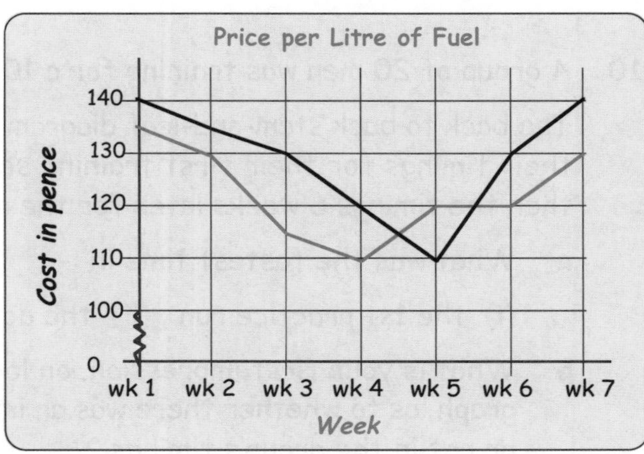

a Find the cost of petrol in week 2.

b Find the cost of diesel in week 3.

c Halfway through week 4, diesel became cheaper than petrol.

When did it become dearer again ?

d In week 7, how much dearer was diesel ?

8. The temperature at noon each day in February was noted, both in Glasgow and in Aberdeen.

• *Glasgow* in red • *Aberdeen* in green.

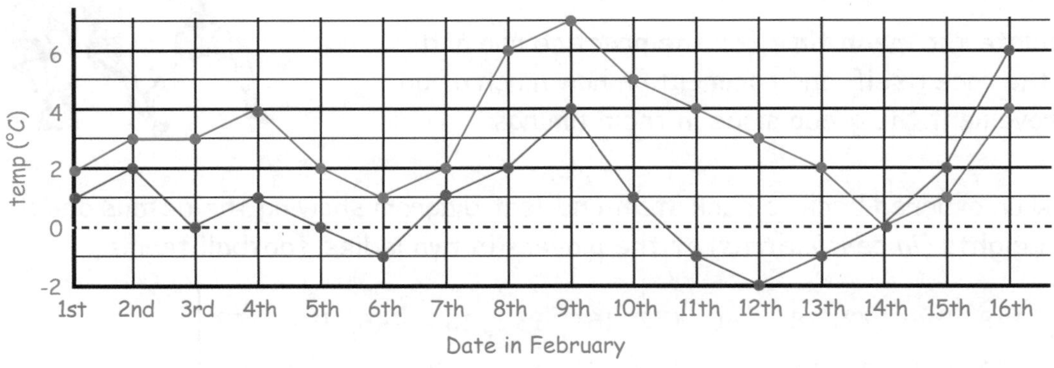

a On February 12th, what was the temperature in :- (i) Glasgow (ii) Aberdeen ?

b Between which 2 days did the temperature rise by the greatest in Aberdeen ?

c Discuss the general temperature trends in both cities.

Remember :- To calculate the **mean** (average) of a set of numbers, add all the numbers together and divide by how many numbers there are.

d Calculate the **mean** temperature for both Glasgow and Aberdeen, and comment.

9. The back to back stem-and-leaf diagram shows the ages of a family group at a 50th birthday party.

a How old was the youngest (i) male (ii) female ?

b Was the oldest person there male or female, and how old was he/she ?

c Was the birthday party for a man or a woman ?

d There was one set of twins at the party.

How old were they and of what sex were they ?

e By calculating the **mean** age of both the males and the females, say which sex were on average older, and by how much.

Ages

male		female
9 7 1	1	0 5 6
8 6 5 0	2	1 3 7 9
9 8 5 3 1	3	0 4 6
8 7 5 4 3	4	1 5
9 7 1	5	0

key :-

	3	0	= 30
3	4		= 43

10. A group of 20 men was training for a 10 K run.

The back to back stem-and-leaf diagram shows their timings for their first training session, then the timings 6 weeks later for the actual race.

a What was the fastest time in :-

(i) the 1st practice run (ii) the actual race ?

b What is your first impression, on looking at the graph, as to whether there was an improvement or not in the group's timings ?

c The man who had the slowest time in practice also had the slowest time in the race.

By how many minutes had his time improved ?

d Calculate the **mean** time for the practice run and for the race itself, and comment on how much of an improvement the group made in their timings.

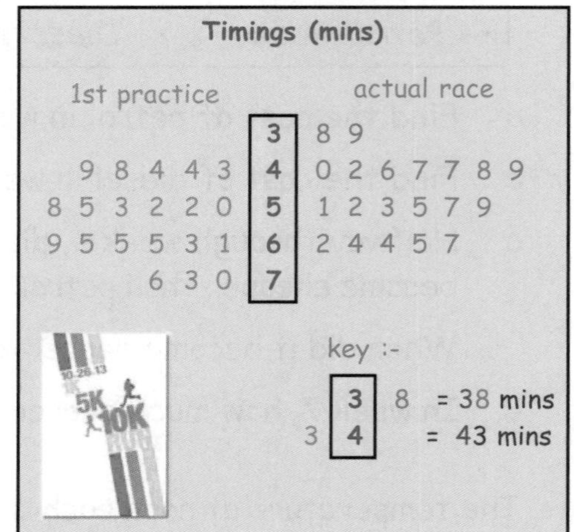

Timings (mins)

1st practice		actual race
	3	8 9
9 8 4 4 3	4	0 2 6 7 7 8 9
8 5 3 2 2 0	5	1 2 3 5 7 9
9 5 5 5 3 1	6	2 4 4 5 7
6 3 0	7	

key :-

	3	8	= 38 mins
3	4		= 43 mins

11. a Draw an ordered back to back stem-and-leaf diagram showing the details about the heights (*in centimetres*) of the players in two ladies' football teams.

Doves	148	156	172	181	160	157	164	132	184	146	157	139
Rovers	182	174	138	145	175	162	159	175	167	173	144	150

Use the key shown opposite :-

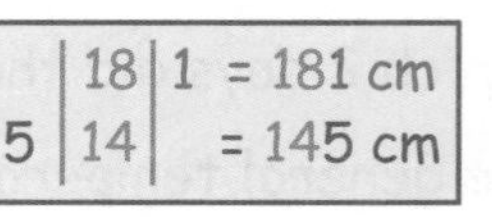

	18	1	= 181 cm
5	14		= 145 cm

b Comment on the distribution of heights of the players in both teams.

c Calculate the **mean** height of both teams and say who will have the greater height advantage.

Pie Charts

Pie Charts are another way of visually representing data.

They can show raw results or display information in fractional or percentage form.

Example :- A group of 1500 people was asked to name their favourite pie filling and this is represented by the pie chart opposite.

How many chose "steak" ?

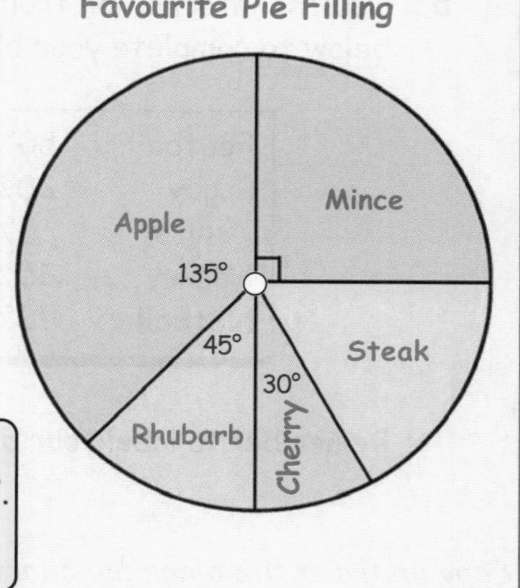

Solution :- By adding the angles :- 135° + 45° + 90° + 30°, and subtracting from 360° => 360 - 300 = 60°.

No. choosing steak = $\frac{60}{360}$ x 1500 = **250** people.

Exercise 2

1. The pie chart shows the results of a class survey into *favourite school canteen food.*

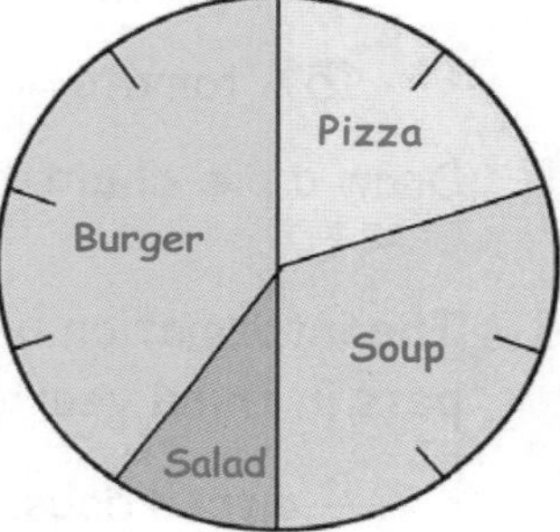

   a What fraction of the class chose :-

   (i) Burger ($\frac{7}{10}$) (ii) Salad (iii) Pizza (iv) Soup ?

   b List the foods in order, from **most** popular to **least** popular.

2. The pie chart shows the results of a year-group analysis of hair colour.

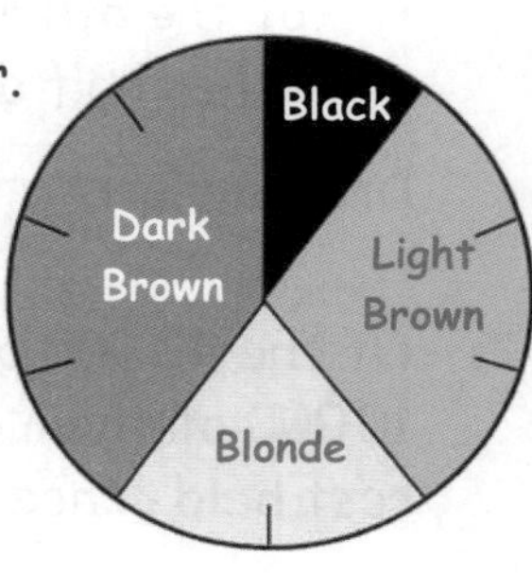

   a What percentage of the year-group had :-

   (i) dark brown (ii) light brown (iii) blonde hair ?

   b If 300 pupils were in the year-group, how many of them :-

   (i) had blonde hair (ii) did not have black hair ?

3. This pie chart shows the type of houses the people at a political meeting live in.

   a What percentage of the people live in a :-

   (i) bungalow (ii) semi-detached villa

   (iii) flat (iv) detached villa ?

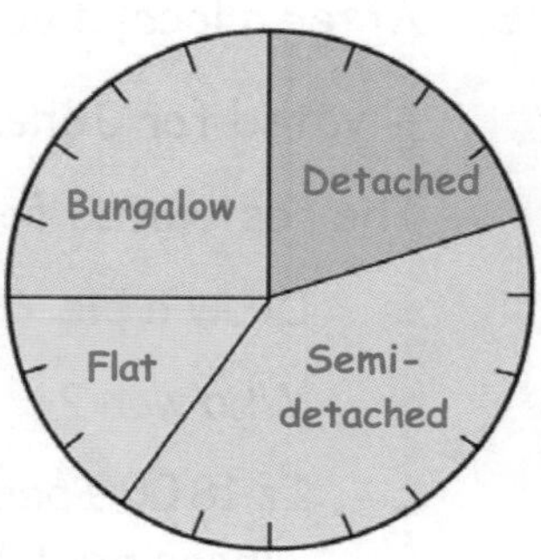

   b If there are 500 people at the meeting, how many live in a :-

   (i) bungalow (ii) detached villa ?

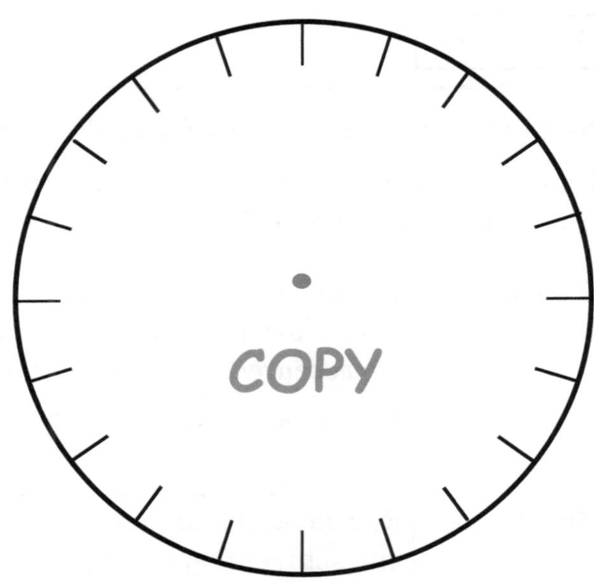

4. a Copy or trace the blank pie chart.

   b Use the information from the table below to complete your blank pie chart.

Football	-	50%
Rugby	-	20%
Tennis	-	5%
Hockey	-	15%
Netball	-	10%

   Remember to label your diagram.

Copy or trace the blank pie chart above to help you draw pie charts for Questions 5 to 7 :-

5. In a bowl of minestrone soup, the ingredients were as follows :-
   - 35% pasta
   - 40% carrots
   - 15% tomato
   - the rest was celery.

   Draw a **pie chart** to show the information above.

6. The information below shows the most popular pets in third year at Greenby High school.
   - $\frac{2}{5}$ owned dogs.
   - $\frac{3}{10}$ owned cats.
   - of the others, half owned fish and the other half owned a bird.

   Draw a **pie chart** to show this information.

7. Of the 40 000 people at a football match, 20 000 of them were season ticket holders, 10 000 of them were ticket sales, 6000 of them were juvenile ticket holders and the rest held concessionary tickets.

   Draw a **pie chart** to show this information.

8. After a local election, the vote count showed the following :-

   $\frac{1}{9}$ voted for Jones, $\frac{1}{6}$ voted for Douglas, $\frac{1}{8}$ voted for Bright, $\frac{3}{10}$ voted for McCann.
   The rest voted for Alexander.

   a Draw a **pie chart** to show how all 5 candidates fared.

   b Who won ?

   c If 18 000 people voted, by how many votes did the winner beat the runner up ?

Scattergraphs

A **Scattergraph** is a statistical graph which shows a possible connection between two sets of data.

Example :- This scattergraph displays the ***heights*** and ***weights*** of the players in a basketball team.

- Lou is 135 cm tall and he weighs 25 kg.

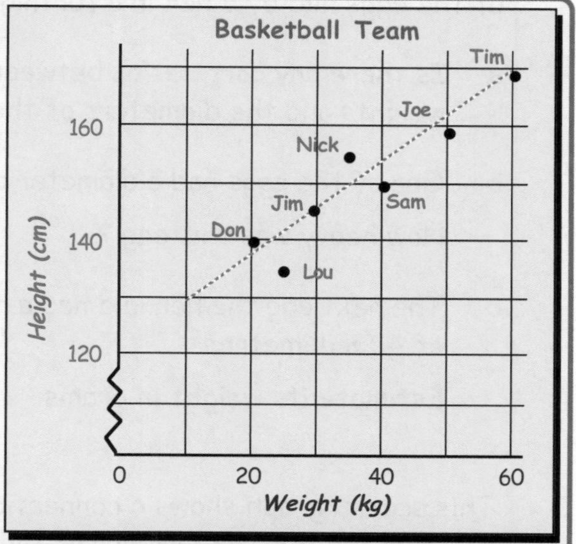

Can you see from the dotted line drawn up the middle of the points, that there is a fairly strong ***connection*** between weight and height ?

If this is true, we say there is a **positive correlation** between the 2 sets of data.

Exercise 3

1. From the scattergraph above, write down the height and weight of each player.

2. This scattergraph shows the ages and weights of several children.

   a Who is the :-

   (i) youngest (ii) lightest

   (iii) oldest (iv) heaviest child ?

   b Write the age and weight of each child.

   c Child "x" is older than Ali, younger than Pat and is lighter than Shaz.

   What is child x's name ?

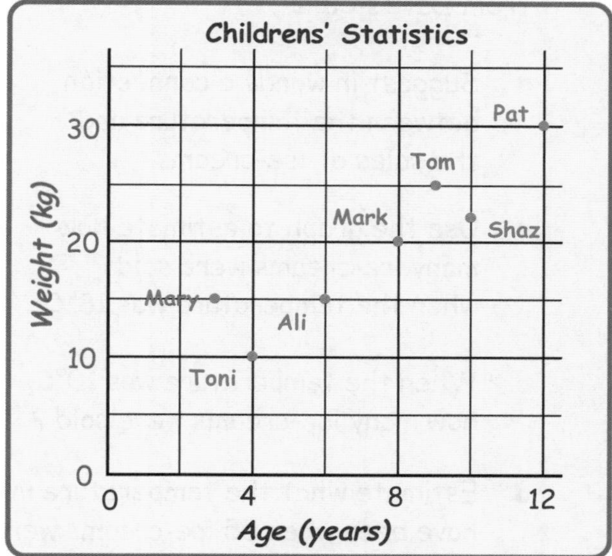

3.

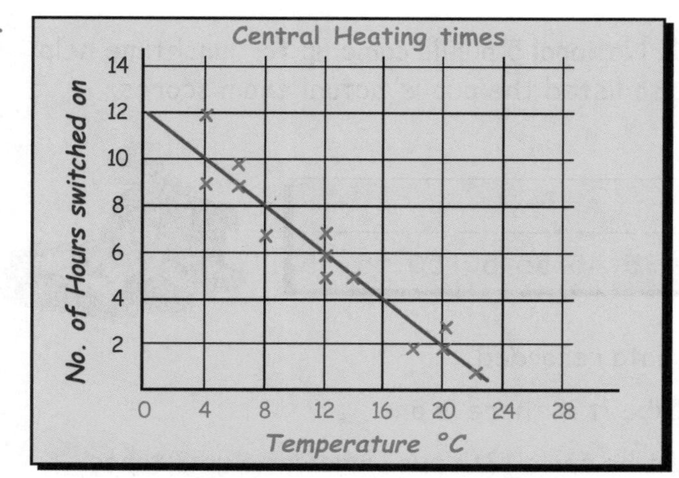

This scattergraph shows the number of hours a lady had her central heating on each day, plotted against the average daily temperature on each of those days.

a When the temperature was 8°C, for how many hours was the heating on ?

b Is there a strong **correlation** between the temperature and the number of hours switched on ?

c What kind of **correlation** is it ?

d Estimate how many hours it was on when the temperature reached 16°C.

4. A researcher noted the diameter and weight of the eggs laid by a hen in a fortnight.

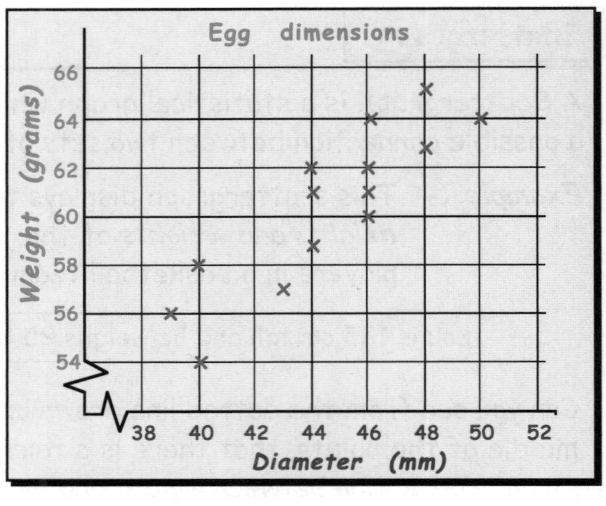

a Is there any **correlation** between the weights and the diameters of the eggs ?

b One of the eggs had a diameter of 50 mm.

How heavy was this egg ?

c The next egg the hen laid had a diameter of 42 millimetres.

Estimate its weight in grams.

5. This scattergraph shows a connection between the temperature during the day and the sales of ice-creams from *Dave's Cafe*.

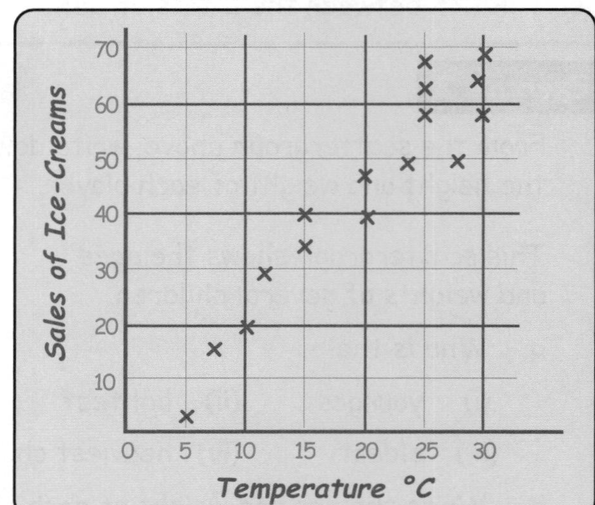

a Suggest in words a connection between the temperature and the sales of ice-creams.

b Use the graph to estimate how many ice-creams were sold when the temperature was 18°C.

c When the temperature was 10°C, how many ice-creams were sold ?

d Estimate what the temperature might have been when 55 ice-creams were sold.

6. Mr Ives recorded the number of times 11 National 5 pupils came up for lunchtime help in the run-up to their Maths exam. He also listed the pupils' actual exam scores.

Here are the results :-

Lunchtimes	1	2	3	4	5	6	7	9	10	11	12
Maths Score	30	35	35	40	35	45	55	50	50	55	55

a Construct a **scattergraph** from the data recorded.

b Can you see any correlation ? Describe it if there is one.

c **Estimate** what the Maths score might be for a 12th pupil who came up 8 times to see Mr Ives for lunchtime tutorials.

Interpreting Tables

Exercise 4

1. A Scottish businessman kept a note of his expenses on 5 business trips.

	Flight	Hotel	Food	Incidentals
London	€75	€85	€49	€30
Paris	€130	€72	€63	€46
Rome	€185	€59	€48	€10
Berlin	€99	€140	€75	€44
Barcelona	€110	€45	€52	€0

   a How much did it cost him for his hotel and food in Paris ?

   b How much did his whole trip to Barcelona cost ?

   c Which capital had the cheapest hotel cost ?

   d If he was told to cut back on expenses, which trip should he miss out next time ?

2. A survey was taken as to which Cola drink people preferred.

	18 to 24	25 to 29	30 to 39	40 to 49	50 to 54	55 to 59	60 or more
Coke-Cola	65%	41%	55%	28%	46%	36%	36%
Diet Coke	2%	10%	13%	15%	8%	12%	23%
Coke Zero	9%	23%	19%	22%	28%	16%	14%
Pepsi Light	0%	3%	0%	3%	3%	6%	9%
Pepsi Max	16%	18%	6%	10%	13%	24%	14%
Pepsi	8%	5%	7%	22%	2%	6%	4%
	100	100	100	100	100	100	100

   a Which was the favourite drink with all age-groups ?

   b What percentage of those 50 or over preferred Diet Coke ?

   c What percentage of those under 25 preferred some sort of diet drink ?

   d If 800 people who took part in the survey were between 40 and 49, how many of them said they preferred some type of Coke rather than some type of Pepsi ?

3. Shown are the temperature and rainfall statistics for Babbington.

	High(°F)	Low (°F)	High (°C)	Low (°C)	Rain (mm)
Winter	54	34	12	1	125
Spring	78	57	26	14	85
Summer	85	66	29	19	37
Autumn	61	41	16	5	46

   a What was the lowest temperature, (in °C), during the Spring ?

   b What was the difference between the highest and lowest temperature (in °F), during the Autumn ?

   c Calculate the **mean** (average) rainfall over the whole year, in mm.

Graphs, Charts & Tables

Numeracy Assessment 9

1. Two drivers recorded their speed every 10 minutes over the first 2 hours of a car journey from Glasgow to Carlisle.

   One went by the M74, the other on the slower route via the M77 and the A76.

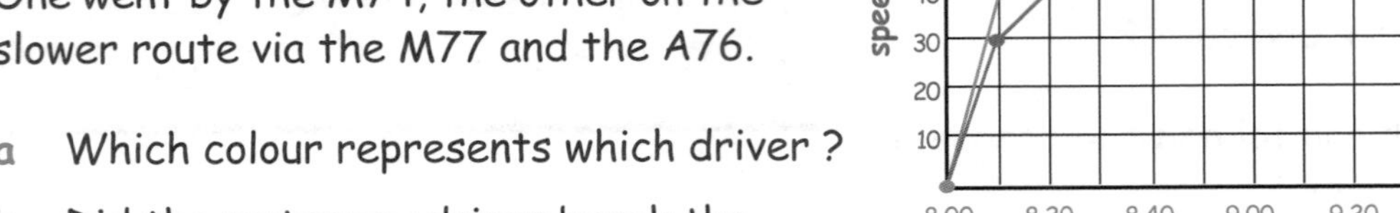

   a Which colour represents which driver ?

   b Did the motorway driver break the speed limit ?

   c At one point, the M74 driver was travelling slower than the other. Why ?

   d At 10.00, they were both travelling at the same speed. Does this part of the graph indicate that they had travelled the same distance ? *Explain.*

2. The public voted for the four finalists in the *Z-Factor* talent show as shown :-

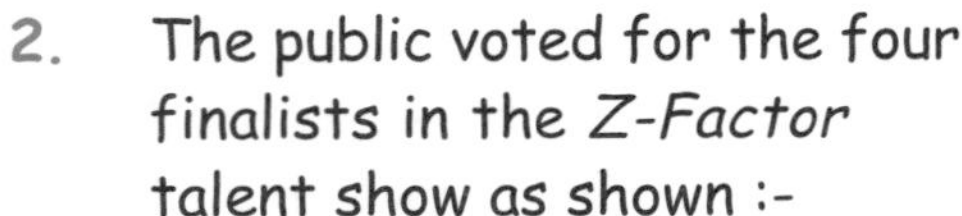

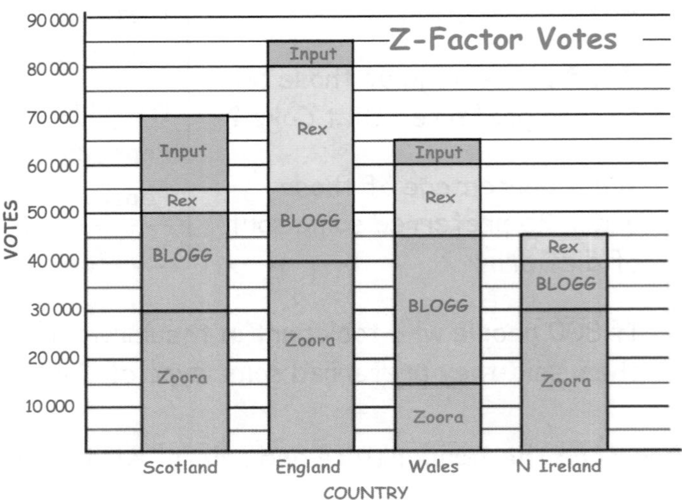

   a How many from England voted for *Zoora* ?

   b How many Scots went for *Input* ?

   c How many votes were cast altogether ?

   d Who won the talent show, and by how many votes did they beat the runner up ?

3. In a survey in a fish market, 540 people were asked which method they preferred to cook a piece of haddock.

   The results are shown in the pie chart.

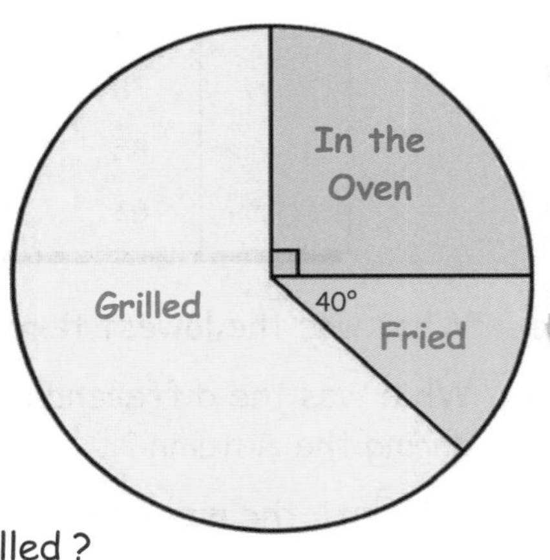

   a What angle at the centre is taken up by grilling the fish ?

   b How many people preferred the haddock :-

      (i) done in the oven (ii) fried ?

   c How many preferred to have their haddock grilled ?

4. Two newly born batches of mice with cancer genes were treated with two different experimental drugs, and it was recorded how long the mice lived, in months.

Mice Ages

ZX-10A		AC/135
	0	1 3 4 4
6 3 2 1	1	3 5 5 5 7 8
8 7 5 5 3	2	0 2 4 5 7
9 7 3 3 1	3	2
1 0	4	

Key :- 3 | 2 = 32 months; 1 | 4 = 41 months

a How old was the oldest mouse ?

b Which of the 2 drugs, ZX-10A or AC/135 appeared to work better ?

c What **fraction** of those mice, treated with ZX-10A, lived to be at least 3 years old ?

d By calculating the mean of both groups of mice, make a statement about the effectiveness of the 2 drugs.

5. 18 people counted the number of coins in their pockets and weighed them.

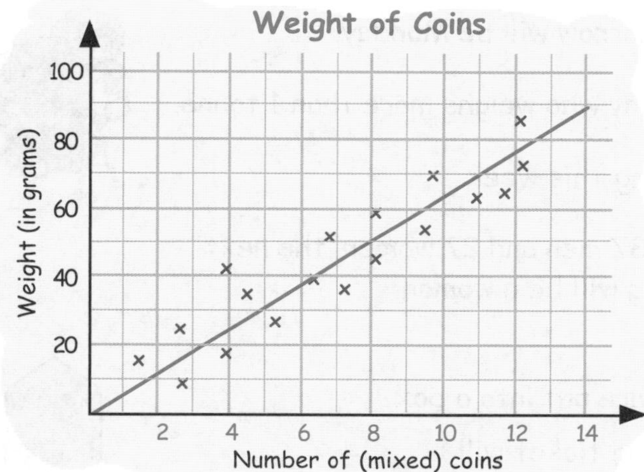

a Why must the line pass through the (0, 0) point ?

b Count how many points are above and how many are below the red line.

c Use the line of best fit to estimate the weight of 10 coins.

d Estimate the weight of 14 coins.

6. *Thistle Holidays* are promoting end of season short holidays.

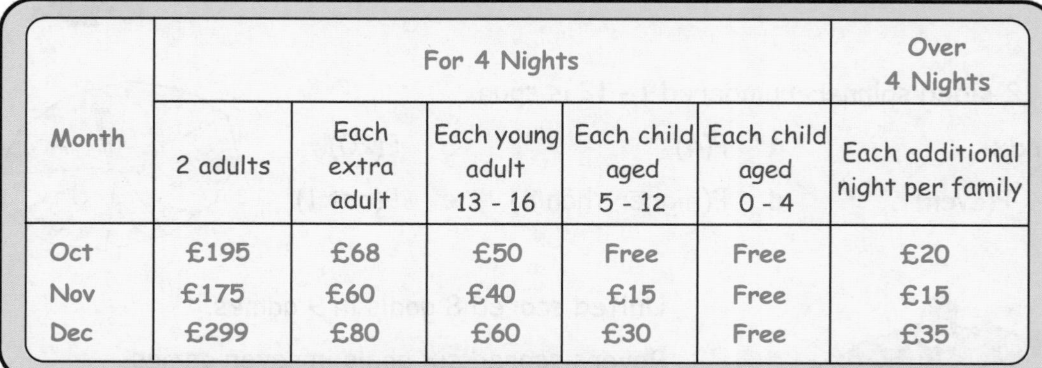

Month	For 4 Nights					Over 4 Nights
	2 adults	Each extra adult	Each young adult 13 - 16	Each child aged 5 - 12	Each child aged 0 - 4	Each additional night per family
Oct	£195	£68	£50	Free	Free	£20
Nov	£175	£60	£40	£15	Free	£15
Dec	£299	£80	£60	£30	Free	£35

Calculate the cost of :-

a A 4 night holiday for 3 adults and 2 children aged 3 and 14 in November.

b A 5 night holiday for 2 adults, a 13 and 15 year old and a 6 year old in December.

c Suggest a reason why December prices are a bit higher.

Probability

Revision of Probability

1. Shown is a "Probability Line".

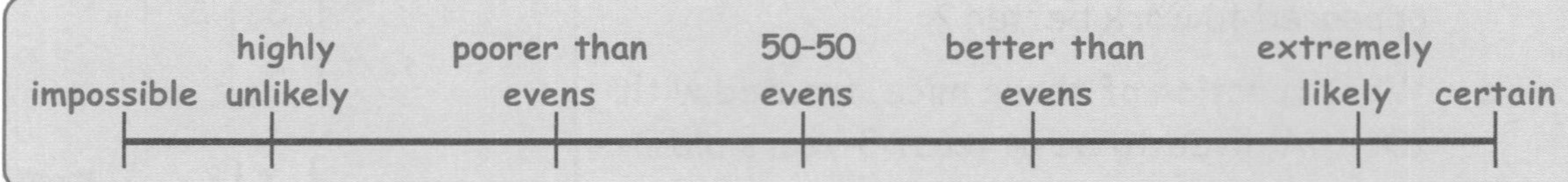

For each of the following, decide what the best choice of probability is :-

A – The next person to walk through the door will be female.

B – If today is Sunday, tomorrow will be Monday.

C – I will meet someone today who weighs more than 1 tonne.

D – I will get hit by lightning this week.

E – At a disco attended by 37 men and 27 women, the next person to get up dancing will be a woman.

2. Raffle tickets numbered 1 to 100 are put into a box.

What is the probability the winning ticket will :-

a be the number 10 b be an odd number

c **not** be the number 78 d be a number bigger than 49 ?

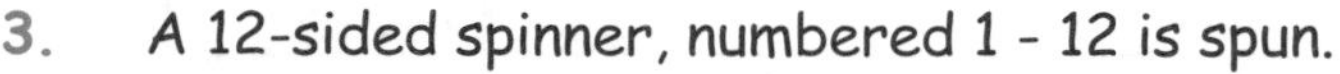

3. A 12-sided spinner, numbered 1 - 12 is spun.

Find :- a P(4) b P(20)

c P(even) d P(higher than 8) e P(not 1).

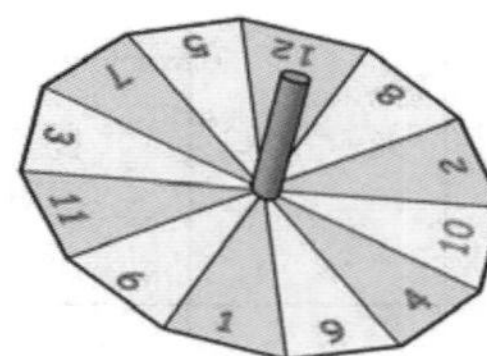

4.

United scored 8 goals in 9 games.

Rovers scored six goals in seven games.

City scored ten goals in twelve games.

Who has the better scoring rate ?

(*Show all your working*).

Probability

Exercise 1

1. There are 27 girls and 42 boys in a playground.

   If I walk through the playground and bump into one of the children, what is the probability it will be a girl ?
   (*Give your answer in its simplest form*).

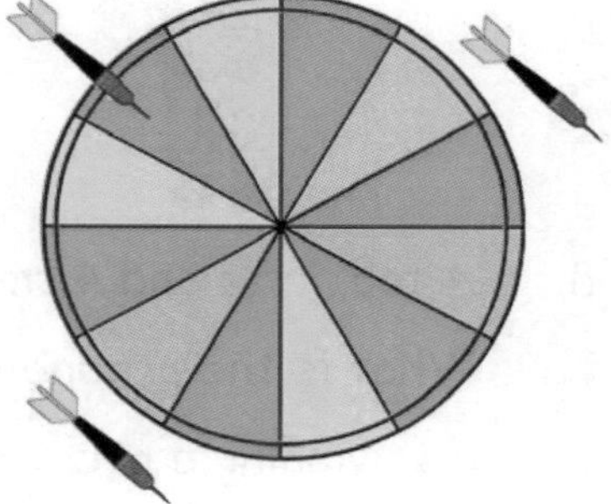

2. A fairground dart board is split into equal sections as shown.

   Red loses and any other colour wins a prize.

   If you actually land on the board, what is the probability of :-

   a losing b landing on the blue part
   c landing on the yellow part d winning a prize ?

3. If you roll two normal 6 sided dice sixty times, approximately how many times would you expect to get a total score of :-

   a 12 b 1 c 7 ?
   (*Note :- it may help to write down all the combinations*).

4. Two 5 sided spinners, numbered 1 to 5, are spun and the 2 numbers are added together.

   a Write down all the pairings of numbers you could get.

   (e.g. (1, 1), (1, 2), (1, 3), etc - There are 25 !

   b Find the following probabilities :-

   (i) P(total = 10) (ii) P(total = 2)
   (iii) P(total = 8) (iv) P(total = 11).

5. A survey shows the types of drinks bought in a cafe during a lunchtime by 30 people.

Water	Orange	Milk	Cola	Energy
14	3	6	5	2

   a What is the probability that the next person to enter the cafe will order water ?

   b What is the least number of bottles of each drink the manager should order for next week if he expects 240 lunchtime customers each day, Monday to Friday ?

6. Mr Jones puts all his students' test results into a table as shown.

	Passed	Failed
Boys	9	3
Girls	11	1

a How many students sat the test altogether ?

b What is the probability that if he picks a pupil at random it will be a :-

(i) boy (ii) pupil who failed (iii) girl who failed ?

7.

Wick Wanderers have scored 55 points in ten games.

Stranraer Stars have scored 48 points in nine games.

Berwick Bears have scored 70 points in twelve games.

Which team has the better scoring rate ?

(*Show all your working*).

8. A top prize and 4 smaller prizes are available when 1000 raffle tickets are sold.

What is the probability of :-

a winning a prize with a single ticket

b winning the top prize

c picking a ticket that ends with a 9

d picking a ticket that ends with at least two zeros ?

9. When a flu virus enters a school, the probability of a person catching it is 0·17.

In a school of 1200 pupils, how many pupils are expected to catch the flu ?

10.

In a *Y-Factor* competition, the success rate of passing the first round is only 8%.

a Find P(fail).

b Find the number of people passing the first round from a group of 2100.

11. *APP Insurance* provides cover in the event of a cancelled town fete due to heavy rain.

They know that the probability of heavy rain is 0·06.

a If they insure 200 fetes, how many are likely to be cancelled ?

b They pay out £2000 for each cancelled fete.

APP want to make £5000 profit from the 200 fetes.

How much must they charge each fete for insurance ?

12. A coin is tossed 1000 times.

Which of the following set of figures would be most likely to occur ?

	A	B	C	D
Heads	200	623	498	488
Tails	800	377	502	522

13. A six sided dice is rolled 1000 times.

Which graph below best represents the expected results ?

Graph 1

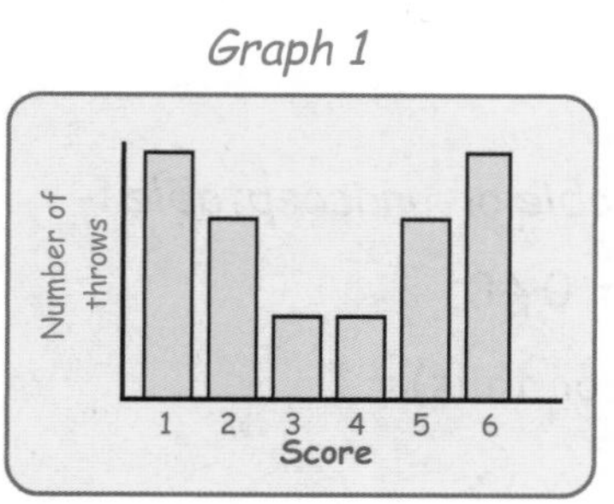

Graph 2

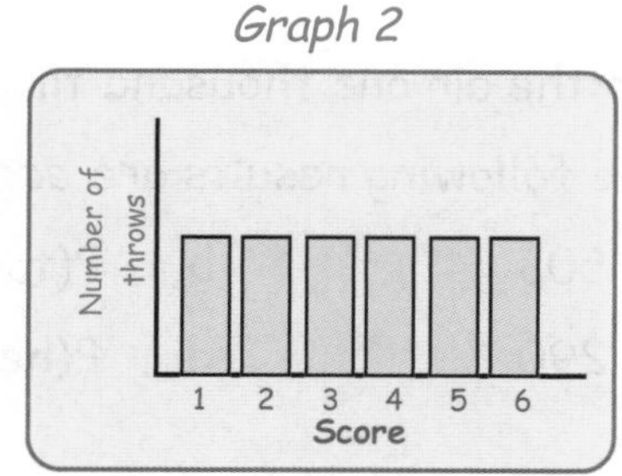

Graph 3

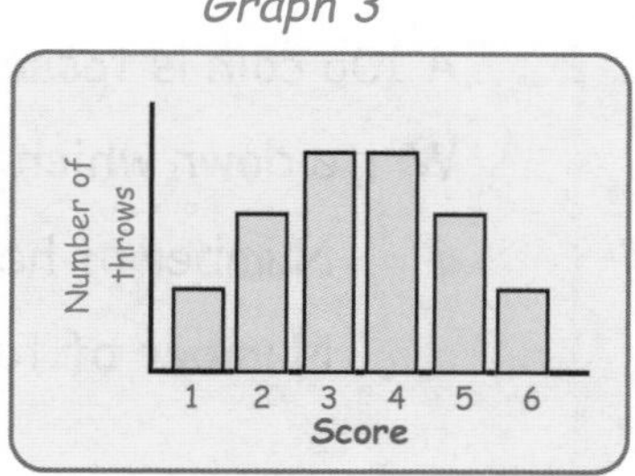

14. **Two** six sided dice are thrown 1000 times, and the 2 numbers added each time.

A total of between 2 and 12 is possible.

Sketch what you would expect the graph of the "totals" to look like.

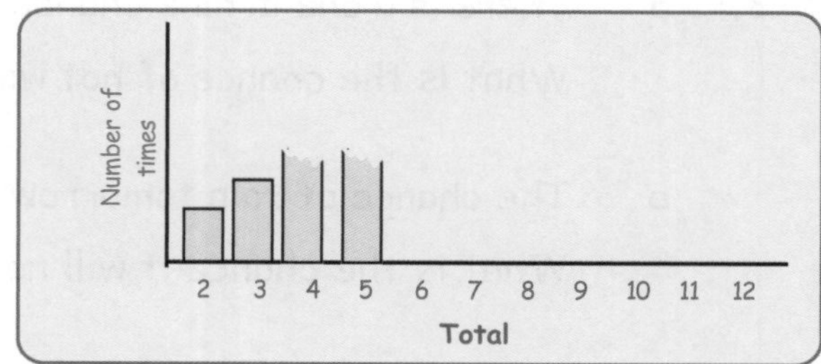

15.

A machine makes precision light fittings.

The optimum (best) speed gives a Prob(*faulty fittings*) = 0·012.

a How many faulty fittings will machine A produce at this speed if it produces 10 000 light fittings ?

b At a higher speed, machine B gives 60 faulty fittings for every 4000 fittings.

Should the machine B be slowed down or speeded up ?

16. There are 3 sizes of book cases for sale in a shop.

The book cases are constructed using either metal or wood.

	3 m by 2 m	4 m by 2 m	1 m by 1 m
Wood	6	4	12
Metal	3	1	4

The table shows the number of each type of bookcase on display.

If I walked into the shop, what is the probability the first bookcase I would see is :-

a 3 m by 2 m and made of wood

b 1 m by 1 m and made from metal

c made from wood

d made from wood or metal ?

Probability

Numeracy Assessment 10

1. An octagonal dice, numbered 1 to 8, is rolled.

   Find :-

   a Probability(3) b P(odd) c P(not 7).

2. A 10p coin is tossed into the air one thousand times.

   Write down which of the following results are *acceptable* or *unacceptable* :-

   a Number of heads = 503 b P(tails) = 0·48

   c Number of tails = 290 d P(heads or tails) = 1.

3. a There is a one in nine chance of winning a prize.

   What is the chance of not winning a prize ?

   b The chance of rain tomorrow is 0·7.

   What is the chance it will not rain ?

4. 

   Dario scored eight goals in eleven games.

   Sergio scored nine goals in thirteen games.

   Who has the better goal scoring rate ?

5. There are two types of car in a repair garage - Sports and Saloon.

   These car engines are either ***below 2000 cc*** or ***2000 cc and above***. (*cc means cm^3 or ml*)

   The table shows the number of different cars being repaired.

   When an inspector arrives, he chooses a car at random to inspect.

   What is the probability, in its simplest form, of the inspector choosing a :-

cc	Sports	Saloon
below 2000	4	2
2000+	6	0

   a 2500 cc sports car b 1600 cc Saloon

   c sports car d 3 litre saloon ?

Unit Assessment

Numeracy

Assessment Tasks

1. Tourists from USA, visiting Scotland, were asked where they enjoyed visiting the most.

   The top four towns/cities are shown in the bar graph.

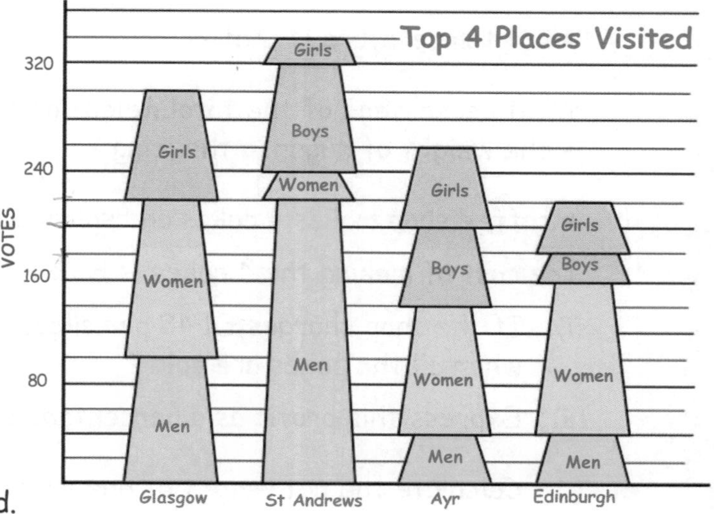

   a How many American men voted for St Andrews ? (1)

   b Which place got the same number of votes from boys and girls ? (1)

   c 1200 people were questioned.

   How many of them voted for a town/city outwith the top four ? (2)

   d Express the number who voted for Edinburgh as a percentage of all who voted, correct to 3 significant figures. (2)

   e 900 tourists from Canada were asked the same question.

   The proportions of their votes are shown in a pie chart.

   How many Canadians voted for "others" ? (4)

Others
Glasgow
Edinburgh
120°
60°
60°
Ayr
St Andrews

2. Shown below is the recipe for a Carrot Cake.

   The recipe is in two parts - the sponge and the icing.

Sponge

4 eggs
300 ml (1/2 pint) vegetable oil
400 g (14 oz) sugar
2 teaspoons vanilla extract
250 g (9 oz) plain flour
2 teaspoons bicarbonate of soda
2 teaspoons baking powder
1/2 teaspoon salt
2 teaspoons ground cinnamon
350 g (12 oz) grated carrots
120 g ($4\frac{1}{4}$ oz) chopped nuts

Icing

125 g ($4\frac{1}{4}$ oz) butter, softened
1 (200 g) tub cream cheese, softened
450 g (1 lb) sugar
dash of vanilla extract
125 g ($4\frac{1}{4}$ oz) chopped nuts

2. a Write in its simplest form :- the ratio of the weight of nuts to the weight of sugar used to make the entire carrot cake. (2)

b The sponge mix has to be baked in a preheated oven for 40-50 minutes at the temperature shown on the thermometer.

What temperature is that ? (1)

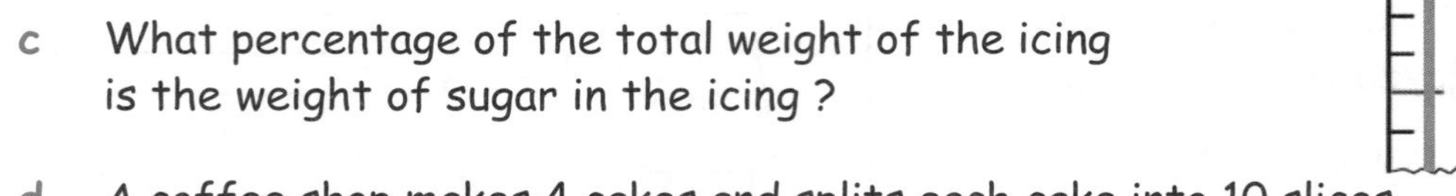

c What percentage of the total weight of the icing is the weight of sugar in the icing ? (3)

d A coffee shop makes 4 cakes and splits each cake into 10 slices.

The cost of making the 4 cakes is £32.

(i) If the shop charges £1·40 per slice, how much profit will be made when all the cakes are sold ? (2)

(ii) Express this profit as a percentage of what it costs to make the cakes. (2)

e (i) Calculate the net weight of one slice of carrot cake to the nearest 10 g. (1)
(*Forget the weight of the eggs, salt, cinnamon, vanilla and oil*).

(ii) One of the shop's customers thinks that £1·40 is too expensive, as the local baker is selling 150 gram carrot cake muffins for £1·05.

Is the customer correct ? Explain. (2)

3. The scattergraph shows some information about the test marks of a few students who sat a maths test and science test, both out of 70, in January.

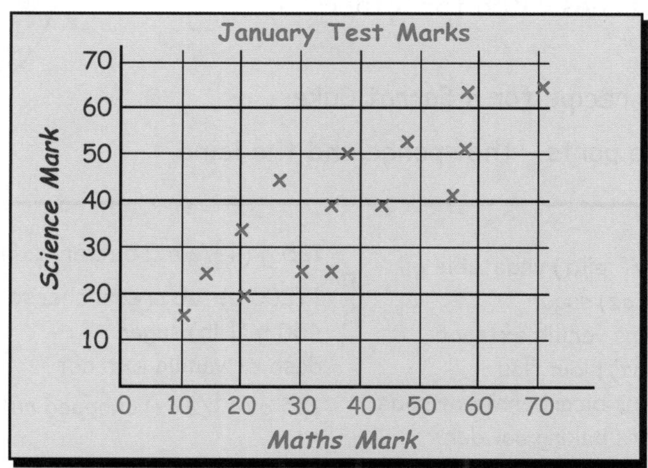

a Describe the correlation between the maths marks and the science marks. (1)

b Hazel scored 38 in maths. What was her science mark ? (1)

3. c The History department recorded their January test marks out of 50, to compare them with the marks of a similar test sat in April, after a spell of intensive revision and supported study.

This back-to-back stem and leaf diagram shows their findings :-

(i) What was the lowest mark in the January test ? (1)

(ii) Which mark occurred most often in the April test ? (1)

(iii) By calculating the mean of both sets of marks, make a statement about how useful all the revision was. (3)

History Marks

January		April
6 4 3 2	1	4 6 8
7 5 2 0	2	2 2 6 6
4 3 2 1 1	3	0 5 5 5 8
5 4 2 1 0	4	4 7 7 9 9
	5	0

Key :- 2 | 6 = 26 marks; 1 | 4 = 41 marks

4. Shown is a picture of a child's play brick.

It is in the shape of a square based cuboid.

To find its height, given the volume and length of one side of the base, we use the formula :-

$$H = \frac{V}{L^2} .$$

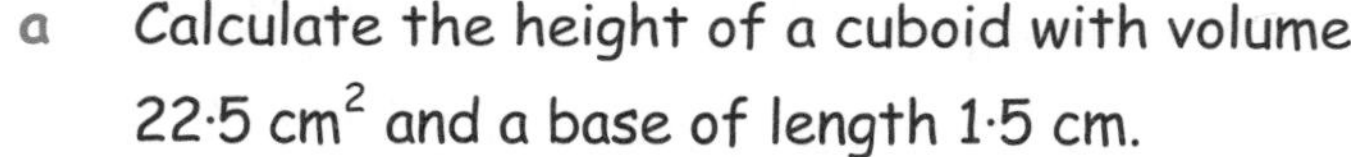

a Calculate the height of a cuboid with volume $22{\cdot}5\ cm^2$ and a base of length 1·5 cm. (2)

b If the volume remains fixed, what happens to the height of the cuboid as the length of the base doubles in size ? (1)

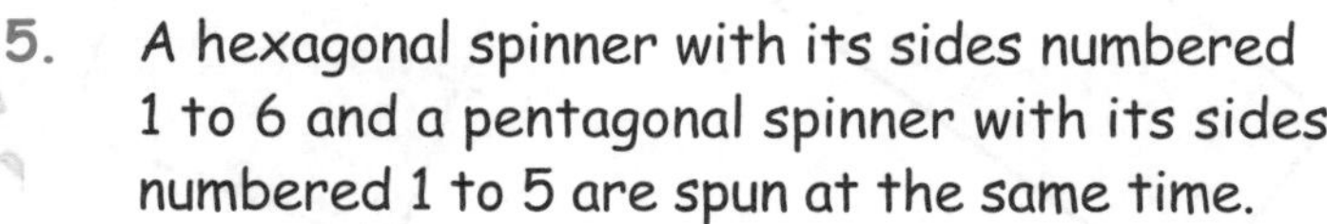

5. A hexagonal spinner with its sides numbered 1 to 6 and a pentagonal spinner with its sides numbered 1 to 5 are spun at the same time.

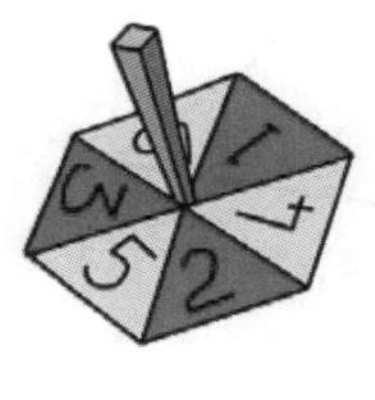

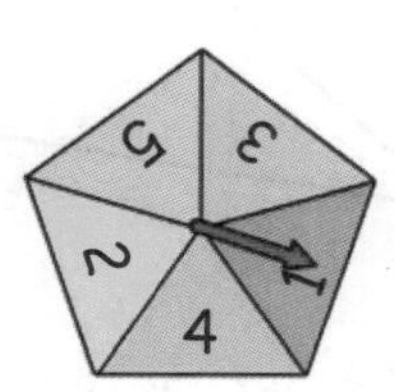

a Write out all the possible combinations of results when they stop spinning and both lie on a numbered side. (2)

b What is the probability of getting a total score of 7 from the 2 spinners ? (2)

c If the spinners are spun 60 times, approximately how many times are you likely to get a total score of 10 ? (2)

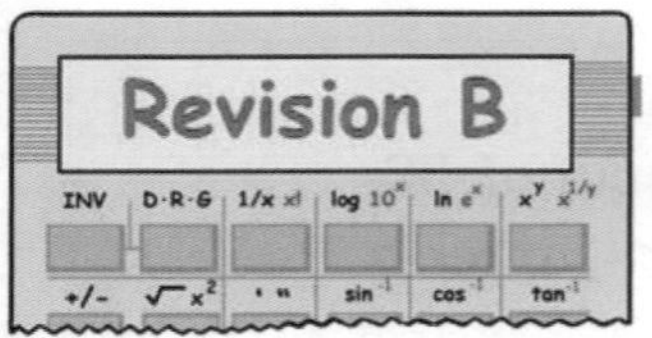

Geometry/Measure Revision

(The following was covered in Nat 4 Lifeskills and should be known, though much of it will be revised later).

Gradients

1. a Write down the gradient of the slope shown on Law Hill, as a fraction.

   b Simplify the fraction.

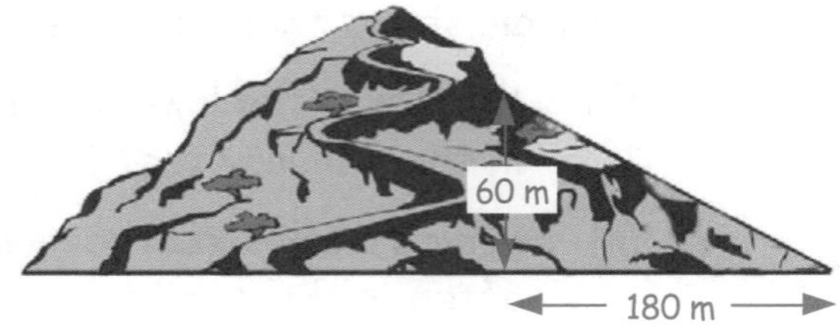

2. 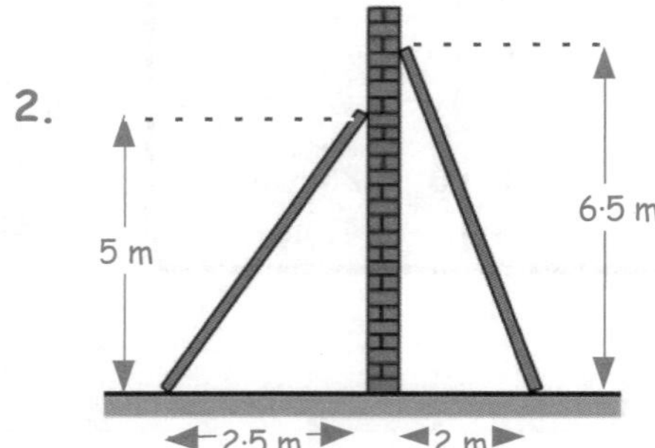

Two wooden planks are placed against a wall as shown.

The planks should have a gradient with a value between **2·5** and **3·5**.

Which of the planks shown meet this requirement ?

3. The gradients of four ramps are given below :-

car ramp	30%,	ski jump ramp	$\frac{7}{20}$,
skateboard ramp	0·38,	building ramp	$\frac{3}{8}$.

List the ramps in order, **steepest** first.

building ramp

Perimeter

4. Calculate the perimeter of each of these shapes :-

a 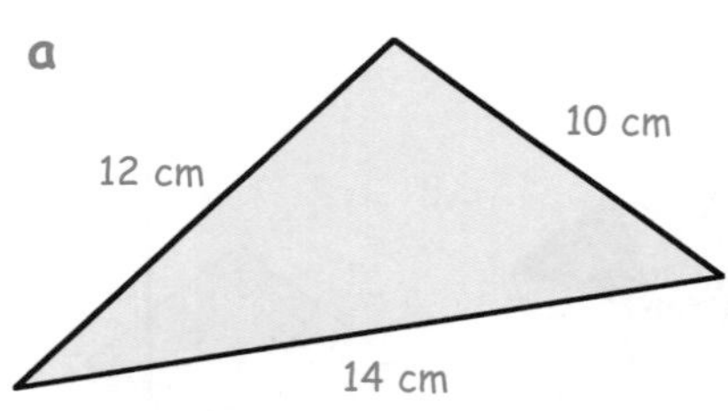

b

c 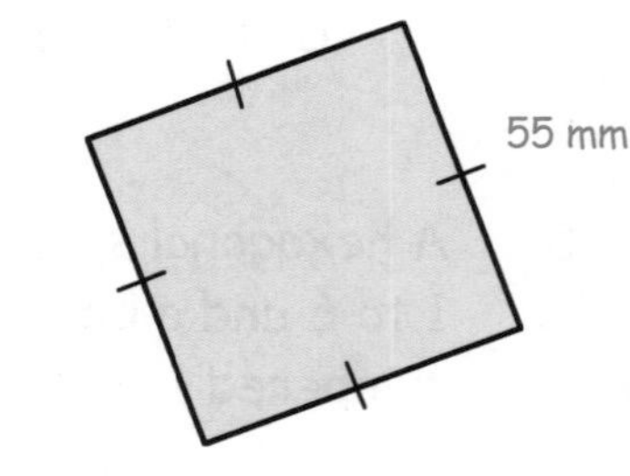

5. The perimeter of this rectangle is 66 cm.

   Calculate the missing side of the rectangle.

? cm

3 cm

6. 

The radius of the top rim of this coffee mug is 72·5 mm.

What is its diameter ?

7. Calculate the perimeter of this shape.

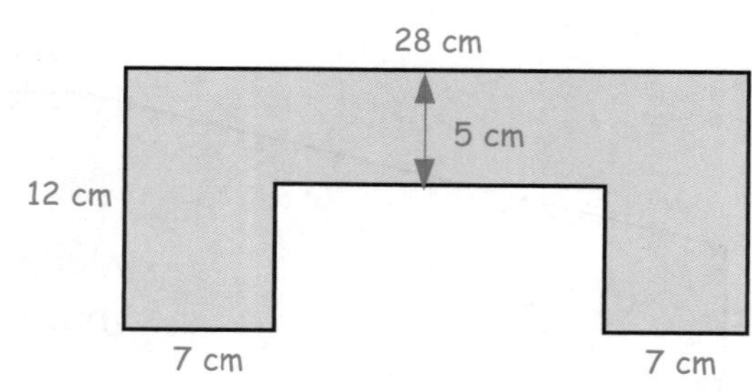

Area

8. Calculate the area of this rectangle.

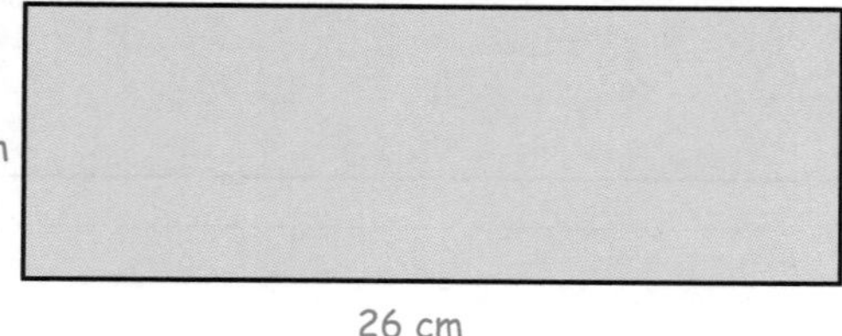

9. Calculate the area of this right angled triangle.

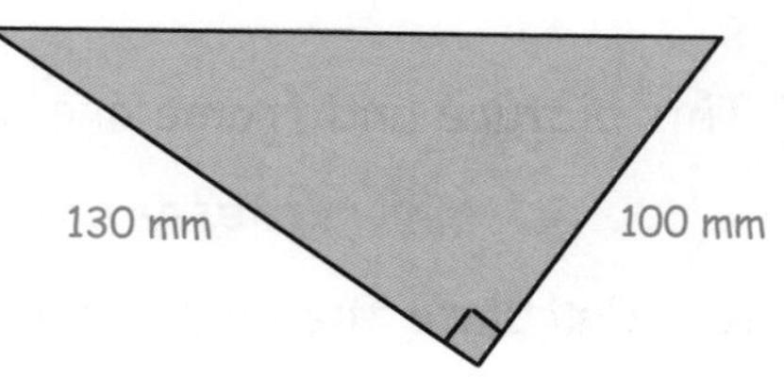

10. Calculate the area of each of the following shapes :-

a

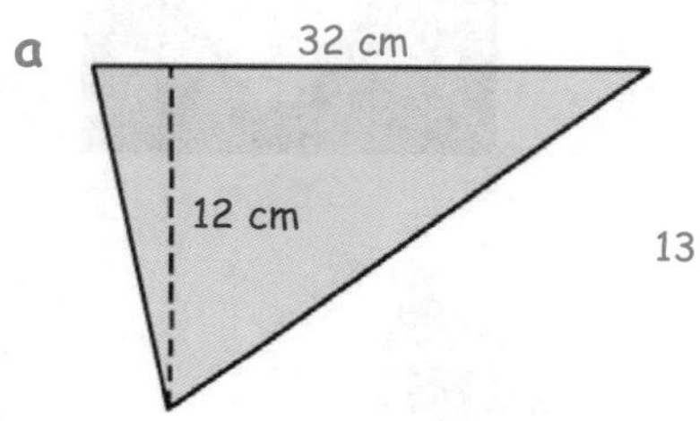

b

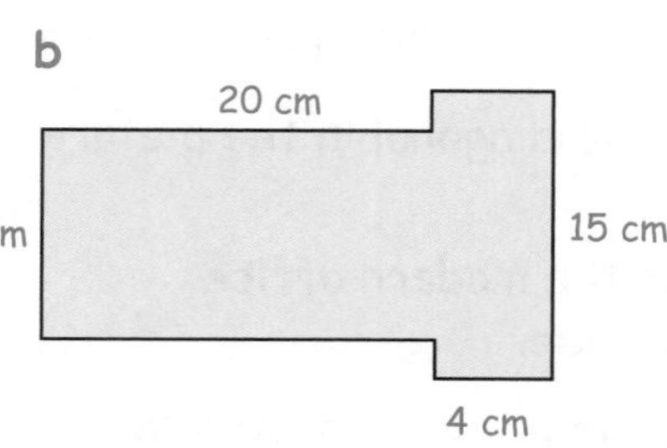

c

14 cm

25 cm

32 cm

11. Calculate the area of each of these shapes :-

a rhombus

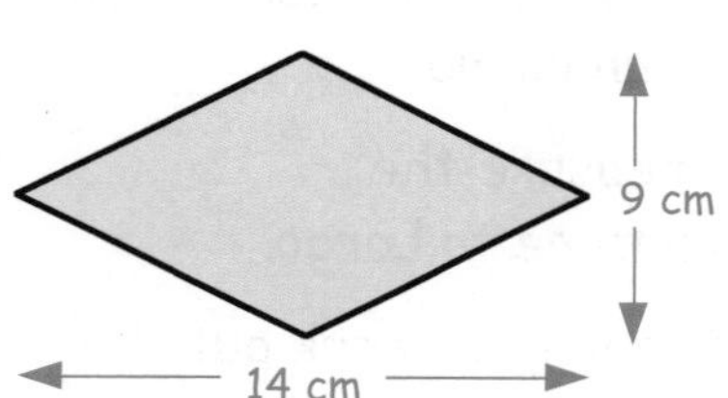

b parallelogram

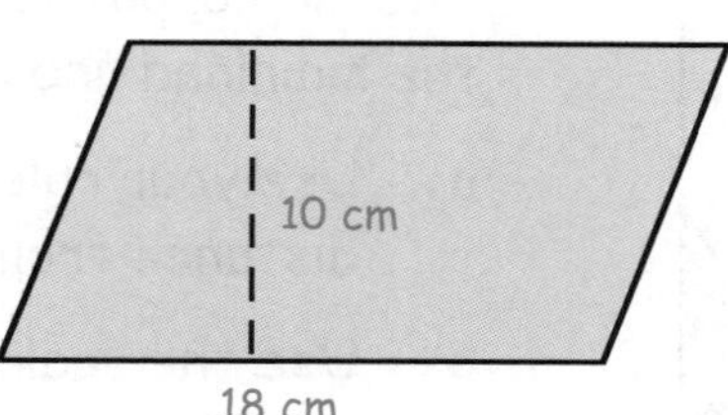

c kite

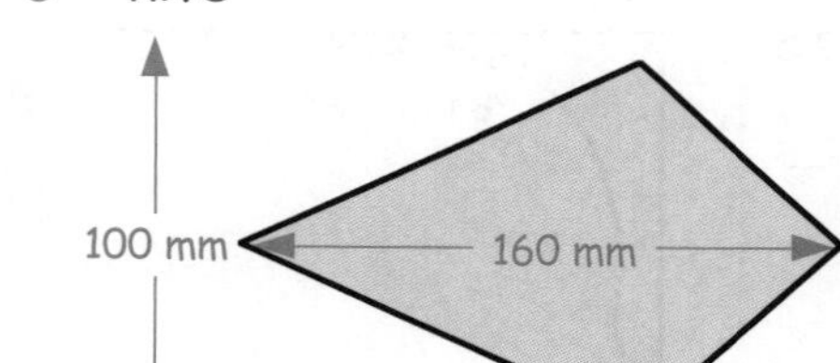

12. Calculate the area of each of these circles :-

a

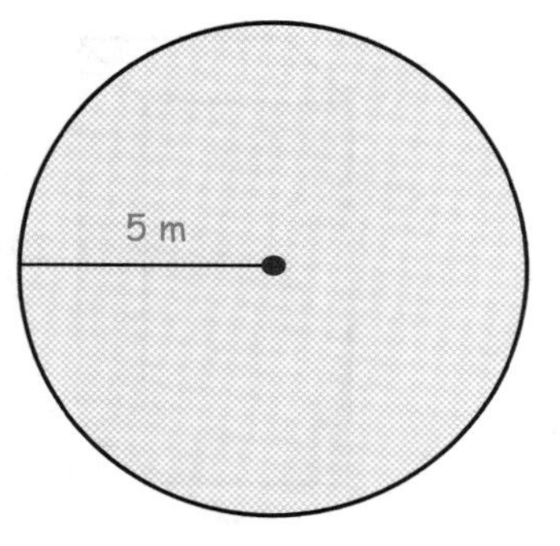

b

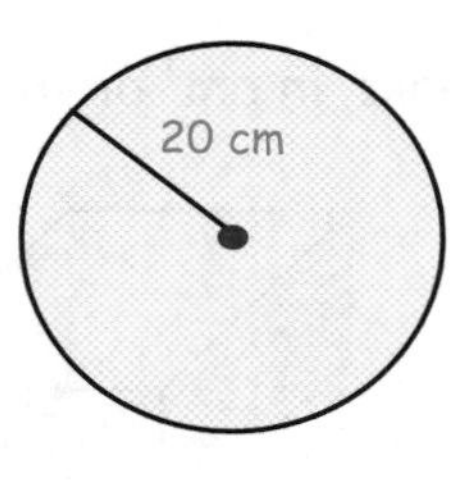

c

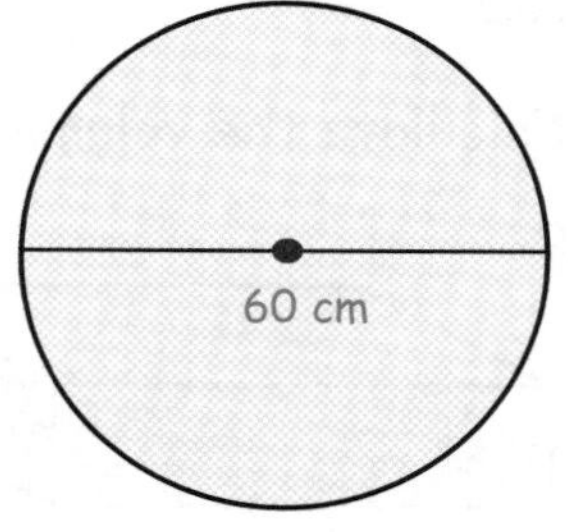

Scales

13.

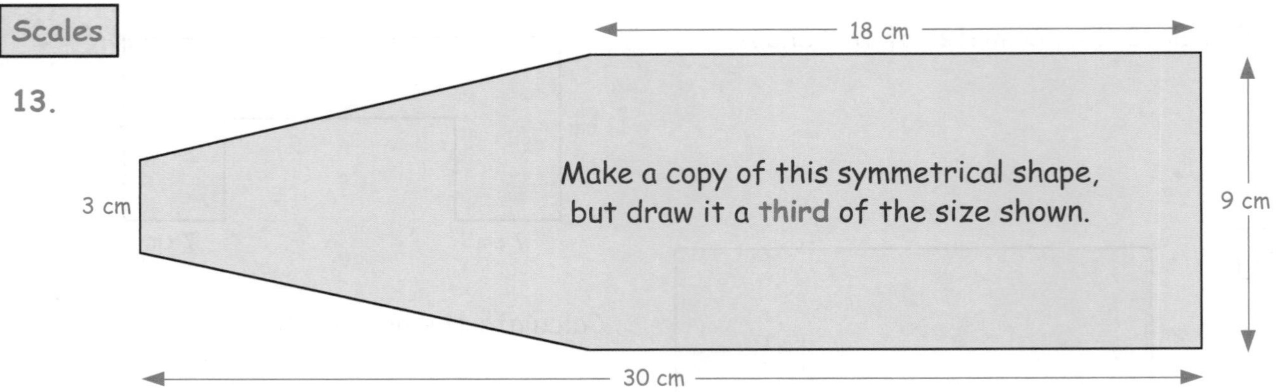

14. This picture and frame are drawn to a scale of :-

1 mm represents 4·5 mm.

a Calculate the real width of the frame, in cm.

b Calculate the real height of the frame, in cm.

c The real length of a diagonal is 22·5 cm.

Calculate the length of the diagonal in the picture.

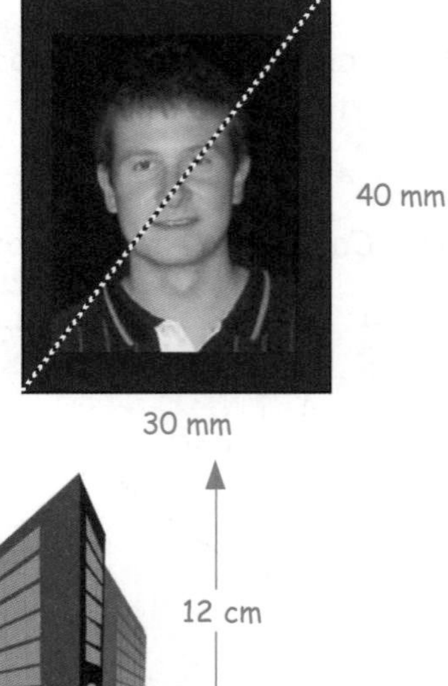

15. Shown is a drawing of one of the modern office buildings in the centre of Dundee.

It has been drawn using a scale :- **1 cm = 3·5 m.**

Work out the real height of the building.

12 cm

16.

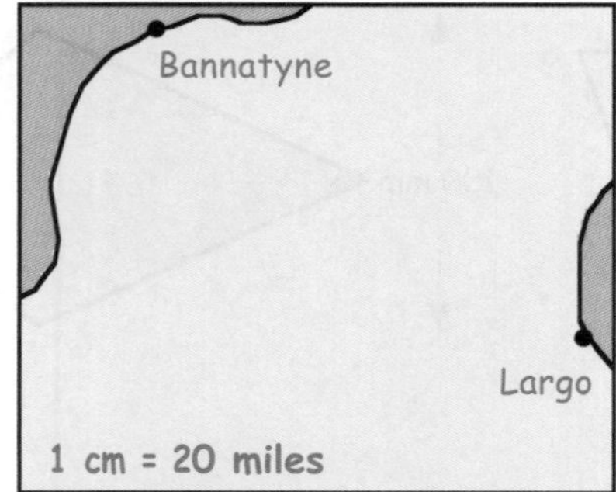

The map opposite shows 2 fishing villages - one on the mainland and one on an island.

a Use your ruler to measure the distance from Bannatyne to Largo.

b Use the scale of the map to work out the real distance between the two villages.

Volume

17. Calculate the volume of each cuboid, in cm^3 or in m^3 :-

a

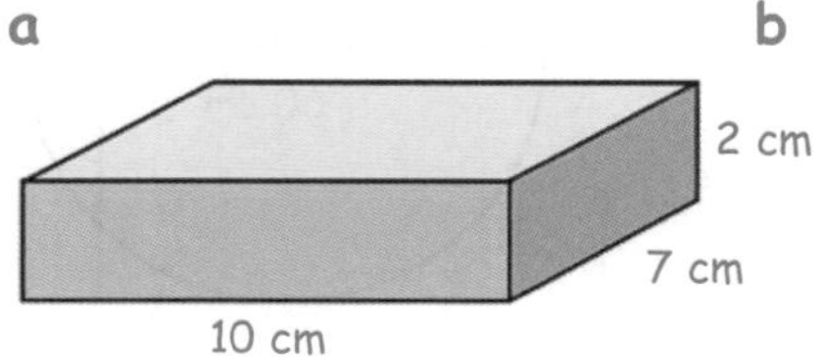

b

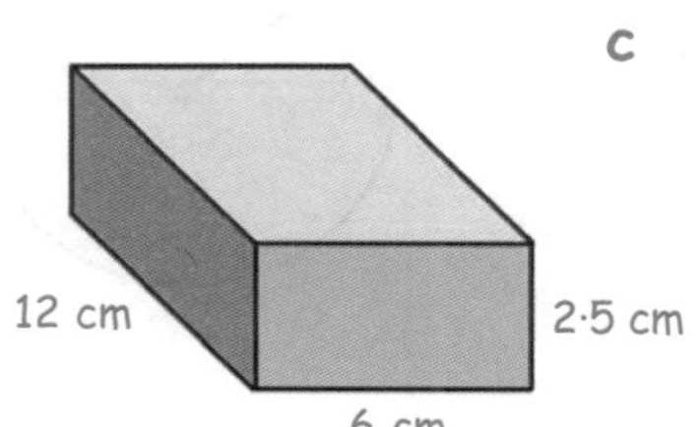

c

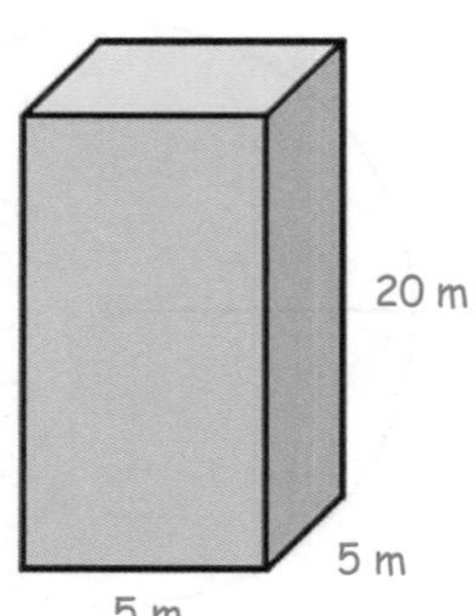

18. This cuboid of ice has a volume of 15 cm^3.
Calculate what its width must be.

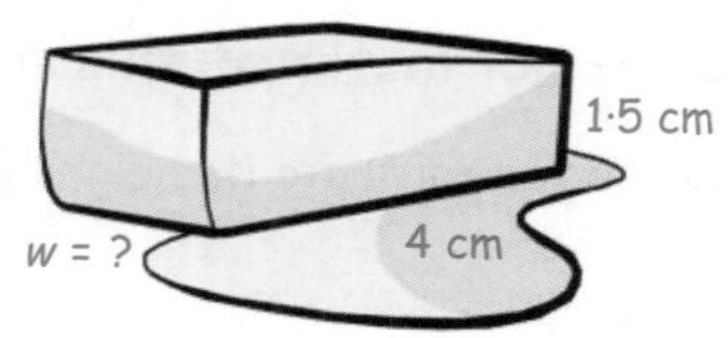

19.

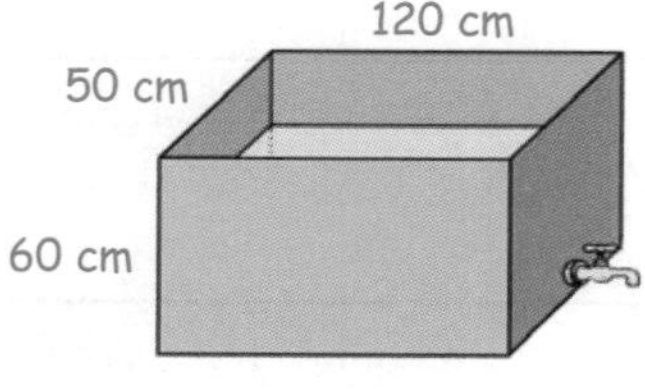

a Calculate the volume of this tank, in cm^3.

b How many millilitres will it hold when full ?

c Write its **capacity** in litres.

20. Calculate the volume of these prisms :-

a

23 cm^2

10 cm

b

40 cm^2

8·5 cm

21.

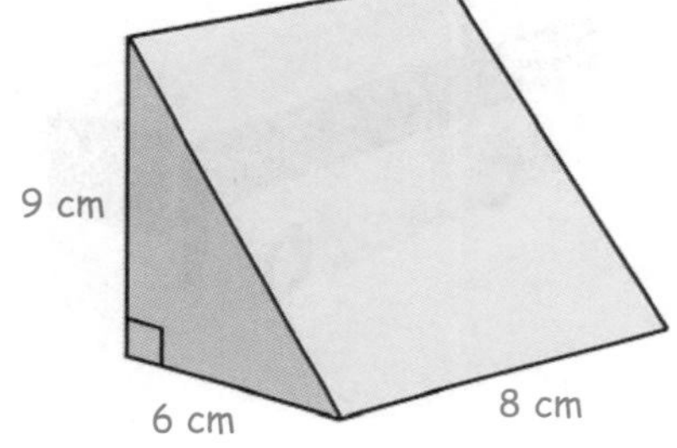

a Calculate the area of the triangular end face of this prism.

b Now calculate its volume.

22. Calculate the volume of this cylindrical tin of cat food with radius 5 cm and height 6 cm.

Pythagoras

23. Calculate the lengths of the sides marked *x* and *y* here.

a

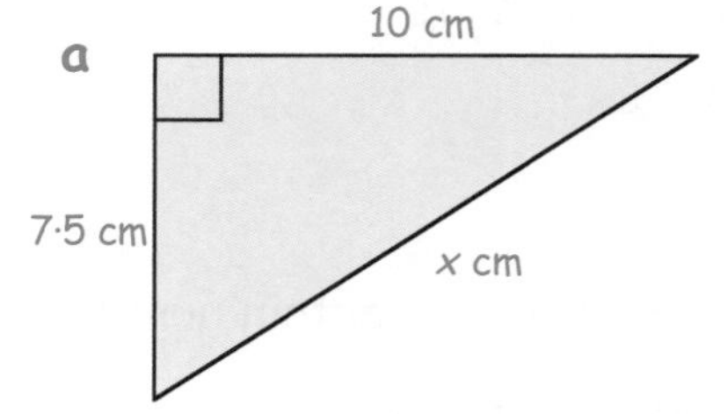

b

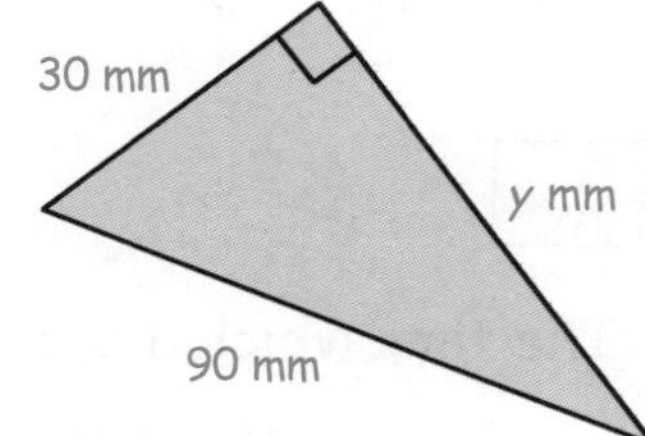

24.

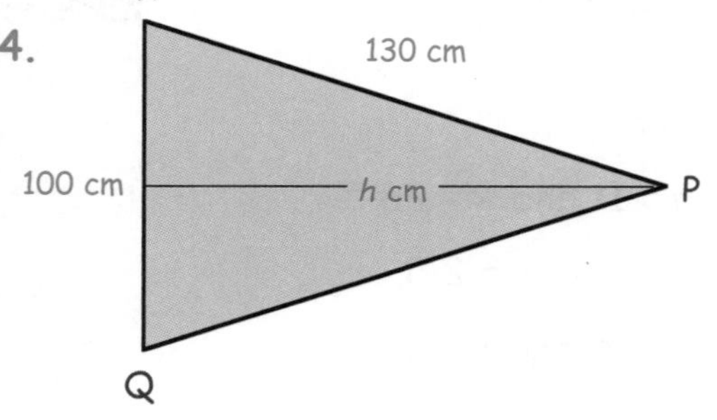

Triangle PQR is isosceles with PR = PQ

a Calculate the value of *h*.

b Now calculate the area of triangle PQR.

25. Calculate the **perimeter** of this shape.

(*Note* - you need to calculate its height first).

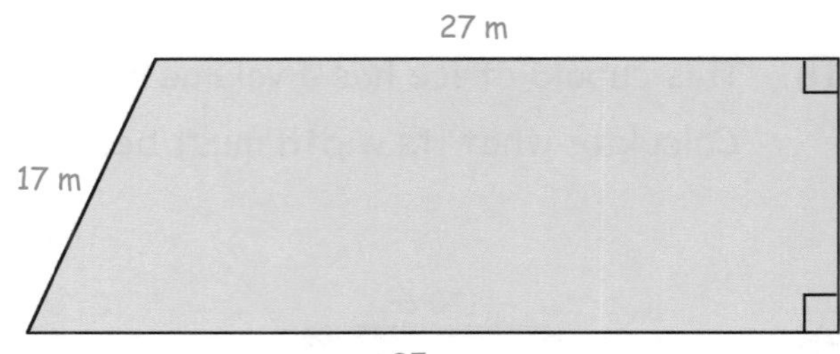

Timetables

26. Shown is a bus timetable from Alberry to Wesley.

Alberry		Gatsburgh		Rodwell		Wesley	
Arrive	Depart	Arrive	Depart	Arrive	Depart	Arrive	Depart
	0810	0844	0849	0905	0910	0953	1001
1107	1112	1146	1151	1207	1212	1255	1303
1419	1424	1458	1503	1519	1524	1607	1615
1731	1736	1810	----	----	----	----	----
----	----	----	1927	1943	1948	2031	----

a When the bus leaves Alberry at 0810, at what time does it arrive at Wesley ?

b A bus arrives at Wesley at 2031.

Where did it set out from and when did it leave there ?

c I am at a bus stop in Gatsburgh at 2:35 pm.

How long do I have to wait for the next bus to Wesley to come along ?

d How long does the journey take from :-

(i) Alberry to Gatsburgh (ii) Alberry to Rodwell

(iii) Gatsburgh to Rodwell (iv) Gatsburgh to Wesley ?

27. It takes 9 hours and 25 minutes to travel by train from London to Madrid, the capital city of Spain.

If I catch the 2145 train from London, at what time will I arrive in Madrid ?

(*Remember - Spain is 1 hour ahead of Britain*).

Formulae

28. The time which a cyclist takes to travel a certain number of miles is found by :-

"Divide the distance travelled by the average speed for the journey".

How long might a cyclist take to travel 27 miles doing 18 mph ?

29. For each formula, find the value of the letter asked for :-

a $W = g - h + k$ find W, when $g = 20{\cdot}5$, $h = 11$ and $k = 26{\cdot}5$.

b $P = a \times b \times c$ find P, when $a = 20$, $b = 1{\cdot}5$ and $c = 2{\cdot}5$.

c $U = p \div q \times r$ find U, when $p = 125$, $q = 25$ and $r = 4$.

30. The final speed of a car is v and can be calculated using the formula :-

$$v = u + at$$

where u is the initial speed, a is the acceleration and t is the time taken.

Calculate the value of v when $u = 5$, $a = 2$ and $t = 3·5$.

Scale Drawing

31. John Baird has monoblocked the rectangular area outside his house but has kept some space for a lawn.

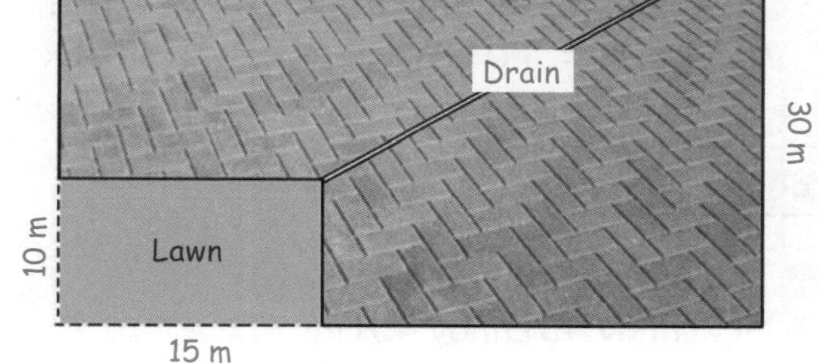

a Make a scale drawing of this area, using a scale :-

1 cm = 5 m.

b Measure the length of the drain from the lawn to the top right corner of his land, (*in cm*), on your drawing.

c Calculate the real length of the drain, in metres.

32. A pilot was flying North East, but on receiving a distress call, turned his plane anticlockwise till he was then flying due West.

By how many degrees had the pilot rotated his plane ?

33. Use a protractor to measure the bearing of each island from Royston Airport.

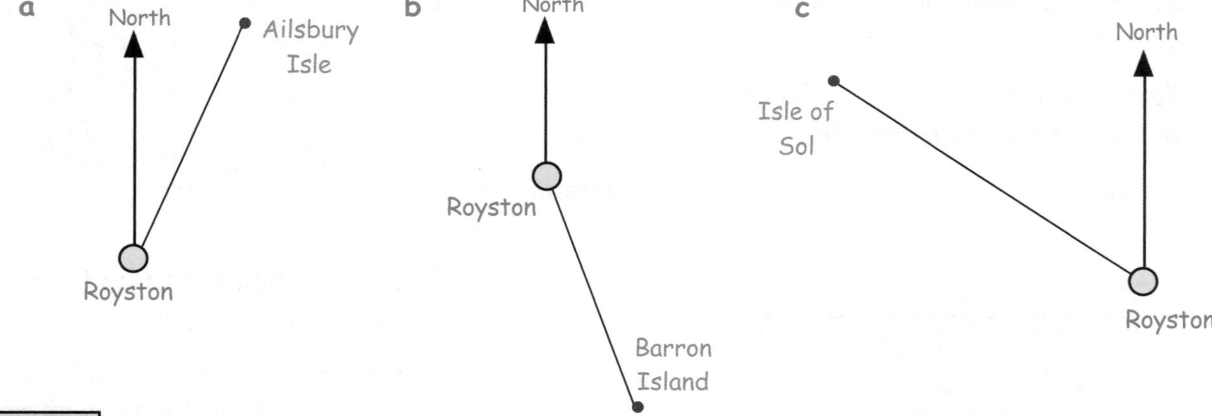

Tolerance

34. Write down the minimum and maximum values for each of the following :-

a (90 ± 4) km b (227 ± 5) g c (120 ± 30) volts

d (2100 ± 250) pounds e (7·2 ± 0·6) litres f (0·3 ± 0·02) cl.

35. 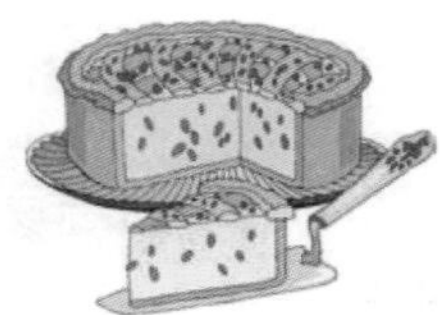

In the baking of a farmhouse sultana cake, the recommended weight of soft brown sugar to be used lies between 7·25 and 8·75 ounces.

Write this in tolerance form as (.... ± ....) ounces.

36. Put the following into tolerance form :-

a min = 40 mm
max = 50 mm

b min = 117 g
max = 123 g

c min = 5200 m
max = 4400 m

d min = 3·9 hrs
max = 4·0 hrs

e min = 36·5 sec
max = 37·1 sec

f min = 0·01 km
max = 0·07 km.

Problem Solving

37. A factory stores boxes 45 cm by 45 cm by 45 cm on a shelf **ten metres** long, **1 metre** deep and **50 cm** high.

a How many boxes can be placed on one shelf ?

b There are 4 shelves in each rack and 80 racks in the factory.

What is the maximum number of boxes that can be stored in the factory ?

38. Each roll of wallpaper Ms Deans buys is 80 cm wide and is 9·5 m long.

She has to wallpaper the 4 walls of a room 8 m by 4·5 m by 3 m.

Calculate the number of rolls of wallpaper Ms Deans requires.

(*Forget the door and window, and there is no pattern to match*).

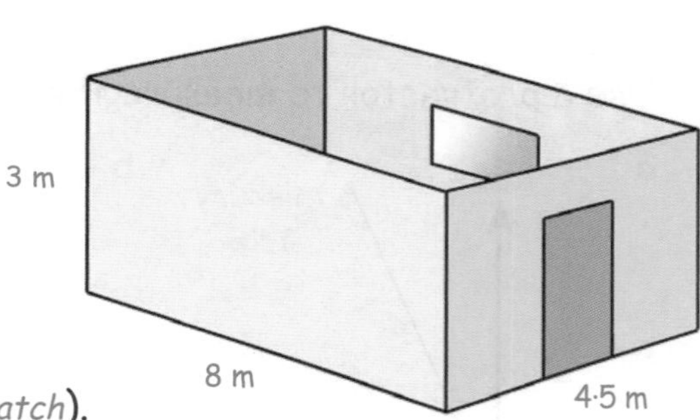

39. 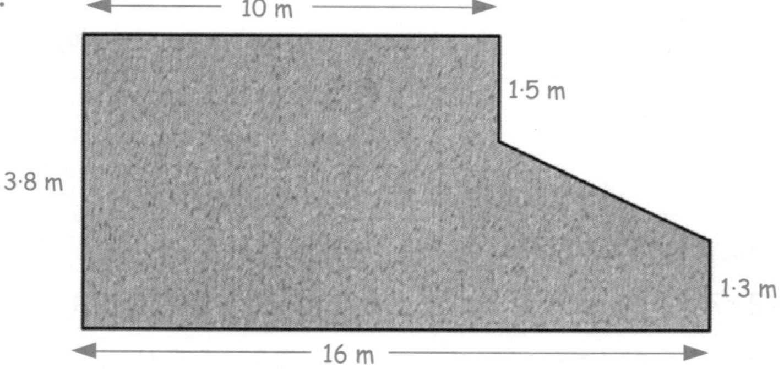

The floor shown is to be fully carpeted with no joins.

The carpet is 4 metres wide, and can be bought to the nearest metre in length.

The carpet costs £28 per m^2.

a Calculate the cost of carpeting this floor.

b Calculate the area of carpet that is "wasted".

Tolerance

Revision of Tolerance

1. Whilst training for a Javelin event, Danny records his throws in metres.

   His distances are (79·5 ± 3·5) metres.

   a What is his longest throw ?

   b What is his worst ?

2. Write down the minimum and maximum values for each of the following :-

   a (50 ± 4) m b (215 ± 8) g c (240 ± 15) amps

   d (1500 ± 150) miles e (7·2 ± 0·4) mg f (0·9 ± 0·05) kg.

3. The price of a standard Bovis Loaf was noted in 10 shops.

   The costs were £(1·05 ± 0·13).

   a What was the cheapest loaf ? b What was the dearest ?

4. A recipe requires (195 ± 10) grams of flour for a cake mix to be successful.

   Which of the following will possibly give rise to a nice cake mixture :-

   a 192 grams b 206 grams c 185·5 grams d 203·5 grams ?

5. 

   During a motorway ride from Glasgow to Manchester, a driver maintained a speed of between 58 and 72 mph.

   Write this in tolerance form as (.... ± ....) mph.

6. Put the following into tolerance form :-

   a min = 40 ml, max = 50 ml b min = 165 g, max = 175 g c min = 1800 m, max = 2100 m

   d min = 2·3 km, max = 2·4 km e min = 19·8 sec, max = 22·4 sec f min = 0·04 mm, max = 0·10 mm.

7. The depth of rain falling each day in the month of April in Dundee city centre ranged from 0 mm to 18·2 mm.

   Write this in tolerance form.

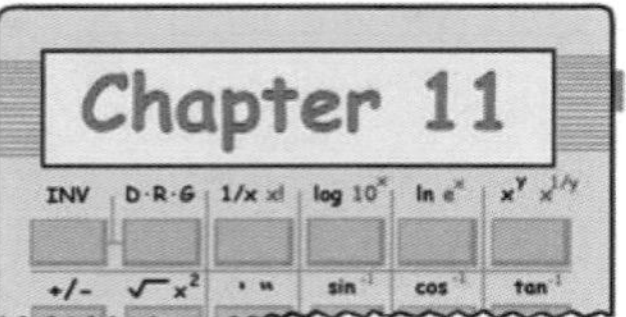

Tolerance

Tolerance involving Percentages

All the tolerance calculations you have dealt with so far refer to "raw" figures :-

Example 1 :- The length and breadth of a rectangle are (15 ± 0·2) cm and (9 ± 0·2) cm.

Calculate the upper and lower limits for the perimeter of the rectangle.

(9 ± 0·2) cm

(15 ± 0·2) cm

Solution :- The length lies between 14·8 cm and 15·2 cm.

The breadth lies between 8·8 cm and 9·2 cm.

=> The perimeter lies between 2 x (14·8 + 8·8) cm and 2 x (15·2 + 9·2) cm

=> The perimeter lies between **47·2 cm** and **48·8 cm** or **(48 ± 0·8) cm.**

NEW :- Sometimes, tolerance is given in terms of **percentages**.

Example 2 :- The captain of a container ship hopes to cross the Atlantic at a speed of **40 mph (± 10%)**, the "tolerance" being due to unknown tidal effects.

Can you see that, since 10% of 40 = 4, then the speed is **(40 ± 4) mph**,

=> the **minimum speed** is **36 mph** and the **maximum speed** is **44 mph** ?

Exercise 1

1. For each of the following, find the minimum and the maximum values :-

   a 120 mm (±10%) b 600 kg (±5%) c 1500 m (±1%)

   d 0·6 cm (±10%) e 25 tonnes (±2%) f 400 ml (±0·5%).

2. 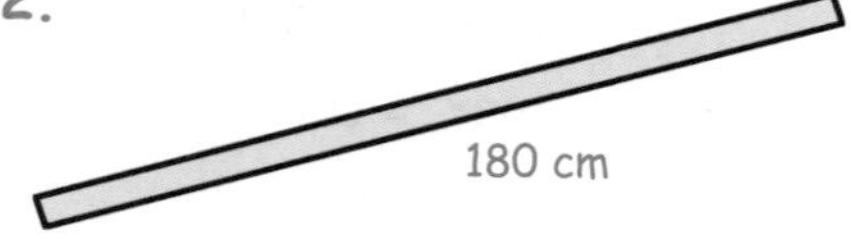

   A metal rod expands and contracts due to heat and cold,

   The length of the rod is given as 180 cm (±5%).

   Write down the upper and lower lengths of the rod.

3. When a doctor uses a thermometer to measure a patient's temperature, there is usually a tolerance of about (±2%).

   What is a patient's range of temperature when the thermometer reads 40°C ?

4. The pressure in a propane gas canister can vary from its advertised pressure by a tolerance of (± 15%).

The pressure in this canister is listed at 70 poundals.

What is the greatest and the least gas pressure in the canister ?

5. 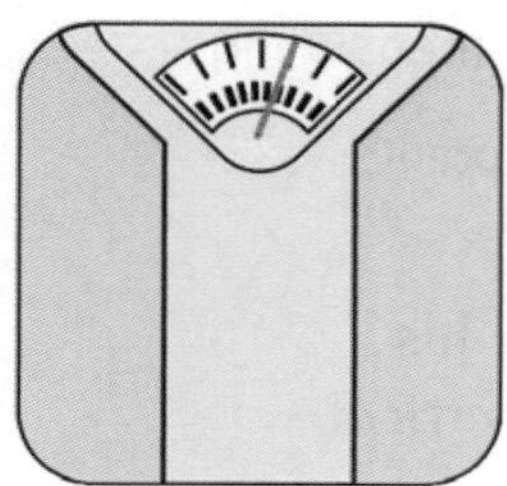

A woman weighs herself every day and finds that the reading on her scales can fluctuate by (± 5%).

One day, her scales indicated she weighed 55 kilograms.

What was her potential upper weight ?

6. The three sides of a triangular wooden board are measured using a tailor's tape measure.

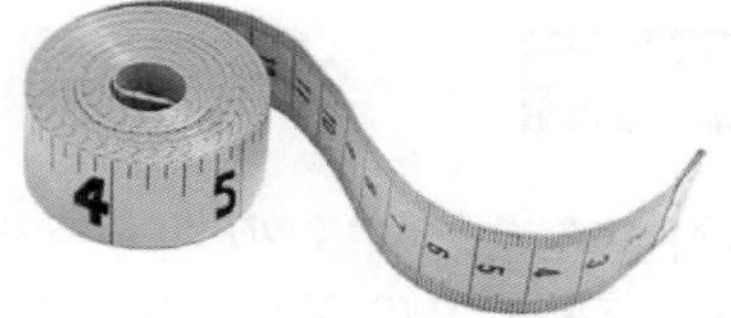

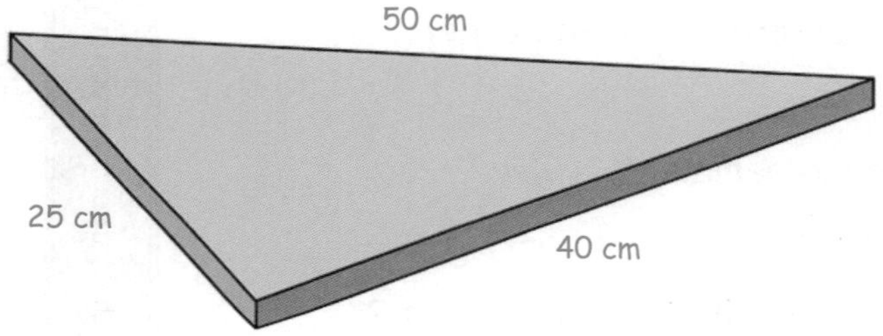

The accuracy of the tape is denoted by a tolerance of (± 2%).

Calculate the maximum and the minimum values of the perimeter of the board.

7. A tolerance of (± 2·5%) is allowed when potatoes are put into a sack and weighed.

Each sack is supposed to weigh 56 pounds.

Which of the following are acceptable weights :-

a 55 pounds   b 57 pounds

c 54·5 pounds   d 57·4 pounds ?

8. 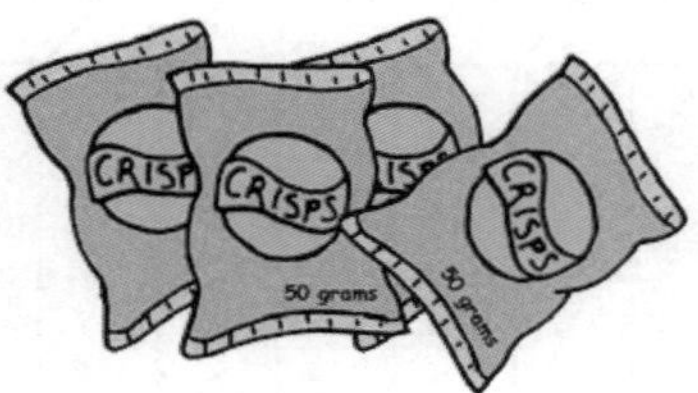

A crisp manufacturer rejects packets of crisps whose weight does not lie within the acceptable tolerance level of 50 grams (± 3%).

Which of these crisp packets should be rejected :-

a 50·8 grams   b 48·8 grams   c 51·6 grams   d 48·5 grams ?

9. **Harder :-** When she was practising for the 10K, Mirin timed herself.

Her times ranged from 66 minutes down to 54 minutes.

a Write her times in tolerance notation as in (.... ± ....) minutes.

b Now calculate her tolerance using percentages as .... mins (± ...%).

The Effects of applying Tolerance

Question :- A man, when measuring something, found he was 1 centimetre "out".
Was this acceptable as far as tolerance was concerned ?

Answer :- We can't say whether it is or whether it is not acceptable, unless we have more information as to what he was actually measuring.

- If he was measuring the length of a football park, a 1 centimetre error is almost negligible.
- If he was measuring a window frame to renew his windows, a 1 centimetre error is much more critical.

Exercise 2

1. Explain in your own words why the 1 centimetre margin of error in the above two examples matter in one case but not in the other.

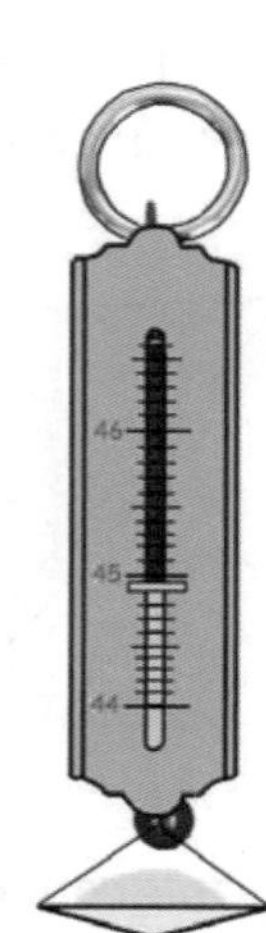

2. A chemical is being weighed for use in an experiment.

   The chemical should weigh (44·6 ± 0·4) grams.

   Is this batch of the chemical suitable for use in the experiment ?

3. 

   When Bobby goes to buy a new hat, depending on the manufacturer, he can generally wear a hat sized ($7\frac{3}{4} \pm \frac{1}{8}$) inches.

   Write down the largest and the smallest hat size Bobby might at least consider trying on.

4. Eight aluminium blocks are packed against each other as shown.

   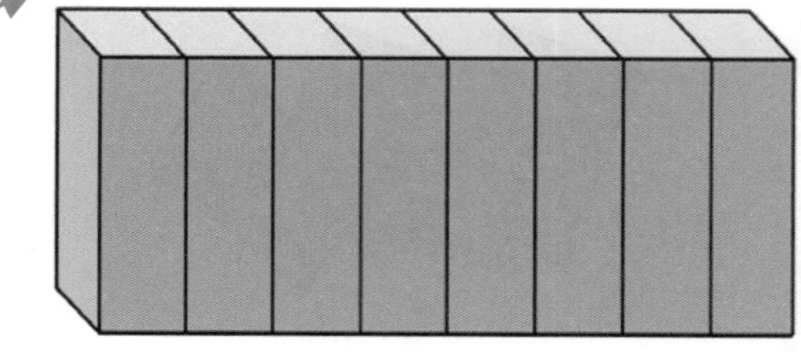

   The width of each block is (13·45 ± 0·08) mm.

   The combined set of blocks is supposed to fit into a box 108·25 mm long.

   Is it a certainty that the set of blocks will fit in the box ? (*Explain*).

5. Four runners in a 4 x 400 metre relay race have their times measured using a stopwatch.

   The watch is accurate to within ± 0·05 seconds.

   The individual times are 47·25 secs, 46·94 secs, 48·01 secs and 45·77 secs.

   What is the team's **best** possible overall time for the relay ?

6. A car's speedometer is known to be accurate to within (± 5 mph).

If the car was travelling at an average speed of 30 mph, as shown on his speedometer, and is driven from 9.00 am till 11.30 am what is the greatest and least distances it could have covered.

(**Remember** :- *Distance = Speed x Time*).

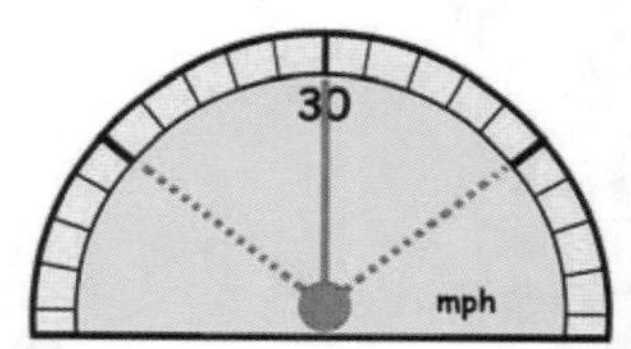

7. 

The captain of a cruise liner sets his ship to cross the Atlantic at a speed of 15 mph (± 10%) (*due to tides and winds*).

He hopes to make the 3450 mile journey from London to New York therefore in 230 hours (*just under 10 days*).

At best, how long will the trip take, and at worst, how long ?

(**Remember** :- *Time = Distance ÷ Speed*).

8. Handley's trial times for the 200 metre hurdles race are (20·8 ± 0·05) seconds.

Calculate his fastest and his slowest speed in the 200 metre race, in metres per second, correct to 2 decimal places each time.

9. 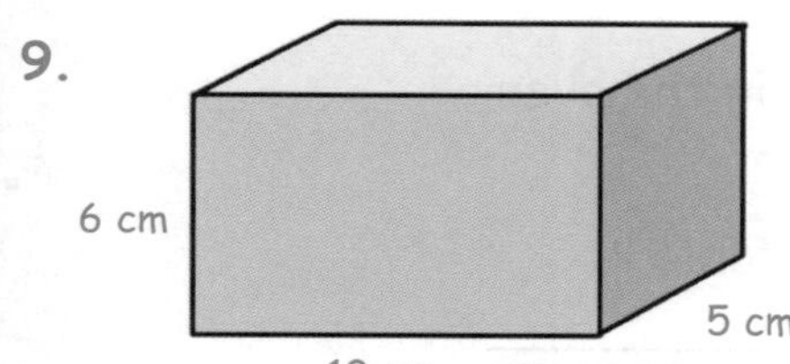

This steel cuboid has its dimensions given in centimetres.

All measurements are within a tolerance of (± 0·05 cm).

a Calculate the minimum and the maximum volume of the cuboid, in cubic centimetres.

b The density (*weight*) of steel is (7·9 ± 0·15) grams per cubic centimetre.

Calculate the maximum possible weight of this steel cuboid.

10. A fish bowl, containing 3500 ml of water, is sitting on a window sill.

Due to the heat, (15 ± 2·5)% of the water evaporates every hour.

What is the least volume and what is the greatest volume of water remaining in the fish bowl after 1 hour in the sun ?

11. In a car plant, *Skazda* set out to produce 6500 cars a year (± 4%).

This is because they predict that is how many cars they will sell.

If they underproduce, they will lose a potential sale of €12 500 per car.

If they overproduce, they will be left with unsold cars with losses of €7200 per car.

Say how much money was wasted, if any, during the following years' productions :-

a 2013 - 6250 cars   b 2014 - 6780 cars   c 2015 - 6210 cars.

Tolerance

Geometry/Measure Assessment 1

1. For each of the following, find the minimum and the maximum values :-

   a 50 cm (± 10%) b 8000 g (± 5%) c £4000 (± 1%)

   d 0·8 ml (± 10%) e 150 kg (± 2%) f 200 ml (± 0·1%).

2. In a chemical experiment, a reading of between 72 mg and 88 mg was acceptable.

   Write this in tolerance notation in the form :- (... mg ± ...%)

3. 

   A commercial tomato grower only sends tomatoes to be sold in the local supermarket if their diameters lie within the tolerance level of 60 mm (± 2%).

   Which of these tomatoes should be rejected :-

   a 58·9 mm b 62·0 mm c 61·2 mm d $59\frac{1}{2}$ mm ?

4. In a smelting plant, the temperature of the molten iron in the oven should be kept at a temperature of (1575 ± 35)°C.

   Is the oven temperature shown on this thermometer suitable ?

   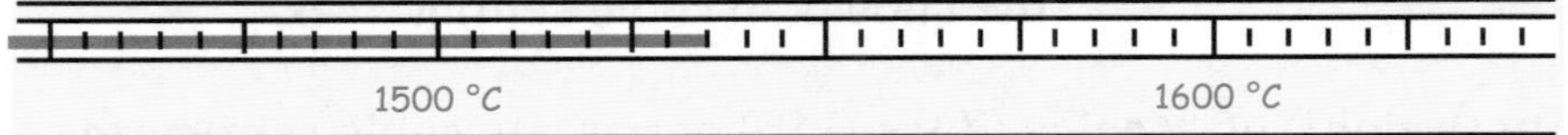

5. The four swimmers in a 4 x 100 metre freestyle relay race are timed (in seconds) as follows :-

   Phelps (47·51), Weber-Gale (47·02), Jones (47·65), Lezak (46·06)

   The stopwatch used was accurate to within ± 0·05 seconds.

   What was the team's **best** possible overall time for the relay ?

6. 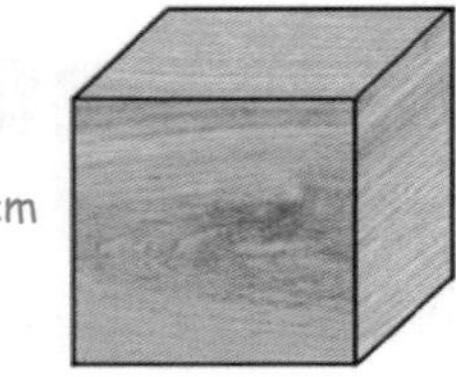

   This wooden cube has each of its sides measured as 4 cm.

   All measurements are within a tolerance of (± 0·1 cm).

   a Calculate the minimum and the maximum volume of the cube, in cubic centimetres.

   b The density (*weight*) of wood is (0·54 ± 0·05) grams per cubic centimetre.

   Calculate the maximum possible weight of this wooden cube.

Rules & Formulae

Revision of Rules & Formulae

1. A fishmonger calculates her profit by :-

   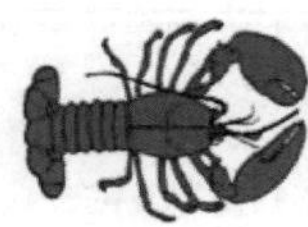

   "Subtracting the price she paid from what she sold it for."

   She buys crates of lobster for £162·99 and sells them all for £204·50.

   Work out her profit.

2. The area of a circular pizza can be calculated as follows :-

   "Halve the diameter to get the radius; multiply the radius by itself, then times the answer by 3·14 on a calculator".

   What is the area of a 16 inch diameter pizza, to the nearest square inch ?

3. For each formula, find the value of the capital letter :-

a	$P = 1{\cdot}5a + 5{\cdot}4b$	find P,	when $a = 6$ and $b = 5$.
b	$F = 61 - \frac{1}{2}g$	find F,	when $g = 98$.
c	$K = (m - n)^2$	find K,	when $m = 2\frac{3}{4}$ and $n = 2\frac{1}{4}$.
d	$A = \sqrt{v + w}$	find A,	when $v = 99$ and $w = 22$.
e	$G = 2h^2 - 12$	find G,	when $h = 6$.
f	$Q = 2as + at^2$	find Q,	when $a = 10$, $s = 3$ and $t = 2$.

4. Polo shirts were advertised :-

   "Buy five polo shirts, get 20% off the total price".

   What would you pay for five Polo shirts costing £7·50 each ?

5. The length of an arc is found by using the formula :-

   $$L = \tfrac{1}{3}(8h - c).$$

   arc

   Find L when $h = 5$ and $c = 1$.

6. The formula for the blue area in the diagram is :-

   $$A = 2y^2 - 4x^2.$$

   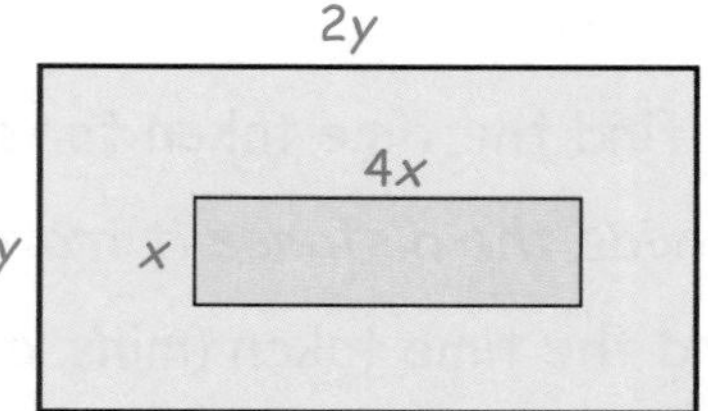

   Work out the value of A when $y = 5$ and $x = 3$.

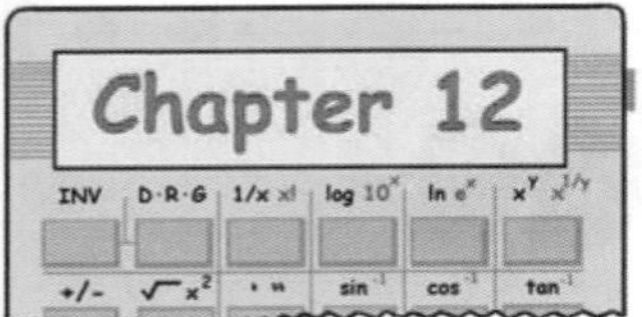

Rules & Formulae

Formulae Expressed in Words

Example 1 :-

The distance a car travels along a motorway can be found as follows :-

"Multiply the speed it is travelling at by the time (in decimal form) it takes for the journey".

How far did a car travel going at 60 mph for 3 hours and 15 minutes ?

Distance = 60 × 3·25 (as 3 hrs 15 mins = 3·25 hrs)
= **195 miles**

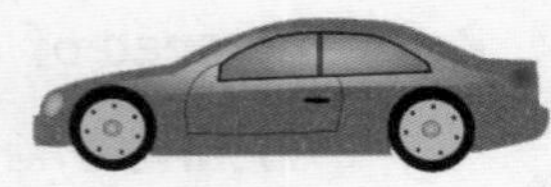

Example 2 :-

To find the area of a triangle :-

"Multiply its base by its height and halve the answer".

Find the area of a triangle with base 9 cm and height 8 cm.

$$\text{Area} = \tfrac{1}{2} \text{ of base} \times \text{height}$$
$$= \tfrac{1}{2} \text{ of } 9 \times 8$$
$$= \tfrac{1}{2} \text{ of } 72$$
$$= \mathbf{36\ cm^2}$$

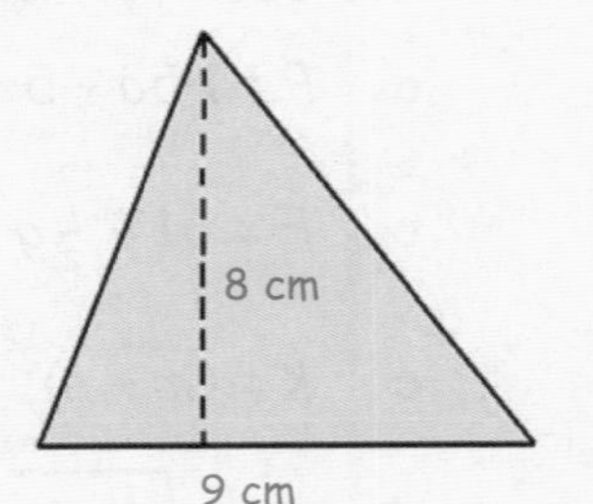

Exercise 1

1. The average speed of a train can be found by :-

   "Dividing the distance travelled by the time taken for the journey".

   Calculate the average speed of a train which travelled 900 km in 4 hours 30 minutes.

2. Work out the volume of this concrete slab by :-

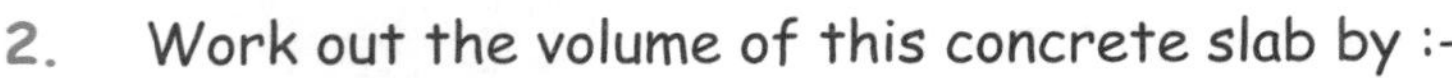

   "Multiplying its length by its breadth by its height".

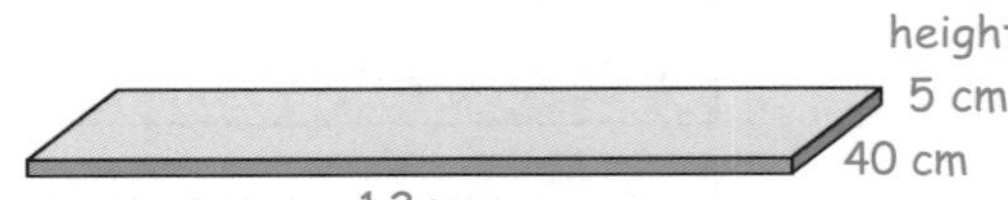

3. To work out the height of this metal support bracket which is in the shape of a parallelogram :-

   "Divide its area by its length".

   Calculate the height of the bracket.

4. To find the time taken for a caterpillar to cross a cabbage patch :-

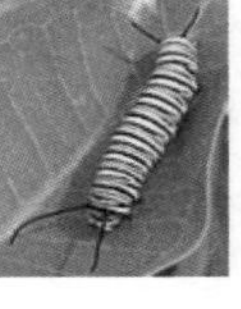

   "Divide the distance it travelled by its average speed".

   Find the time taken (mins. and secs.) for a caterpillar to cover 60 cm at 0·6 cm/sec.

5. When buying a pair of jeans from a catalogue :-

"Multiply the number of jeans by 25 and add on 3·99".

a Work out the cost of 6 pairs of jeans.

b Why the 3·99 ? What is this charge for ?

6. How to find a length of a side of a square, given its area :-

? cm | 121 cm²

"Simply, find the square root of the area".

Calculate the length of a side in the square shown.

7. To change from degrees Fahrenheit (°F) to degrees Celsius (°C) use the following rule :-

"Subtract 32 from the temperature in °F, then divide the answer by 1·8".

Use the rule to change 86 °F to °C.

8. Here's how to change a number of kilometres to a number of miles :-

"Multiply the kilometres by five and divide the answer by eight".

Change 32 kilometres to miles.

9. 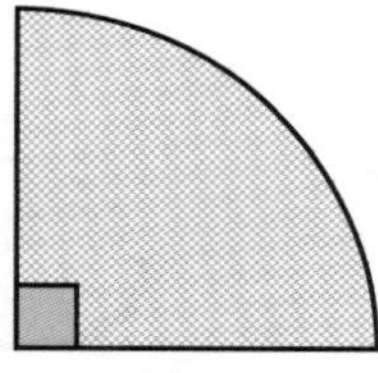

The area of a quarter circle can be calculated as follows :-

"Multiply the radius of the circle by itself; multiply by 3·14 on a calculator; then divide the answer by four".

Work out the area of a quarter circle with radius 10 cm.

10. The cost of hiring a jet ski is given by the rule :-

"Multiply the cost per hour by the number of hours hired and add on a fixed amount".

Find the cost of hiring a jet ski for 2 hours at £18·75 per hour, with a fixed amount of £20.

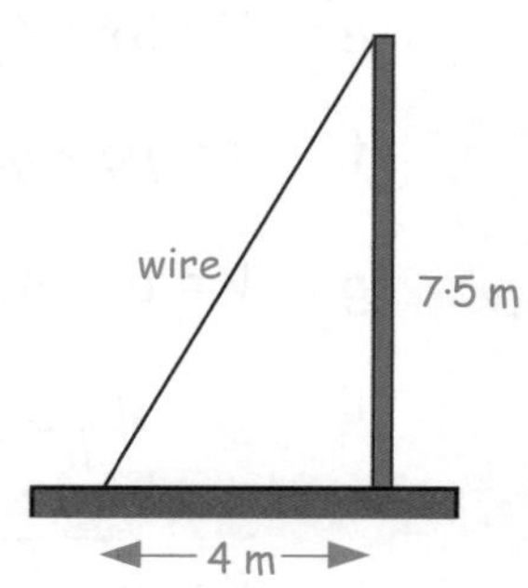

11. In a right angled triangle, to calculate the hypotenuse :-

"Square one of the lengths; square the other length and add the two answers; find the square root of the answer you now have".

Calculate the length of the wire holding the vertical pole.

12. 

To cook a turkey :-

"Give it half an hour per pound and then add an extra twenty five minutes".

I cooked my turkey for the correct amount of time, 5 hours and 55 minutes.

What was the weight of the turkey ?

Formulae with Symbols

Example 1 :-

The final speed of a car is v and can be calculated using the formula :-

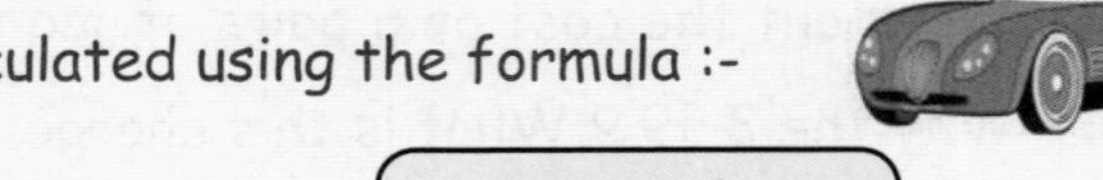

$$v = u + at$$

where u is the initial speed, a is the acceleration and t is the time taken.

Calculate the value of v when $u = 4$, $a = 2$ and $t = 9{\cdot}5$.

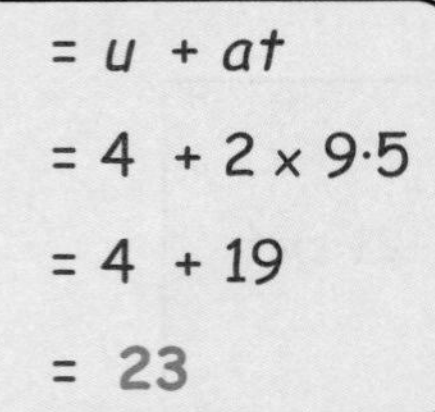

$$v = u + at$$
$$= 4 + 2 \times 9{\cdot}5$$
$$= 4 + 19$$
$$= \mathbf{23}$$

Example 2 :-

$A = \frac{1}{2}\pi r^2$ is the formula for calculating the area of a semicircle.

Find the area of Mr Howie's semicircular lawn shown.

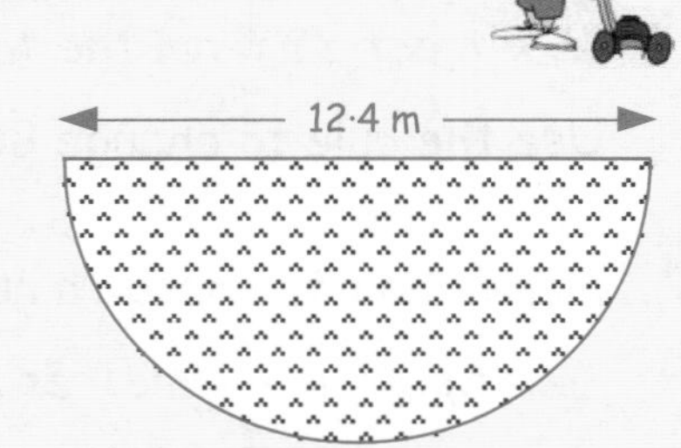

$$A = \frac{1}{2}\pi r^2$$
$$\Rightarrow \quad A = 0{\cdot}5 \times 3{\cdot}14 \times 6{\cdot}2 \times 6{\cdot}2$$
$$\Rightarrow \quad A = \mathbf{60{\cdot}4\ m^2} \ \textit{(to 3 sig. figs.)}$$

Exercise 2

1. For each formula, find the value of the letter asked for :-

Q = 4a + 3b
=> Q = 4 x 15 + 3 x 5
=> Q = ...

a	$Q = 4a + 3b$	find Q,	when $a = 15$ and $b = 5$.
b	$R = st - 12$	find R,	when $s = 8$ and $t = 9$.
c	$T = p^2 + q^2$	find T,	when $p = 20$ and $q = 40$.
d	$W = \dfrac{x + 12}{y}$	find W,	when $x = 42$ and $y = 3$.
e	$E = 3f + 4g - 5h$	find E,	when $f = 20$, $g = 15$ and $h = 24$.
f	$T = pq + qr$	find T,	when $p = 8$, $q = 4{\cdot}5$ and $r = 6$.
g	$V = u + at$	find V,	when $u = 20$, $a = 8$ and $t = 10{\cdot}25$.
h	$G = \dfrac{d + e}{h}$	find G,	$d = 80$, $e = 20$ and $h = 25$.
i	$K = \sqrt{m - n}$	find K,	when $m = 62$ and $n = 13$.
j	$R = \dfrac{1}{a} + \dfrac{1}{b}$	find R,	when $a = 4$ and $b = 5$.
k	$U = \dfrac{rs}{r + s}$	find U,	when $r = 10$ and $s = 5$.

2. The length, (L) of a spring, when compressed, is given by the formula $L = 20 - 0{\cdot}08F$, where F is the size of force applied to the spring to compress it.

Find L when $F = 15$.

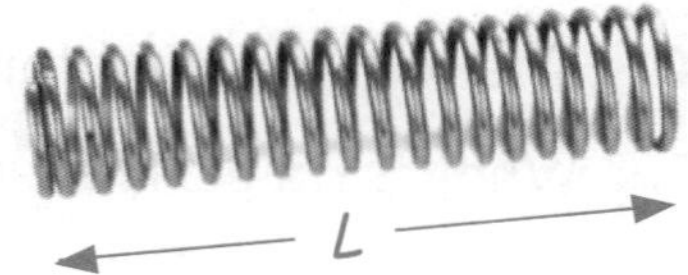

3. 

The formula $P = 120n - 500$ gives the profit, £P, made when n cars are sold in a day at a showroom.

a What profit is made when 20 cars are sold ?

b What is the situation when only 1 car is sold ?

c How many cars must be sold to make a profit ?

4. To find the volume of this gutter, use $V = \frac{1}{2}\pi r^2 L$, where $\pi = 3{\cdot}14$, r is the radius and L is its length.

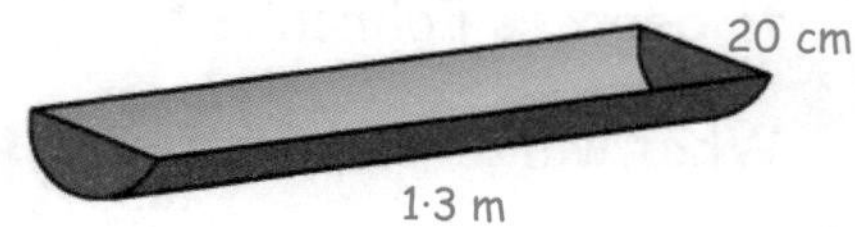

5. 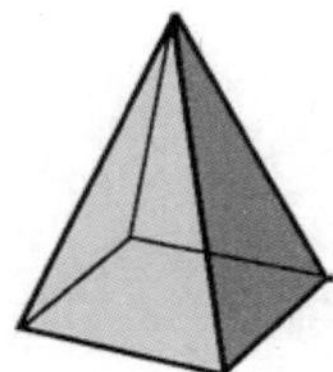

The volume of a pyramid can be found using the rule :-

Volume = $\frac{1}{3}$ x Area of base x height.

Calculate the volume of a pyramid with base area 45 cm^2 and height 12 cm.

6. The formula $s = \frac{1}{2}(u + v) \times t$ is used to calculate the distance s, that an object travels if it starts with a speed u and has a speed v, t seconds later.

Find the value of s when $u = 1{\cdot}6$, $v = 2{\cdot}9$ and $t = 4$.

7. 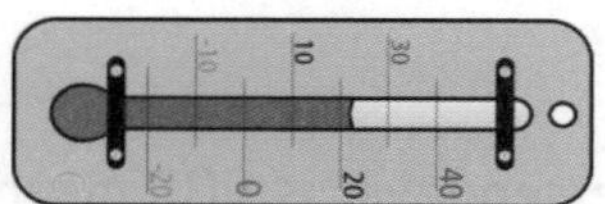

To convert from degrees Fahrenheit (°F) to degrees Celsius (°C), use the rule :- $C = \frac{5}{9}(F - 32)$.

What will a temperature of 50°F be in °C?

8. The equation of this straight line is $y = \frac{1}{2}x + 5$.

Find y when $x = 12$.

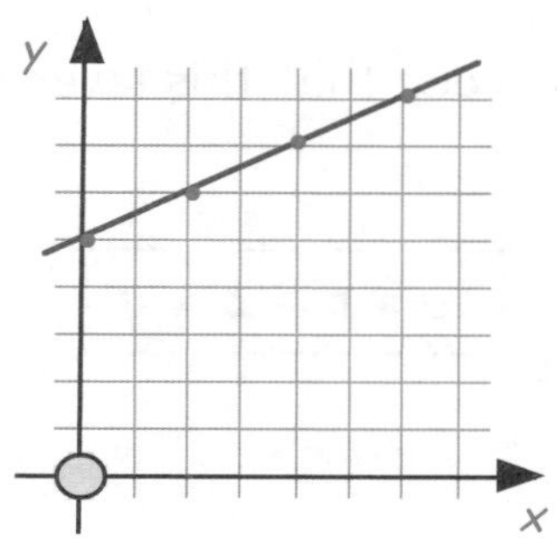

9. 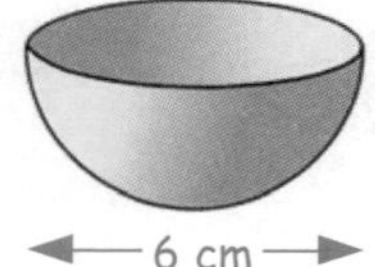

The volume of a hemisphere is found using the formula $V = \frac{2}{3}\pi r^3$, with $\pi = 3{\cdot}14$ and r is its radius.

Calculate the volume of the hemisphere shown.

10. The perimeter of this rectangle is given by :- $P = 2a + 2b$.
What is its perimeter when $a = 7{\cdot}5$ and $b = 2{\cdot}25$?

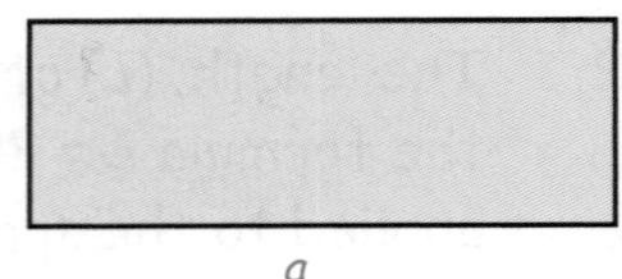

11. 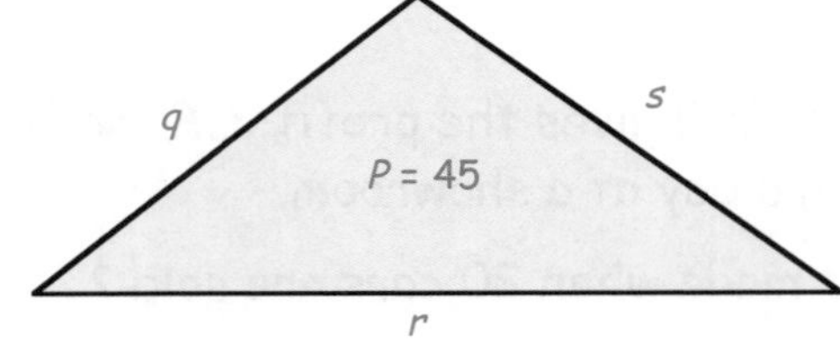

To find the length of a side of this triangle, given its perimeter P, use $s = P - (q + r)$.

Find s if $P = 45$, $q = 12{\cdot}8$ and $r = 17$.

12. To change a temperature given in degrees Celsius (°C) to degrees Fahrenheit (°F), use the rule :- $F = 32 + \frac{9C}{5}$.
What will a temperature of 15°C be in °F ?

13. 

The illumination from a light bulb is $I = \frac{C}{d^2}$.

Calculate the value of I when $C = 2000$ and $d = 20$.

14. At a height h metres above sea level, the distance d kilometres to the horizon is given by the formula :- $d = 5\sqrt{h}$.

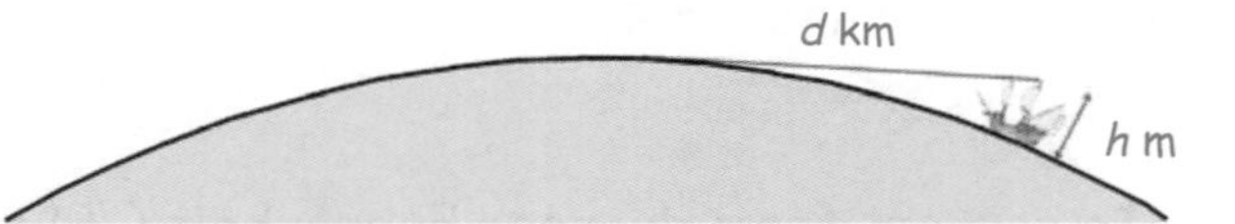

Calculate the distance to the horizon when the height above sea level is 900 metres.

15. In order that this lever system is balanced, it is known that :-

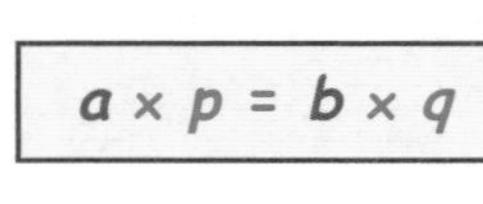

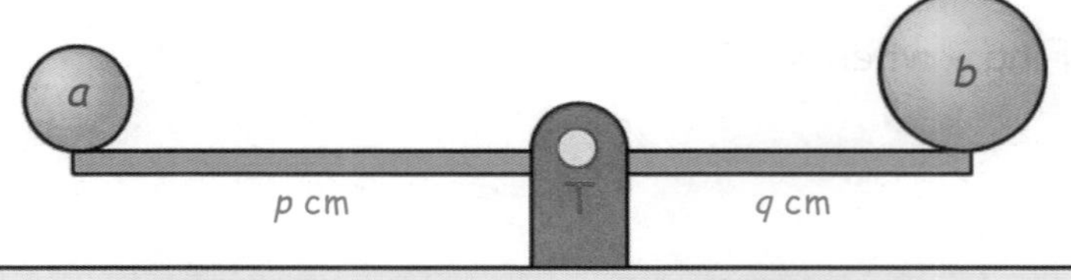

where • a and b are the weights of the 2 objects
and • p and q are the distances from each object to the point T.

Determine the value of a when $p = 54{\cdot}0$, $q = 21{\cdot}6$ and $b = 37{\cdot}5$.

Formulae - Further Examples

Exercise 3

1. a For the formula $A = \frac{ab^2}{c}$, calculate the value of A when $a = 3$, $b = 5$ and $c = 100$, giving your answer as a fraction in its simplest form.

   b Using $R = \frac{x^2 + y^2}{x + y}$, determine R when $x = 3$ and $y = 6$.

2. The formula $f = \frac{uv}{u + v}$ is used in the study of lenses.
   Calculate f when $u = 15$ and $v = 10$.

3. The area of a trapezium is found using the formula :-

$$A = \tfrac{1}{2}(a + b) \times w\ .$$

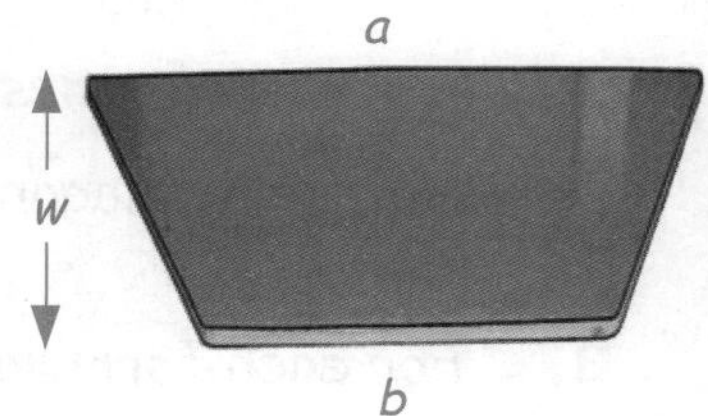

Work out the area of this trapezoidal shaped desk top with parallel sides of length 150 cm and 100 cm, and width 50 cm.

4. The length of one of the shorter sides in a right angled triangle can be calculated using the formula $a = \sqrt{c^2 - b^2}$.
   Calculate a when $c = 13$ and $b = 5$.

5. The formula $A = \frac{C^2}{4\pi}$ is used to find the area of a circle when you are given its circumference.
   Calculate the area of a circle with circumference 15·7 cm.
   (*Give your answer correct to two significant figures*).

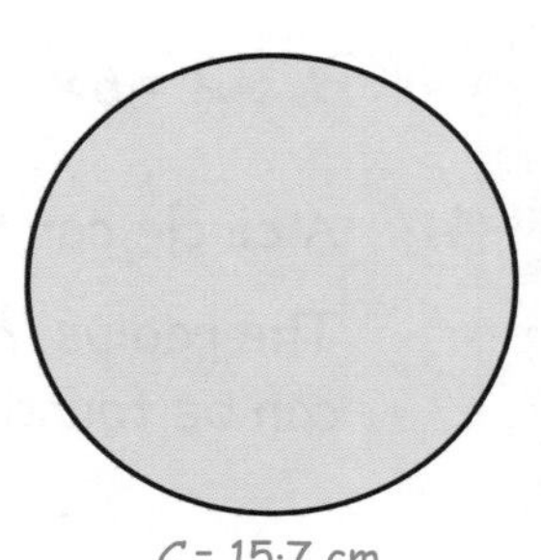

C = 15·7 cm

6. a A cylindrical box of biscuits with a radius of 10 cm has a volume of 2198 cm^2.
   Use the formula $h = \frac{V}{\pi r^2}$ to find its height.

   b A cylindrical can of juice with height 40 cm has a volume of 3140 cm^2.
   Use the formula $r = \sqrt{\frac{V}{\pi h}}$ to find its radius.

Rules & Formulae

Geometry/Measure Assessment 2

1. Given the mean age of five boys and the individual ages of four of them, to obtain the age of the 5th boy use the rule :-

> *"Multiply the mean age by 5, then subtract the total of the four ages given".*

Apply the rule to find Mark's age, given that Tom is 13, Bob is 14, Joe is 17 and Donnie is 19, the mean age for the five of them being 15.

2. The number of diagonals in a polygon with a given number of sides is found by :-

> *"Multiplying the number of sides by itself and subtracting three times the number of sides; then halving your answer".*

How many diagonals has a polygon with 8 sides ?

3. For each formula, find the value of the letter asked for :-

a $R = \dfrac{mn}{m - n}$ find R, when $m = 30$ and $n = 5$.

b $P = \dfrac{50}{w} + \dfrac{7}{y}$ find P, when $w = 20$ and $y = 28$.

c $C = \sqrt{a^2 - b^2}$ find C, when $a = 25$ and $b = 24$.

d $A = 6x - 3x^2$ find A, when $x = 2$.

4. A circle can be drawn inside a triangle, as shown.

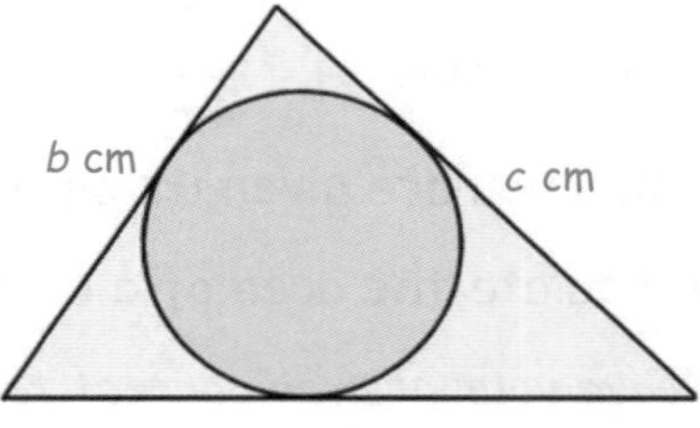

The radius, r centimetres, of this circle can be found using the formula :-

$$r = \sqrt{\frac{(P - a) \times (P - b) \times (P - c)}{P}} \quad \text{where} \quad P = \tfrac{1}{2}(a + b + c).$$

Use this formula to calculate the radius (*to 2 decimal places*) of the circle shown in the diagram.

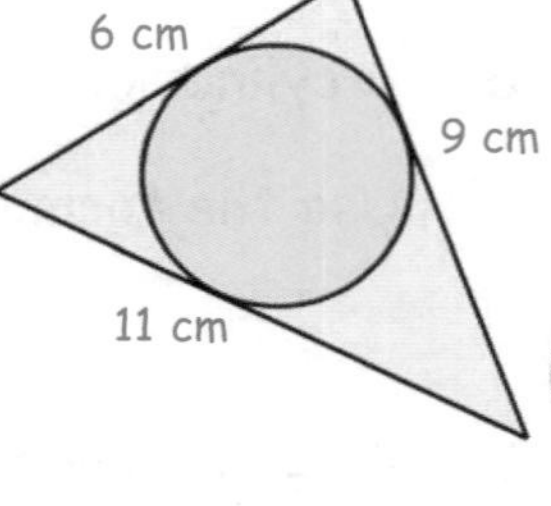

5. The intensity of light, I, emerging after passing through a liquid with concentration, c, is found by the formula given opposite :-

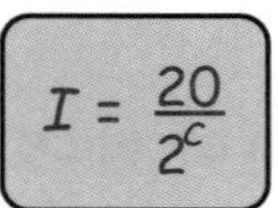

(2^c means $2 \times 2 \times 2$ x.. c times)

a Find the intensity of light when the concentration is 4.

b Find the concentration of the liquid when the intensity is 5.

Scale Drawings

Revision of Scale Drawings

1. This light aircraft runway at Aberdeen measures 300 metres by 45 metres.

   The scale is :- ***1 : 1500.***

   a What does 1 cm represent in metres ?

   b Make a scale drawing of the runway.

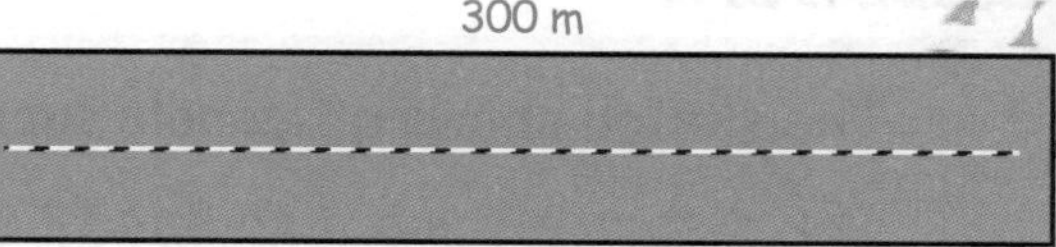

2. Make a scale drawing of the television screen using a scale :-

   1 cm represents 12 centimetres.

3. Measure and write down the 3 figure bearing for these towns :-

a

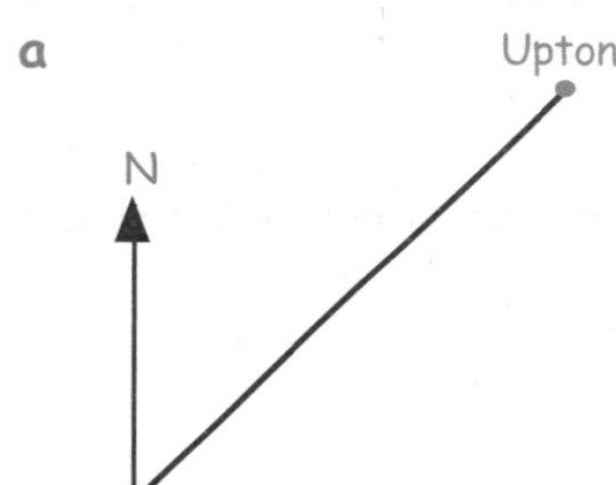

b c

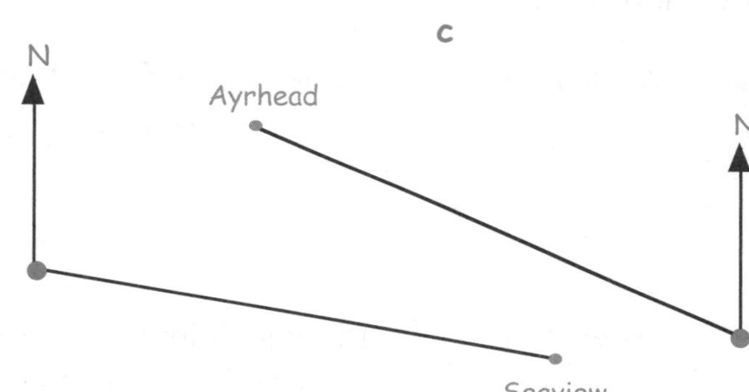

4. Use your protractor to draw 3 figure bearings of :-

   a 090° b 160° c 225° d 320°.

5. A pilot was flying South East, but on receiving a distress call, turned his plane clockwise till he was then flying due North.

   By how many degrees had the pilot turned his plane ?

6. a Make a scale drawing of this swimming pool,

   scale 1 cm = 4 metres.

   b Alana swam from corner P to corner R.

   Show this as a dotted line on your drawing.

   c Measure the length of this dotted line, in centimetres.

   d Calculate the real distance swam by Alana, in metres.

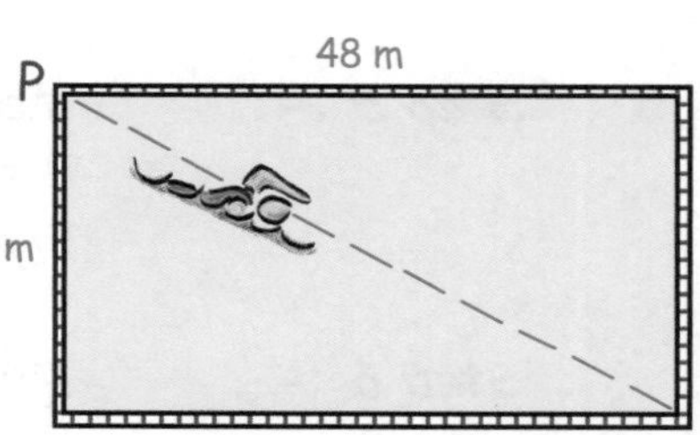

Scale Drawings

Making a Scale Drawing Using a Protractor

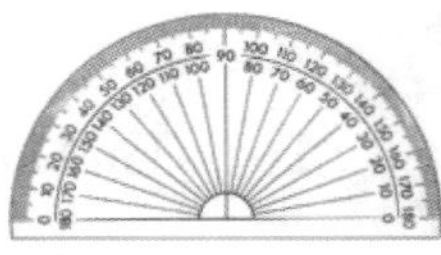

Exercise 1 *You will need a ruler and protractor to draw the figures in this exercise.*

1. The sketch shows a flagpole supported by a wire (AC).

   The distance from A to B is 12 feet.

   ∠CAB = 55°.

   a Make a scale drawing using a scale :-

   1 cm = 4 feet

   b Use your drawing to calculate the real height of the flagpole.

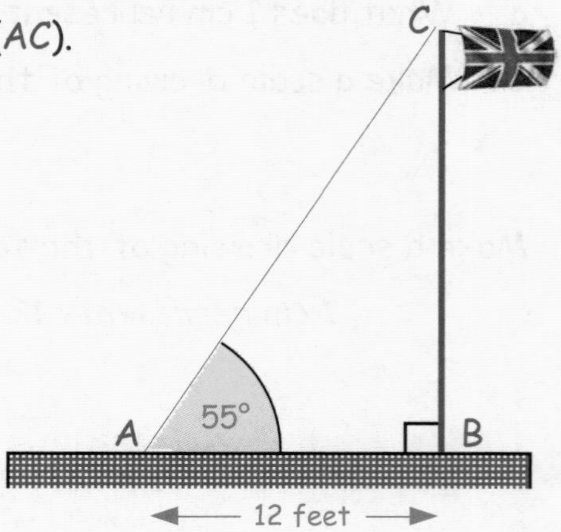

C
A
55°
B
12 feet

Here's how to do it :-

a *Step 1 :-* Scale 4 ft = 1 cm

=> 12 ft = (12 ÷ 4) = 3 cm. => draw AB = 3 cm.

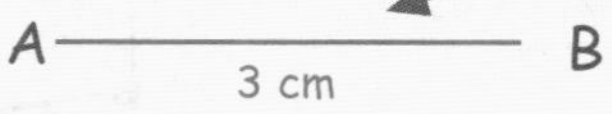

A — 3 cm — B

Step 2 :- Draw a (feint) line straight up from B to show the pole.

Step 3 :- Put your protractor on A and mark out an angle of 55°.

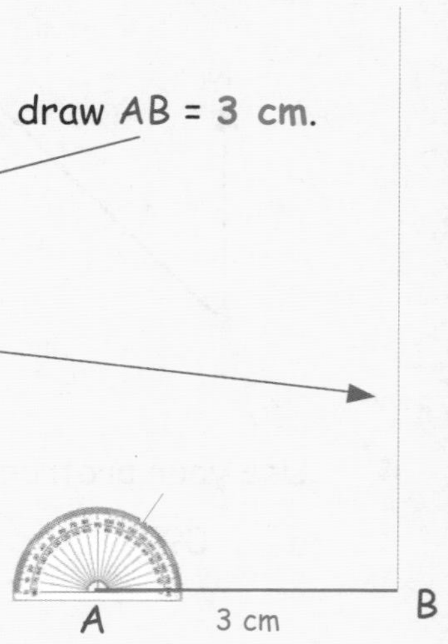

A 3 cm B

Step 4 :- Draw the 55° line from A till it crosses the line drawn up from B.

C top of flagpole

b *Step 5 :-* Measure the length from B to C, where the two lines cross (= 4·3 cm).

Step 6 :- Multiply this length by the scale (x 4) to obtain the real height in feet. (= 17·2 feet)

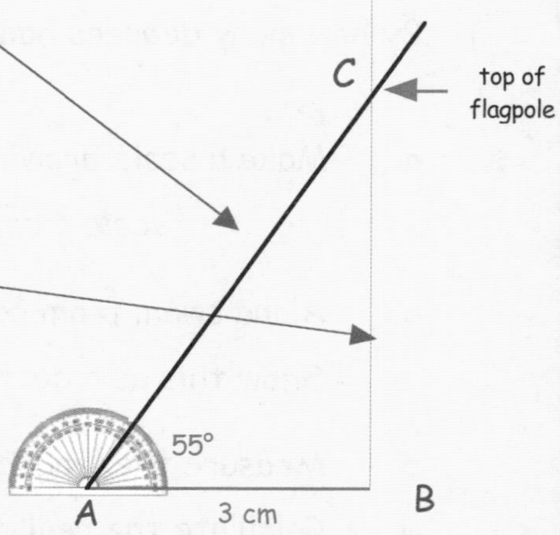

55°
A 3 cm B

2. a Make a scale drawing to show this tree as it is viewed from point R.

Use a scale of :- *1 cm = 2 metres*

- Start by drawing the line representing RS.
- Draw a feint line straight up from S.
- Use your protractor to measure out ∠R = 50°.
- Complete the drawing.

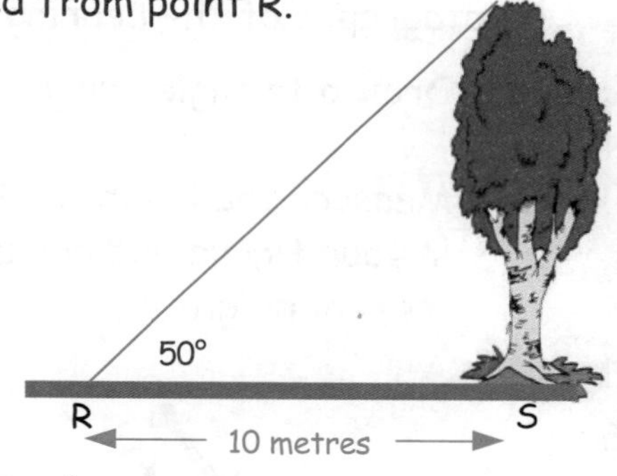

b Measure, in centimetres, the height of the tree in your drawing.

c Calculate the height of the real tree.

3. A keeper is standing on the rocks 18 metres from his lighthouse.

The angle between his feet and the top of the lighthouse is 60°.

a Make an accurate scale drawing of the sketch.

scale :- *1 cm = 3 metres*

b Calculate the height of the real lighthouse.

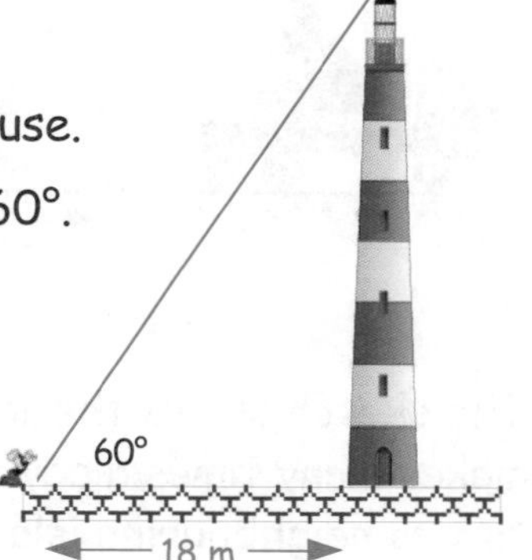

4. For each of the following :-

(i) Make a scale drawing using the given scale.

(ii) Calculate the real height of the given object.

a

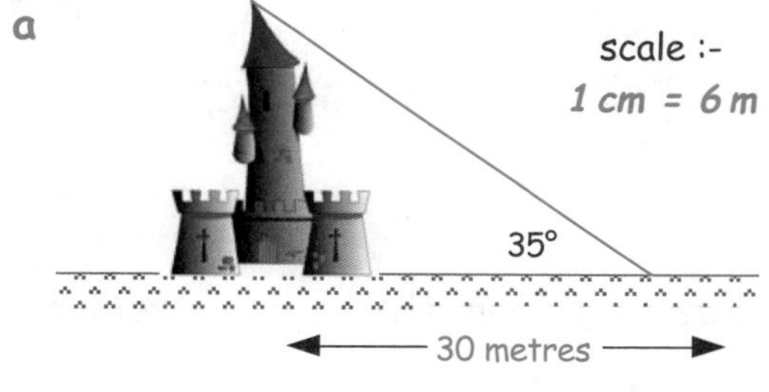

b

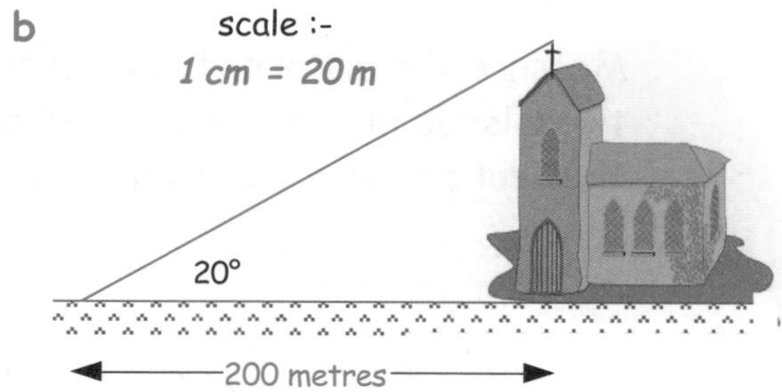

c

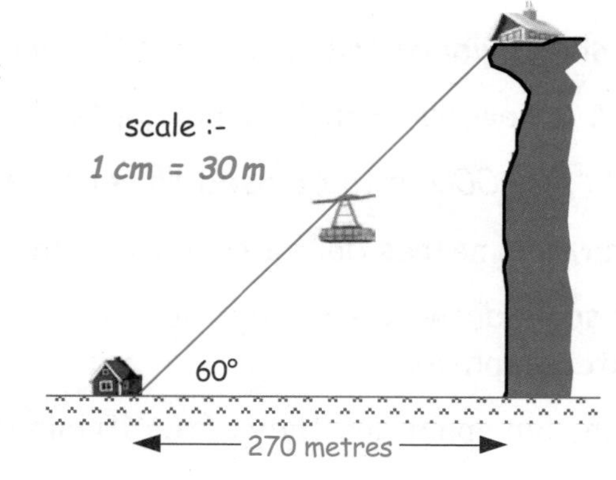

d

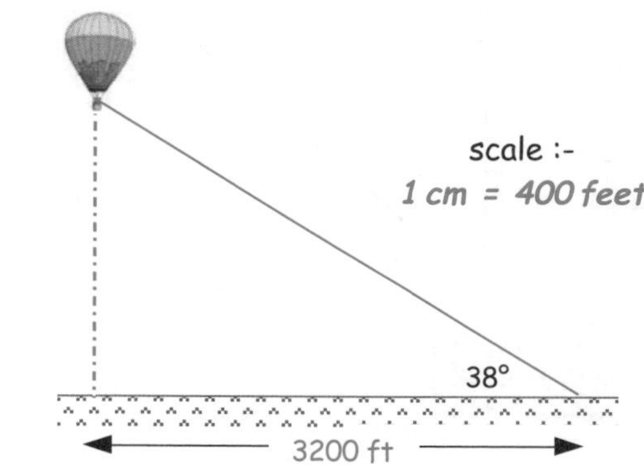

5. The picture shows Mr Paganelli taking photographs of the Leaning Tower of Pisa.

   a Draw a triangle using the scale :- *1 cm = 7 m.*

   b Measure the height of the Tower in your figure and calculate its real height.

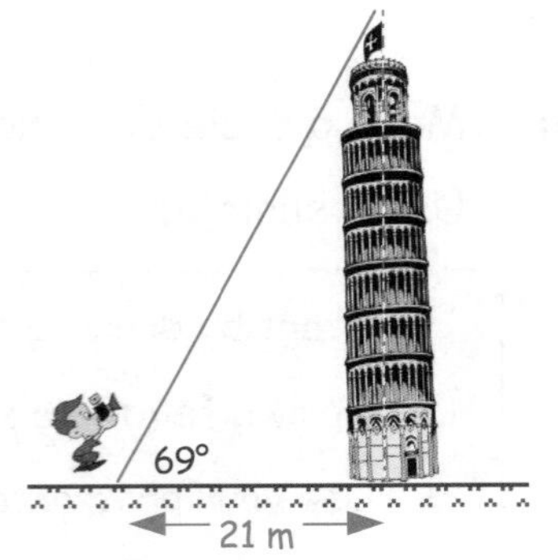

6.

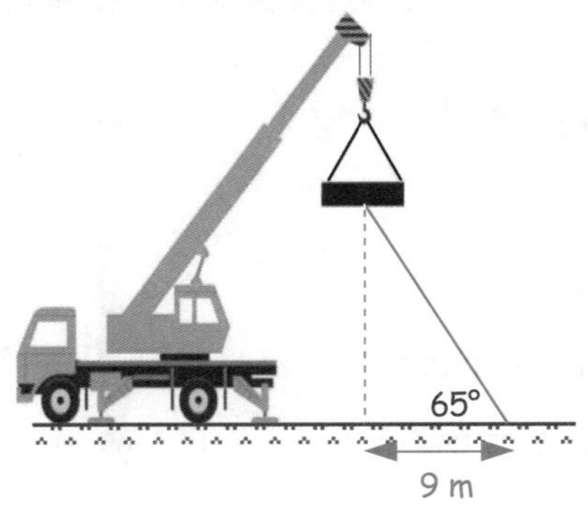

Shown is a concrete block being raised from the ground by a portable crane.

   a Make a scale drawing to represent the height of the block above the ground, using a scale :- *1 cm = 1·5 m.*

   b Measure how high the block is from the ground in your scale drawing and calculate how high it really is at this moment.

7. The sketch shows the journey a car ferry makes many times a day from the mainland to two neighbouring islands.

   Isle of Jute is due East of the Mainland and Arrun Island is North of Jute.

   a Draw a triangle to scale, showing the ferry's journey.

      scale *1 cm = 2·5 miles.*

   b Measure the distance between the two islands in centimetres and calculate the real distance between them in kilometres.

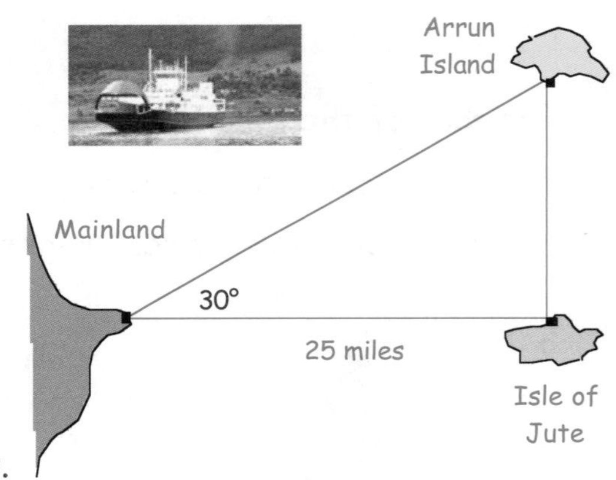

8.

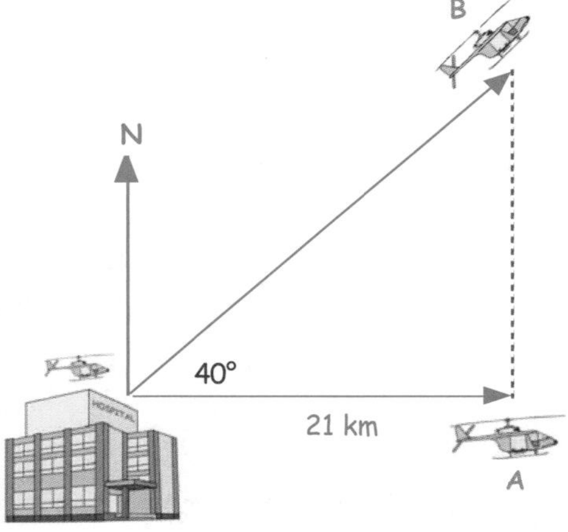

2 helicopters set off from the roof of Kiel Hospital.

Helicopter A heads off on a course due East.

Helicopter B flies in the direction shown.

The sketch shows where they are after 15 minutes.

Helicopter A is now due South of helicopter B.

A scale of *1 : 300 000* is to be used to represent it.

   a How many kilometres does 1 cm represent ?

   b Make a scale drawing showing the two helicopters' routes.

   c How many km apart are they after 15 minutes ?

Scale Drawings Involving Bearings

You will need a ruler and protractor to draw the figures in this exercise.

You should already know :-

- the points of a compass and their 3 figure bearings
- that bearings are measured clockwise from the North and always have 3 figures
- how to read bearings and measure them using a protractor.

In this exercise we use all three to make scale drawings involving directions and bearings.

Exercise 2

1. Use a protractor to measure the bearing of each town from Arkleston.

a

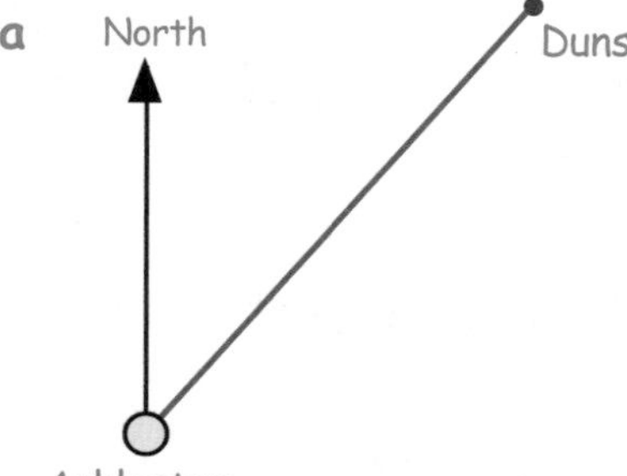

b

c

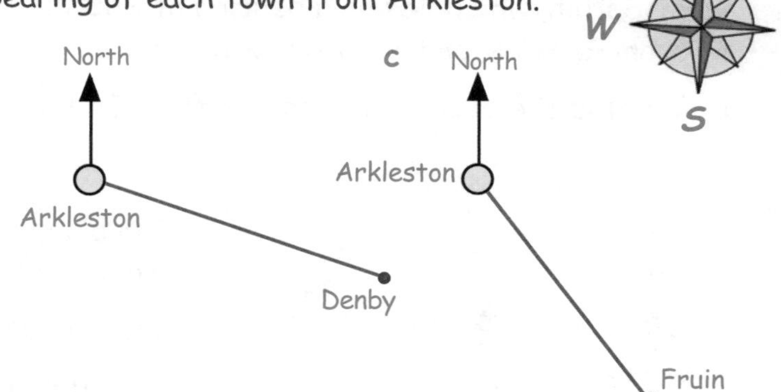

2. Use a protractor (turned round) to measure the bearing of each town from Norton.

a

b

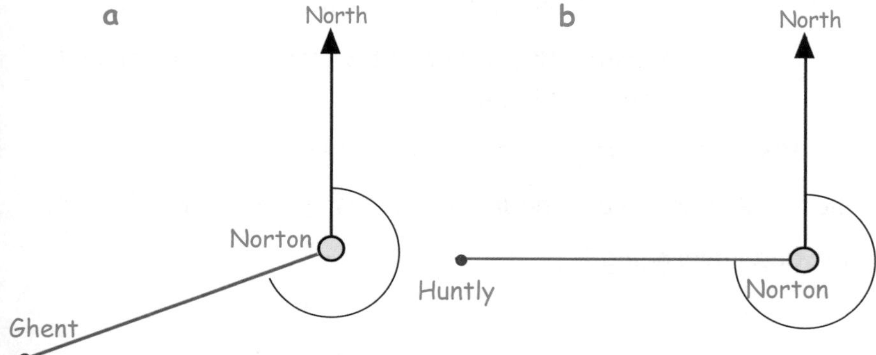

c

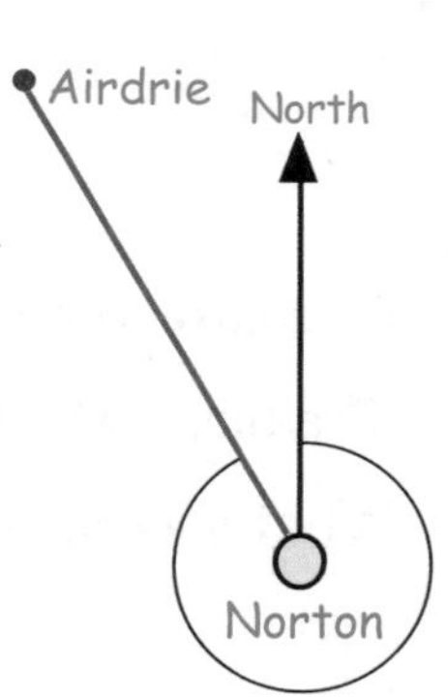

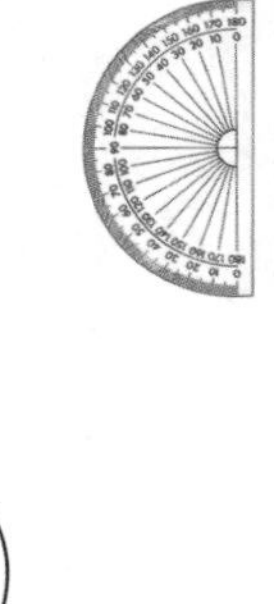

3. Aberdown (A) is 80 miles due North of Pembroke.

Inverbain is a city which lies on a bearing of 110° from Aberdown and 050° from Pembroke.

a Use a scale of *1 cm = 10 miles* to show where Aberdown and Inverbain are situated in relation to Pembroke.

start by choosing a point for Pembroke

- start by marking a point on your page to show Pembroke
- use your protractor at Pembroke to show 50° from North and draw a line
- use your ruler to measure the "scaled 80 miles" North from Pembroke - plot A
- use your protractor at Aberdown (A) to show 110° from North and draw a line
- the lines will meet at Inverbain

3. b From your drawing, measure the distance in centimetres from Inverbain to Pembroke and hence calculate the actual number of miles between them.

   c Mr Bain travels daily from home in Pembroke to his work in Inverbain.

   He usually travels at an average speed of (30 ± 5) mph.

   Calculate the minimum and maximum time, to the nearest minute, his journey takes.

4. Mark a point on the page of your exercise book and call it Renwick.

   Draw a North line through your point.

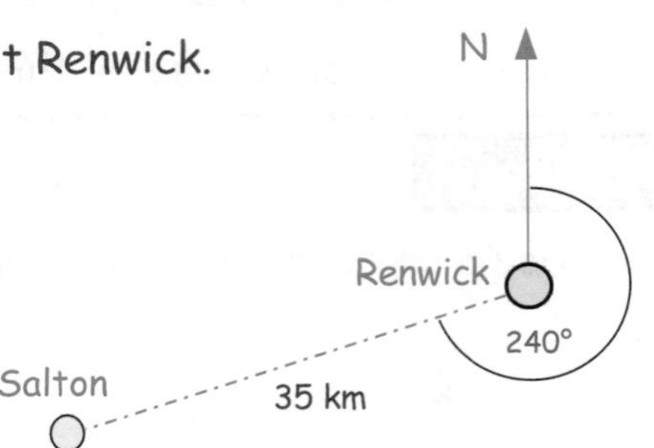

   a Use a scale of *1 cm = 5 km* to show the town of Salton, which lies on a bearing of 240° from Renwick, and is 35 km away.

   b What is the bearing of Renwick from Salton ?

5.

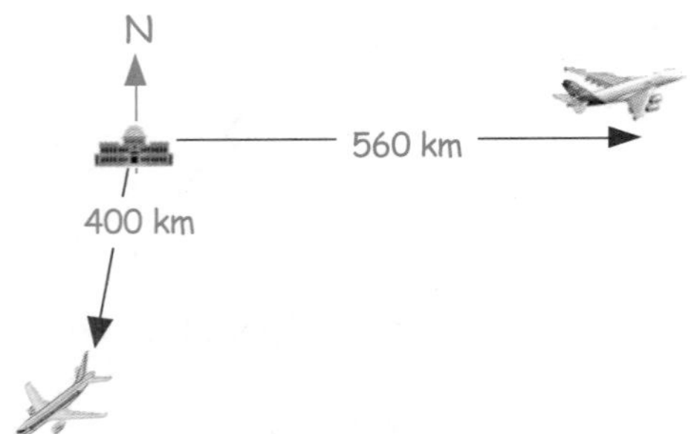

Two planes leave Edinburgh Airport one after the other.

One flies due East for 560 km.

The other flies on a bearing of 190° for 400 km.

   a Make a scale drawing of both flights.

   scale *1 cm = 80 km*

   b Measure the distance between the two planes, in centimetres.

   c Calculate the real distance between the two planes, in kilometres.

   d The plane which had travelled East had taken 1 hour 15 minutes to cover the 560 km.

   What speed, in km/hr, had it been averaging ?

6. The map shows the position of three places.

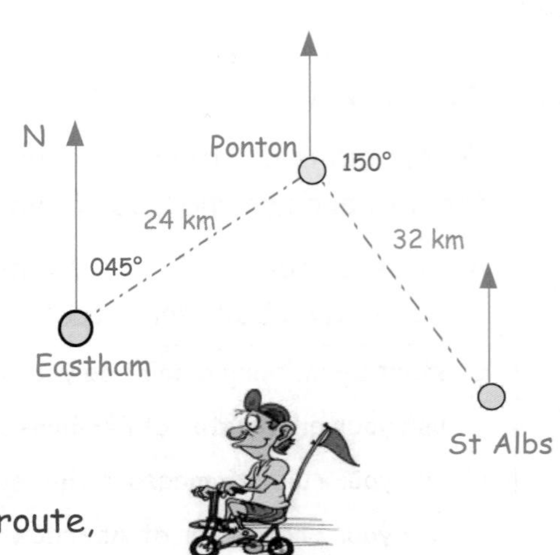

   a Make a scale drawing showing the journey from Eastham to St Albs going through Ponton, using a scale *1 cm = 4 km*.

   b Measure and write down the bearing of Eastham from St Albs.

   c Measure, in centimetres, how far the direct route from Eastham to St Albs is and calculate the real distance between them, in kilometres.

   d How long would it take Gerry to cycle this direct route, going at an average speed of 10 km/hr ?

7. The sketch shows a beginners' orienteering course with markers A, B and C.

B is 900 metres due East of A.

C is 700 metres from A and on a bearing of 025°.

a Use a scale of *1 cm = 100 metres* to make a scale drawing of the course.

b How many metres is B away from C ?

c What is the bearing of C from B ?

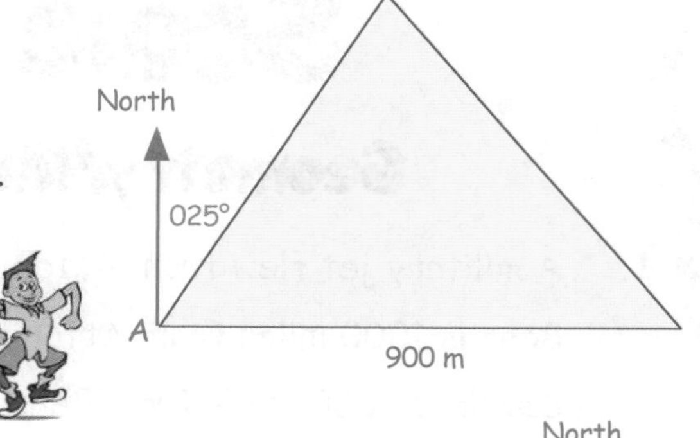

8. A small plane, flying to Edinburgh Airport, is 150 km due South of Edinburgh when the pilot receives instructions to change her course because of fog.

She is told to fly to Prestwick Airport on a bearing of 320°.

The bearing of Prestwick from Edinburgh is 255°.

a Make a scale drawing of this route, using the scale *1 cm = 10 km*, and measure the distance from the plane to Prestwick.

b Calculate how far in kilometres the plane is from Prestwick.

c If the plane's speed varies between (200 ± 30) km/hr, calculate the quickest and the slowest time, (*to the nearest minute*), it will take to reach Prestwick.

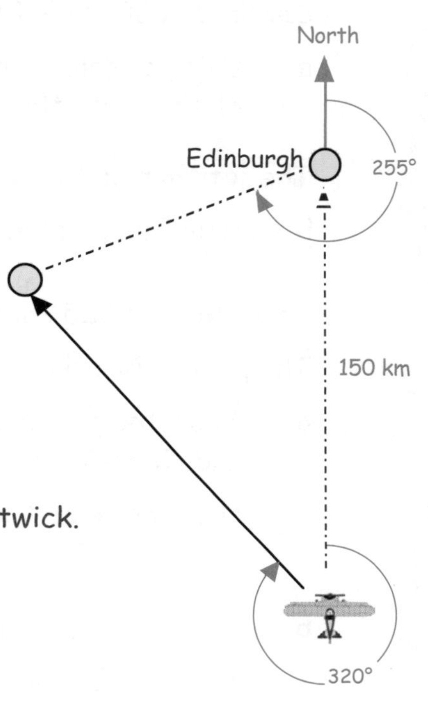

9. This sketch highlights the maiden cruise made by the new liner *Ocean Sea*.

It sailed for 150 km on a bearing of 045° from Med Isle to Gran Canape.

From there, it sailed on a bearing of 130° for 120 km to Port Lanza.

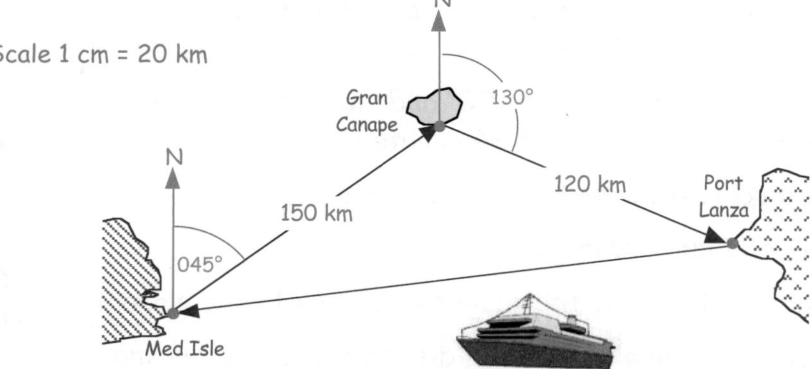

a Make a scale drawing, using the given scale, to show this voyage taken by *Ocean Sea*.

b Find the distance the liner had to travel to return to Med Isle from Port Lanza.

c It took 8 hours to go from Port Lanza to Med Isle. What was its average speed ?

Scale Drawings

Geometry/Measure Assessment 3

1. A military jet flew from Afton to Benz, and then on to Dowlin.

   Benz is 1000 miles from Afton on a bearing of 080°.

   Dowlin is 1200 miles from Benz on a bearing of 170°.

   a Using a scale 1 cm = 200 miles, make a scale drawing of the route the jet took.

   The jet then left Dowlin and returned to Afton.

   b How far is Afton from Dowlin and on what bearing ?

2. Greer Rock is 325 km from the coastal town of Levern on a bearing of 070°.

   The port of Neeskin is 450 km from Levern on a bearing of 100°.

   a Show the position of Greer Rock and Neeskin on a scale drawing.

   Use a scale of 1 cm to represent 50 km.

   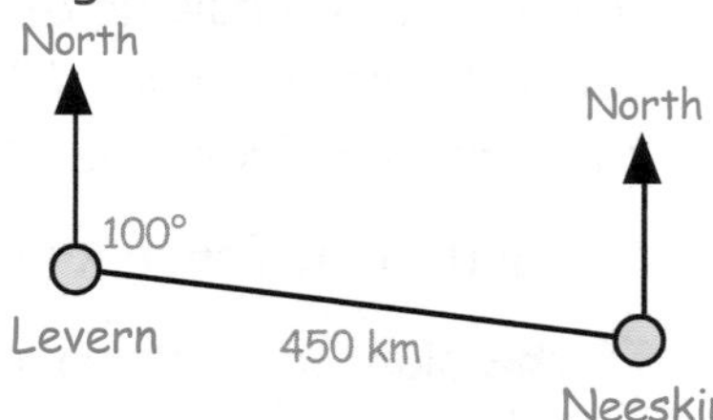

   b A cruise ship issues an SOS call which is received by Levern and Neeskin.

   It is on a bearing of 120° from Levern and 260° from Neeskin.

   (i) Mark the position of the cruise ship on your drawing.

   (ii) Find the distance (km) and bearing of the cruise ship from Greer Rock.

3. A light aircraft flies from an airport on a bearing of 055° at a speed of 200 mph for 48 minutes.

   It then turns onto a new bearing of 190° and flies at the same speed for a further 1 hour and 24 minutes.

   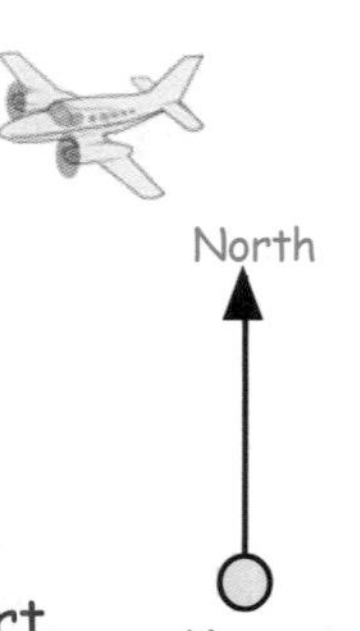

   a Construct a scale drawing to illustrate this journey.

   Use a scale of 1 cm : 40 miles.

   b The aircraft continues at the same speed back to the airport.

   Use your scale drawing to find the distance and the bearing of the airport from the light aircraft.

   c The aircraft burns fuel at 40 litres per hour.

   The cost of aviation fuel is £2·05 per litre.

   Calculate how much the fuel costs for the entire journey.

Time-Distance-Speed

Revision of Time, Distance & Speed

1. Change each of the following to 24 hour notation :-

   a 3 pm b 8 am c 7:19 pm d 11:45 am.

2. Change each of the following to 12 hour clock times :-

   a 1330 b 2215 c 0105 d 0001.

3. Change each of these times to hours and minutes :-

   a $2\frac{1}{2}$ hours b $5\frac{1}{4}$ hours c 600 minutes d $8\frac{3}{4}$ hours

   e 3·5 hours f $6\frac{2}{3}$ hours g 1·25 hours h 10·75 hours.

4. Find the missing quantity in each of the following :-

   a
   Distance - 60 miles
   Speed - 20 mph
   Time ?

   b
   Speed - 25 mph
   Time - 4 hours
   Distance ?

   c
   Distance - 210 miles
   Time - 3 hours
   Speed ?

   d
   Speed - 8 m/sec
   Time - $2\frac{1}{2}$ seconds
   Distance ?

5. a A car travels at 40 mph for 3 hours. Find the distance the car travelled.

   b Al runs for 4 km at an average speed of 8 km/hr. How long did it take him ?

   c A jet travels 600 km in 2 hours. What is the average speed of the jet ?

6. 

   A jet left Scotland and flew 3600 miles to America.

   The jet left at 3:20 pm and its average speed was 600 mph.

   At what time (*British time*) did it arrive in America ?

7. Mary ran the 10 km race at an average speed of 8 km/hr.

   Jake ran the 10 km race in 1 hour and 12 minutes.

   a Did Mary beat Jake's time ? Explain.

   b Lucy Jane ran the race at three quarters of the speed Mary ran it.

   How long did Lucy Jane take to run the race ?

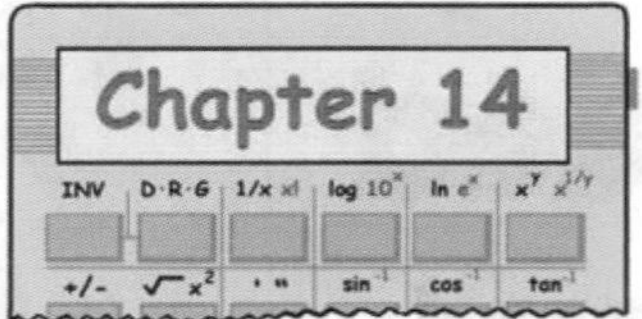

Time-Distance-Speed

Converting Hours/Minutes => Decimal Times

You should already know that :- $\frac{1}{2}$ hour = 0·5 hr and $\frac{1}{4}$ hour = 0·25 hr.

Further investigation into decimal times is required to deal with more complicated problems.

Changing Hours and Minutes => Decimals

Examples :-

45 minutes is $\frac{45}{60}$ of an hour = 45 ÷ 60 = 0·75 hr

12 minutes is $\frac{12}{60}$ of an hour = 12 ÷ 60 = 0·2 hr

2 hrs 21 minutes is 2 + $\frac{21}{60}$ = 2 + (21 ÷ 60) = 2·35 hrs.

RULE :- to change minutes to a decimal fraction of an hour => ÷ by 60

Exercise 1

1. Use your calculator to change the following to decimal times :-

a 6 minutes = $\frac{6}{60}$ hour (= 6 ÷ 60) = ... hour

b	12 minutes	c	24 minutes	d	36 minutes	e	9 minutes
f	33 minutes	g	54 minutes	h	27 minutes	i	40 minutes.

2. Use your calculator to change these times to decimal times, giving your final answers, correct to 2 decimal places :-

a	20 minutes	b	1 minute	c	59 minutes	d	25 minutes
e	19 minutes	f	11 minutes	g	70 minutes	h	205 minutes.

3. Use your calculator to change the following times to decimal times :-

a 3 hours 45 minutes = 3 + $\frac{45}{60}$ = 3 + (45 ÷ 60) = ... hours

b	2 hrs 36 mins	c	1 hr 24 mins	d	5 hrs 33 mins	e	2 hrs 55 mins
f	10 hrs 8 mins	g	19 hrs 28 mins	h	30 hrs 10 mins	i	100 hrs 3 mins.

4. A truck travels at 90 km/hr for 12 minutes.

How far does it travel in that time ? Copy and complete :-

D = S × T
= 90 × $\frac{12}{60}$
= 90 × 0·....
= .... km

5. Calculate the distance travelled each time :-

a A bus going at 60 km/hr for 40 minutes.

b A car speeding at 75 mph for 10 minutes.

c A tortoise crawling up a hill at 10 m/hr for 18 minutes.

d A train travelling for 33 minutes at 120 km/hr.

6.

Sally and Simon take turns driving a long distance.

Sally drives at 72 km/hr for 40 minutes.

Simon drives at 60 km/hr for 50 minutes.

Who drove further, Sally or Simon and by how much ?

7. A shark swam at 30 km/hr for 1 hour 48 minutes.

How far did it travel ?

8. For each of the following, calculate the distance travelled :-

a A spaceship flies at 1000 mph for 8 hours 32 minutes.

b A bicycle goes at 15 mph for 1 hour 8 minutes.

c A jogger runs at 9 km/hr for 1 hour 24 minutes.

d A skier travels at 75 km/hr for 9 minutes.

9.

A battleship, on an exercise, sails a distance of 3 kilometres in 36 minutes.

Calculate its speed, in km/hr.

10. Find the **average speed** for each of these questions :-

a A bird flies 21 miles in 42 minutes.

b An ambulance travels 8 kilometres in 6 minutes.

c A rocket covers 3000 miles in 15 minutes.

d A van travels 45 kilometres in 27 minutes.

e A canoe covers 8·2 km in 1 hour 22 minutes.

f A walker travels 8·1 miles in 2 hours 42 minutes.

g A comet flies 61 600 miles in 1 hour 6 minutes.

h An eel swam 12·1 miles in 2 hrs 12 mins.

i A tortoise crawls 8·2 metres in 4 minutes.

Converting Decimal Times => Hours/Minutes

In the last exercise, you learned a rule for changing hours and minutes into decimal form.

RULE 1 :- to change minutes to a decimal fraction of an hour => ÷ by 60

When using a calculator to find the time taken for a journey, the answer might appear as a decimal, like 0·65 hrs. There is an easy way of changing this to minutes.

RULE 2 :- to change a time in decimal form back into minutes => x by 60

Decimals => Minutes

Examples :-

0·7 hr	=	(0·7 x 60) mins	=	**42 minutes**
0·75 hr	=	(0·75 x 60) mins	=	**45 minutes**
2·6 hrs	=	2 + (0·6 x 60) mins	=	**2 hours 36 minutes**

Exercise 2

1. Each calculator display shows a time as a decimal part of an hour.

   Change each time to minutes :-

a 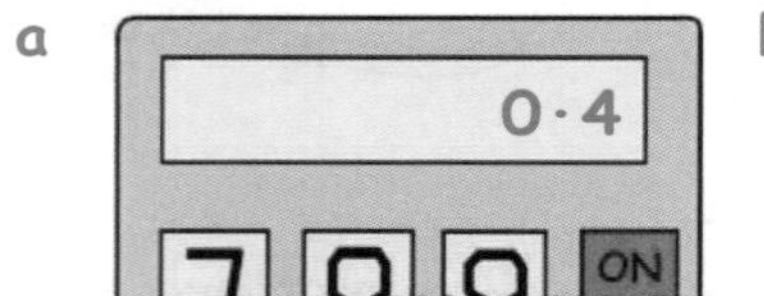

b 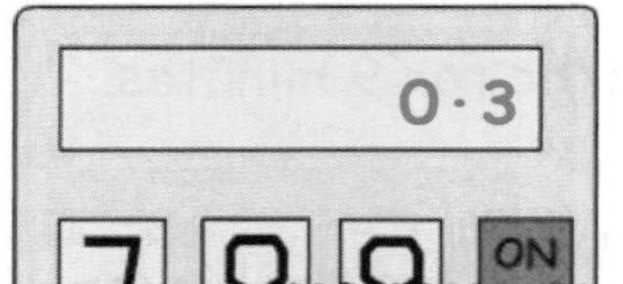

c 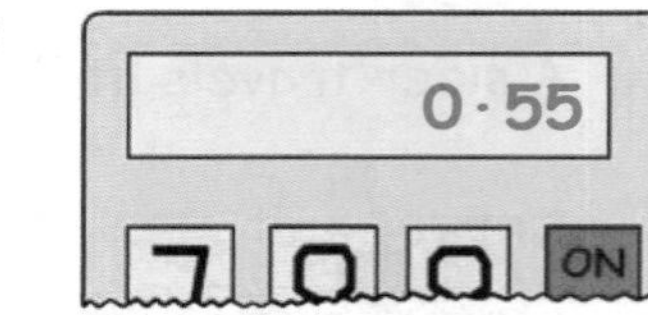

d 

e 

f 

2. If you want to change 4·2 hours to hours and minutes :-
   - Leave the hours as they are (4 hours)
   - Multiply the 0·2 by 60 => .... minutes

   => *Answer = 4 hrs .... mins.*

3. Use the same method as question 2 to change these times to hours and minutes :-

   a 2·3 hours = 2 hour + (0·3 x 60) minutes = 2 hours ... minutes.

   b 5·45 hours c 14·25 hours d 0·75 hours e 8·4 hours

   f 7·66666 hours g 9·9 hours h 2·833333 hours i 15·7 hours.

4. A boat covers 76 kilometres at 20 km/hr.

a Calculate the time taken, in hours. ($T = D/S$) (*as a decimal*).

b Change your answer to hours and minutes.

5.

A lorry travelled 132 kilometres at an average speed of 48 km/hr.

a Calculate how long it took (*as a decimal*).

b How long did it take, in hours and minutes.

6. Calculate the time taken (*as a decimal*) for each of the following, and then give your answer in hours and minutes :-

a A jet flies 638 miles at an average speed of 440 mph.

b A bus travels 24 kilometres at an average speed of 40 km/hr.

c A meteor travels 28 000 miles at an average speed of 6000 m.p.h.

d A swimmer covers 1·65 miles at an average speed of 6 mph.

7. An orienteer jogs along the course shown at an average speed of 10 km/hr.

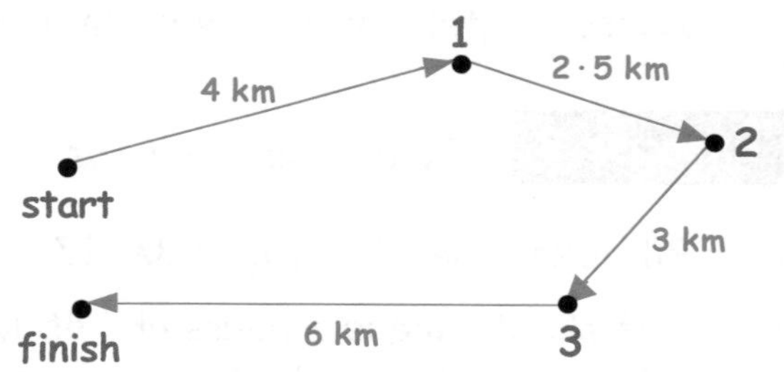

How long does he take :-

a to travel from the **start** to station **1** ?

b to travel from station **2** to station **3** ?

c to complete the course from start to finish ?

8. Eddie covers a distance of 250 metres in 50 seconds.

a What is Eddie's speed, in metres per second ?

b **Copy** the working below and **complete** it to show how to change Eddie's speed from **metres per second** to **km/hr** :-

- ***Step 1*** Change the speed to metres per minute, then metres per hour

  => 5 m/sec => 5 × 60 = 300 m/min => 300 × 60 = 18 000 m/hr.

- ***Step 2*** Change the metres to kilometres (÷ 1000)

  => 18 000 m/hr => 18 000 ÷ 1000 = ... km/hr.

9. Change these speeds from metres per second to km/hr :-

a 20 m/sec b 50 m/sec c 400 m/sec d 12·5 m/sec.

10. Which is faster :-

- a van travelling at 14 m/sec,
- or a car driving at 50 km/hr,

and by how much ?

11. The sprint speeds of 3 animals are recorded.

Big Cat	-	**25 metres in 1 second**
Greyhound	-	**0·2 km in 0·2 minutes**
Horse	-	**$\frac{3}{10}$ km in 0·25 minute.**

List the animals in order, fastest first.

12. A kilometre is five eighths of a mile approximately.

The London Marathon is 26·2 miles.

Approximately, how many kilometres, *to 3 significant figures*, is the London Marathon ?

Exercise 3 *Exam type questions*

1. Bill takes the 1435 flight BA147 from Edinburgh to Moscow.

The flight time is 3 hours and 45 minutes, but the flight take-off is delayed by 1 hour and ten minutes due to fog.

Moscow time is 4 hours ahead of Edinburgh.

At what time (*local time*) should he arrive in Moscow ?

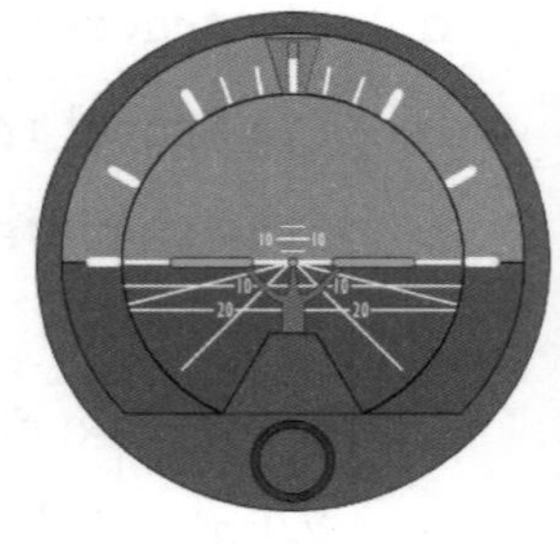

2. Usain Bolt ran the 100 m final in Berlin 2009 in 9·58 seconds.

a Calculate his speed, in km/hr, to 2 decimal places.

b Tyson Gay (*2nd place*) ran at a speed of 36·36 km/hr.

How many seconds, to two decimal places, did he end up behind Usain ?

3. James prepares for a half marathon.

He jogs round the perimeter of Strathclyde Park 6 days a week for 4 weeks.

His average speed is 10 km/hr and his recorded total running time for the month is 14 hours 24 mins.

Find the perimeter distance of the park.

4. Janice records the London Marathon programme on television.

The programme records for 4 hours and 30 minutes.

At 8 pm she decides to watch the playback using a fast-forward replay.

She watches the first third of the programme at twice the normal speed, and then watches the remainder at three times normal speed.

At what time does the programme end for Janice ?

5. Cara drove from Glasgow to Berlin, a distance of 1215 km, to visit her Great Grandmother.

She drove at an average speed of 75 km/hr.

a For how long was she driving ?

b Germany time is 2 hours ahead of GMT.

Cara decided to drive at night, when there was less traffic.

She phoned her Great Grandmother at 2215 to tell her she was leaving Glasgow.

Was this an appropriate time to phone ? *Explain.*

c Cara left her house at 2225 and on her journey she made 3 stops :-

1 hour and 45 minutes, 50 minutes and 1 hour and 25 minutes.

The ferry crossing took a total of 1 hour and 35 minutes.

At what time (local time) did she arrive in Berlin ?

6. A tourist helicopter leaves Glasgow at 2 pm and travels to Bruin, 30 km away.

It then turns and flies for 45 km to Talloch.

From Talloch, it turns and flies directly back to Glasgow, a distance of 30 km.

It arrives back in Glasgow at 5:30 pm.

Bruin
45 km
Talloch
30 km
30 km
Glasgow

a What was the helicopter's average speed for the journey ?

The next day, the helicopter leaves at 1 pm and makes the same journey.

This time, the helicopter sets off at an average speed of 25 km/hr.

b If the pilot does fly at this speed for the first 2 parts of the journey to Talloch, but he wants to be back at Glasgow by 4.45 pm, what would his minimum average return speed need to be from Talloch to Glasgow ?

7. A nail sticks into a tyre which rotates at an "angular speed" of 8 m/sec.

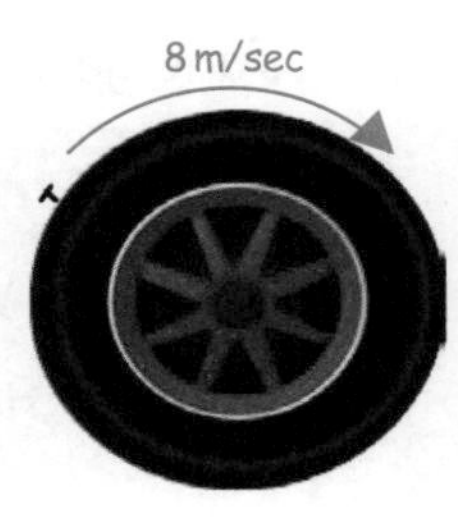

The nail, upon entering the tyre, takes a quarter of a second to do a complete revolution and reach the ground again.

Find the diameter of the tyre, *to the nearest centimetre.*

8. Trevor decided to travel round the world in his private jet.

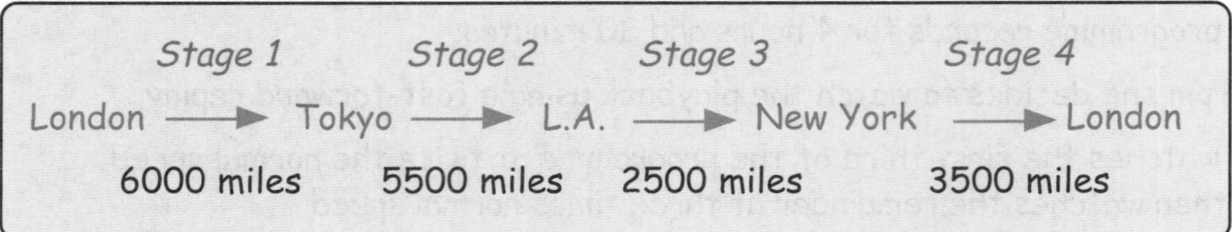

After each stage of the journey, he stopped for 7 hours (sleep).

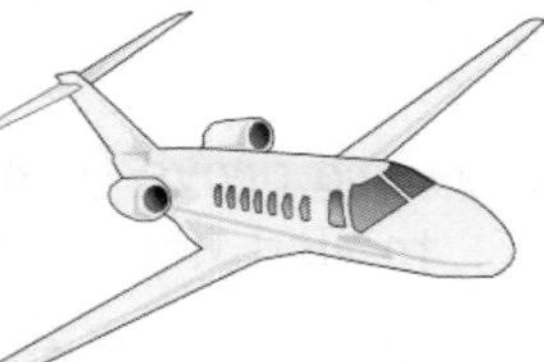

The whole journey was covered at an average speed of 400 km/hr.

a How many hours did his round the world journey take ?

b If he left at noon on Monday, when did he arrive back in London ?

c In his original plan, he wanted to leave at noon on Monday, fly at a constant average speed for the whole trip, make the same 7 hour stops and arrive back in London on Wednesday exactly at midnight.

What must his planned average speed have been in his original plan, to the nearest 10 miles per hour ?

9. An orienteering course is as shown.

A competitor managed to maintain an average speed from start to finish of 12 km/hr.

She completed the course in exactly 20 minutes.

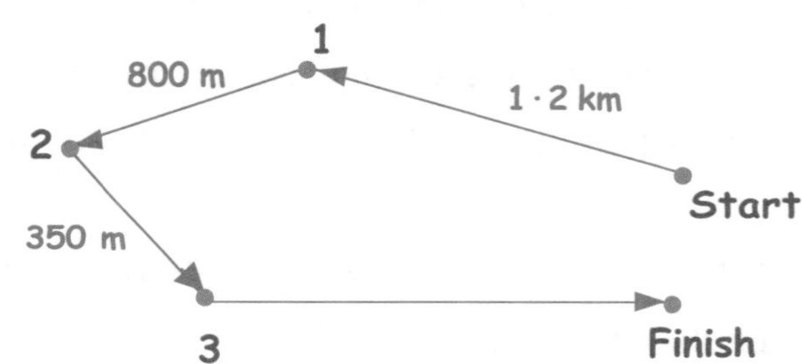

What was the distance from **Stage 3** to the finish ?

10. Jamie runs a Marathon (42·2 km) at an average speed of 9 km/hr.

What was his running time in hours, minutes and seconds ?

11. Wullie walks to school, a distance of 700 m.

He leaves the house at 8:30 am and walks at an average speed of 4·2 km/hr.

Jane gets her dad to drive her to school which is $2\frac{1}{2}$ km away.

The car travels at an average speed of 25 km/hr.

Jane and Wullie arrive at school at exactly the same time.

At what time must Jane have left her house to go to school ?

12. A fox, a rabbit and a rabbit hole are all in a straight line.

The fox is 40 m away from the rabbit and the rabbit is 80 m away from the rabbit hole.

They both start running at the same time towards the rabbit hole .

The fox runs at 24 km/hr and the rabbit runs at 18 km/hr.

a Will the rabbit reach safety, (*the rabbit hole*), before the fox catches it ?
(*Hint :- Change 24 km/hr and 18 km/hr to metres per second*).

b How fast would the fox need to be running, if it hoped to catch the rabbit ?

13. On Saturday, Janek drove a delivery truck 340 miles from the depot to a superstore.

a He left at 12.20 pm and his average speed was 50 mph.

He needed to be at the superstore by 7 pm (± 10 mins).

Did he make it on time ? *Explain.*

b On Sunday, when the roads were quieter, Janek made the same delivery.

Because there was less traffic on the roads, he found his average speed was 20% greater than that on Saturday.

He needed to arrive at the superstore at 10.25 pm, (± 15 mins).

What was the latest time he had to leave the depot ?

14. The Glasgow Half-Marathon race is over 13·1 miles.

Jane took part in her wheelchair.

She travelled at an average speed of 10 mph.

a Find her time for this event in hrs, mins and secs.

b Jane also took part in a 10 km competition.

The large wheel on her chair has a radius of 40 cm.

How many revolutions did the wheel make covering the 10 kilometres ?

c Jane's best time in the 10 km race was 37 minutes.

What was her average speed in km/hr, (*to 2 decimal places*), when she managed her best time ?

15. A comet travels at 3700 metres per second.

How many kilometres will it travel in a week ?

Time Distance Speed

Geometry/Measure Assessment 4

1. Use your calculator to change each of the following into decimal times giving your answer, where necessary, to 2 significant figures :-

   a 12 minutes b 28 minutes c 2 hrs 42 mins d 1 hr 3 mins.

2. Change each of these times to hours and minutes :-

   a 3·3 hrs b 8·4 hrs c 2·3333 hrs d 0·7 hrs.

3. a A train travelled at 44 km/hr for 2·5 hours. How far did it travel ?

   b What is the speed of a jogger who covers 8 km in 1 hour 15 minutes ?

   c A truck travelled 240 km at an average speed of 45 km/hr.

   How long did the journey take ?

4. Change each of these speeds to km/hr :-

   a 100 m/sec b 45 m/sec c 12 m/min d 40 cm/sec.

5. Which is faster, a car travelling at 25 m/sec or a truck at 0·3 km in 0·25 minutes ?

6. Sara walks to work at 8·15 am every morning, a distance of 1·2 km.

   Her average walking speed is 5 km/hr.

   a At what time, to the nearest minute, will she arrive at work ?

   b Jan drives to work, 4·5 km away, at an average speed of 30 km/hr.

   She arrives at work at 8:45 am.

   At what time does she leave her house ?

7. Frank arrived at Edinburgh Airport to find that his 1445 flight to Delhi was delayed by 50 minutes.

   The flight journey was 6804 km, and the plane travelled at an average speed of 540 km/hr.

   Delhi is 4·5 hours ahead of BST, (*British Standard Time*).

   At what time (*local time*) did Frank land in Delhi ?

Pythagoras' Theorem

Revision of Pythagoras

1. Find the following :-

   a $\sqrt{81}$ b $\sqrt{1}$ c $\sqrt{100}$ d $\sqrt{55}$.

2. Use Pythagoras' Theorem to calculate the length of the hypotenuse :-

   a

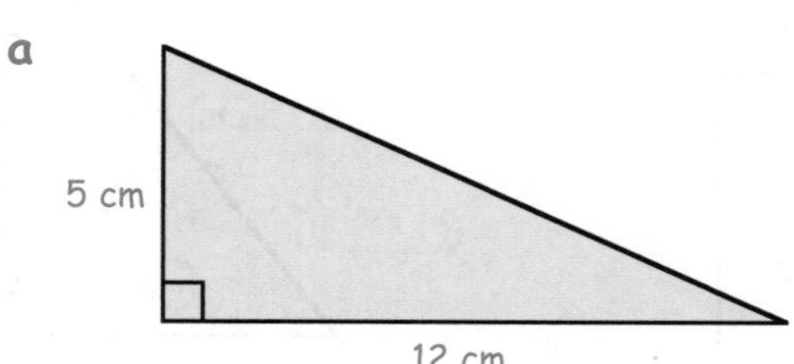

   b

16 cm

12 cm

3. Find the length of the shorter side in each of the following :-

   a

26 cm

10 cm

a cm

   b

7 cm

b cm

9 cm

4. Jackson is flying his kite.

   The string is 22 metres long and he is 15 metres from a point directly below the kite.

   How high, to the nearest metre, is the kite above the ground ?

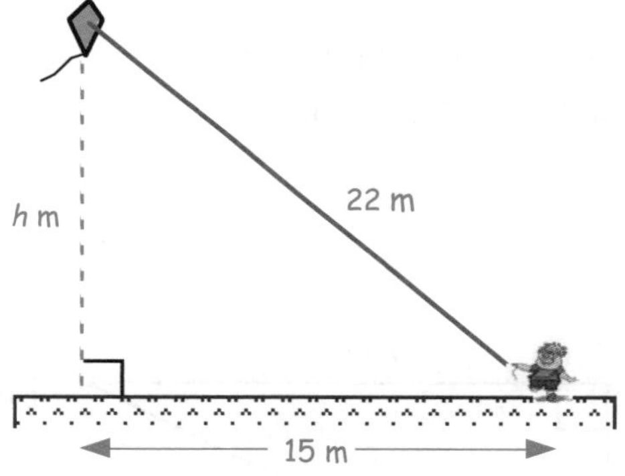

5. The base of an isosceles triangle is 200 cm.

   Its height is 75 cm.

   Find the perimeter of the isosceles triangle.

75 cm

200 cm

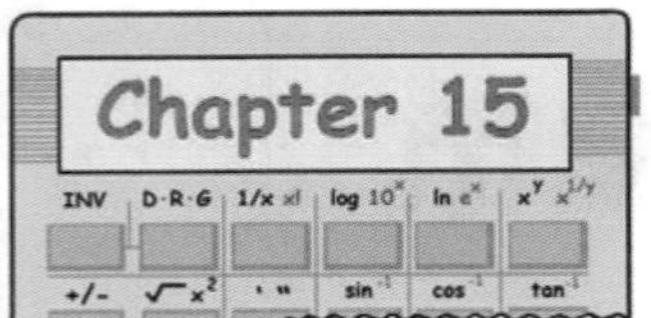

Pythagoras' Theorem

Problem Solving Using Pythagoras' Theorem

Some problems, involving the use of Pythagoras' Theorem, can be a bit more complex.

Example :- Find the **area** of this right angled triangle.

Notice this must be done in two steps.

5 cm

4 cm

x cm

Step 1 Find the base length (x).

$$x^2 = 5^2 - 4^2$$

$$\Rightarrow \quad x^2 = 25 - 16 = 9$$

$$\Rightarrow \quad x = \sqrt{9} = 3 \text{ cm}$$

Step 2 Now find the area

$$A = \tfrac{1}{2}(B \times H)$$

$$A = \tfrac{1}{2} \text{ of } (3 \times 4)$$

$$A = 6 \text{ cm}^2$$

Exercise 1

1. Find the **area** of the right angled triangle shown.

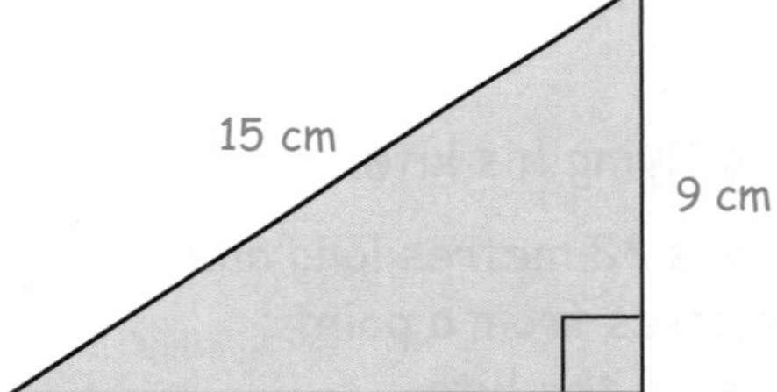

2. Find the **perimeter** of this right angled triangle.

(*Give your answer to 3 significant figures*).

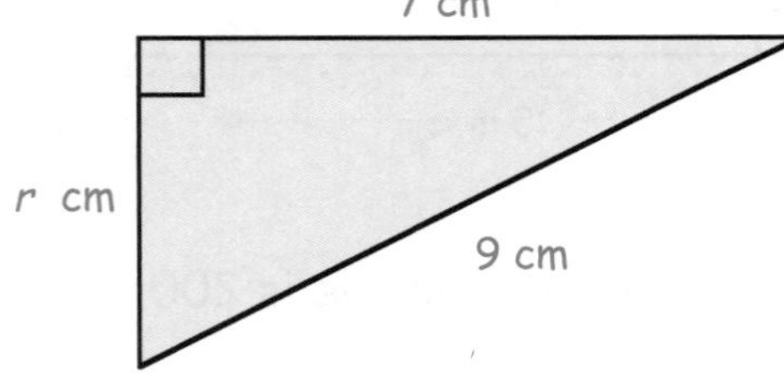

3. Shown is a right angled triangle.

    a Find the **perimeter**

    b Find the **area**.

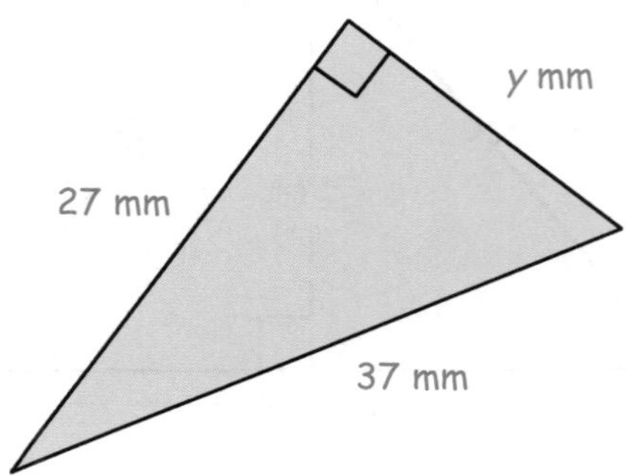

More complicated questions can arise requiring the use of Pythagoras' Theorem.

Example :- Find the value of x.

Notice this must be done in two steps both using Pythagoras twice.

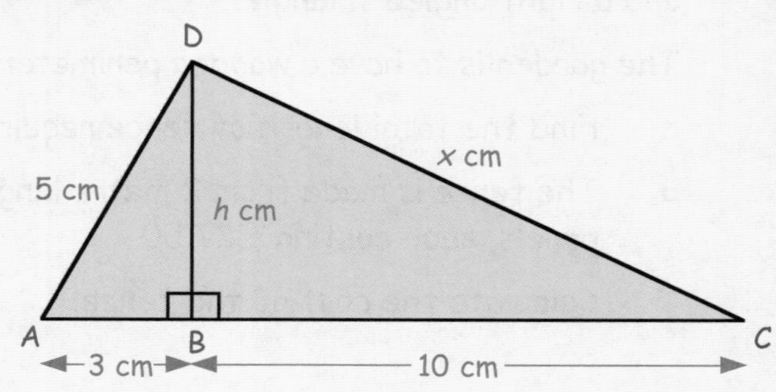

Step 1 Find the height **BD** in triangle **ABD**.

$$h^2 = 5^2 - 3^2$$
$$\Rightarrow h^2 = 25 - 9 = 16$$
$$\Rightarrow h = \sqrt{16} = \mathbf{4\ cm}$$

Step 2 Now find the hypotenuse (x) in triangle BCD.

$$x^2 = 10^2 + 4^2$$
$$\Rightarrow x^2 = 100 + 16 = 116$$
$$\Rightarrow x = \sqrt{116} = \mathbf{10 \cdot 77\ cm}$$

4. Find the value of x in this right angled triangle.

(*Use the steps in the example above to help you*).

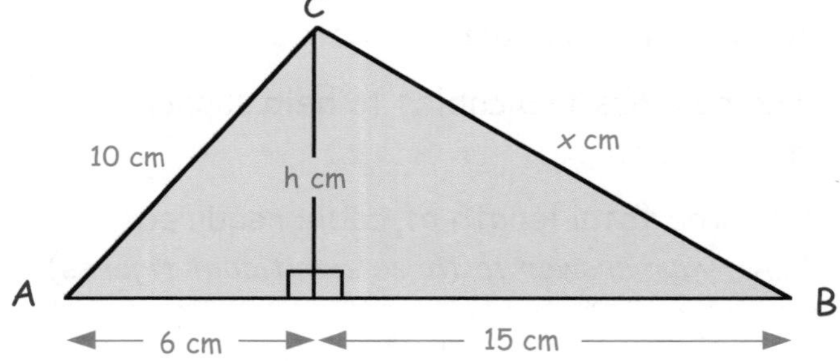

5. Use the diagram and your answers from Question **4**, to find :-

a the **area** of triangle ABC

b the **perimeter** of triangle ABC.

6. A composite shape is made from two right angled triangles, as shown.

a Find the length of the line marked x.

b Find the perimeter of this composite shape.

c Find the total area of this composite shape.

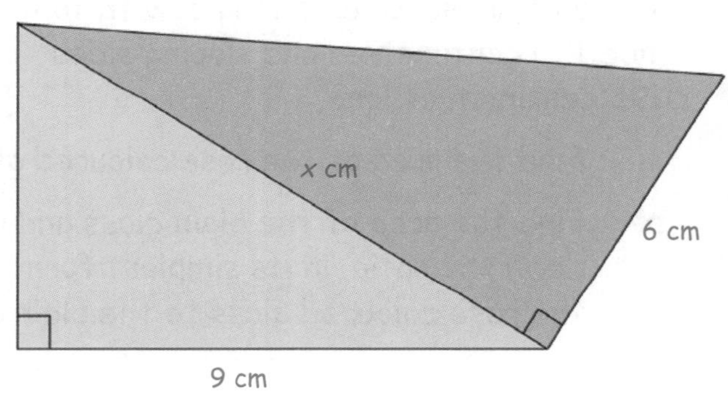

7. A garden lawn is in the shape of a rectangle and a right angled triangle.

The garden is to have a wooden perimeter fence.

a Find the total length of fence required.

b The fence is made from 2 metre length panels, each costing £27·50.

Calculate the cost of the fence.

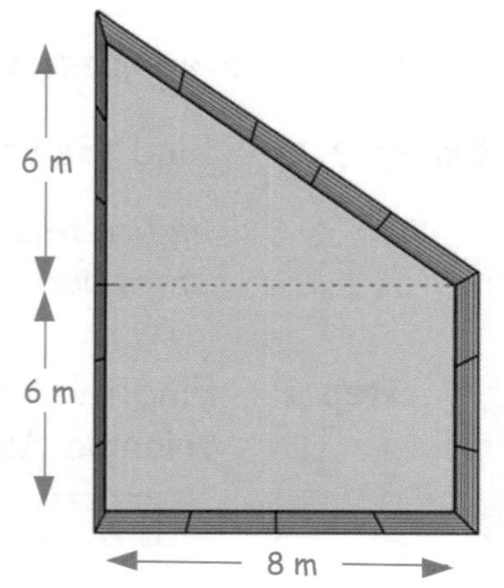

8. 

Tank A leaves HQ at noon and drives due East at 20 km/hr until 2 pm.

Tank B leaves HQ also at noon and travels due North at 12 km/hr for 90 minutes.

Tank A then breaks down and Tank B drives directly to Tank A.

How far does Tank B travel in total ?
(*Do NOT use a scale drawing - but it would help to draw a sketch*).

9. An 8 metre tall pole is erected.

The pole has two cables to help support it, as shown.

Find the total length of cable required.
(*Give your answer to three significant figures*).

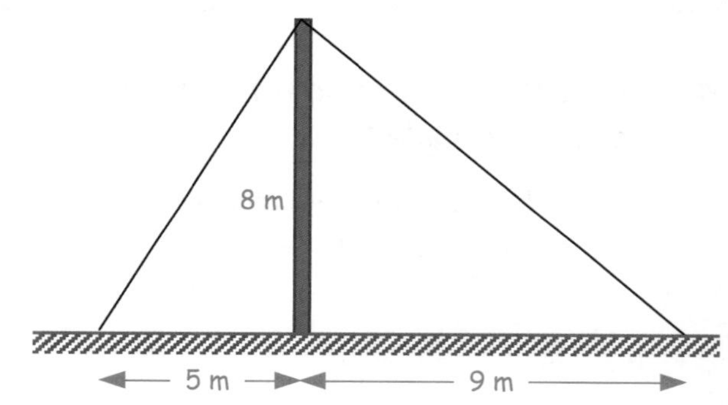

10. A church window is filled with a mixture of plain and rose coloured glass panels.

The window is surrounded by a wooden frame.

The rose coloured glass panel is in the shape of an isosceles triangle, with top side 150 centimetres and sloping sides 195 centimetres long.

a Find the area of the rose coloured glass.

b Find the area of the plain glass and write down the ratio, in its simplest form, of the rose coloured glass to the plain glass.

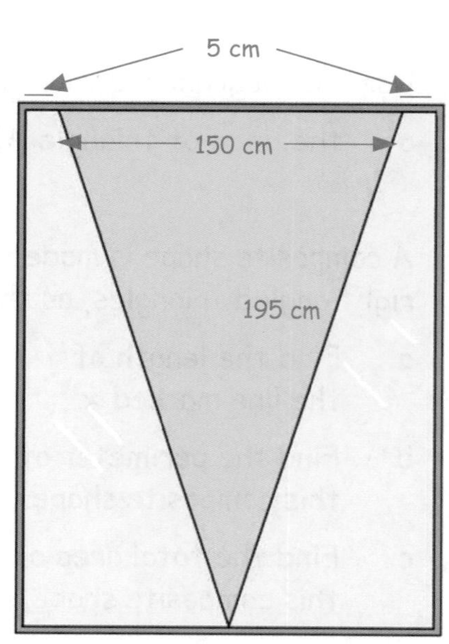

11. A new flag is designed with a green triangle on top of a yellow background.

The flag measures 2·6 m by 1·8 m.

The green triangle AEF has E as the midpoint of BC and F as the midpoint of DC.

Find the area of the green triangle.

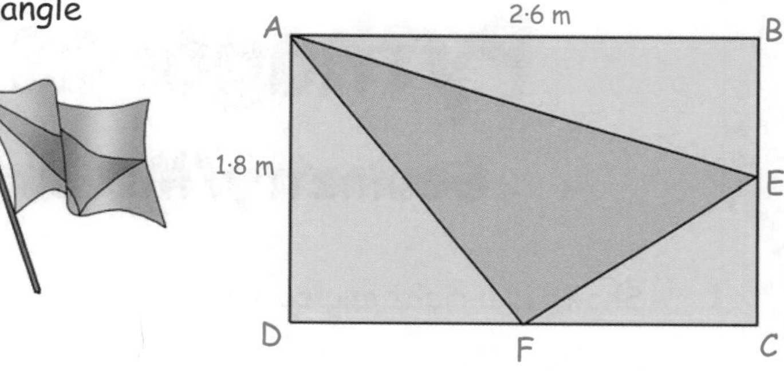

12. 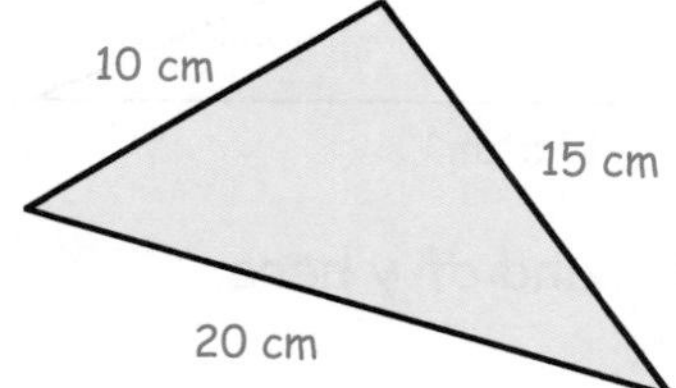

A triangle has sides 10 cm, 15 cm and 20 cm.

Explain why this triangle **cannot** be a right angled triangle.

13. A cycle race has been organised, and the route taken is in the shape of a right angled triangle, as shown.

The two shorter sides have been measured out as 8 km (±10%) and 5 km (±10%).

The total distance travelled over the triangular route should be **no more** than 25 kilometres.

Can the race organisers guarantee that the maximum distance has **not** been exceeded ?

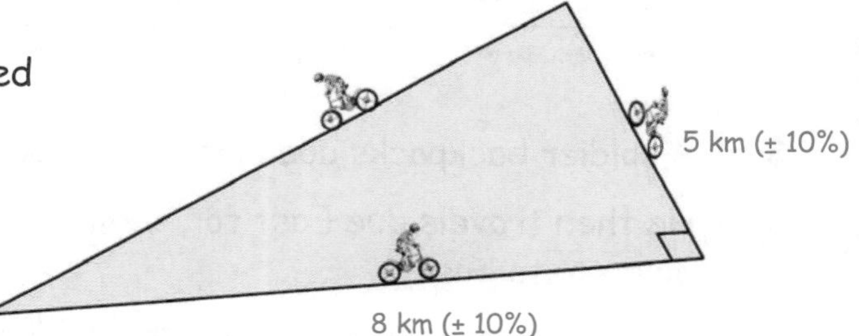

14. A wheelchair ramp is built as shown.

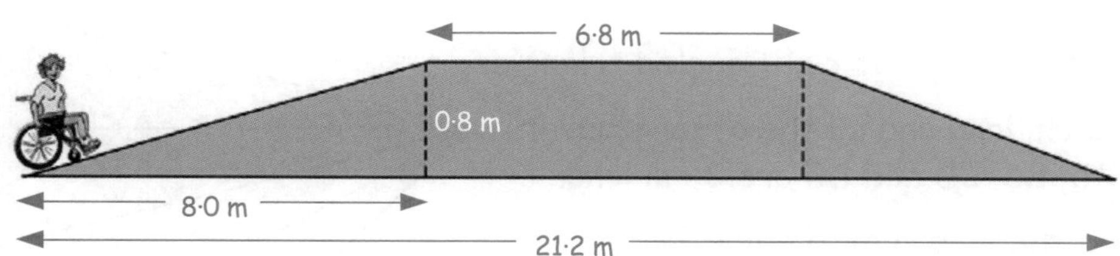

Find the total distance a wheelchair user must travel to get from one end to the other, giving your answer to one decimal place.

15. In a cross country running event, the runners must begin at the starting point and run to Checkpoint 1, then 2, then 3, before returning to the starting point.

- *Checkpoint 1* - 4 km due North.
- *Checkpoint 2* - 2 km due West of the start.
- *Checkpoint 3* - 1 km due South of *Checkpoint 2*.

What is the total running distance, to the nearest metre ?

Pythagoras' Theorem

Geometry/Measure Assessment 5

1. Shown is a right angled triangle.

   a Find the perimeter of the triangle.

   b Calculate its area.

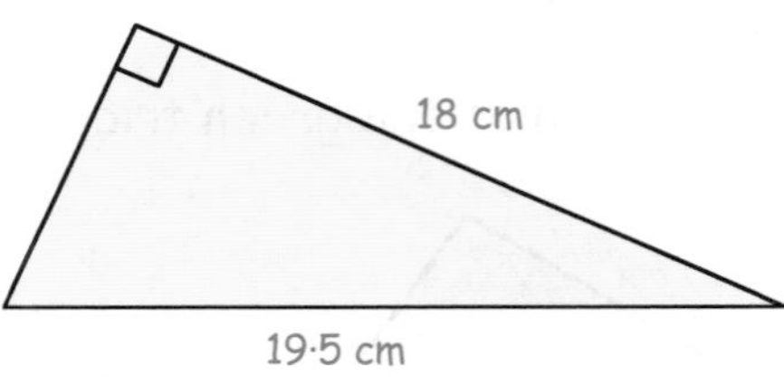

2. Find the value of x and of y here.

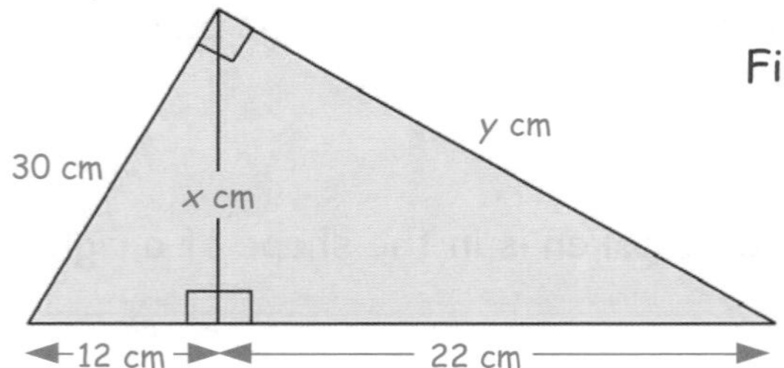

3. A soldier backpacks due North from base for 7 km.

   He then travels due East for 4 km, before returning directly to base.

   a How many kilometres had the soldier covered ?

   b If he left base at 1430 and travelled at an average speed of 7 km/hr, at what time, to the nearest minute, did he arrive back at base ?

4. Shown is a "spiral" of right angled triangles.

   PA is 10 cm long and all the other smaller sides AB, BC, CD and DE are 3 cm long.

   a Find the length of the line PB.

   b Find the length of the line PE.

   c How many more triangles, with small side 3 cm, must be added to the spiral in order that the final line P... will be greater than 13 cm ?

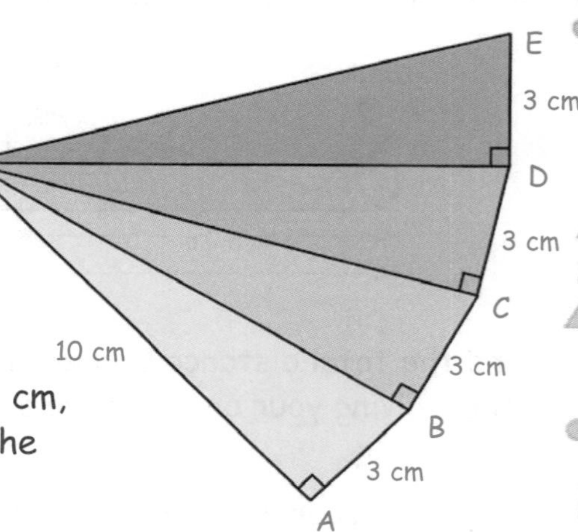

5. Two sides of this right angled triangle have been measured and are given as (9·7 ± 0·05) cm and (4·3 ± 0·05) cm.

   Calculate the maximum and the minimum values of the area of the right angled triangle.

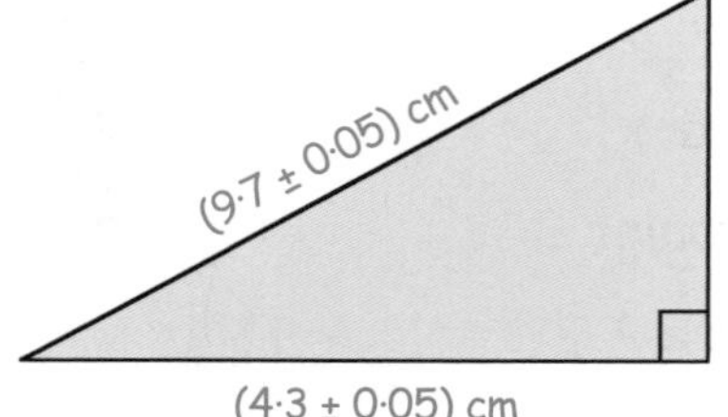

Gradients

Revision of Gradients

1. a Write down the gradient of Stoney Brae as a fraction.

   b Simplify the fraction.

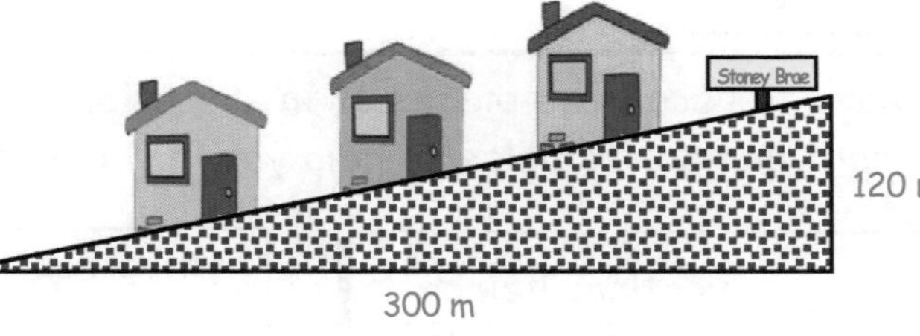

2. a Calculate the gradients of Viscount Street and Vanguard Way as fractions.

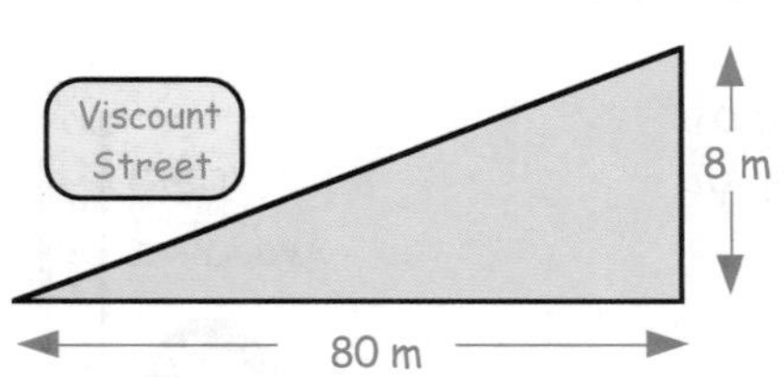

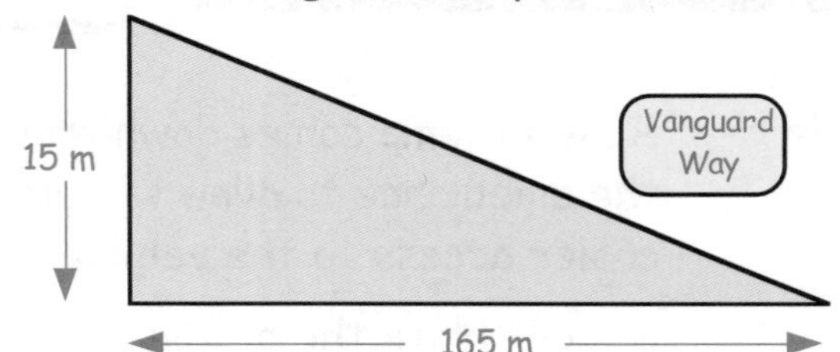

   b Which of the 2 slopes is steeper ?

3. The picture shows a lady on a treadmill.

   She has elevated it from its horizontal starting position to a more inclined position.

   Work out the treadmill's gradient, as a decimal, in its present position.

4. 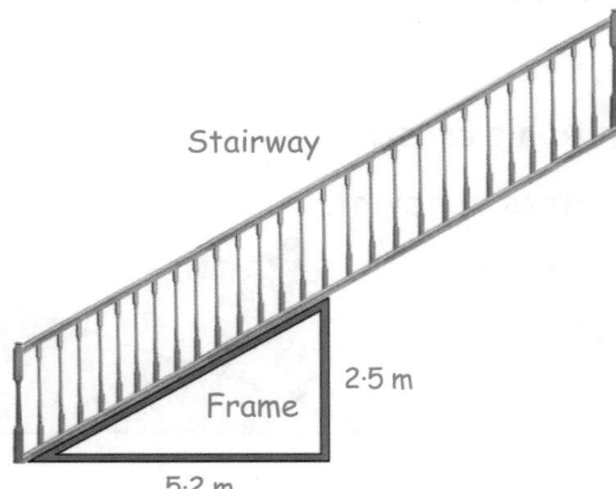

   Patryk is making a frame to strengthen a stairway in an apartment block.

   The horizontal distance is 5·2 metres and he has erected a frame support 2·5 metres high.

   Regulations state that the gradient of the stairway should be no larger than 0·5.

   Does the stairway meet the requirements ?

5. Shown is a house with a front porch.

   The roof of the porch has a horizontal distance of 320 cm and a vertical height of 48 cm.

   The house roof has a horizontal distance of 900 cm and a vertical height of 630 cm.

   Express the gradient of each roof as a decimal and calculate how much steeper the house roof is.

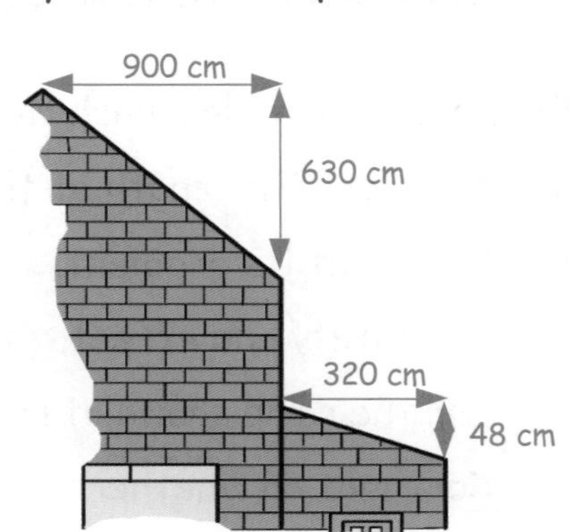

Gradients

Using Gradients

You will have to recall two pieces of information from National 4 about right angled triangles to help you in this chapter.

$$\text{Gradient} = \frac{\text{vertical height}}{\text{horizontal distance}}$$

Pythagoras' Theorem

$c^2 = a^2 + b^2$ or

$a^2 = c^2 - b^2$

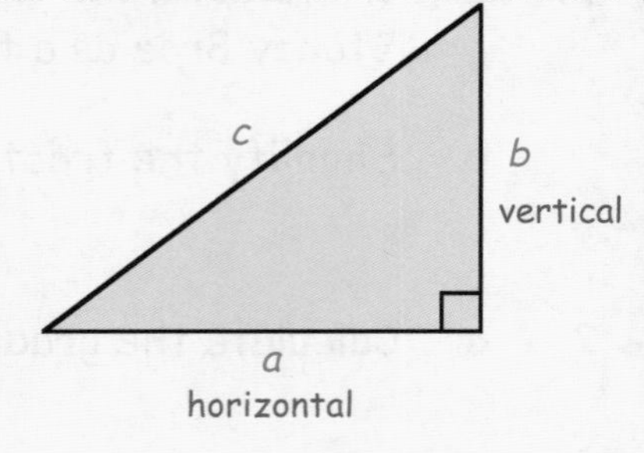

Example :- A metal ramp comes down from the rear of the ambulance to allow wheelchairs to have easier access to the vehicle.

a Calculate the gradient of the ramp.

b Work out the length of the ramp.

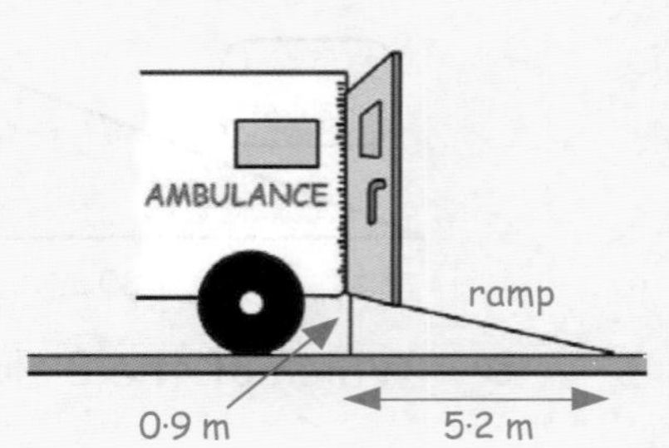

$$\text{Gradient} = \frac{\text{vertical height}}{\text{horizontal distance}}$$

$$\text{grad} = \frac{0{\cdot}9}{5{\cdot}2} = 0{\cdot}173.$$

$c^2 = a^2 + b^2$

$c^2 = 5{\cdot}2^2 + 0{\cdot}9^2$

$= 27{\cdot}04 + 0{\cdot}81$

$= 27{\cdot}85$

$c = 5{\cdot}3$ Ramp = 5·3 m to 2 sig. figs.

* Note - In this chapter, you may be asked to make judgements regarding whether a slope was safe or not or if a ramp would be deemed legal or illegal !

Exercise 1

1. Mr Baines has a wooden wheelchair ramp built on to his conservatory.

   It has a sloping side 6·5 metres long and is 0·9 metres in height.

   a Work out how far it comes out from the conservatory.

   b A wheel chair ramp with gradient less than 0·15 will give a safe ride downwards.

   Is Mr Baines' ramp safe ?

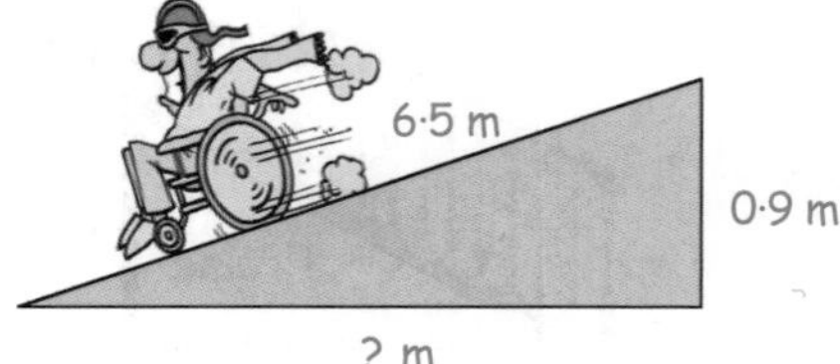

2. Shown is a portable launch ramp for skate boarders.

   a Calculate the length of the slope on this ramp.

   b Work out its gradient.

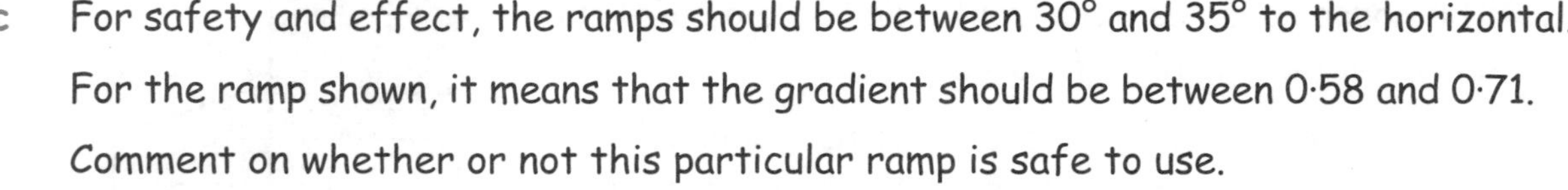

   c For safety and effect, the ramps should be between 30° and 35° to the horizontal.

   For the ramp shown, it means that the gradient should be between 0·58 and 0·71.

   Comment on whether or not this particular ramp is safe to use.

3. A garage owner uses 2 different lever ramps to test the effectiveness of car brakes.

A car is driven on to the ramp, the hand brake pulled up and the brakes are tested.

a Calculate the gradient of each ramp.

b Which ramp will test the brake's effectiveness more fully ?

4. The diagram shows an escalator connecting two levels in a new shopping centre.

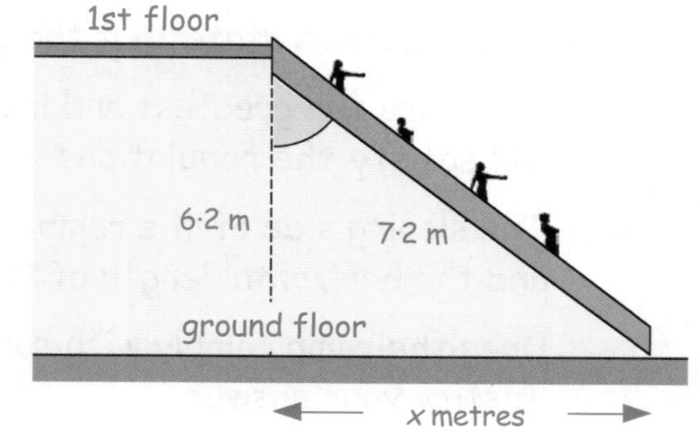

a Calculate the horizontal distance (x).

The "steepness" should not be more that 1·5.

b On completion, the site engineer confirmed that the escalator met the regulation.

Did it ? Explain your reasoning.

5. A new swimming pool is to be 25 metres long and 12 metres wide.

The depth of the pool at the shallow end is to be 0·9 metre.

It is proposed that the deep end is 2·5 metres.

Regulations state that the slope of the bottom of the pool must be (0·06 ± 0·005).

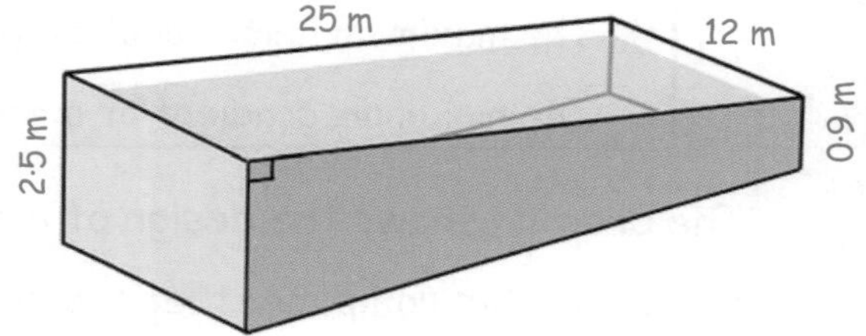

a Will the new pool satisfy the regulations ? Give a reason for your answer.

b Calculate the length of the sloping floor.

6. The glide path of a plane as it comes into land should have a steepness of 0·06 ± 0·01.

An air traffic controller at the airport must tell the pilot whether he is too high, too low or on the correct glide path.

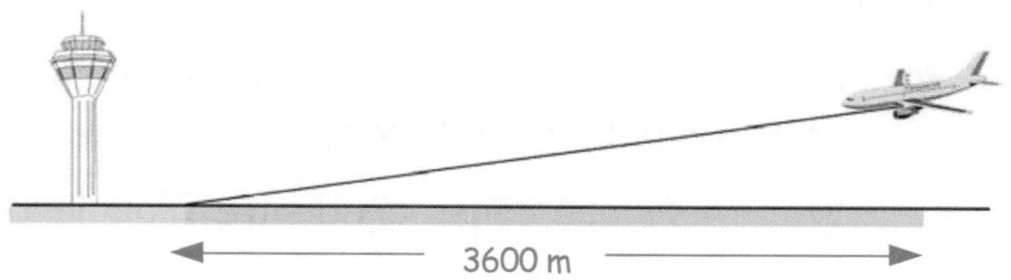

a An incoming plane is 3600 metres away from its landing point and is at a height of 162 metres.

What advice should the air traffic controller give to the pilot ?

b At its present height, calculate the distance the plane has still to travel (*to the nearest metre*), and how long it will take, flying at a speed of 70 metres per second.

7. A ship is berthed at high tide and a gangway is secured to link the ship with the pier.

   It is said that the gradient of the gangway should not be greater than 0·4, to allow passengers safe access to the ship.

   a Is this gangway ok ?

   b Calculate the length of the gangway.

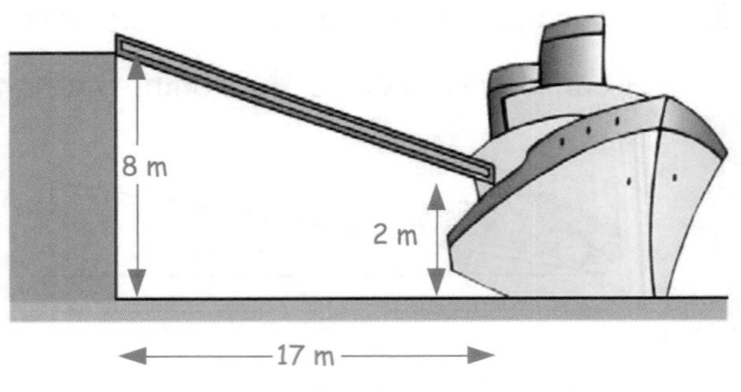

8. A mechanical ramp is provided on an airport vehicle to load luggage onto a small plane.

   Safety regulations state that the gradient of the ramp has to be 2·6 ± 15%.

   a What are the greatest and least gradients that will satisfy the regulations ?

   b The sloping side of the ramp is 4·3 metres long and the horizontal length of the ramp is 1·4 metres.

   Does the ramp comply with safety regulations ? Justify your answer.

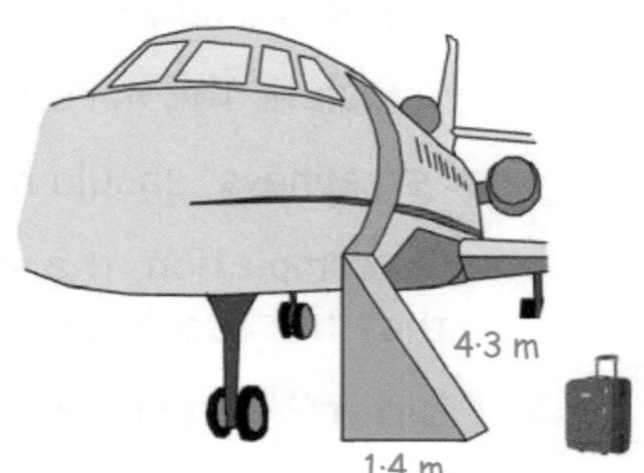

9. When hotels are considering wheelchair access for their guests, at least two legal points have to be adhered to :-

   - The maximum height shall be 650 mm for any length of ramp.
   - The maximum gradient of a ramp shall be 1 in 12.

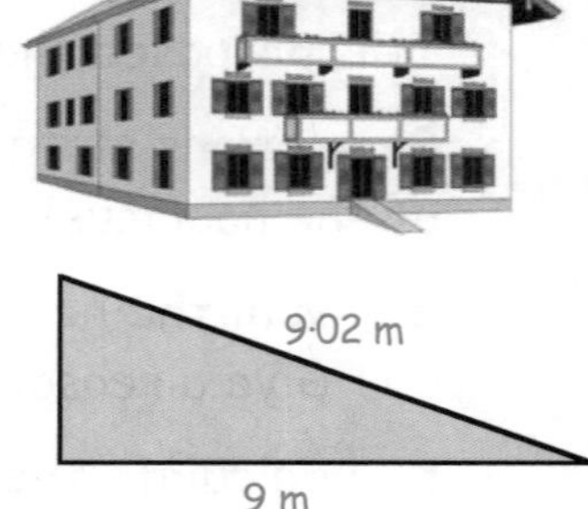

   The drawing shows the design of a new ramp.

   a Does this ramp meet legal point 1 ? *Explain your answer.*

   b Does this ramp meet legal point 2 ? *Explain your answer.*

9·02 m

9 m

10. Many landslides occur on slopes with gradients which lie in the range 0·7 to 1·0.

   A survey was carried out in a mountainous area prone to landslides.

   a One survey was done on a 100 foot slope from a height of 935 feet to 1000 feet.

   Was this slope considered safe from landslides ?

   b The lower part of the mountain was considered safe as it had a gradient of $\frac{1}{3}$.

   It rose from a height of 785 feet up to 935 feet.

   What is the length of the slope, to the nearest foot, on this part of the mountain ?

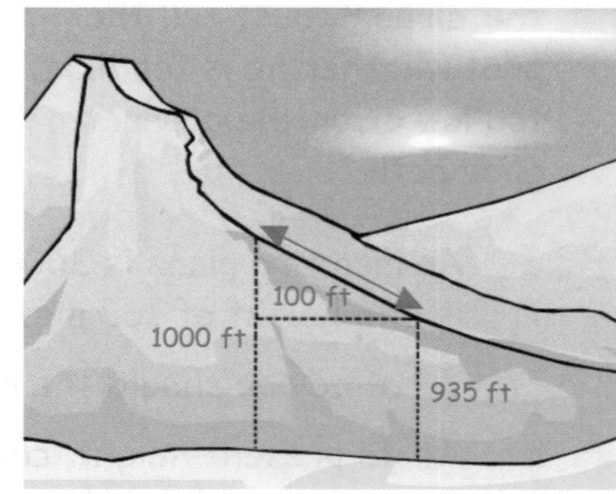

Gradients

Geometry/Measure Assessment 6

Tread depth
40 cm

1. The diagram shows a staircase Mary had installed in her home.

   The dimensions of the riser and tread of each step is shown.

   Mary's joiner had to adhere to the rules below for safety reasons.

Riser height - 16 cm

- The horizontal tread depth plus twice the riser height had to be $(70 \cdot 5 \pm 1 \cdot 5)$ cm.
- The gradient of each step had to be no more than $\frac{2}{5}$.

The joiner thought that he had met both rules.

Was he correct ? Explain your answer.

2. A toy company is designing new children's outdoor play slides.

   Each type of slide has to comply with the following company rules :-

Rule 1	The gradient has to be within $0 \cdot 95 \pm 0 \cdot 03$.
Rule 2	The maximum rise shall be 3650 millimetres for any slide.

The proposed two designs shown below have already been rejected.

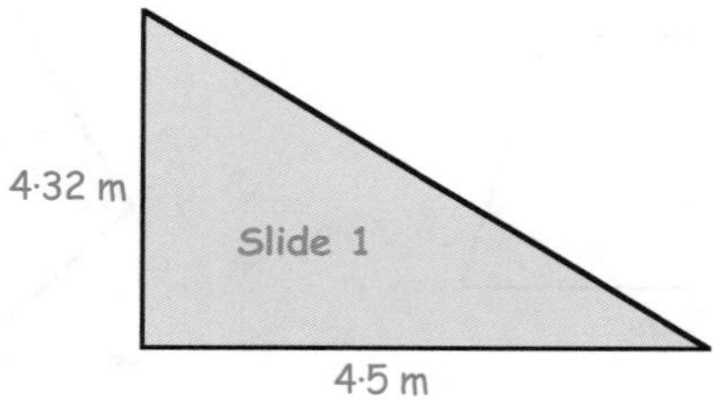

3·5 m
Slide 2
3·4 m

a Which rule(s) did slide 1 fail on ?

b Which rule(s) did slide 2 fail on ?

3. A new regulation states that the gradient of all ramps into a community centre must be less than 0·23.

   This sketch shows the entrance ramp to Braidbank Community Centre.

   It is 492 cm long and has a horizontal distance of 480 cm.

   Does it satisfy the new regulation ?

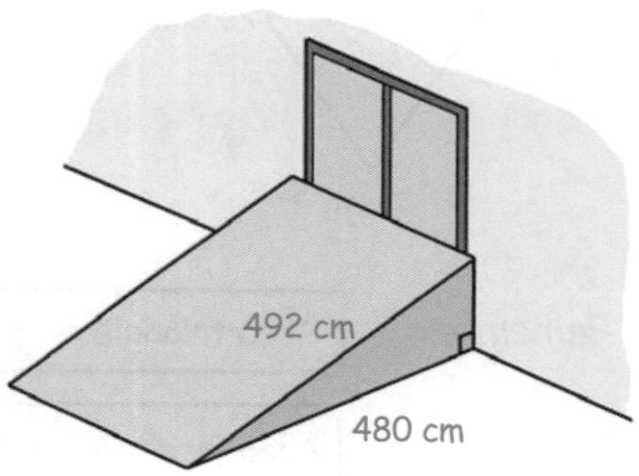

Revision of Area

1. Calculate the area of each of the following rectangles.
   (Write down the rule $A = L \times B$ and remember to use the correct units) :-

a

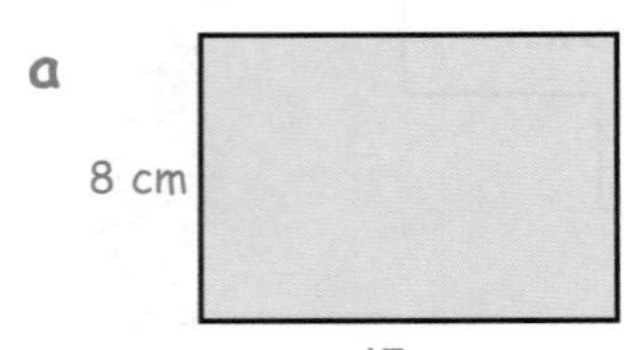

b

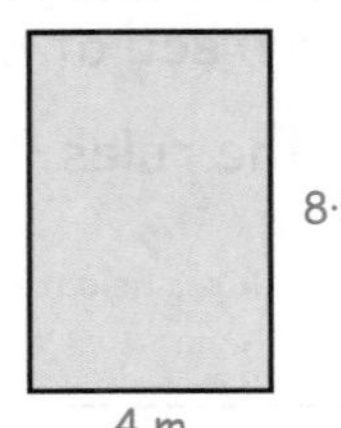

c

40 mm
22 mm

2. Calculate the **area** of each right angled triangle :-

a

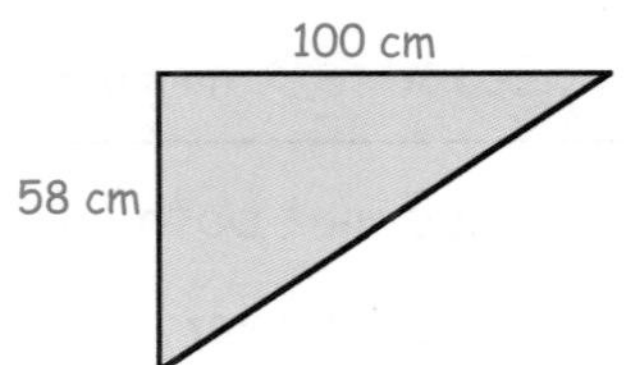

b

35 mm
50 mm

3. Calculate the area of each of the following shapes :-

a

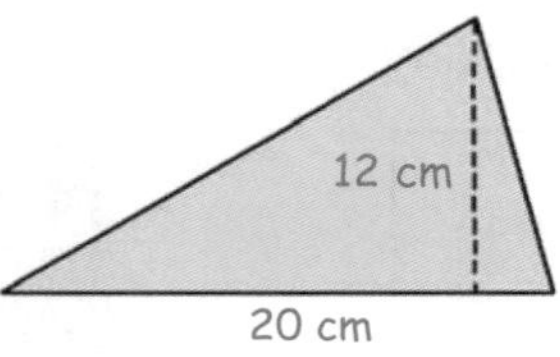

b

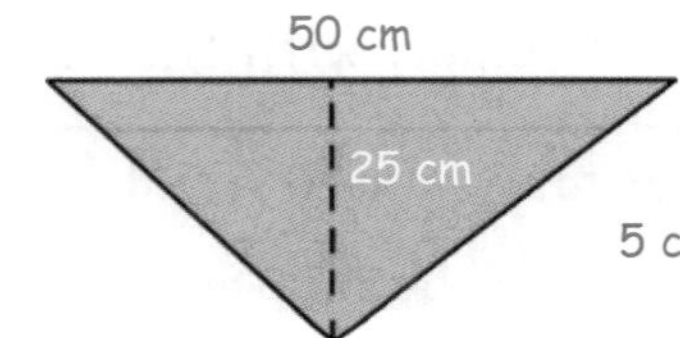

c

16 cm
11 cm
5 cm
12 cm

d

9 cm
6 cm
16 cm

e

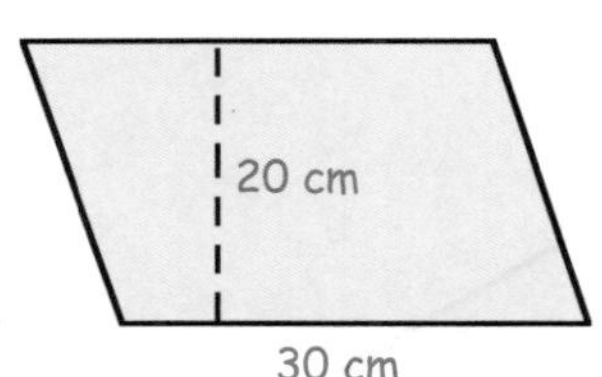

f

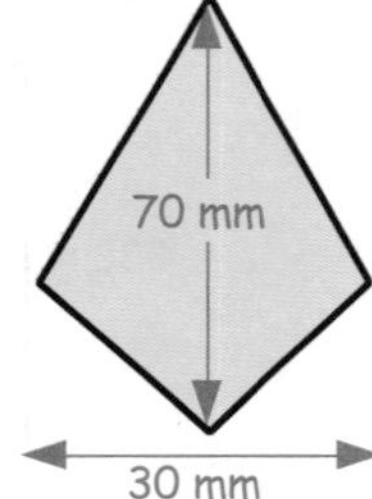

g

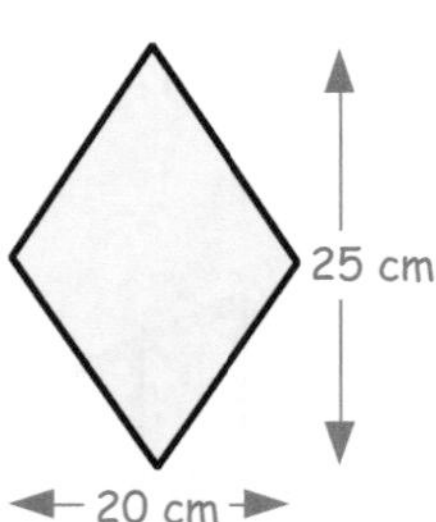

h

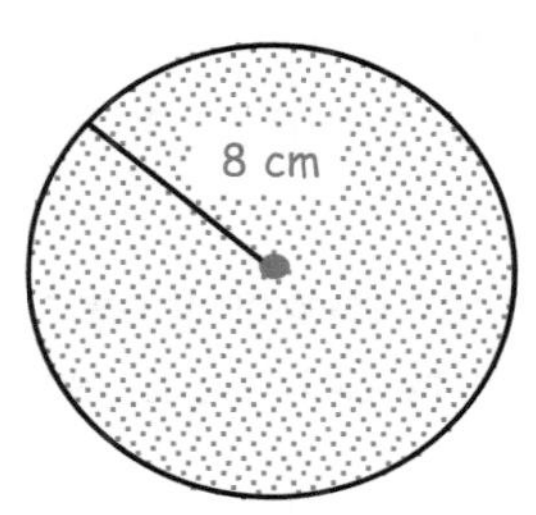

i

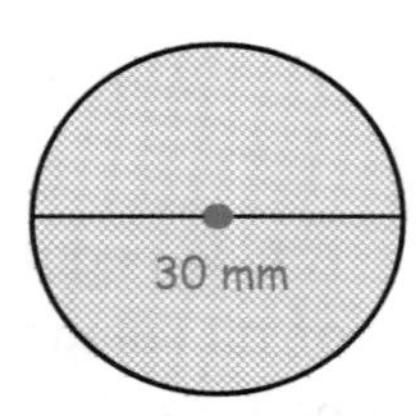

Remember :-

Area triangle = $\frac{1}{2}$(*base* x *height*)

Area parallelogram = *base* x *height*

Area kite = Area rhombus = $\frac{1}{2}(D \times d)$

Area of circle = πr^2

Area of a Circle

In Chapter 6, you were asked to accept that the area of a circle was given by :- $A = \pi r^2$.

It is difficult to calculate exactly the area of a circle because of its curved edge.

Let us try the following idea to show why the formula does in fact work :-

- Cut a circle (with radius r) from a piece of card.
- Divide the circle into 8 parts as shown and half one part.
- Cut the 9 parts out and lay them as shown below :-

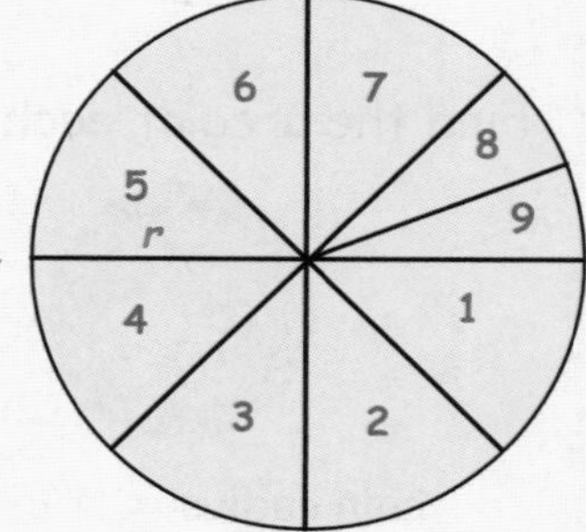

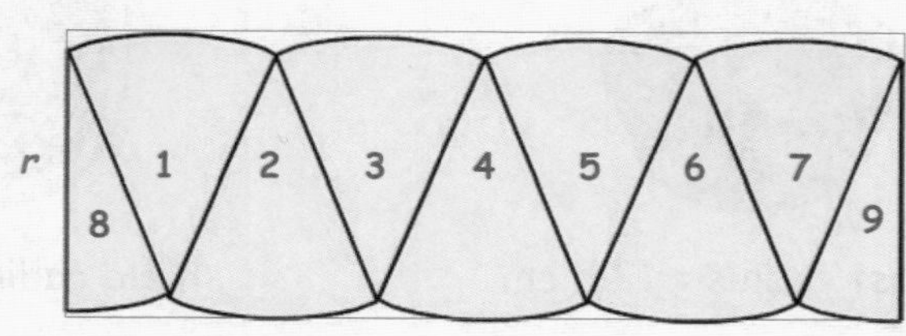

Can you see that our circle has turned into a (rather bumpy) rectangle ?

Try doing this again, but this time cut the circle into 16 parts and half one of them.

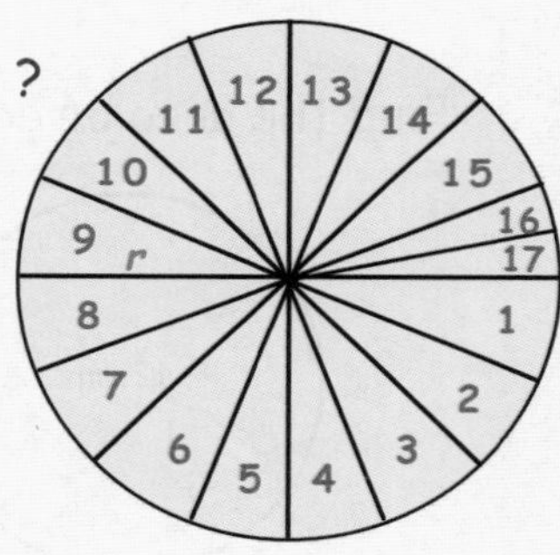

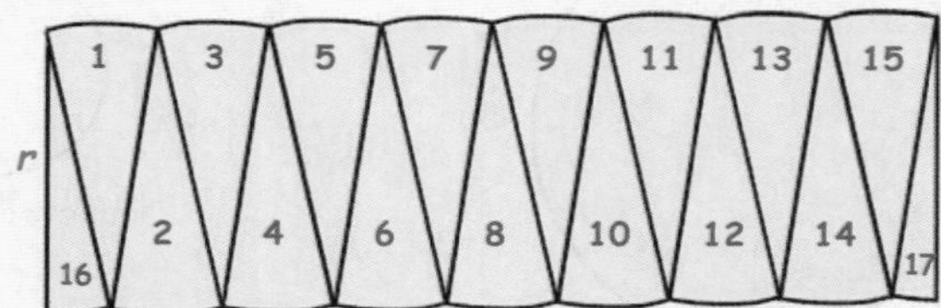

Our circle has turned into a better looking rectangle.

If you kept doing this with more and more cuts, the circle would look even more like a rectangle.

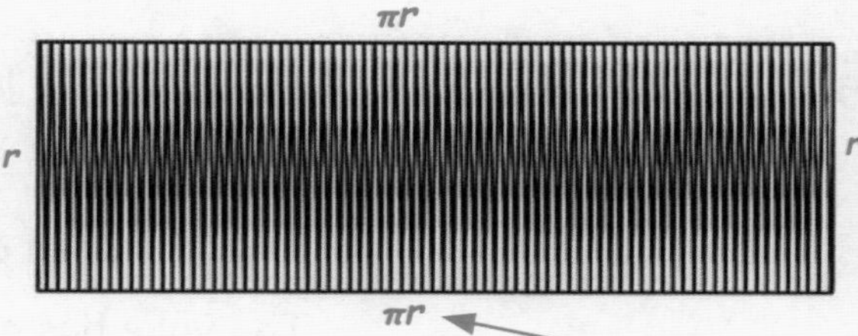

The width of the rectangle is obviously r.

Can you see that the length of the rectangle = $\frac{1}{2}$ of the circumference = $\frac{1}{2}$ of $2\pi r = \pi r$.

This means that, since the area of a rectangle = *length* x *breadth* = $\pi r \times r = \pi r^2$.

=> **Area of a circle = πr^2** or **$A = \pi r^2$.**

Example :- Calculate the area of this circle with radius 5 cm.

$A = \pi r^2$

=> $A = 3{\cdot}14 \times 5 \times 5$

=> $A = 78{\cdot}5 \text{ cm}^2$.

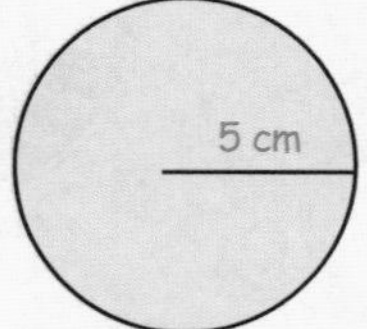

Exercise 1 **Revision** *Give each answer in this exercise correct to 3 significant figures, where possible.*

1. Find the area of a circle with radius 3 cm. **Copy** and **complete** :-

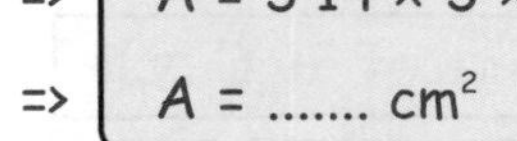

$A = \pi r^2$

=> $A = 3{\cdot}14 \times 3 \times 3$

=> $A = \ldots\ldots\ \text{cm}^2$

2. Calculate the area of each circle below :-
(*You must set down 3 lines of working*).

a

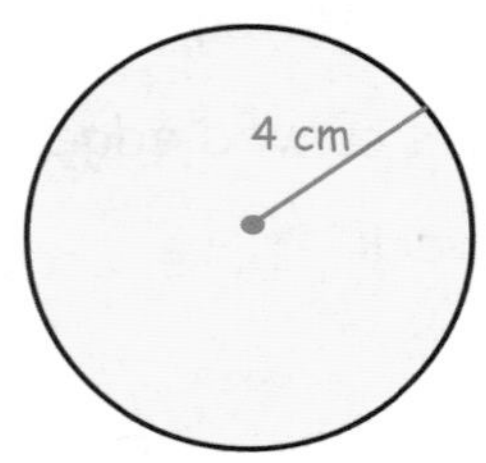

b

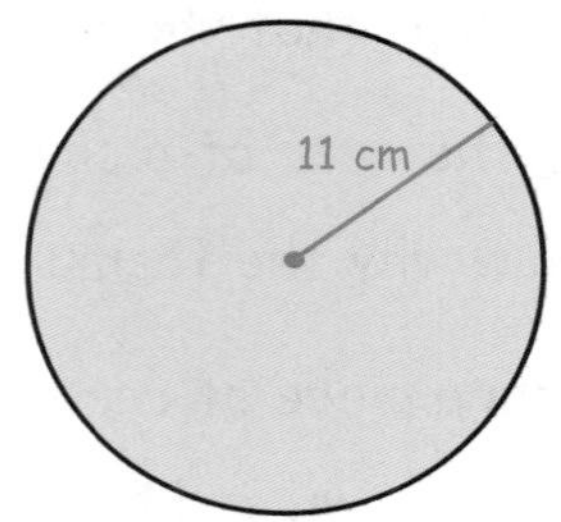

c

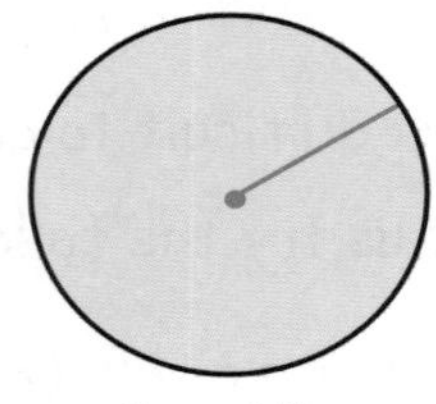

radius = 6·5 cm

3. Find the area of each object below : -

a

coin radius = 14·2 mm

b

top crust radius = 12·5 cm

c

shield radius = 0·5 m

4. Find the area of each circle below : - (*Remember to find the radius first*)

a

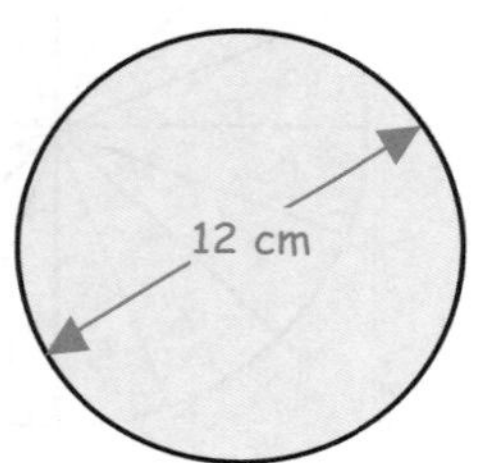

b

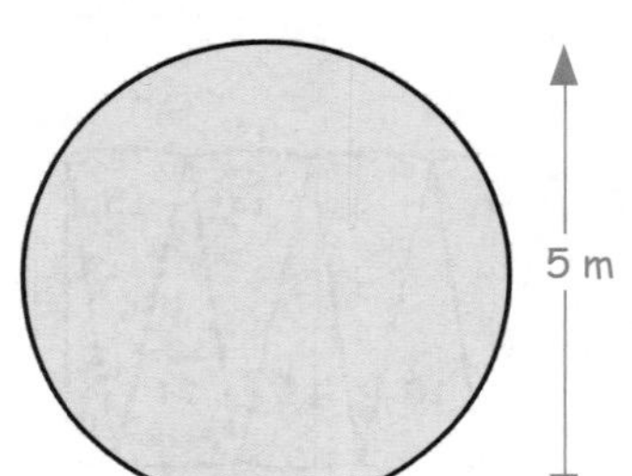

c

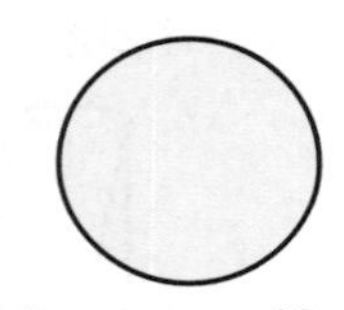

Diameter = 40 mm

5. a The diameter of a golf hole is 10·8 centimetres. Find its area.

b

Find the area of the circular yoke in this fried egg.
The yoke has a radius of 2·1 cm.

c Find the area of the lid of this drinks carton with diameter 66 mm.

d

This no entry sign has a radius of 0·25 metres.
Find the area of the sign.

Circle Problems

Example :- Calculate the area of Sandy's semicircular lawn.

$$A = \pi r^2$$

=> $A = 3{\cdot}14 \times 6{\cdot}2 \times 6{\cdot}2$

=> $A = 121$ m (*to 3 sig figs.*)

Area of Circle = $121\ m^2$

Area of semicircle = $60{\cdot}5\ m^2$

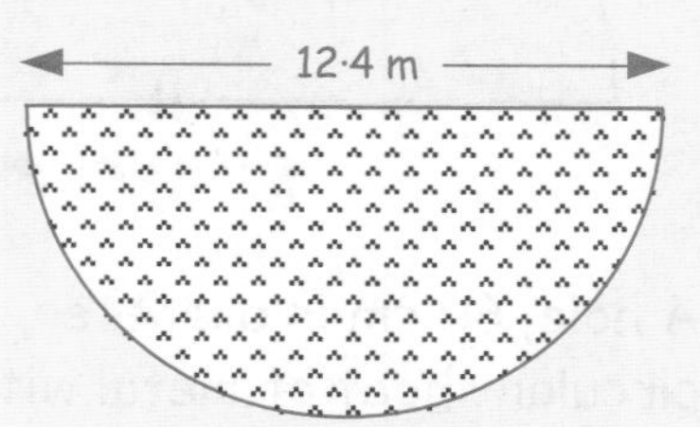

* For a quarter circle ... find the area of the full circle and then ÷ 4.

* For a composite shape ... find the area of each part and add.

Exercise 2

1. Find the area of each semicircle : -

a
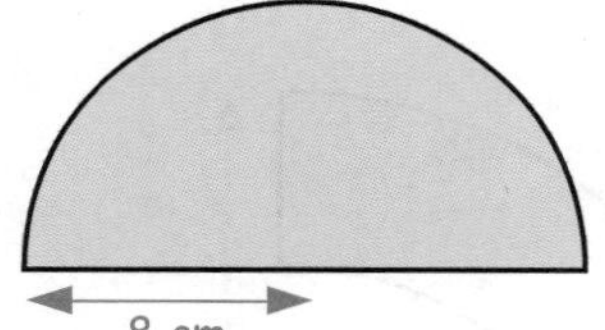

b
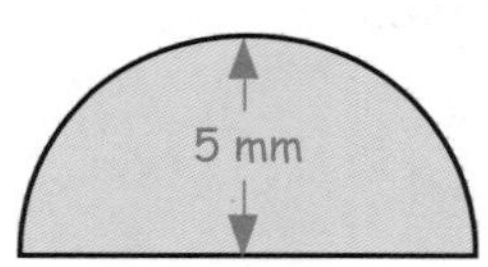

c
4·4 m

2. Find the area of each of these quarter circles : -

a
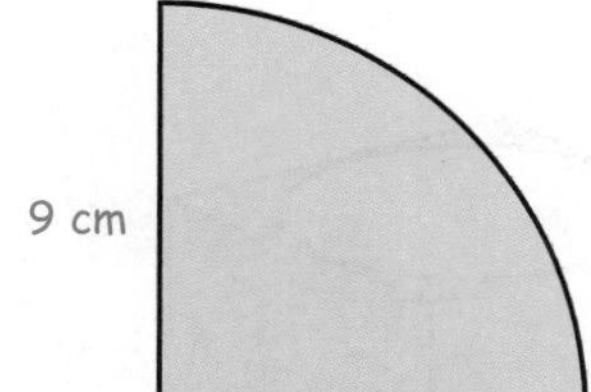

b
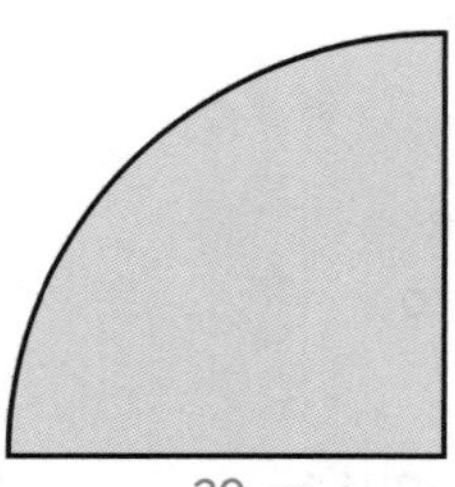

c
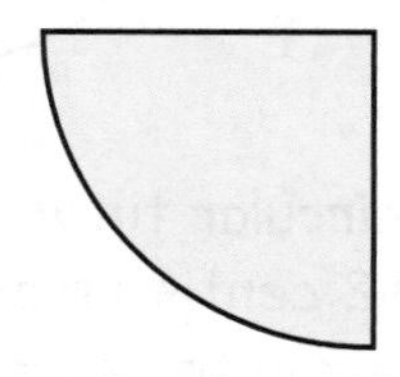

Quarter circle with 1·6 metre diameter

3. Find the area of each of the shapes below :-

a
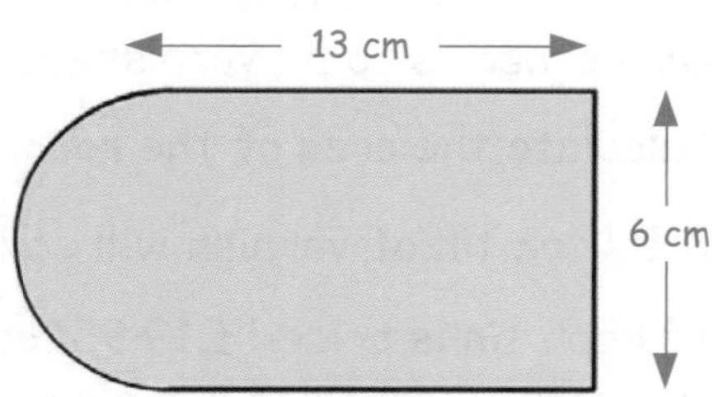

b
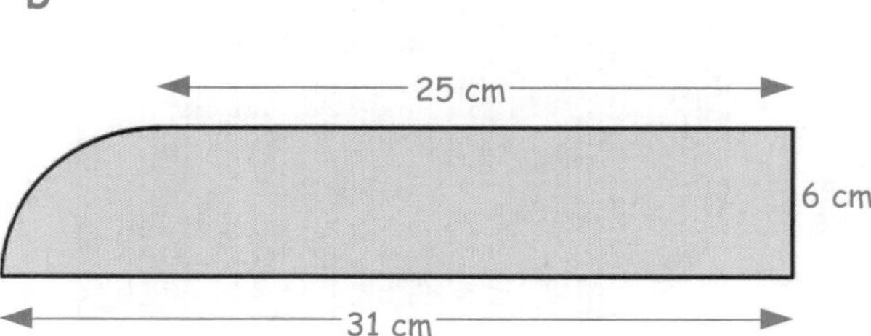

3. c

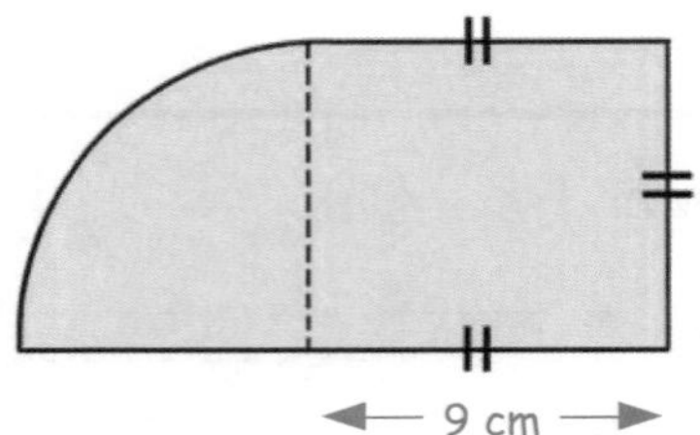

d

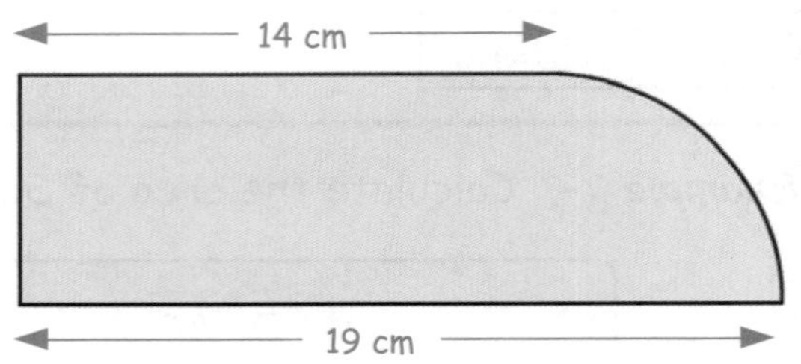

4. A hole, 60 cm in diameter, has been cut from a flat circular sheet of metal with a 60 cm radius.

Find the area of the metal remaining.

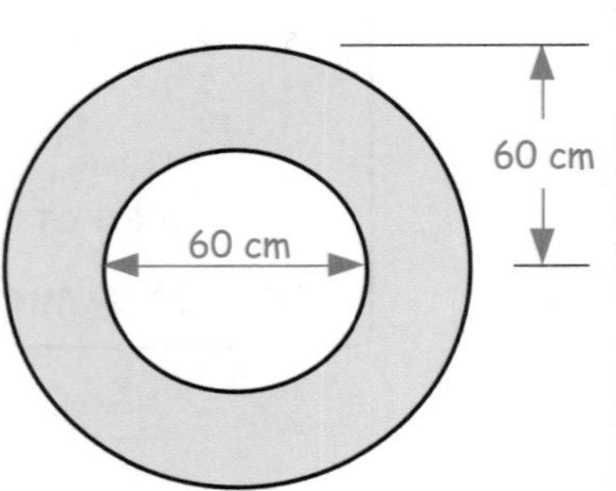

5.

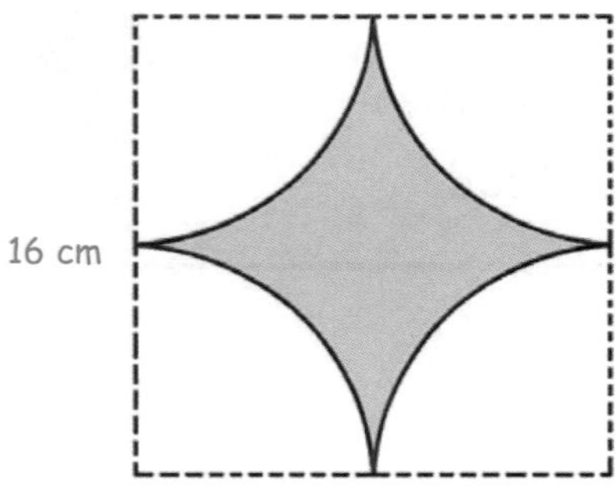

A square with side 16 centimetres has four identical quarter circles cut out from each corner as shown.

Calculate the area of the part remaining.

6. Find the area of each of these shapes : -

a

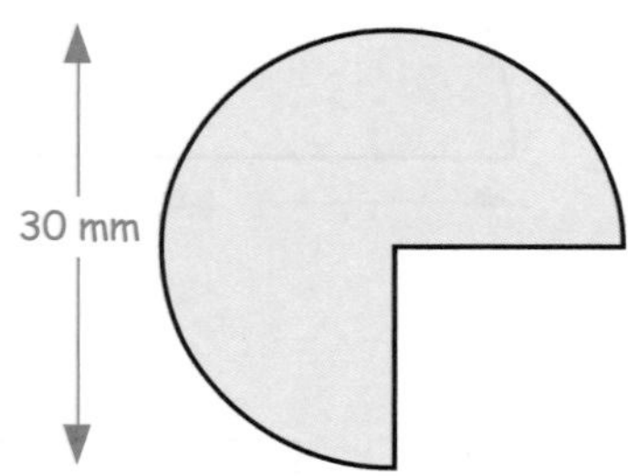

b

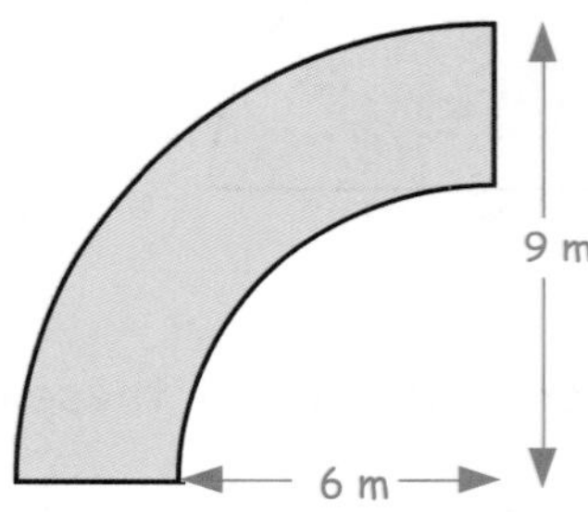

7. A circular tin with circumference 94·2 centimetres fits exactly into a box in the shape of a cuboid.

Calculate the diameter of the cylinder and hence find the volume of the tin.

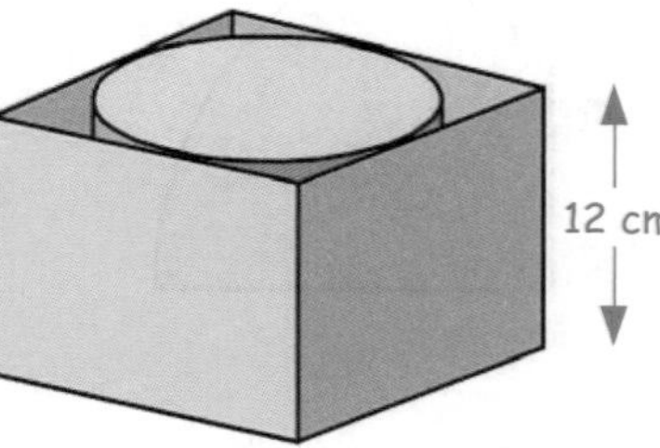

8.

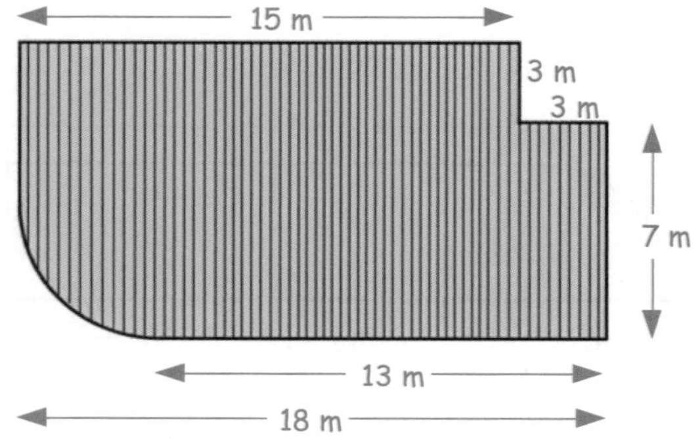

The floor of this meeting room, with a quarter circular corner, is to be varnished.

a Calculate the area of the room's floor.

b A 5 litre tin of varnish will cover 20 m^2.

If each tin is priced £19·95, calculate the cost of covering the floor with two coats of varnish.

9. The radius of this circular disc is given as (12 ± 0·5) cm.

Calculate the maximum and the minimum values of its area.

(Use $\pi = 3{\cdot}14$).

(12 ± 0·5) cm

10. A new church is being built and there is a competition to design the stained glass window.

Here are the three finalists' designs :-

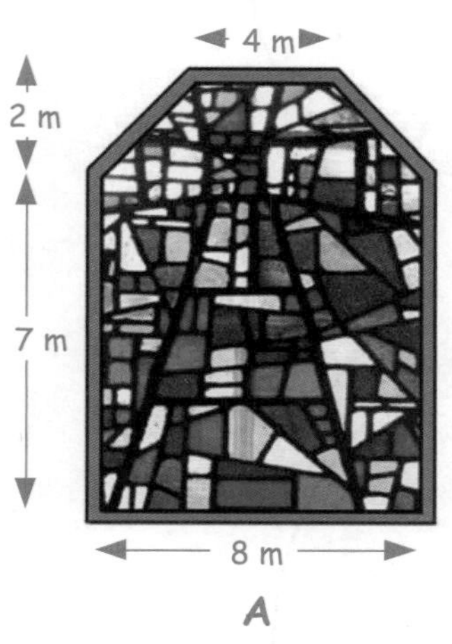

A

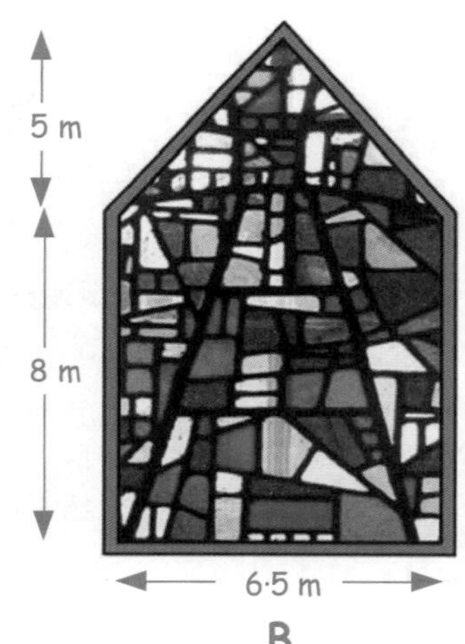

B

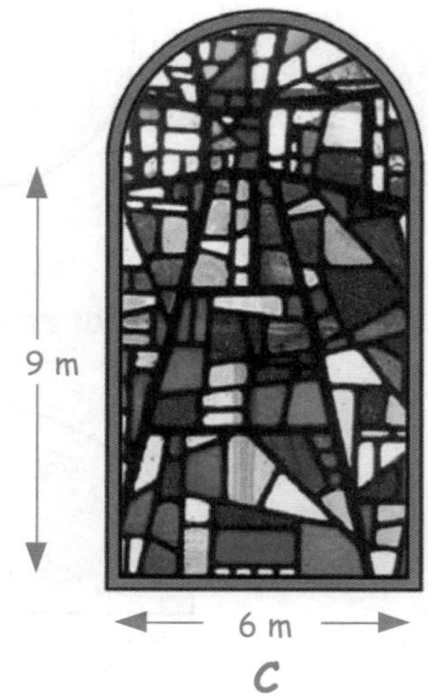

C

Which window design will let in most light ? (*Support your answer with working*).

11. Shown is a lawn which needs re-turfed.

a Calculate the area of the lawn.

b If new turf costs £1·80 per m^2 and the labour costs £105, calculate how much it would cost to re-turf the lawn.

(*Round the lawn's area to the nearest m^2*).

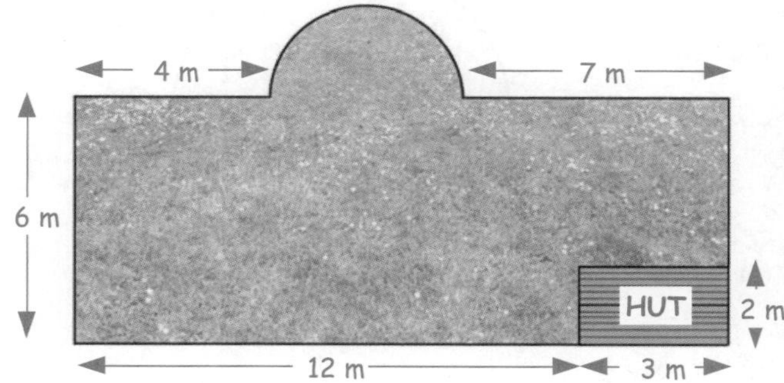

12.

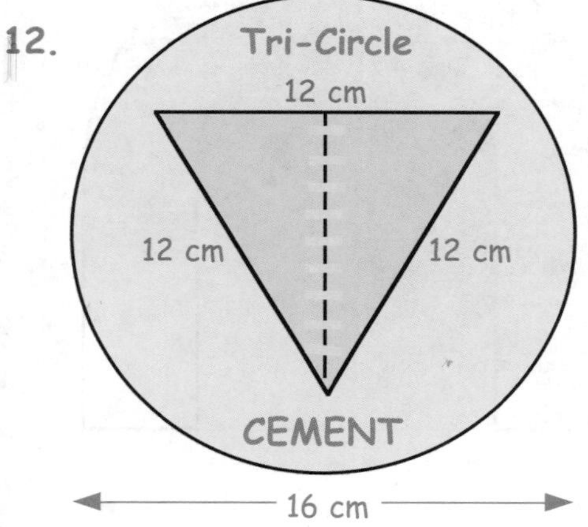

This is a possible design for the logo for the *Tri-Circle Cement*" company.

The company stipulated that the area of the triangle should be between 30% and 35% of the area of the circle.

Does the design meet the company's specification ?

Geometry/Measure Assessment 7

1. Calculate the area of each of these circles :-

a

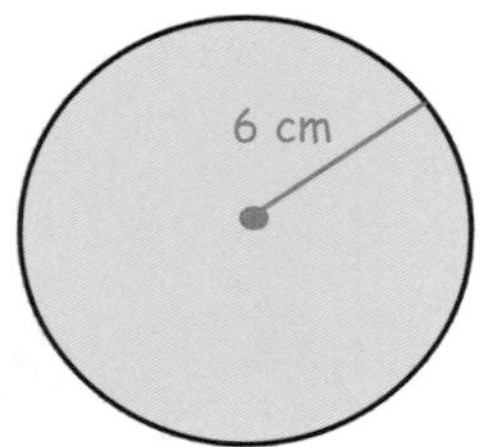

b

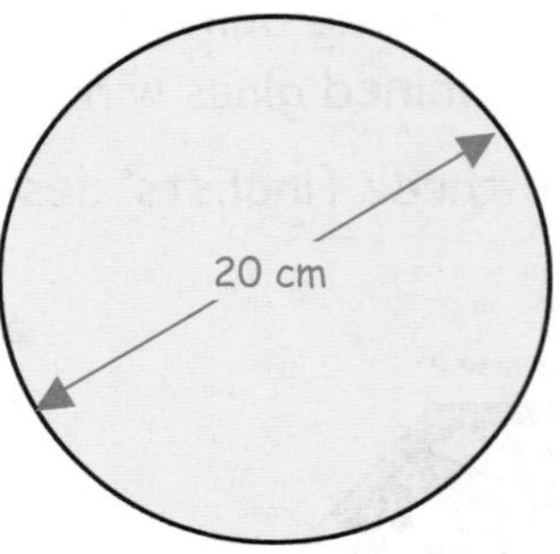

2. Find the area of the semicircle and the quarter circle :-

a

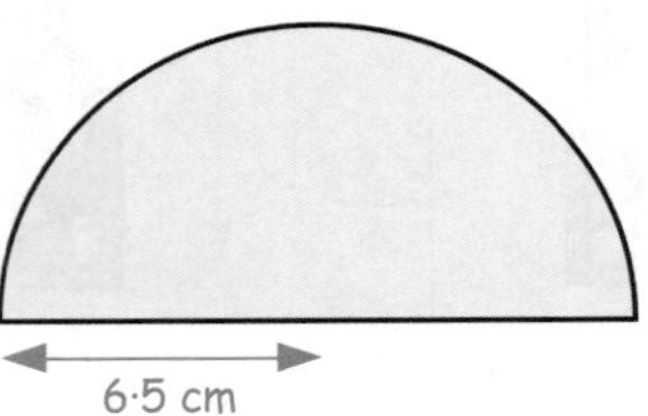

b

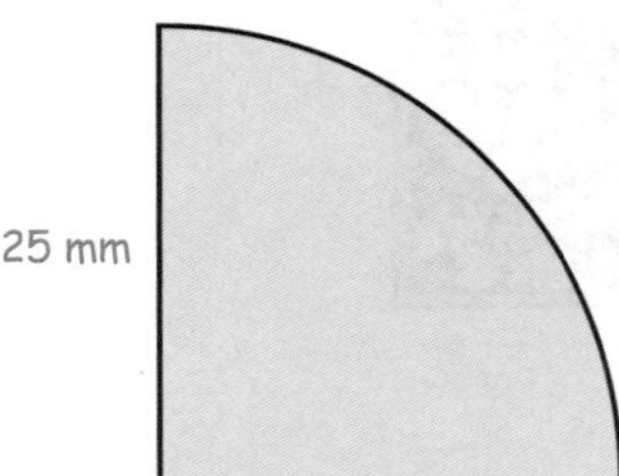

3. Find the area of both of these shapes :-

a

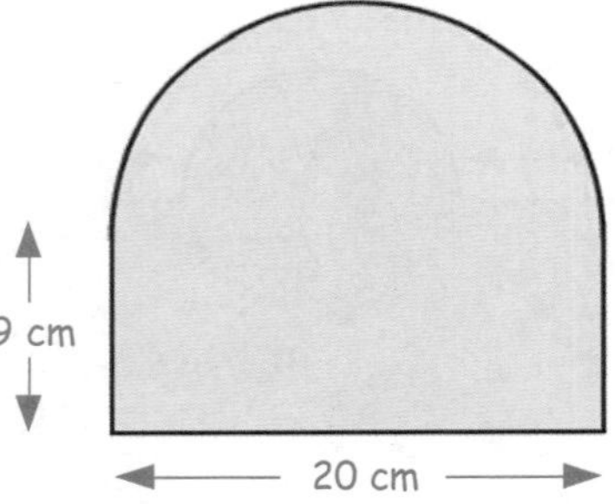

b

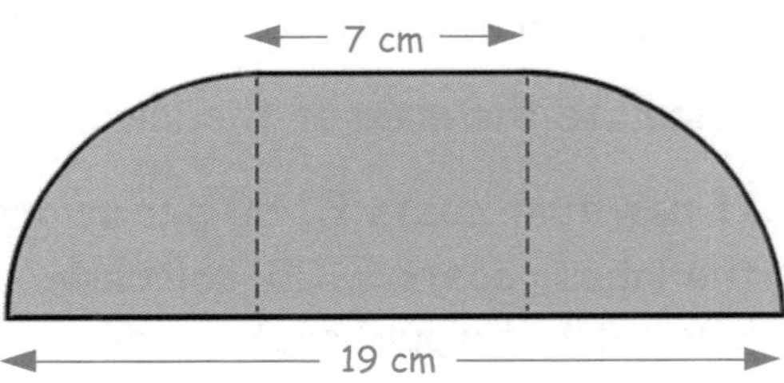

4. The brick wall entrance to this tunnel is to be painted white. It will require 2 coats of paint.

   a Calculate the area of the brickwork that needs to be painted, in m^2.

   The paint comes in 1 litre tins and each tin can cover 5 m^2.
   A range of paints can be bought costing £(22·50 ± 2·75) per tin.

   b How much will it cost to paint the wall using the cheapest quote ?

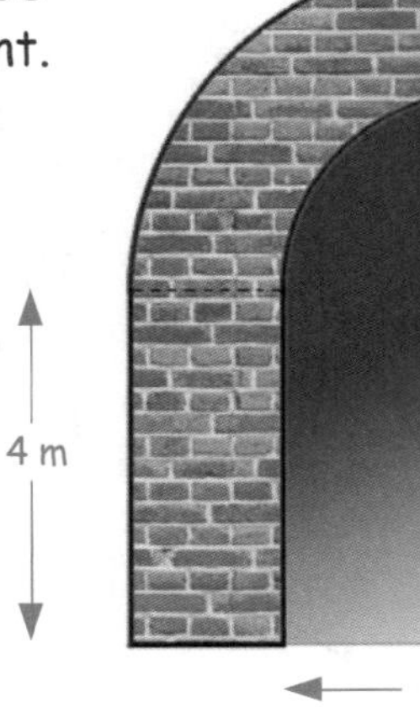

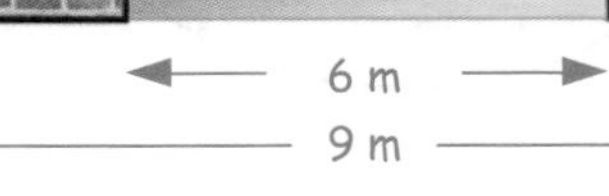

Problem Solving

Revision of Problem Solving

1. A 3 metre long shelf holds identical copies of an encyclopaedia.

   If each book is 4·5 cm in width, what is the maximum number of books the shelf can hold ?

2. A wall, 12 metres long by 2·5 metres high, is to be wallpapered.

   Each roll of wall paper is 60 cm wide and is 8 metres long when unrolled.

   a How many rolls of wallpaper are required ? (*Assume no pattern - hence no extra wastage*).

   b Each roll of wallpaper costs £27·85.

   A small packet of paste costs £1·35, and each packet will cover 3 rolls of paper.

   What will it cost to paper this wall ?

3. 

   A truck has a storage capacity 3 m long by 2 m wide by 2 metres high.

   What is the maximum number of boxes that the truck can hold if each box measures :-

   a 50 cm by 50 cm by 50 cm

   b 30 cm by 25 cm by 20 cm ?

4. A large aluminium sheet consisting of a square and a right angled triangle, is as shown.

   Find the area of this metal sheet.

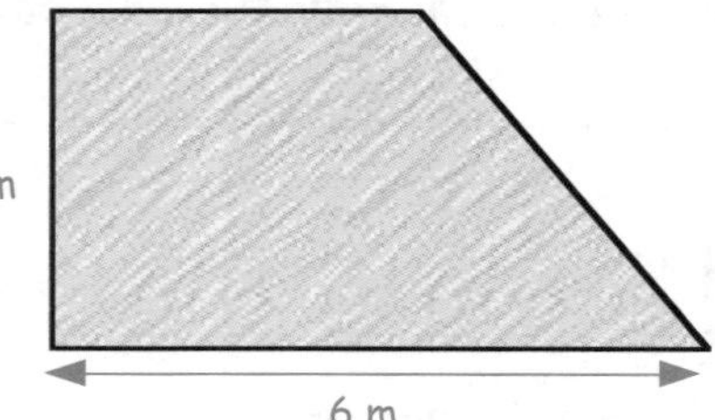

5. A rectangular assembly hall 18 m by 15 m is to have its floor replaced.

   - It costs £8·50 per square metre to lift the existing floor.
   - The flooring comes in 60 cm square sections costing £7·90 each.
   - Labour works out at £65 for every 10 square metres.

   Can the floor be replaced for under £10 000 ? (*A sketch might help*).

Chapter 18 Problem Solving

Real Life Problems involving Volume

Problems involving space and volume occur often in everyday life.

Example :-

A storage unit is in the shape of a cuboid, 3 m by 4 m by 2 m high.

What is the maximum number of boxes 80 cm by 75 cm by 50 cm that will fit into the unit ?

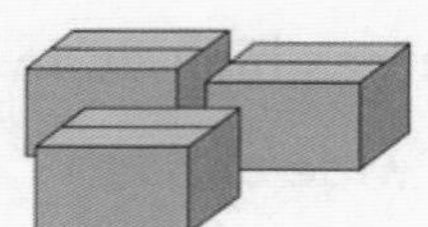

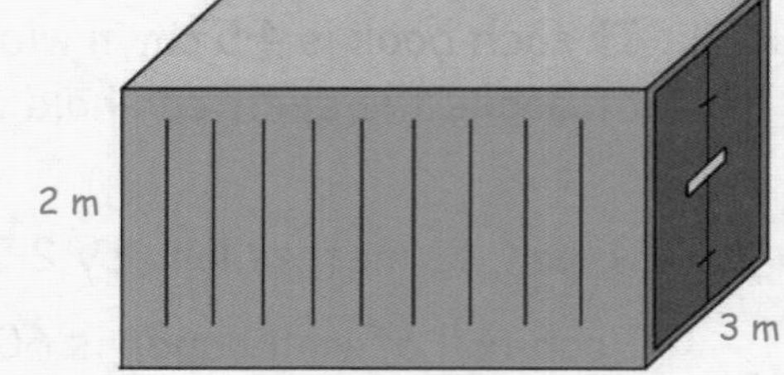

Step 1 :-

Length (3 m) => 300 cm ÷ 80 cm = **3 boxes.** *(wasted space)*

Breadth (4 m) => 400 cm ÷ 75 cm = 5 boxes.

Height (2 m) => 200 cm ÷ 50 cm = 4 boxes.

*Unit will hold 3 x 5 x 4 = **60** boxes.*

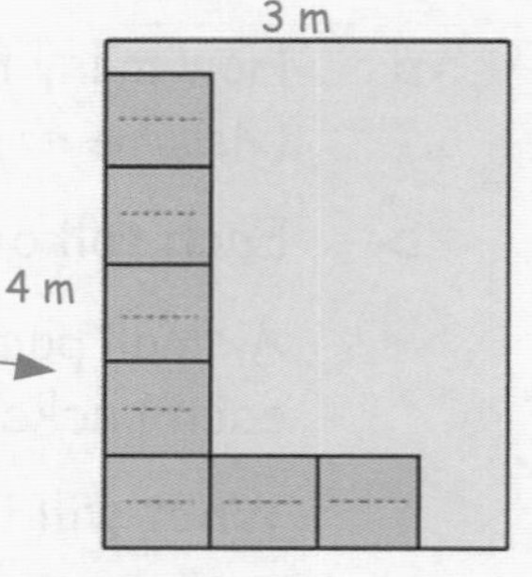

However, we could configure the boxes in a different way by turning the boxes 90°.

Step 2 :-

Length (3 m) => 300 ÷ 75 cm = 4 boxes.

Breadth (4 m) => 400 ÷ 80 cm = 5 boxes.

Height (2 m) => 200 ÷ 50 cm = 4 boxes.

*Unit will hold 4 x 5 x 4 = **80** boxes.*

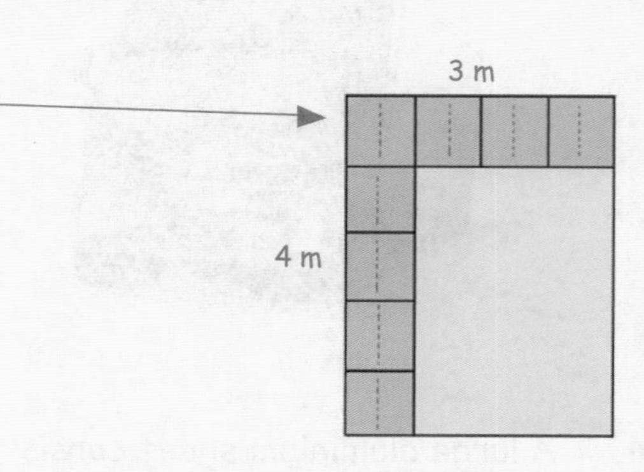

The space will hold a maximum of 80 boxes.

Exercise 1

1. What is the maximum number of boxes that will fit into the red storage unit above if the boxes measure :-

   a 1 m by 1·5 m by 1 m

   b 30 cm by 50 cm by 20 cm

   c 65 cm by 55 cm by 45 cm ? (*Harder !*)

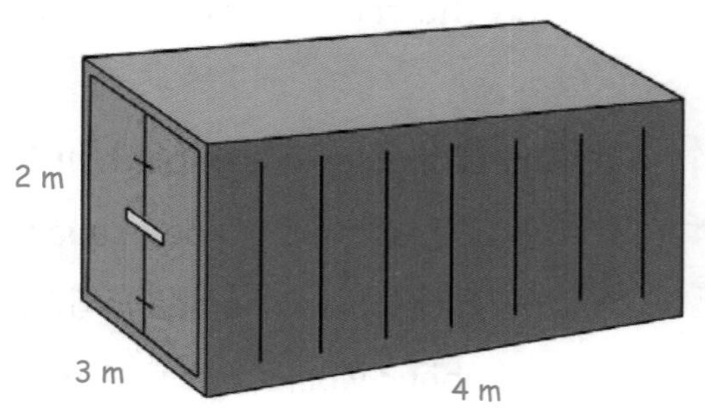

2. A factory warehouse is used to store large metal beams.

The area designated to store these beams is 20 m by 10 m by 3 m.

What is the maximum number of beams that could be stored if each one measures :-

a 4 m by 1·5 m by 1·5 m

b 3 m by 50 cm by 40 cm

c 85 cm by 45 cm by 30 cm ?

3.

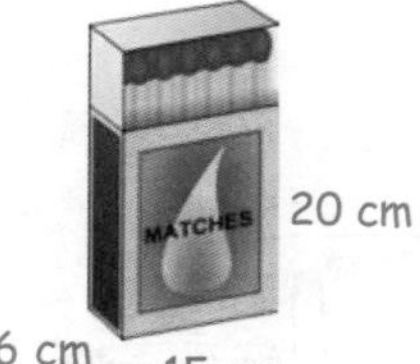

Large match boxes have dimensions as shown.

These boxes are packed into a cardboard box 180 cm by 100 cm by 60 cm.

What is the maximum number of matchboxes that can be packed into the cardboard box ?

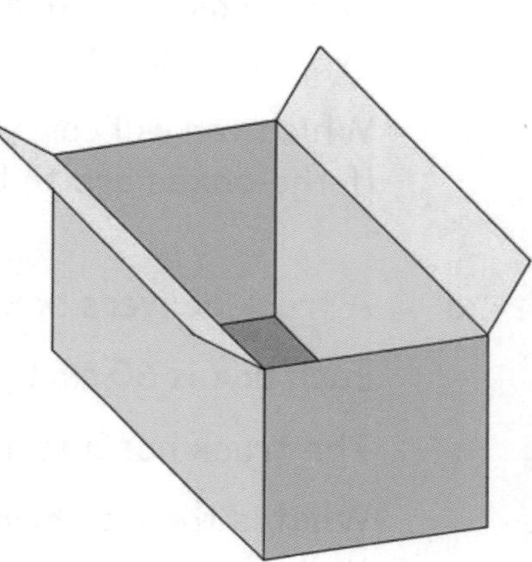

4.

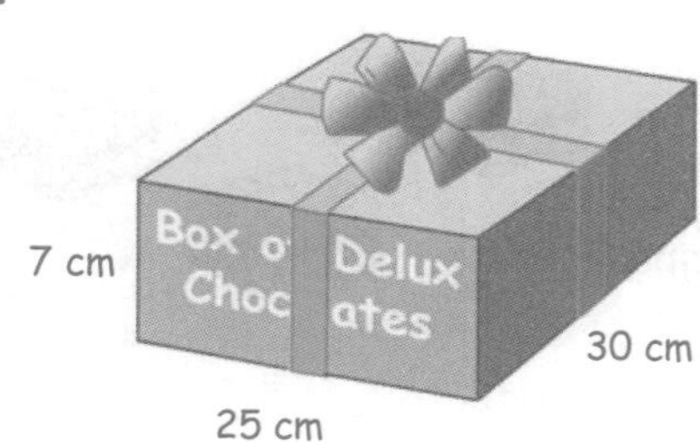

Delux make boxes of chocolates, measuring 30 cm by 25 cm by 7 cm and these are packed into crates for transportation.

Each crate is 1·5 m by 0·75 m by 0·75 m.

Fifty crates are loaded onto a juggernaut.

How many boxes of chocolates are being transported in the juggernaut ?

5. Planks of wood, 2 m long by 30 cm wide by 8 cm deep, are to be stacked in storage containers measuring 4 m by 3 m by 2 m.

These containers are then packed tightly into a warehouse measuring 20 m long by 10 m wide by 7 m high.

a How many planks can be packed into a container ?

b How many planks can be stored inside the containers in the warehouse ?

6. Cartons of Apple Juice measure 7 cm by 5 cm and are 20 cm tall.

The cartons are packed into boxes as shown.

a What is the greatest number of cartons that can be packed into this cardboard box if the cartons must be stored upright ?

b The boxes are to be transported by van and there are 2 types of van available.

Van A has a storage space 2 m long by 1·5 m wide and is 1·5 m high.

Van B has a storage space 1·8 m long by 1·7 m wide and is 1·6 m high.

Which van will carry the greater number of cartons, if the boxes are to be stored upright ? *Explain.*

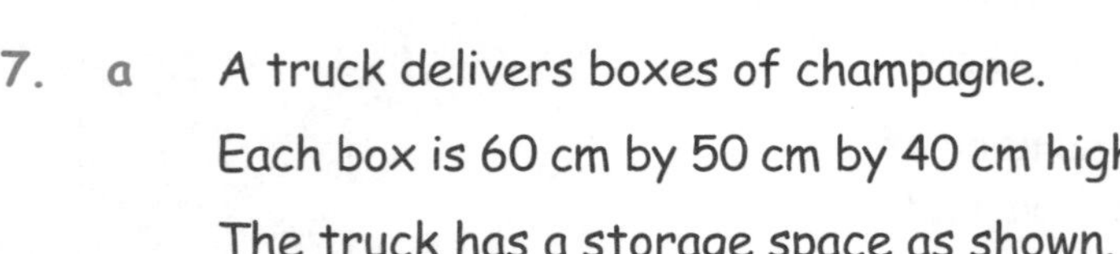

7. a A truck delivers boxes of champagne.

Each box is 60 cm by 50 cm by 40 cm high.

The truck has a storage space as shown.

What is the maximum number of boxes that can be transported if the bottles are to be kept upright ?

b Calculate the volume of wasted space in the truck.

c A second truck has a storage space of 3 m by 3 m by 2 m.

Would this truck be more suitable to carry the champagne ? *Explain.*

8. A ship's hold measures 120 m by 40 m by 16 m high.

Containers, each 11 m long by 7 m wide by 4 m <u>tall</u> are to be transported upright in the ship's hold.

Crates which are 3·5 m by 3 m by 2 m are to be stored in each container.

Each crate has to hold boxes measuring 30 cm by 30 cm by 20 cm.

Each box contains 2 Rag Dolls.

What is the maximum number of Rag Dolls that the ship's hold can carry ?

Problem Solving

Problem solving can be a difficult concept in Mathematics.

There are many different strategies that can be used to solve problems.

Here are just some of them :-

Look for a pattern	*Make an organised list*	*Trial & improvement*
Construct a table	*Draw a diagram*	*Work backwards*
Use a mathematical model	*Use logical reasoning*	*Solve a simpler problem...*

Your teacher may discuss some of these with you.

Exercise 2

You might want to work in pairs or groups for this exercise.

1. The scales shown are in balance.
(i.e. *Each side weighs the same*).

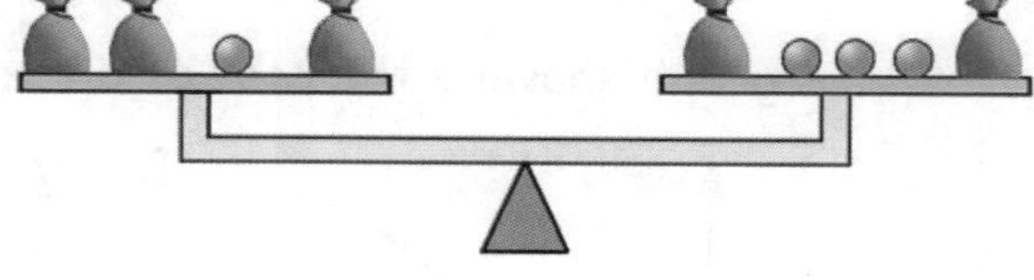

Each bag is the same weight.

Each ball is the same weight.

For each scale below, decide which side of the scale will tip down. *Justify your answer.*

a

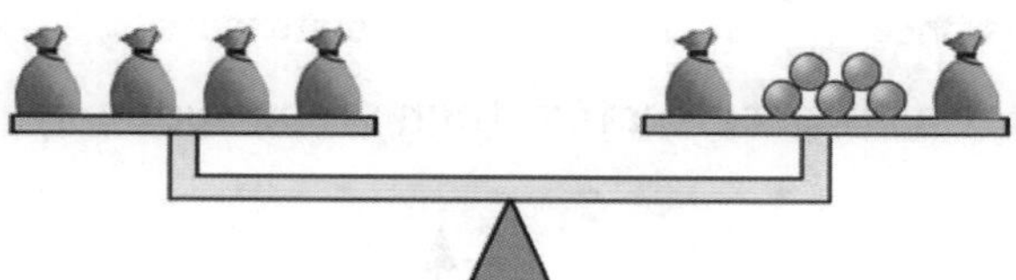

b

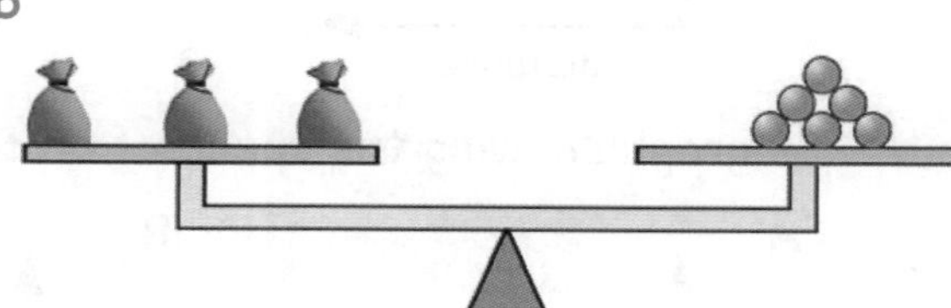

c A situation where on the left scale there are 19 bags and 11 balls and on the right scale there are 22 bags and 6 balls.

2. Sixty four small cubes are placed as shown to make one large cube.

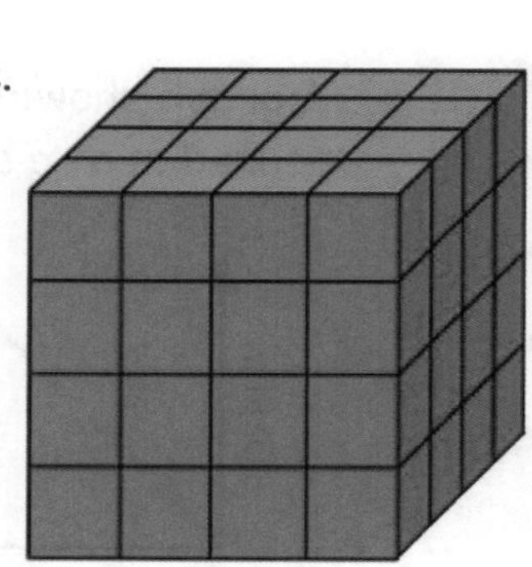

The surface of this large cube is then painted red.

How many of the 64 small cubes will then have :-

a one side red   b two sides red

c three sides red   d no sides red ?

3. Repeat question 2 for a large cube made up of 10 by 10 by 10 smaller cubes whose outside surface is then painted red.

4. Find the sum of the first 100 even positive numbers, 2 + 4 + 6 + 8 + ... without using a calculator !

Hint :- Look at the pattern :-					
	first even number	*2 =*	*2*	*or*	*1 x (1 + 1)*
	first 2 numbers	*2 + 4 =*	*6*	*or*	*2 x (2 + 1)*
	first 3 numbers	*2 + 4 + 6 =*	*12*	*or*	*3 x (3 + ...).*
	first 4 numbers	*2 + 4 + 6 + 8 =*	*20*	*or*	*4 x (... + ...) etc*

5. An old man died and in his will he left these instructions :-

His fortune was to be split as follows :-

- Half to his wife.
- One seventh of what is then left to his son.
- Two thirds of what is then left to his daughter.
- The remaining £2000 to his sister.

How much money did the old man leave altogether ?

6. For each of the following, decide which graph is the most appropriate :-

a A graph showing the cost of a taxi ride based on the distance travelled.

A
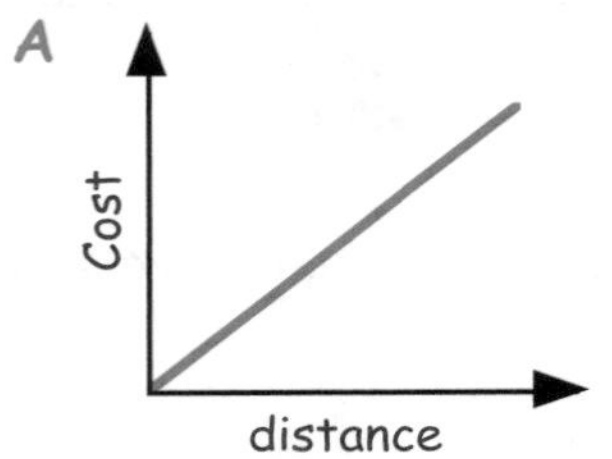

B
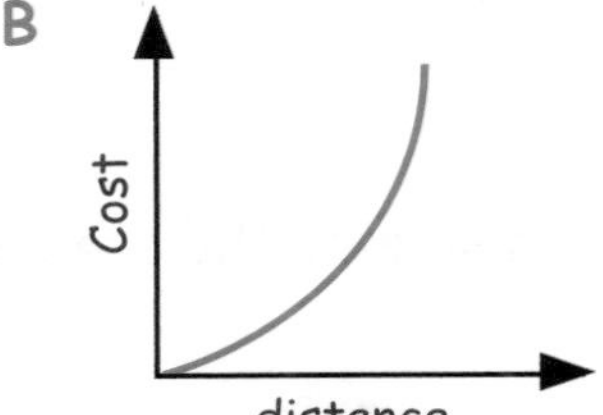

C
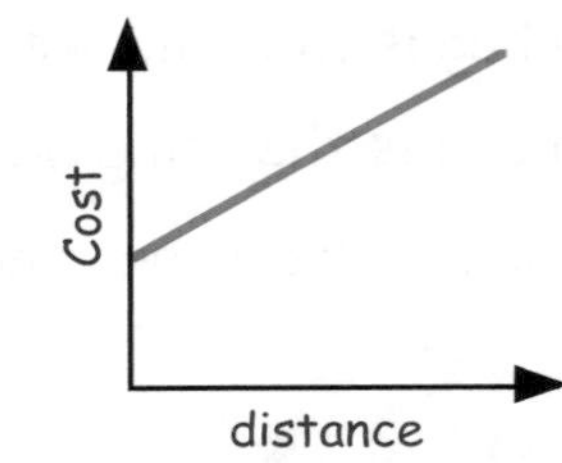

b A graph showing the speed of an object as it accelerates, then stops suddenly.

A
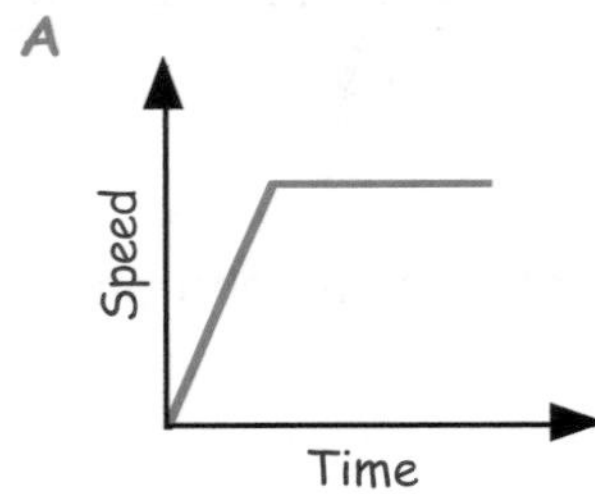

B
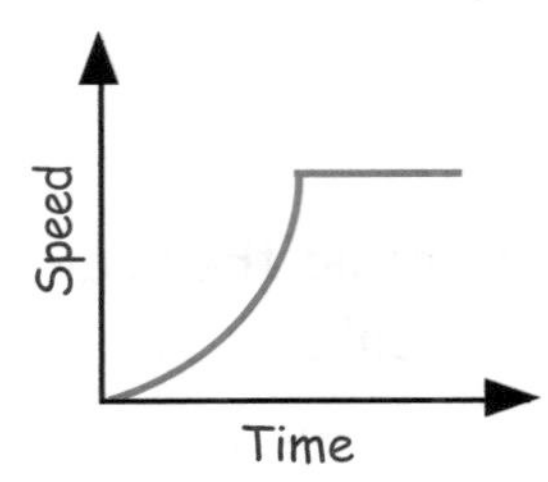

C
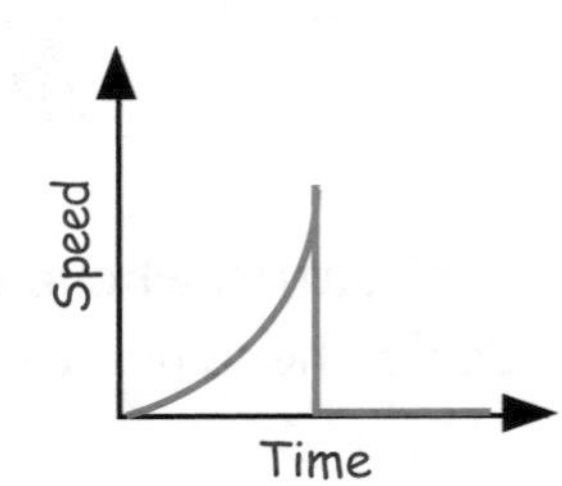

c A graph showing the depth of water in a conical paper cup as water is poured in at a steady rate.

A
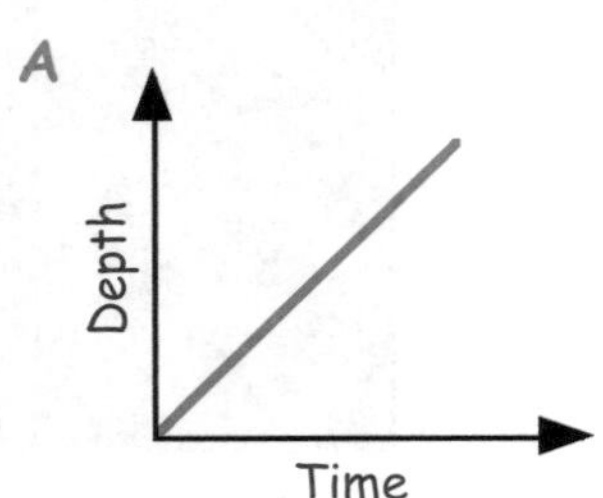

B
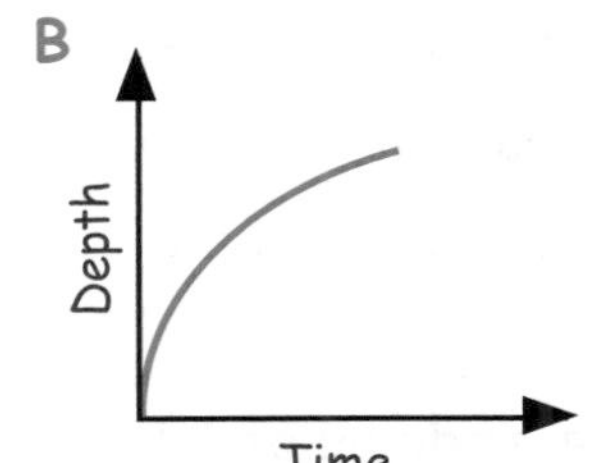

C
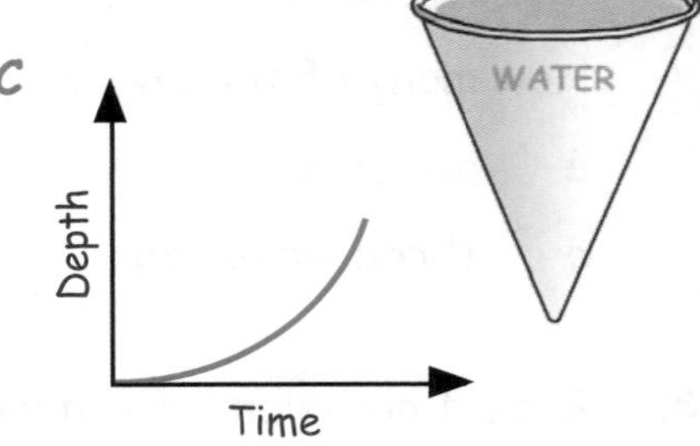

6. d A graph showing the heart rate of a man walking, then running, then stopping.

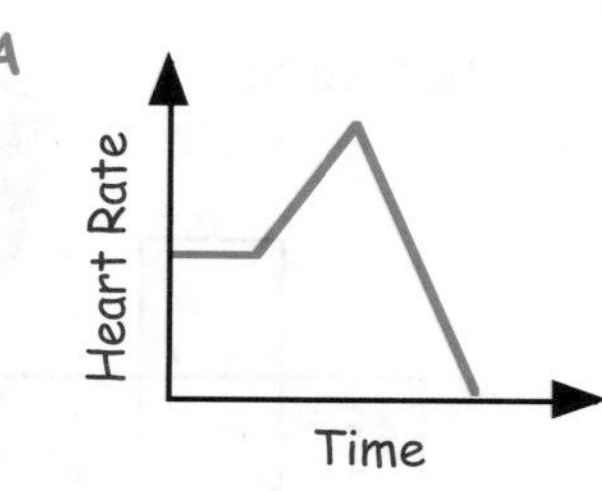

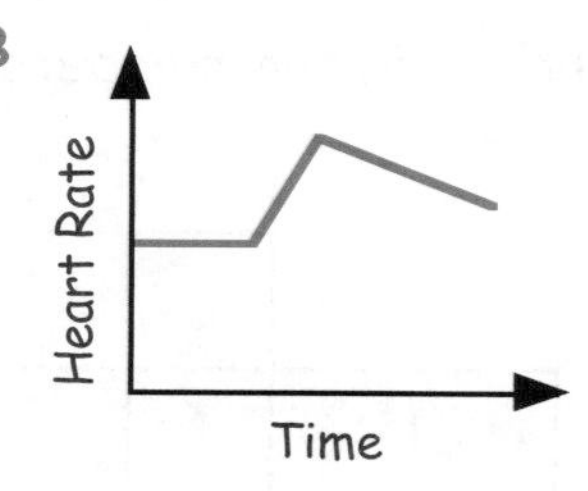

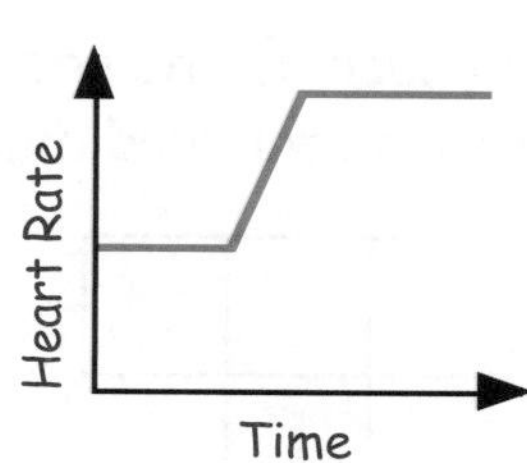

7. A janitor is responsible for turning the heating on and off in a school.

The temperature in a classroom, on a cold day, is recorded from 6 am to 6 pm.

Sketch a possible graph to show the general changes in temperature.

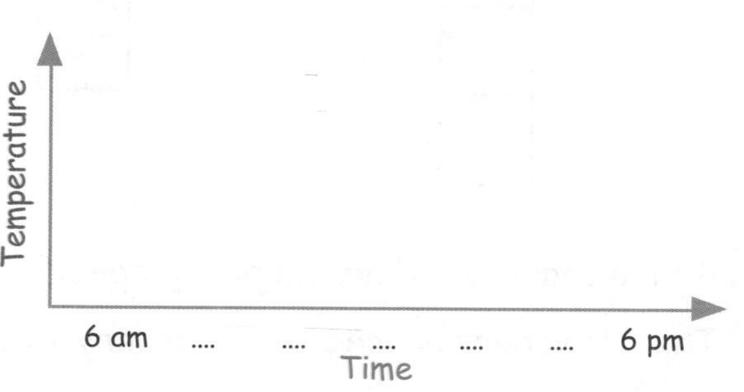

8. One of these containers, when full, holds exactly 3 litres.

The other, when full, holds exactly 5 litres.

There are no markings on the containers.

a Explain how, by filling and emptying the two containers, you can measure exactly **1 litre**.

b Now explain how you can use them to measure out **4 litres**.

9. I was driving along the A5554, when I saw this road sign.

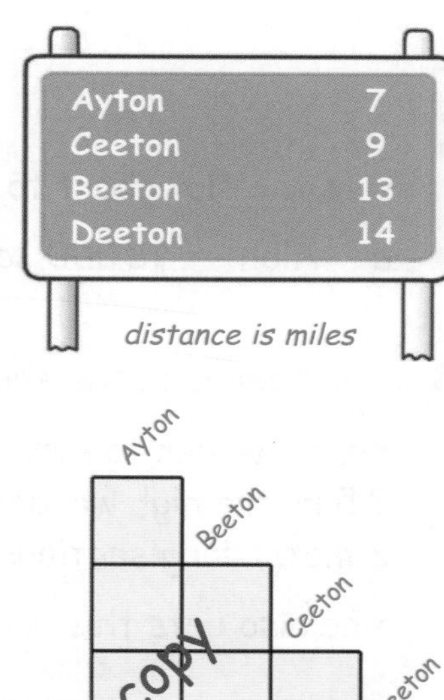

I knew the towns were ahead of me like this :-

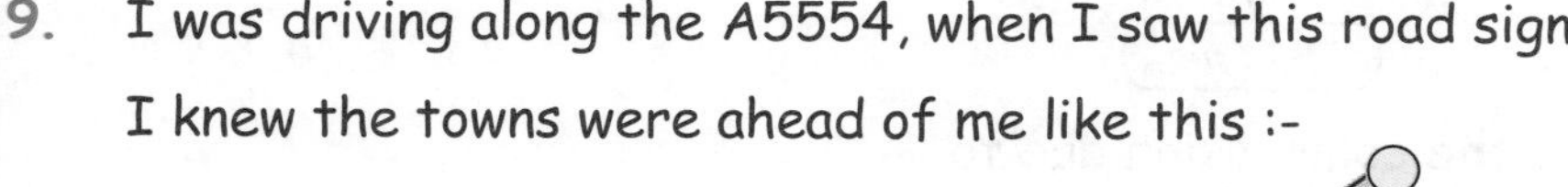

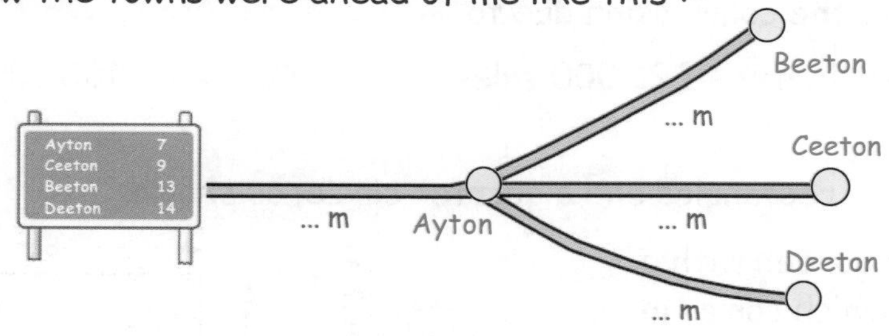

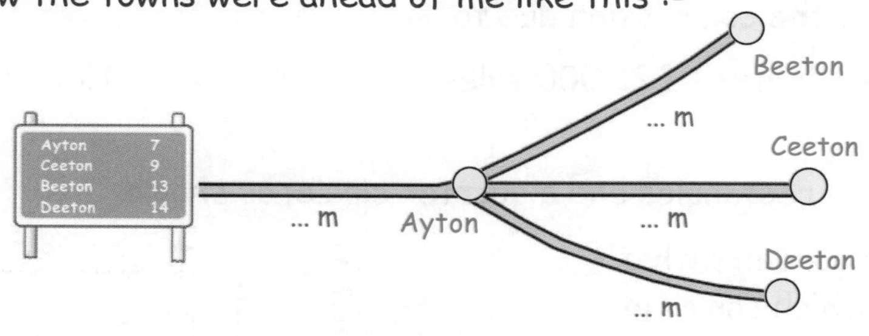

a Sketch the map and fill in the distances, in miles.

b Assuming there are no other roads joining the 4 towns, copy and complete this mileage distance chart.

10. Sara collects £1 coins and loads them into this cylindrical tube.

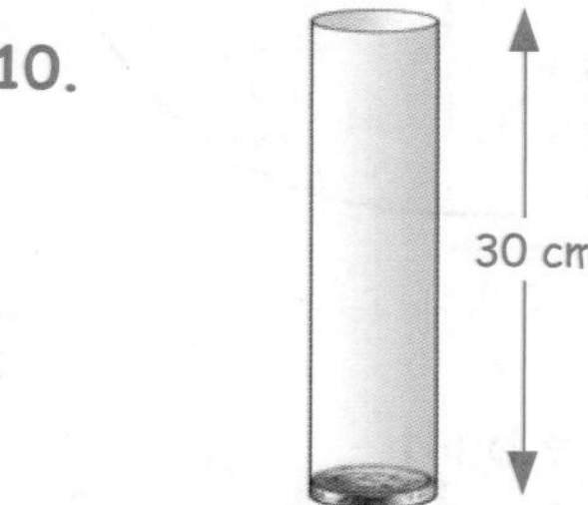

The coins fit exactly into the tube which has an internal diameter of 2·25 cm.

The volume of a £1 coin is known to be 1·25 cm^3.

How many coins can the tube hold ?

11. The numbers on the opposite sides of a standard six sided dice always add up to seven.

Sketch each of the nets below and fill in the numbers 1 to 6 so that each will form a standard dice.

a

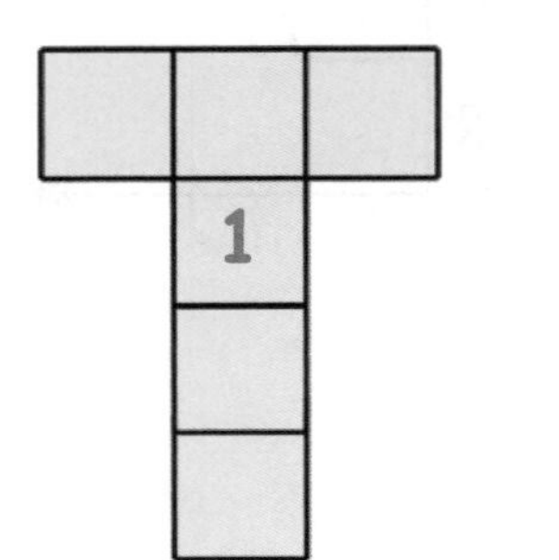

b

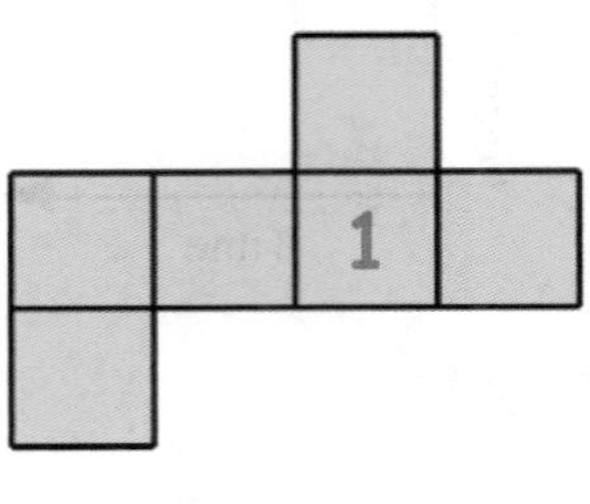

c

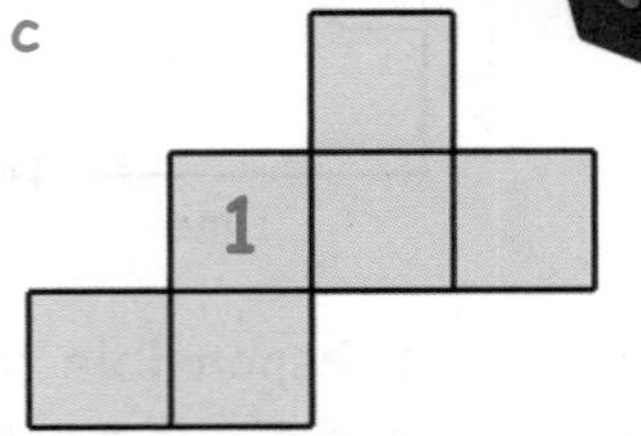

12. A flowchart is a diagram giving specific instructions.

This flowchart is used by a company to calculate commission owed to sales staff.

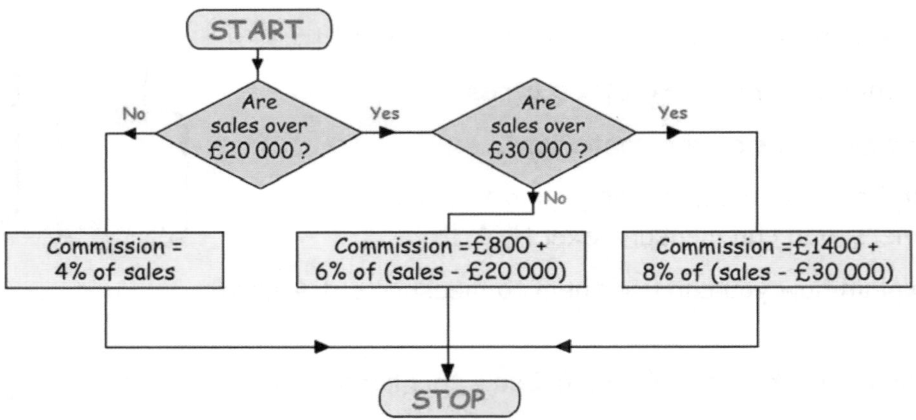

Use the flowchart to calculate the commission due to :-

a Alan - £18 000 sales b Benny - £22 000 sales c Carrie - £100 000 sales.

13. A garden is in the shape of two rectangles and a quarter circle, as shown.

Karen wishes to surround the garden with a 2·5 metre high wooden fence which comes in 2 metre long sections, at a cost of £18·50 each.

2·5 m
2 m

She also gets this quote from a gardening company.

Gardener & Sons		
Labour costs	-	£650
Turf	-	£22 per m^2.

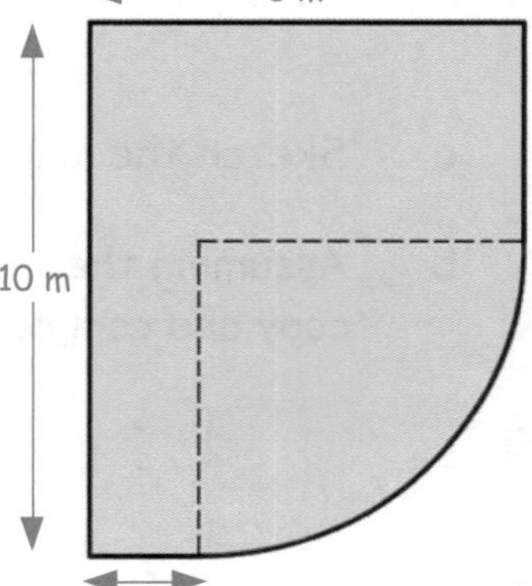

Karen decides to go ahead with the quote from Gardener & Sons.

How much is her total bill for turfing the garden, and having the fence built, if VAT is added on at 20% ?

14. Shown is a red circle with a yellow right angled triangle inside it.

The hypotenuse of this triangle is also the diameter of the circle.

The two shorter sides of the triangle are 6 cm and 7 cm.

Find, *to 3 significant figures*, the total red area.

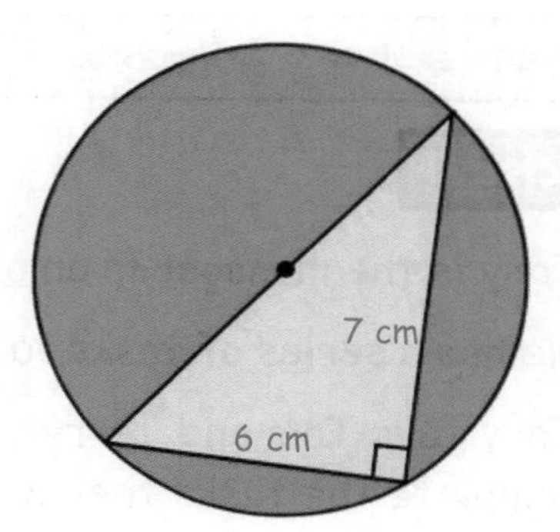

15. A coin is tossed twice and the possible outcomes are shown in this **probability tree**.

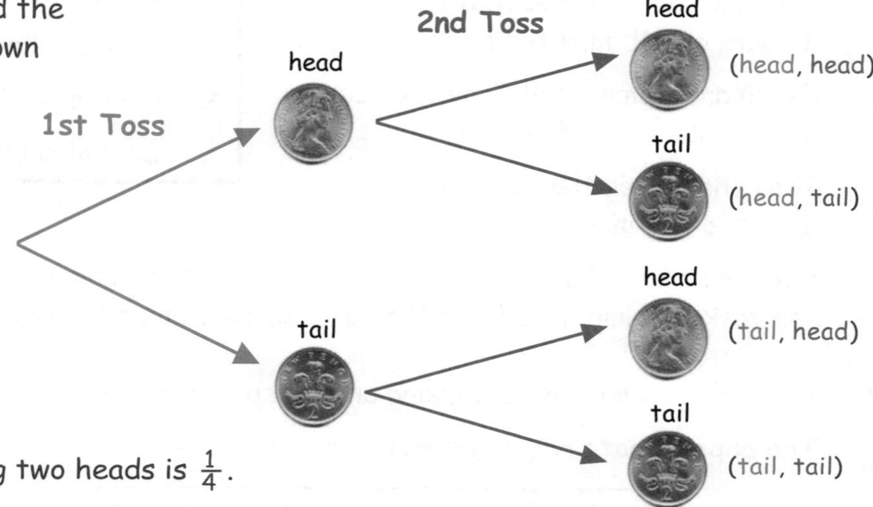

The probability of tossing two heads is $\frac{1}{4}$.

Find :-

a Prob(a head followed by a tail) b Prob(2 tails) c P(a head and a tail).

16. Draw a similar tree, but showing what happens when you toss the coin 3 times. Find :-

a Prob(3 heads) b P(2 tails and 1 head). c P(not all 3 coins are the same).

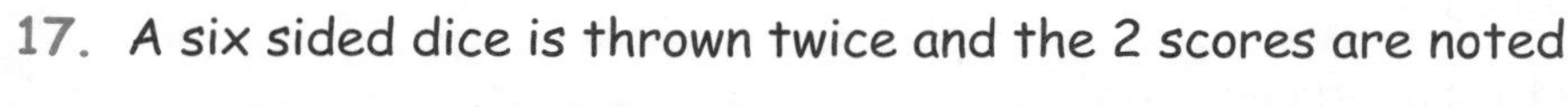

17. A six sided dice is thrown twice and the 2 scores are noted.

a Draw a probability diagram to show all the possibilities.

b Find :- (i) P(total = 12)

(ii) P(total = 4).

18. Repeat, but this time roll the dice 3 times.

a Draw a probability diagram to show all the possibilities this time.

b Find :- (i) P(total = 18)

(ii) P(total is less than 5).

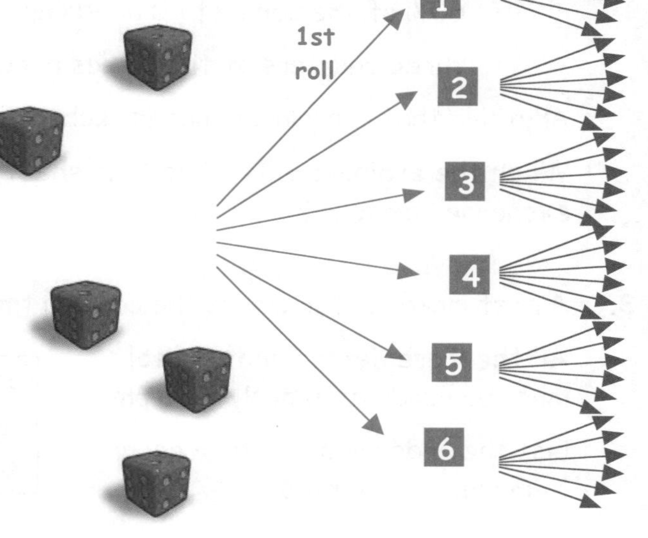

Problem Solving involving Time Management

Exercise 3

1. Tony is the manager in an office.

   He has a series of tasks to be done.

   Tony tells Tom and Jerry that if they complete the tasks they will get a nice bonus at the end of the week.

   Tom and Jerry agree that it will take 8 hours and 15 minutes to do the work.

   Jenna and Jemma tell Tony they can do it in almost half the time.

   Tony then gives the tasks and the bonus to the girls.

	Task	Time it will take 1 person
1.	Create new database on computer	4 hours
2.	File folders into office cabinets	1 hour
3.	Tidy office	30 minutes
4.	Restock main cupboard	2 hours
5.	Do full cupboard inventory	45 minutes.

   Explain using a diagram or table how the girls can complete all of the tasks in almost half the time quoted by Tom and Jerry.

2. A telephone engineer is working on a telephone exchange box.

   The approximate repair times are as follows :-

Replace one cable	2 mins 45 secs
Check one cable	25 secs
Replace cable connector	3 mins 20 secs
Check one cable connector	40 secs

   After a major power surge, the engineer checks all 60 junction boxes at the exchange.

   When he checks them, he finds :-

   - 60% of the connectors need replaced.
   - three quarters of the cables need replaced.

   Anything that is replaced, needs rechecked.

   When the engineer fills in his time sheet, how long in total did the job on the exchange box take ?

3. A chef makes a dish where the cooking times must be adhered to :-

   All the ingredients for the meal must be ready at exactly 8:30 pm.

   List the order and the time each item must be started.

Steak	- 11 minutes	Broccoli	- 8 minutes
Potatoes	- 27 minutes	Carrots	- 12 minutes
Salad	- 3 minutes	Sauce	- 9 minutes.

4. A large company logo, using mathematical shapes, is to be painted.

Each shape - circle, ellipse, square, rectangle and triangle is fully painted.

Each shape takes 3 minutes to paint.

Each shape must be left to dry before another colour can be applied on top of it.

Each paint takes a different time to dry :-

Red - 2 minutes,

Blue - 4 minutes,

Green - 6 minutes.

What is the shortest time in which the whole logo can be painted and it is all dry ?

5. There are seven jobs to be done to complete a project - constructing a greenhouse.

Each job has a specific time for completion.

Below is a list of the jobs and their completion times.

•	*Place glass into greenhouse*	*2 hours*
•	*Level ground*	*3 hours*
•	*Pour concrete into base*	*30 mins*
•	*Secure greenhouse to concrete*	*15 mins*
•	*Let concrete set*	*8 hours*
•	*Build frame for concrete*	*1 hour*
•	*Build greenhouse frame*	*3 hours.*

The last job must be to place the glass into the greenhouse.

a List the jobs in order.

b What activities can be done at the same time ?

c What is the minimum time taken for this project ?

6. A gardener is paid £12·85 per hour. He painted the shed which needed 2 coats.

Each coat took 1 hour 30 minutes and a drying time of 2 hours is allowed for each coat.

- Replanting all geranium pots took 1 hour.
- Mowing the lawn took 15 minutes.
- Edging the lawn took 45 minutes.

The gardener then charged Mr Robb £115·65 for 9 hours work, using his standard hourly rate.

Mr Robb agreed with all the individual times but said he would not pay him for nine hours work.

How much should he pay the gardener ?

(*Explain your reasoning, possibly with a diagram or table, and show all working*).

Problem Solving

Geometry/Measure Assessment 8

1. A boy opened a box which was **completely full** of identical shaped coloured toy bricks measuring 7 cm by 5 cm by 3 cm.

   Calculate how many bricks were in the box.

2. Sue is asked by her boss to stack these 8 parcels side by side onto the two shelves below.

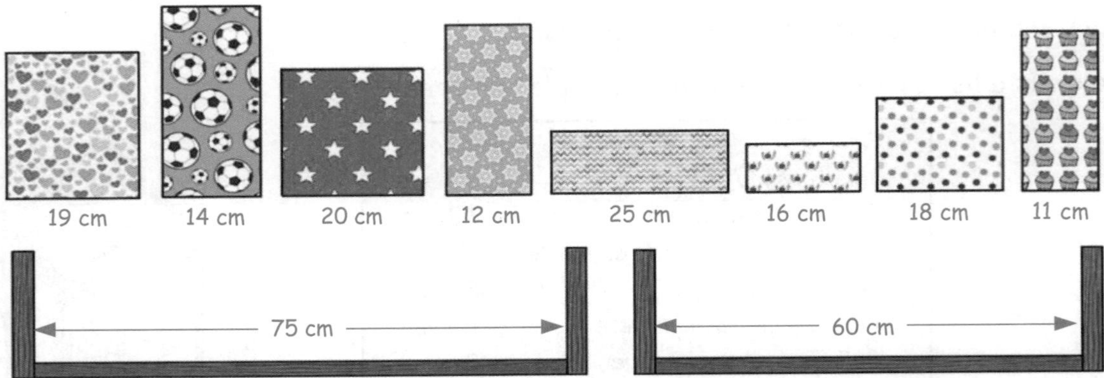

   She manages it with no room to spare. Show how Sue managed to do this.

3. Bill and Ted decide to build a 3 drawer bedside cabinet.

   Here are the tasks required to be done :-

• open the flat pack and lay out pieces	10 mins
• count all the screws	6 mins
• join left side to top	8 mins
• join right side to top	8 mins
• join base plinth to left and right sides	10 mins
• fit back panel to frame with panel pins	12 mins
• make up 3 drawers	10 mins each
• fit 3 handles	7 mins each
• tidy up and throw out packaging	5 mins

   a Draw up and complete this diagram.

   b What is the quickest time the 2 men can build the unit and tidy up ?

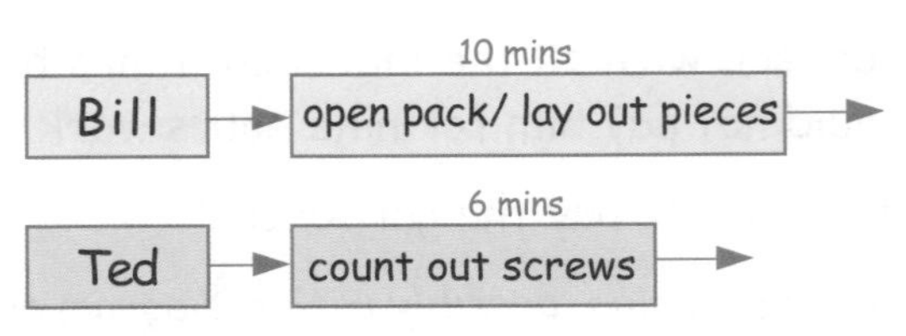

Volume 2

Revision of Volume

1. Calculate the volume of this cuboid :-

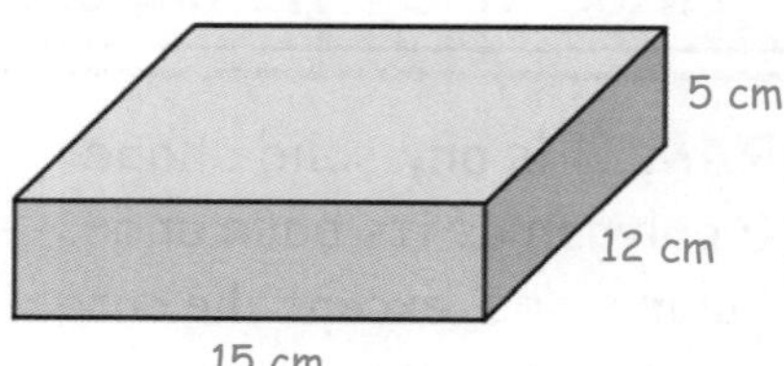

2. This square based cuboid has a volume of 320 cm^3. Calculate what its height must be.

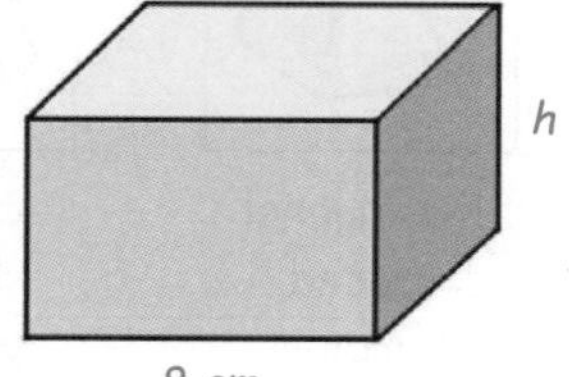

3. a Calculate the volume of this old fashioned petrol can, in cm^3.
   b How many millilitres of petrol will it hold when full ?
   c 1 gallon = 4·5 litres. Will this can hold more than a gallon ?

4. Calculate the volume of this prism.

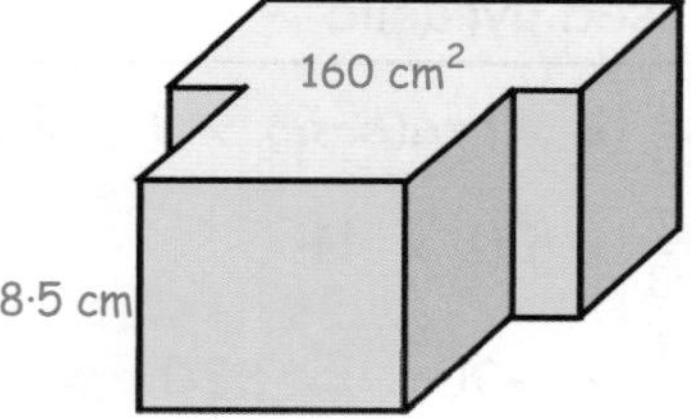

5. a Calculate the area of the triangular end face of this prism.
   b Now calculate its volume.

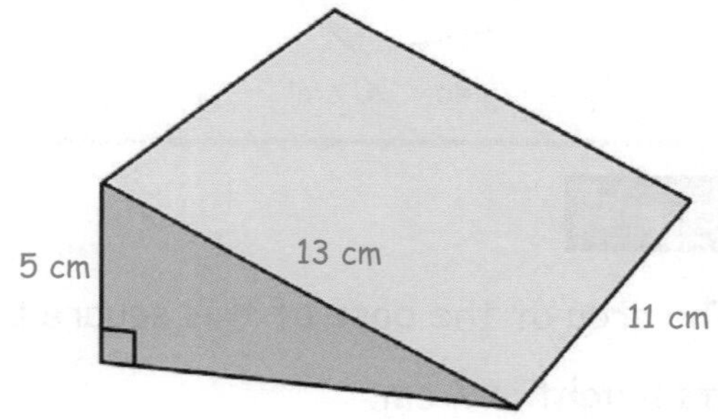

6. If this cylindrical tin is filled to the brim with water, will it be able to hold 6 litres ?

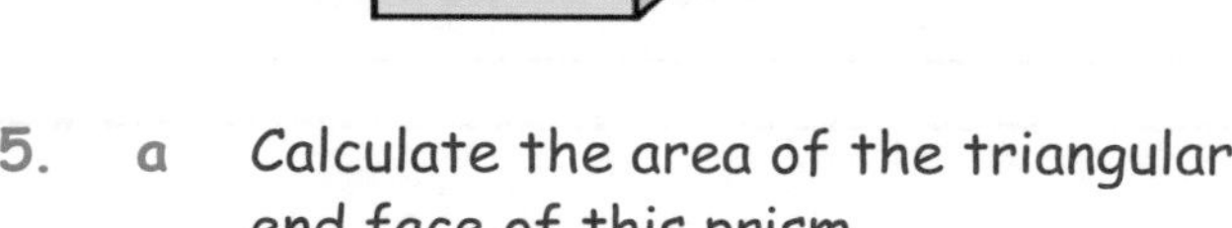

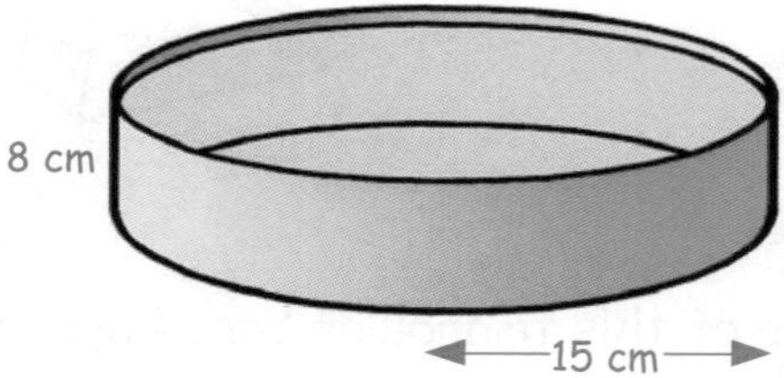

7. Calculate the length in part a and the radius in part b below :-

a

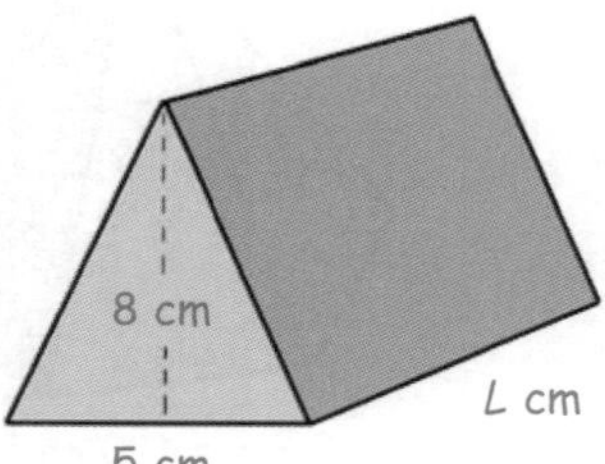

b

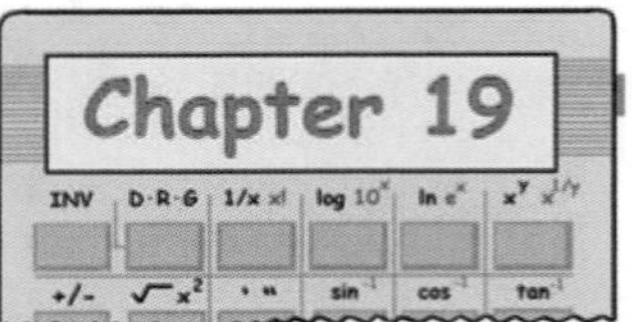

Volume 2

The Volume of a Pyramid and a Cone

A PYRAMID is any solid shape with a polygon as its base and triangular sides, except the cone, with a common vertex.

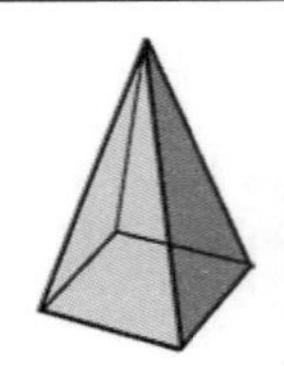
square based pyramid

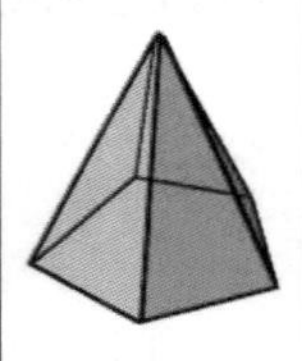
pentagonal based pyramid

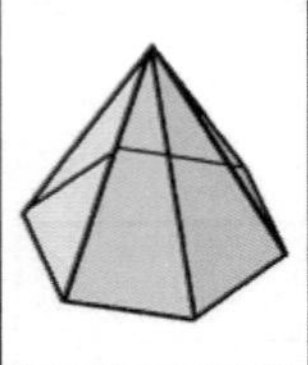
hexagonal based pyramid

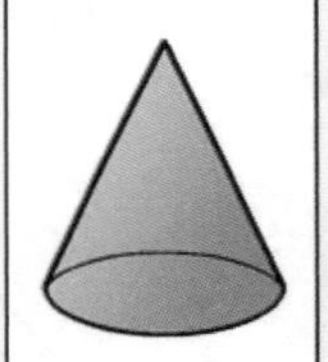
circular based pyramid

Volume of a Pyramid

It is possible to calculate the volume of a pyramid if you know the area of the base.

VOLUME (*pyramid*) $= \frac{1}{3} \times$ **Area** (*of base*) $\times$ **height**

$V = \frac{1}{3}Ah$

Example :-

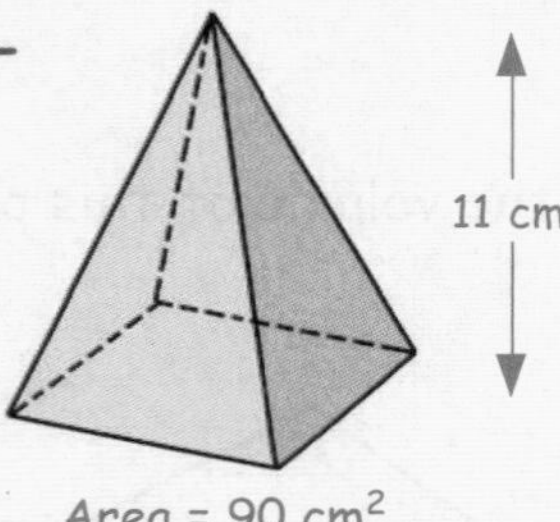

For this square based pyramid :-

$$\text{Volume} = \frac{1}{3} \times \text{Area(base)} \times \text{height}$$
$$= \frac{1}{3} \times 90 \times 11$$
$$= \frac{1}{3} \times 990 = 330 \text{ cm}^3$$

Exercise 1

1. The area of the base of this square based pyramid is 15 cm^2.

   Its height is 7 cm.

   Calculate its volume.

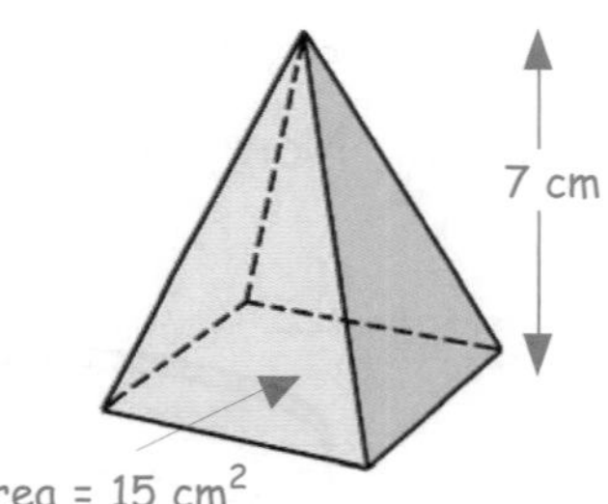

2. Calculate the volume of this triangular based pyramid.

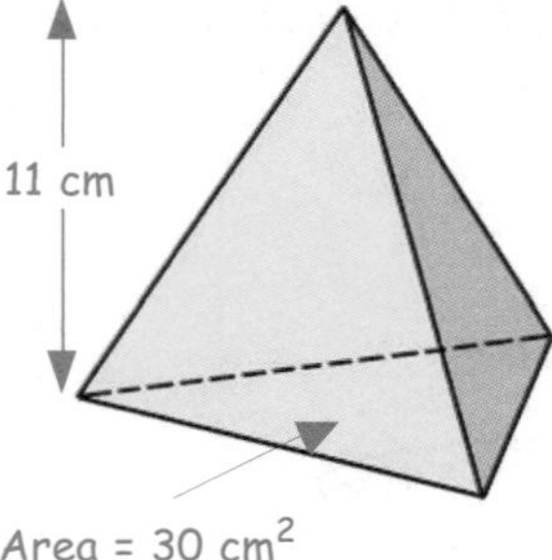

3. Calculate the volume of this hexagonal based pyramid.

9·5 cm

Area = 120 cm^2

4. The base of this pyramid is a square with each side 15 cm. It is 20 cm tall.

20 cm
15 cm

a Calculate the area of its square base.

b Calculate its volume.

5. Shown are two cartons used to hold popcorn.

How much **more** does the big one hold than the small one ?

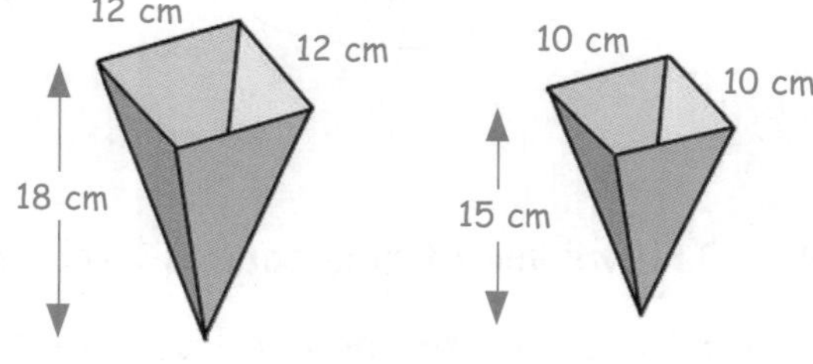

6. The base of a pyramid is an isosceles triangle with the length of its sides shown.

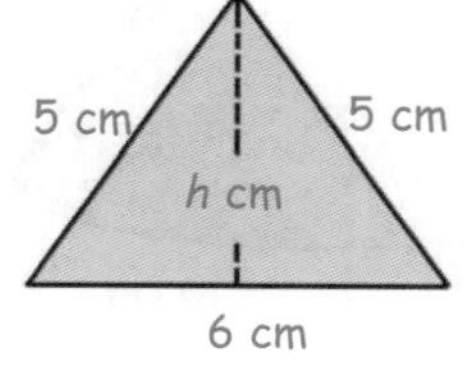

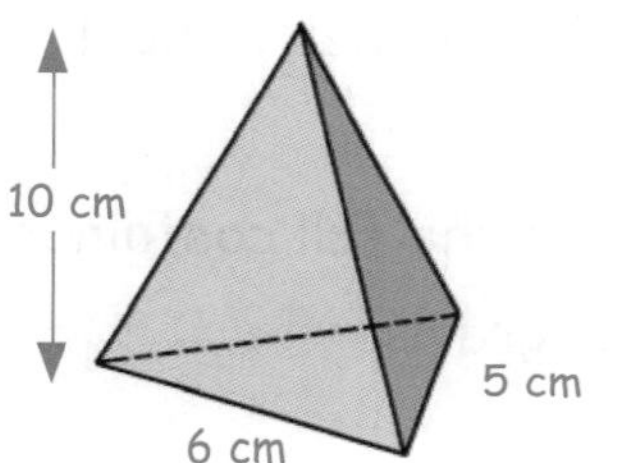

a Use Pythagoras' Theorem to calculate the height of the triangle.

b Now calculate the area of the triangle.

c Work out the volume of the pyramid.

Volume of a Cone

A pyramid with a **Circular Base** is simply called a **CONE**.

The volume of a prism is given by :- $V = \frac{1}{3}$ ***Area** (base)* $\times$ ***height***

and the area of the base (*a circle*) is given by :- $A = \pi r^2$

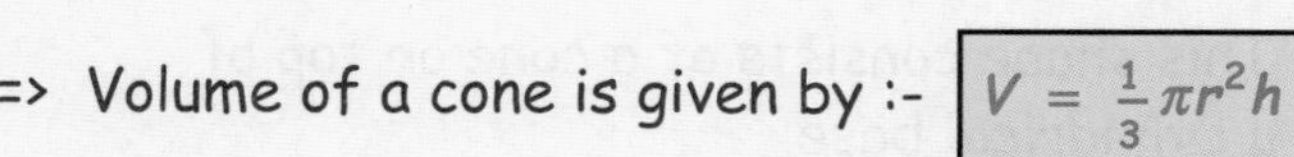

=> Volume of a cone is given by :- $V = \frac{1}{3}\pi r^2 h$

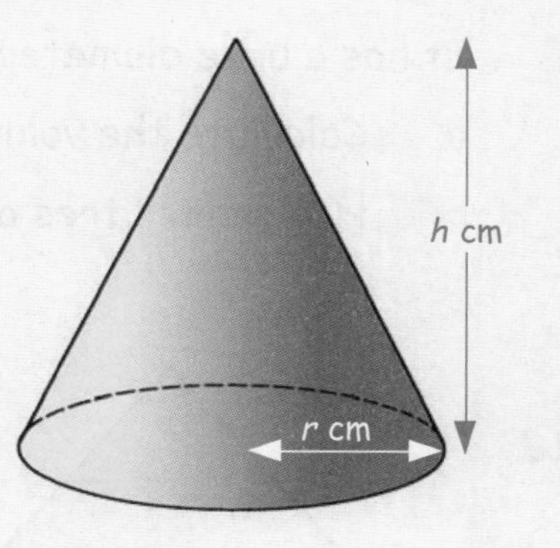

7. The radius of the base of this cone is 5 cm and its height is 12 cm.

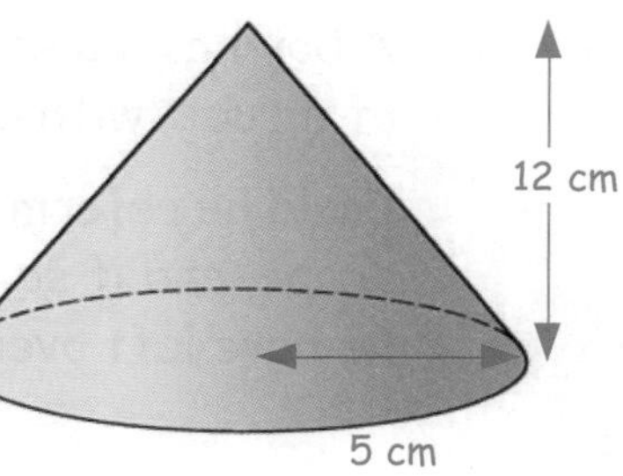

Copy and complete :-

$V = \frac{1}{3}\pi r^2 h$

=> $V = 3{\cdot}14 \times 5 \times 5 \times 12 \div 3$ *note

=> $V =$ .... cm^3

8. Calculate the volumes of these cones :-

a

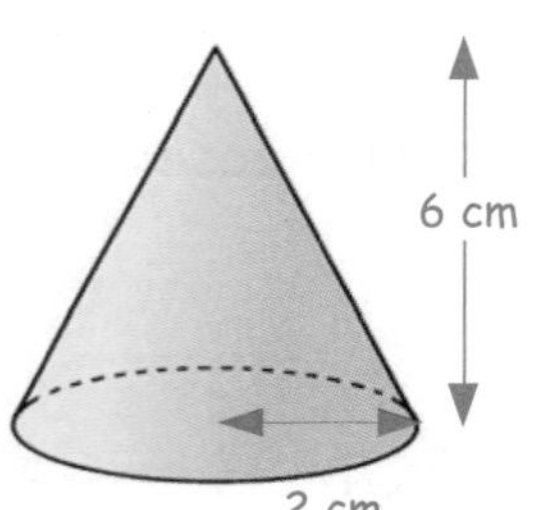

b

9 cm

8 cm

c

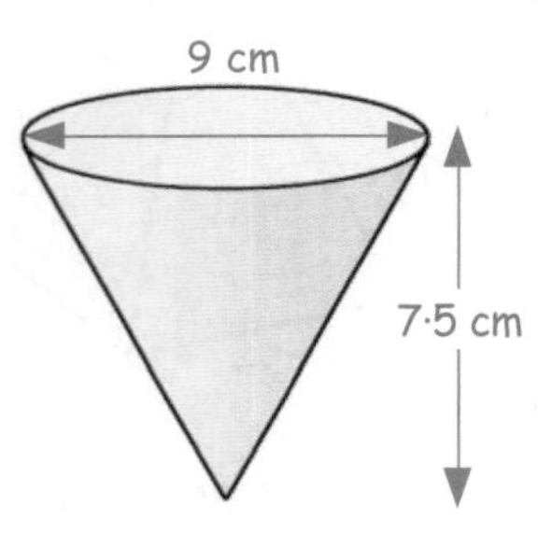

9. The volume of this cone is 1570 cm^3.

a Calculate the area of its circular base.

b Now calculate the height (h cm) of the cone.

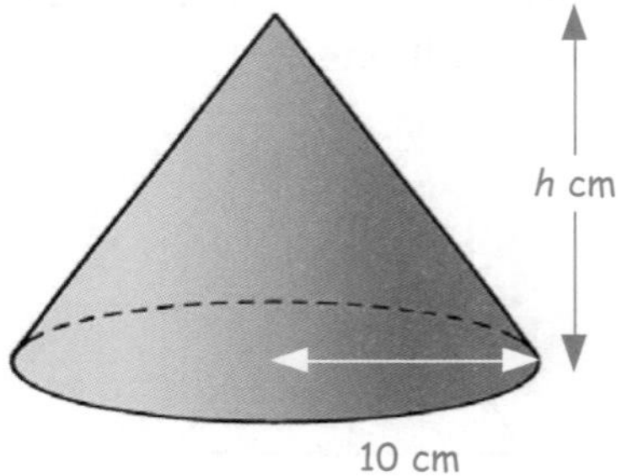

10.

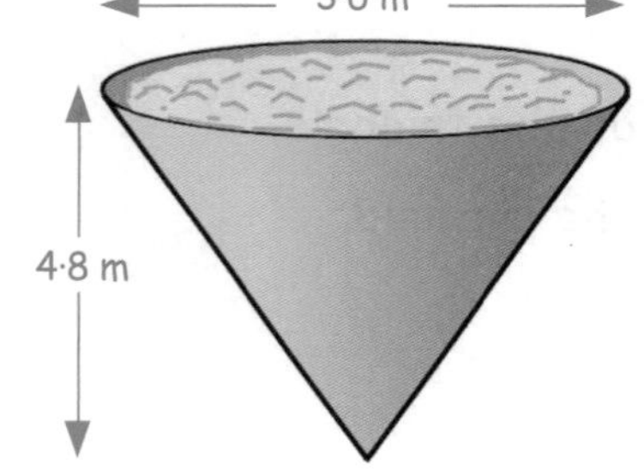

A pig farmer uses this conical container to hold grain for his pigs.

Calculate the weight of grain in the full container, if 1 m^3 of grain weighs 600 kilograms.

11. This oil lamp is in the shape of a cone.

It has a base diameter of 18 cm and is 24 cm tall.

a Calculate the volume of the lamp.

b How many litres of oil will the lamp hold when full ?

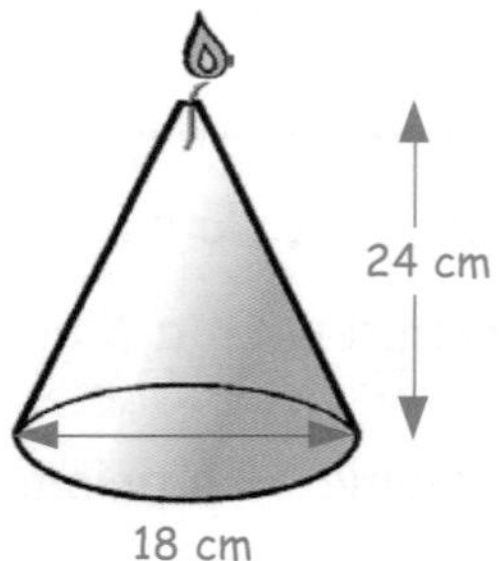

12.

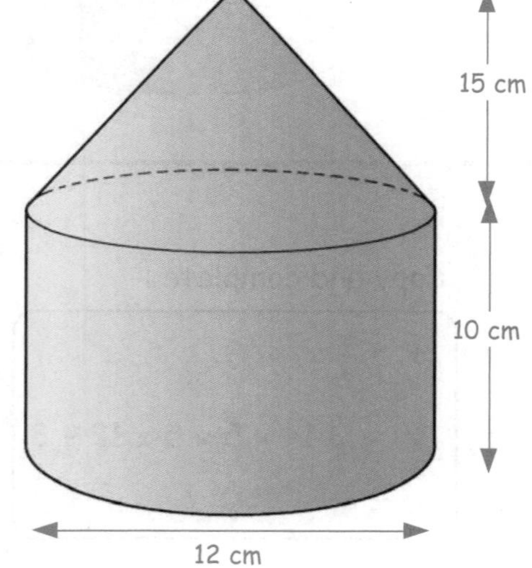

This shape consists of a cone on top of a cylindrical base.

a Calculate the volume of the base.

b Calculate the volume of the conical top.

c A boy has a piece of plasticine in the shape of a cube, with each of its sides 12 cm.

Could he reform the cube to make this shape, and if so, how much plasticine will he have left over ?

The Volume of a Sphere

The correct name for a "ball" shape is a SPHERE.

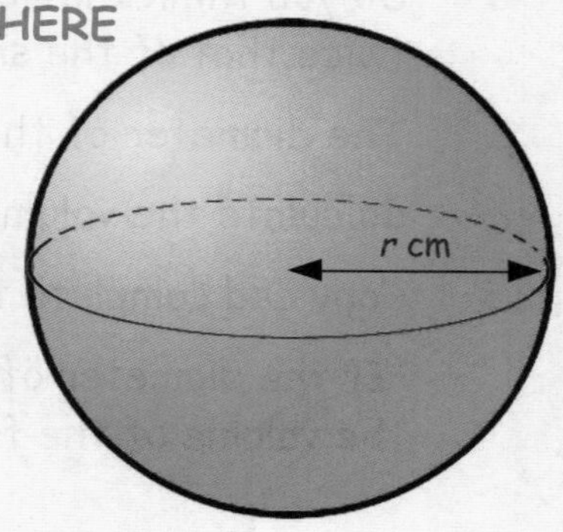

The volume of a sphere is obtained by :-

- Finding the value of r^3,
- Multiplying this by π,
- Finding $\frac{4}{3}$ of this answer.

=> $Volume = \frac{4}{3}\pi r^3$

Example :- Calculate the volume of this baseball which has a **diameter** of 7·6 cm.

7·6 cm

$D = 7{\cdot}6$ cm => $r = 3{\cdot}8$ cm

$V = \frac{4}{3}\pi r^3$ *note

$V = 4 \times 3{\cdot}14 \times 3{\cdot}8 \times 3{\cdot}8 \times 3{\cdot}8 \div 3$

$V = 229{\cdot}7 \text{ cm}^3$

Exercise 2

1. Calculate the volume of a globe with radius 12 cm.

2. Calculate the volume of this football with diameter 30 cm.

30 cm

3. Calculate the volume of this golf ball which has a diameter of 40 mm.

4. This box is tightly packed with 3 tennis balls.

   Calculate the volume of one tennis ball.

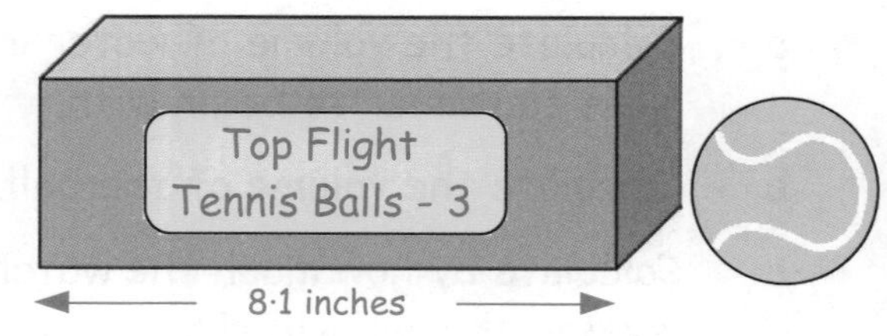

5. The larger beach ball shown has its diameter twice that of the smaller one.

   a Do you think that the volume of the larger ball will also be twice that of the smaller one ?

   b The diameter of the large ball is 20 cm. Calculate its volume.

   c Calculate the volume of the smaller ball.

   d Copy and complete this statement :-

   "If the diameter of one sphere is 2 × that of a second sphere, then the volume of the first sphere will be ... × the volume of the second.

6. 

This hemispherical fruit bowl has a radius of 15 centimetres.

Calculate the volume of the bowl.

7. The diameter of this hemispherical fish bowl is 24 cm.

   a Calculate its volume.

   b Will it be able to hold 3·5 litres of water ?

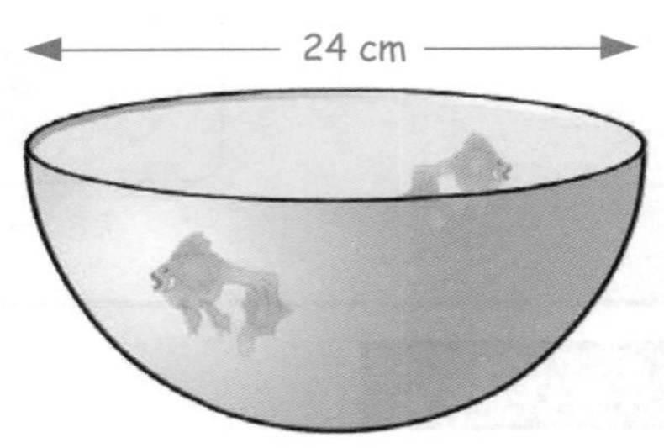

8. Which of these 3 plastic containers holds the most and which holds the least ?

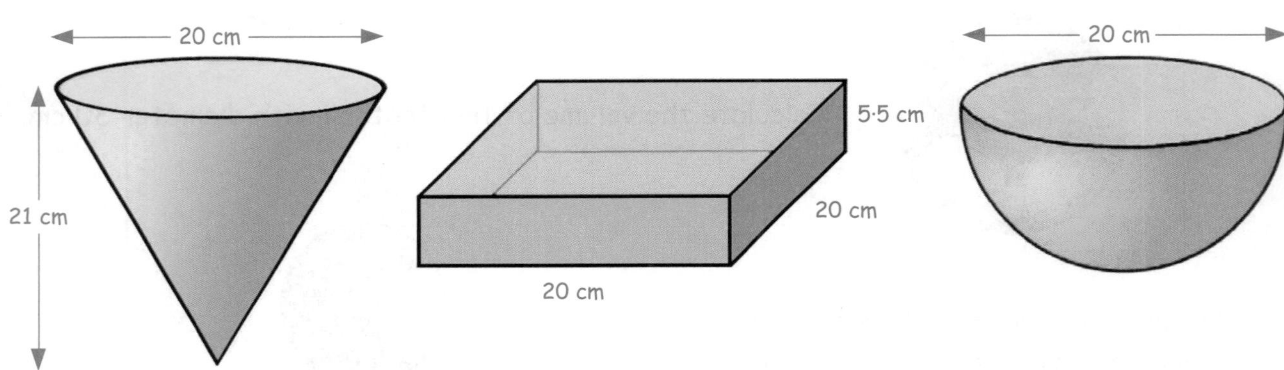

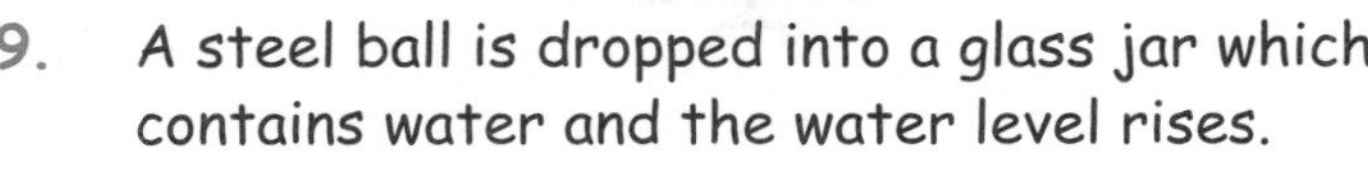

9. A steel ball is dropped into a glass jar which contains water and the water level rises.

   a Calculate the volume of water in the glass container to begin with.

   b Calculate the volume of the ball.

   c Calculate by how much the water level in the jar will rise.

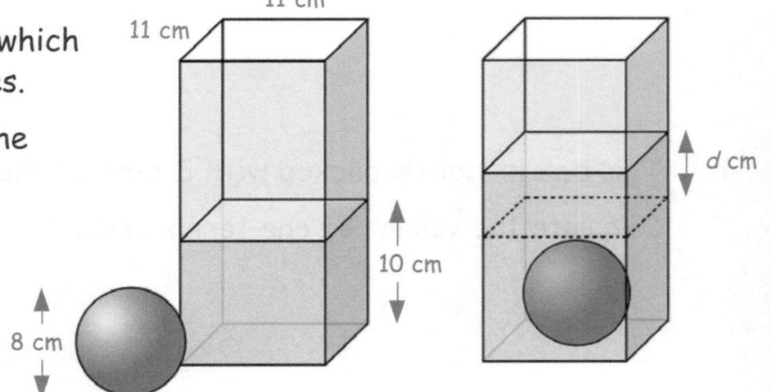

The Volume of a Composite Shape

A 3-D shape made up of cubes, cuboids, cones, prisms, cylinders and spheres etc is called a **composite shape**.

To find its volume, you simply find the volume of its individual shapes, then add them together.

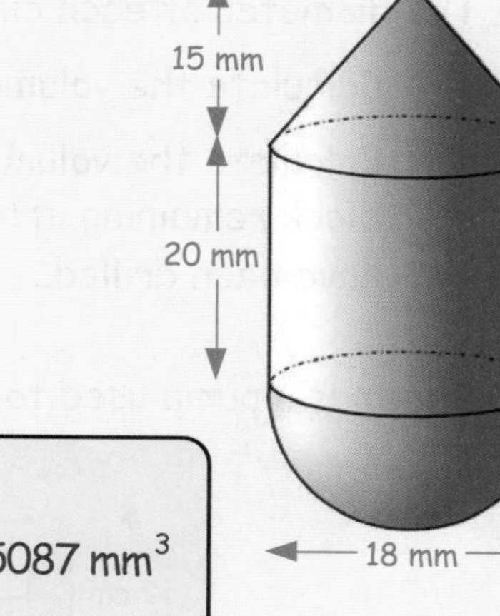

Example :- Calculate the volume of this lead sinker used as a weight by fishermen.

Solution :-

Vol(*cyl*) $V = \pi r^2 h$

$V = 3{\cdot}14 \times 9 \times 9 \times 20 = 5087\ \text{mm}^3$

Vol(*cone*) $V = \frac{1}{3}\pi r^2 h$

$V = 3{\cdot}14 \times 9 \times 9 \times 15 \div 3 = 1272\ \text{mm}^3$

Vol(*hemisphere*) $V = \frac{4}{3}\pi r^3 \div 2$

$V = 4 \times 3{\cdot}14 \times 9 \times 9 \times 9 \div 3 (\div 2) = 1526\ \text{mm}^3$

Total Volume = $(5087 + 1272 + 1526)\ \text{mm}^3 = \mathbf{7885\ mm^3}$

Exercise 3

1. This hot water tank consists of a hemisphere on top of a cylinder.

   The diameter of both the cylinder and hemisphere is 75 cm and the cylinder is 60 cm tall.

   Calculate the total volume.

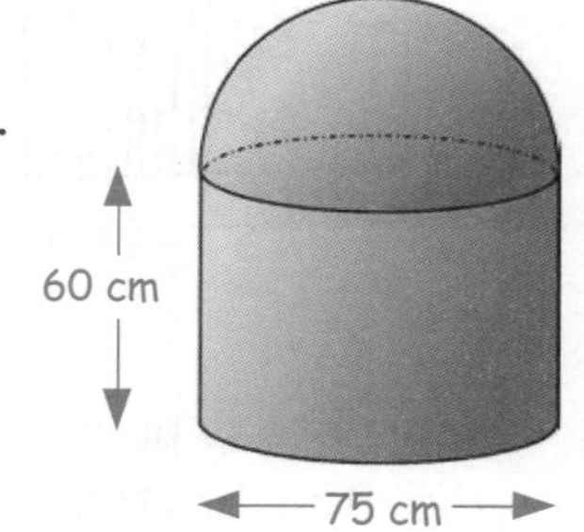

2. This shape is to be erected outside an ice-cream shop in Largs.

   It consists of a hemisphere on top of a cone.

   Work out the total volume of the shape.

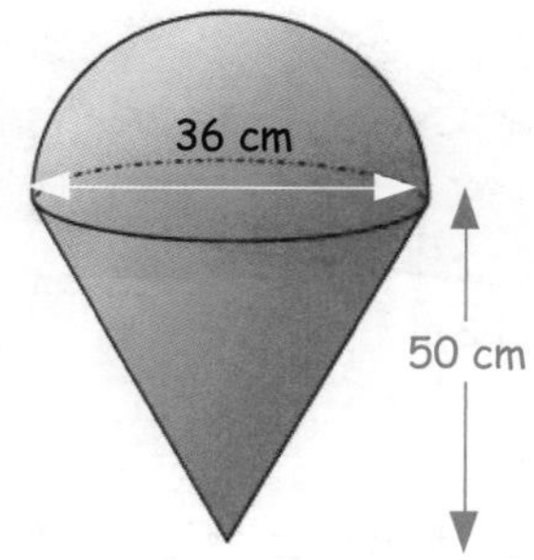

3. This gate post outside a house is made of concrete.

   Calculate the volume of concrete needed to make a pair of identical gate posts.

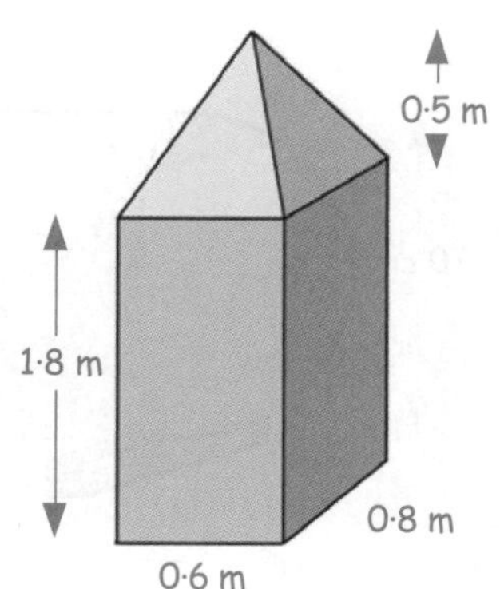

4. This metal block has 4 identical cylindrical holes drilled out of it, as shown.

   The diameter of each circle is 8 cm.

   a Calculate the volume of one of the holes.

   b Calculate the volume of the metal block remaining after the holes have been drilled.

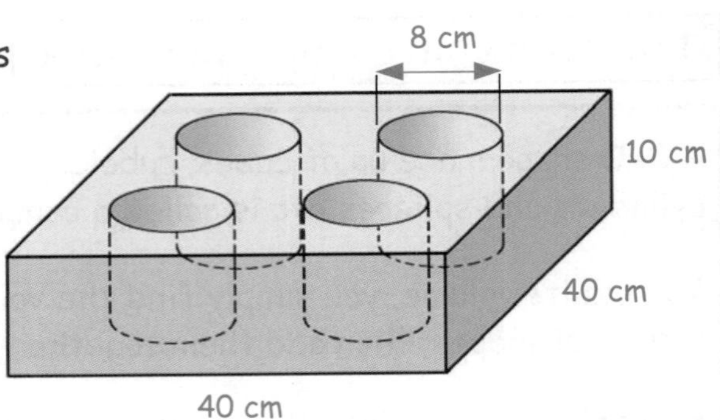

5. Shown is a pump used to blow up inflatable beds and paddling pools.

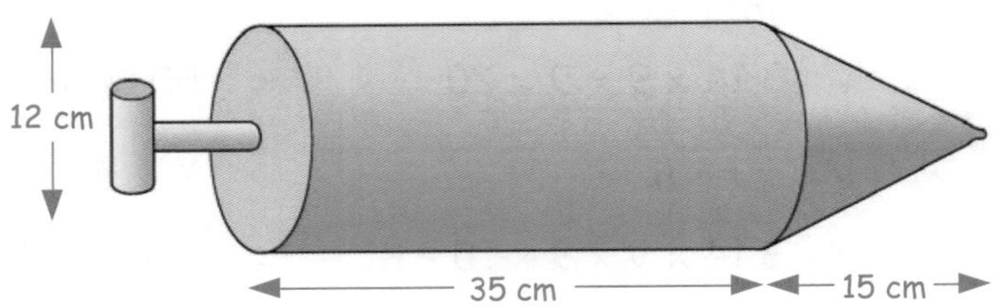

   Calculate the volume of air it can hold when the piston is pulled back.

6.

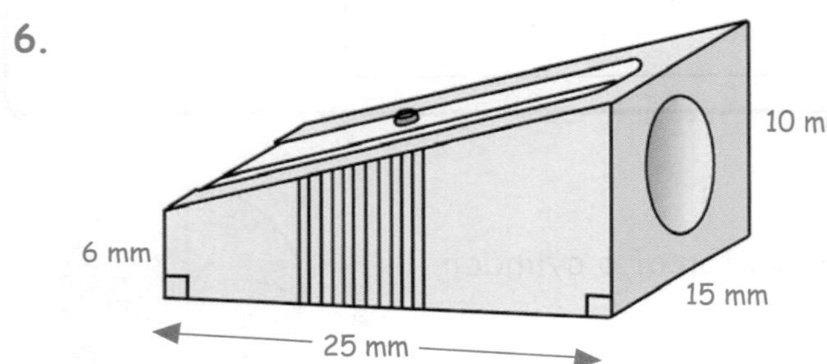

A metal sharpener is made from the block shown opposite with a hole drilled through it and a blade attached.

Calculate the volume of the original metal block, in mm^3.

7. Concrete is poured into a frame to make a top step, bottom step and sloping ramp.

   Calculate the volume of concrete required, (*in* m^3).

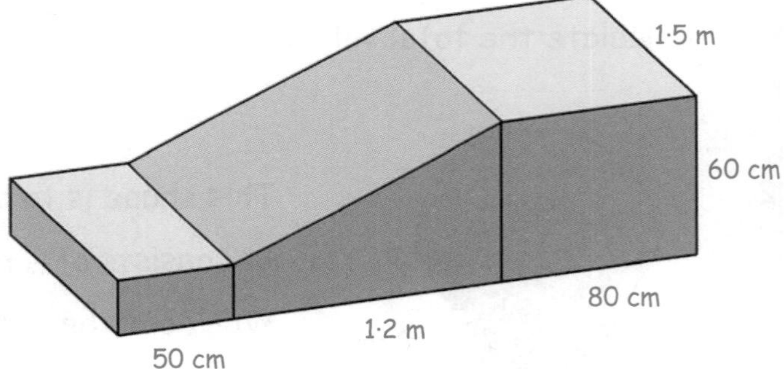

8.

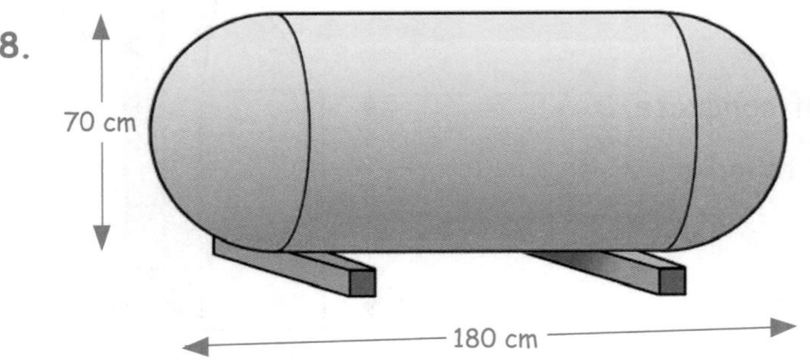

This oil storage tank consists of a cylindrical middle, with two hemispherical end pieces.

The total length of the tank is 180 cm.

At present, it holds 250 litres of oil.

How many litres will it take to fill it ?

9. This conical paper cup has a top diameter of 12 cm and is 16 cm tall.

It was filled with blueberry juice and then some of the juice was poured out.

a Calculate the volume of juice in the paper cup when it was full.

b Was more or less than half of the juice poured out ?

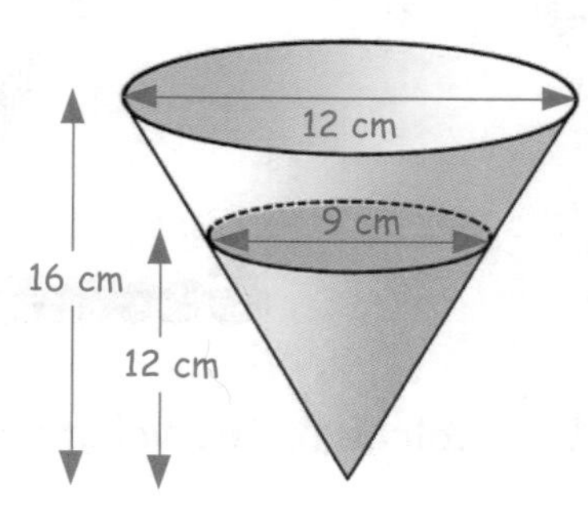

10. 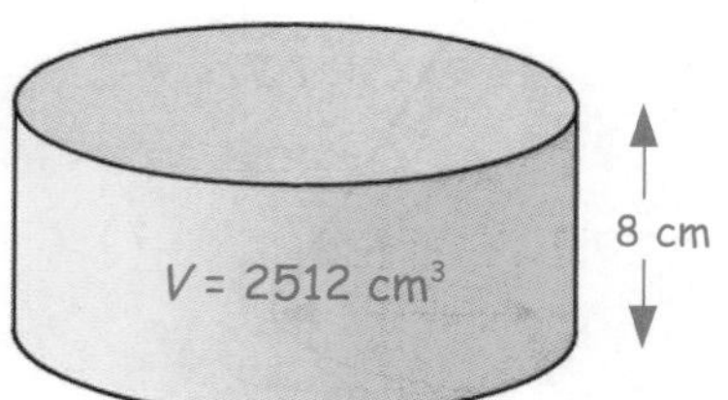

This cylinder is 8 centimetres tall and has a volume of 2512 cm^3.

Calculate the size of the **radius** of the base.

11. Nick has a piece of Play Doh in the shape of a cone.

a Calculate the volume of the cone.

b He then re-forms it and makes a cylinder having the same height, and with the same volume as his cone.

Calculate, to 1 decimal place, the **radius** (*r* cm) of this cylinder.

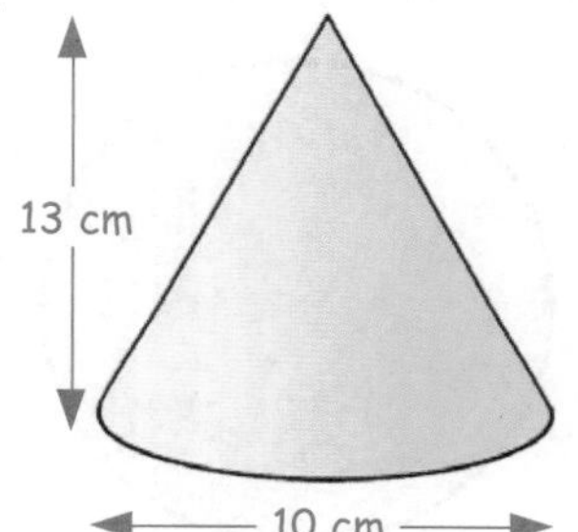

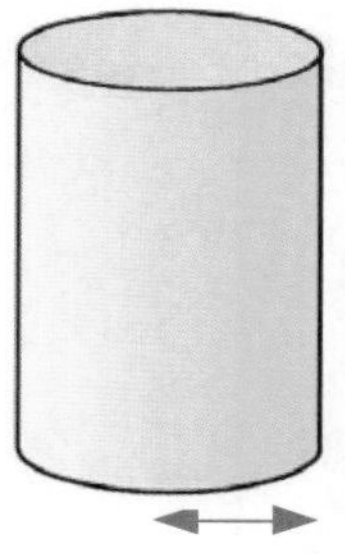

12. 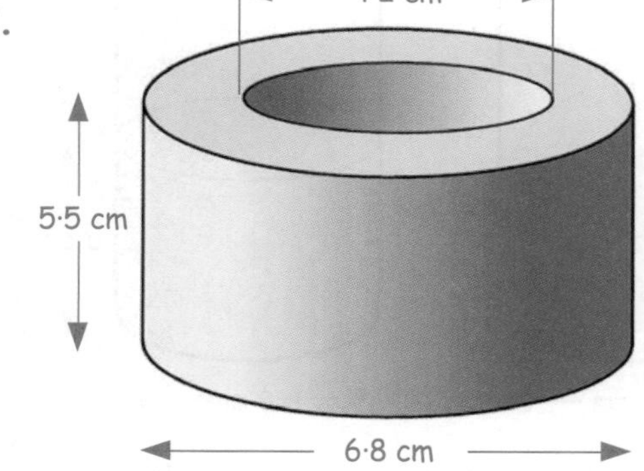

This steel ring has an outer diameter of 6·8 cm and an inner diameter of 4·2 cm.

The height of the ring is 5·5 cm.

a Calculate the volume of steel needed to make the ring.

b If the density (*weight*) of steel is 7·8 grams per cm^3, calculate the weight of the ring.

13. A marble birdbath is made by drilling out a hemisphere from a square based cuboid.

The diameter of the hemisphere is 15 cm.

Calculate the volume of marble used to make the birdbath.

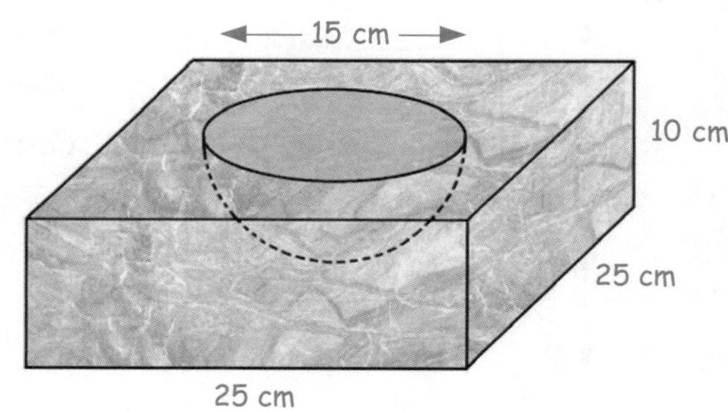

Volume 2

Geometry/Measure Assessment 9

1. Calculate the volume of this pyramid and of this cone :-

a

Area = 120 cm²

9·5 cm

b

7·5 cm

7 cm

2. Calculate the volume of the sphere and of the hemisphere :-

a

5 cm

b

50 mm

3. A spherical ice cube of diameter 6 centimetres, is dropped into a glass beaker, with internal diameter also 6 centimetres, and allowed to melt.

   Calculate how deep the water will be in the jar when the ice cube completely melts.

4. 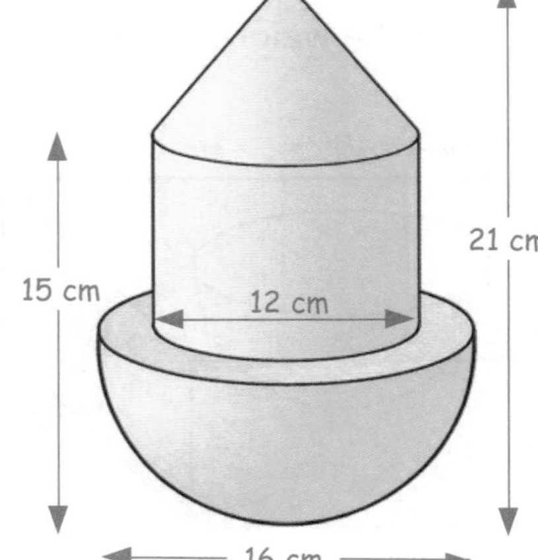

   Shown is the base of a rocking toy, consisting of a hemispherical bottom with a cylinder and cone on top.

   Calculate its total volume.

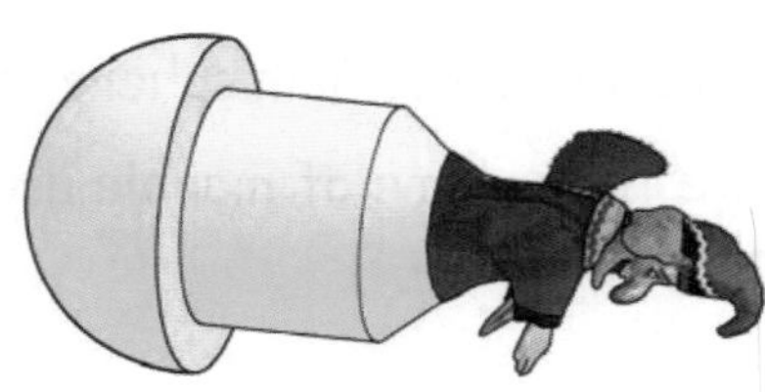

Unit Assessment

Geometry & Measure

Assessment Tasks

1. Sia works as a flight attendant and her next flight is from Glasgow to Los Angeles.

    - The flight time from Glasgow to New York is 6 hrs 51 minutes and from New York to Los Angeles is a further 5 hours 42 minutes.
    - There is a stop-over in New York for 1 hour and 47 minutes.
    - Los Angeles time is 8 hours behind GMT (*UK time*).

    a Calculate how long it will take from Glasgow to Los Angeles, including the stopover. (3)

    Give your answer in hours and minutes.

    b The flight leaves Glasgow at 1320.

    At what time will it arrive in L.A. (*local time*) ? (2)

    c Just before she leaves, Sia phones her old Gran in L.A.

    Is this a suitable time to phone her Gran ? (*Explain*). (2)

    d What would be a suitable UK time to phone her Gran to say she is leaving ? (1)

2. A cruise ship travels between three islands.

    From Aria Island, it sails 200 km on a bearing of 060° to go to Berry Island.

    From Berry Island to Calia Isle the ship sails on a bearing of 170° for 150 km.

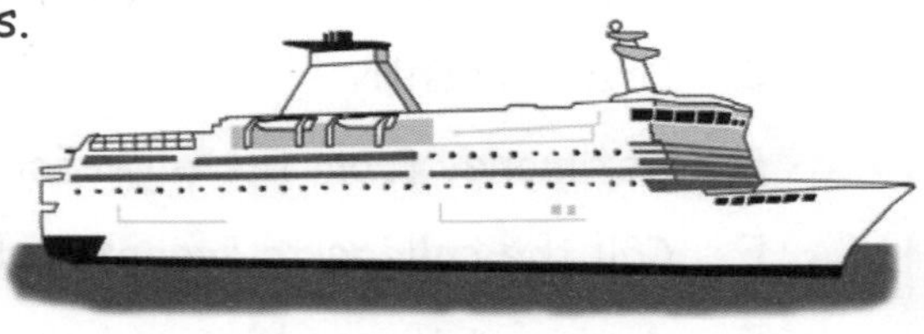

    a Using a scale of *1 cm = 20 km*, make a scale drawing of the ship's journey. (4)

    b From Calia Isle, the ship then sails directly back to Aria Island.

    Use your drawing to find the distance and bearing of Aria Island from Calia Isle.

    c The ship sails at an average speed of 40 km/hr (± 5 km/hr). (3)

    Calculate the minimum and maximum journey times, in hours, minutes and seconds, for this round trip. (6)

    (*Ignore any stopping time at Berry and Calia*).

3. A gold ingot is in the shape of a cylinder.

A jeweller has 0·1 litre of gold which he melts and pours into moulds to make ingots like this.

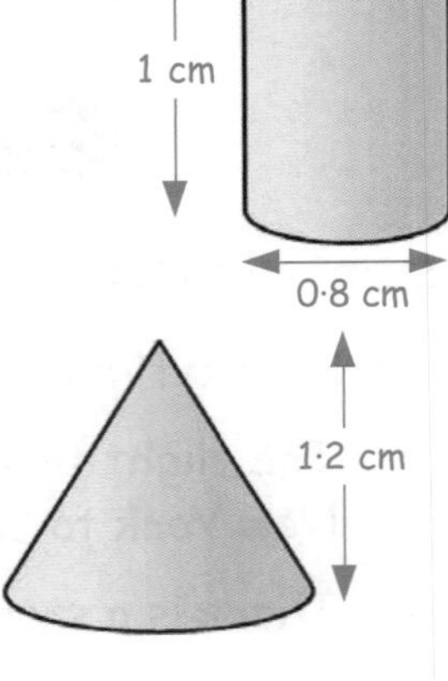

a How many full ingots can he make ? (5)

b One of the cylinders is to be melted down again and made into a cone with height 1·2 cm.

The cone and cylinder will have the same volume.

Calculate the radius of the cone. (2)

4. A storage container has dimensions :-

length	-	3·2 m
breadth	-	2·5 m
height	-	1·9 m.

What is the maximum number of boxes, identical to the one shown, that can be stored in this container ? (4)

5. Mr Hobbs has been invited to give a speech at a college.

The following is a list of things he needs to do :-

A Travel by train to the college (1 hour)

B Walk to the train station (5 minutes)

C Dress smartly

D Get money from the ATM for the journey

E Call the college to accept and confirm

F Arrive at the college and give speech

G Half hour of practising the speech

H Write the speech (2 hours).

Activity order	Activities

Some of the activities can be done at the same time.

Copy and complete this precedence table by putting the activities into a logical order.

Show where some of the activities might overlap and be done at the same time. (2)

6. When a wheelchair ramp is to be designed, safety regulations stipulate that the gradient must be $0{\cdot}24 \pm 0{\cdot}02$.

a Two ramps (A and B) are shown below :-

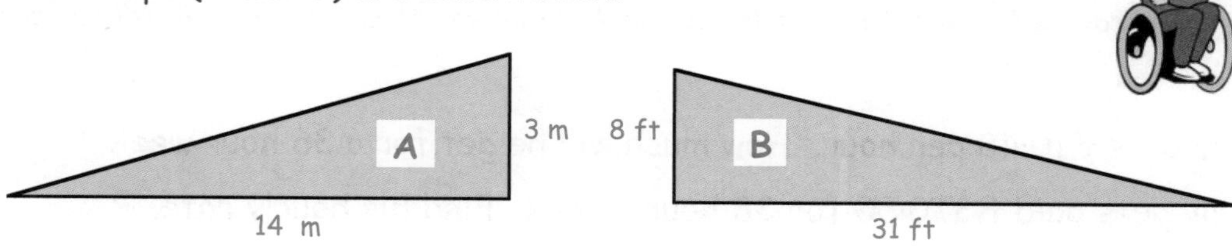

Is either of the ramps safe ? *Explain.* **(5)**

b Here is a third ramp (C), in which both of the sloping parts have a gradient of 0·25, and the height is 1·5 m.

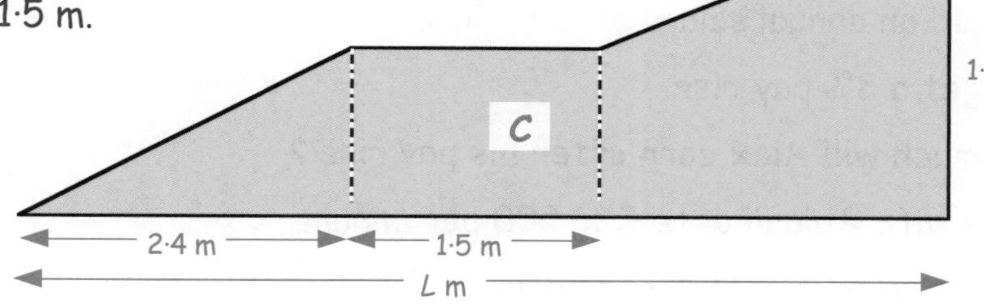

What is the total length (L) of the ramp ? **(3)**

7. Kevin wishes to paint his living room.

The brown door going into the room and each of the patio doors are 2 m high and 1·5 m wide.

Window 1 is 3 m by 1 m.

Window 2 is 2 m by 1 m.

Kevin is going to paint all the walls on the inside of the living room.

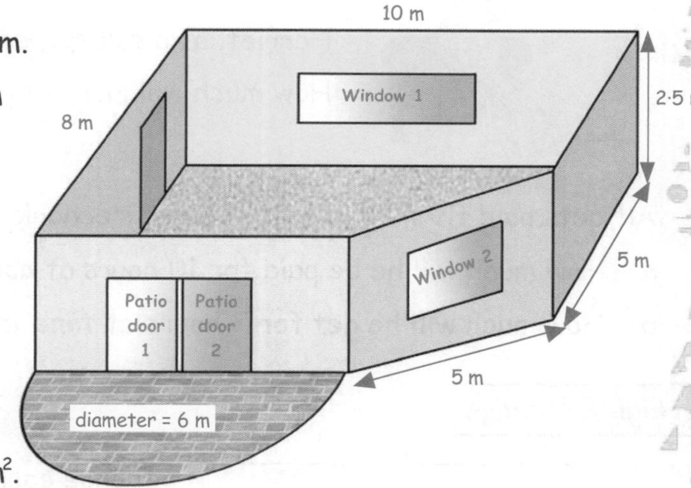

A 1 litre tin of paint will cover $9\,m^2$.

a How many litre tins will he need ? **(5)**

b Paint is sold in two tin sizes :- 1 litre - £9·50 and 2·5 litres - £20·25.

What combination of tin sizes will give him the minimum costing ? **(3)**

c Kevin also wants to lay a semicircular red brick patio.

He has a budget of £1100 and the cheapest quote he has been given is £82 per square metre.

Is the patio within his budget ? *Explain.* **(4)**

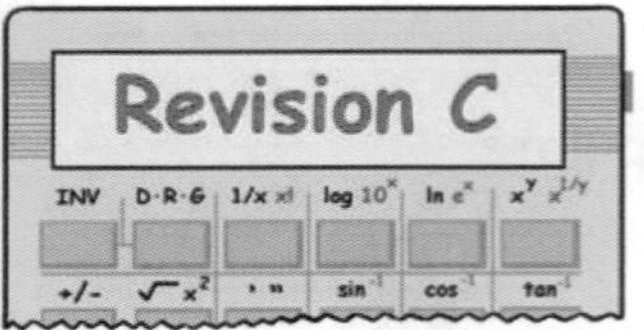

Finance/Statistics Revision

(The following was covered in Nat 4 Lifeskills and should be known, though much of it will be revised later).

Income

1. a Jaz gets £10·48 per hour. How much will he get for a 36 hour week ?
   b Billy gets paid £370·50 for 38 hour's work. Find his hourly rate.
   c Gillian earns £312·25 every week. What are her yearly earnings ?
   d Tina earns £22 230 a year. How much does she earn weekly ?
   e Arch gets £18 750 per annum. How much does he get paid monthly ?

2. Alex is paid an annual salary of £32 000.
   He is to get a 3% pay rise.
   a How much will Alex earn after his pay rise ?
   b Alex's wife Abigail gets £36 500 per annum.
   She has to take a 2·5% pay decrease.
   Who now earns more and by how much ?

3.  Harriet, as a salesperson, earns 12% commission on all sales.
   How much will Harriet get on £3200 of sales ?

4. Alf gets paid £9·70 per hour as a car mechanic.
   a How much will he be paid for 10 hours at ***double time*** ?
   b How much will he get for 7 hours at ***time and a half*** ?

Foreign Exchange

5. £1 sterling can be exchanged for :-
   - 1·95 Australian dollars
   - 429 Hungarian Florints
   - 10·25 Danish Kroner
   - 97·8 Indian Rupee

   Change each of the following :-
   a £40 to Florints b £250 to Rupees
   c 156 Aus dollars to £'s d 1230 Kroner to £'s.

6. Deborah went on a weekend break to Rome.
   She took £350, which she changed to euros at a rate of €1·32 to the £.
   How many euros did Deborah receive ?

Banking

7. Henry won £1200 in the lottery and invested it in *Floyd's Bank*.

   How much interest will he be due if he removes his money 1 year later ?

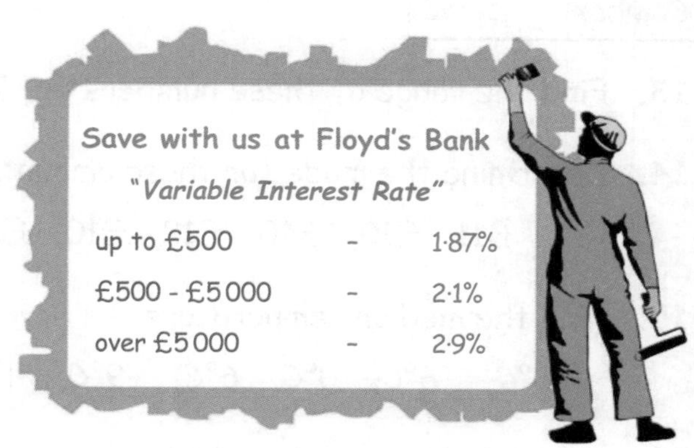

8. Fraz deposited £2000 in one account and his wife paid into £4000 to her account, both with *Floyd's bank*.

   How much **more** interest would they have received if they had invested the £6000 in one single account ?

9. Mr Ghee has a *Viza Card* which has an APR of 15%.

   a What is the APR for just 1 month ?

   b How much would he owe after one month if he had used each of the following amounts on his card :-

   (i) £600 (ii) £2400 ?

10. Ross needs to borrow £1200 to buy a second hand car.

    Sands' Bank charge an annual interest rate of 7·25% on loans.

    a Calculate how much interest will be due if the loan is for 1 year.

    b How much will Ross' monthly payments be ?

Comparing Prices

11. Which pack of Raspberry Cooler is the better buy - the 3-pack or the 5-pack ?

12. I need to hire a van to help me move furniture to my new flat.

    I estimate it will need to be hired for 4 hours.

    The Van Man charges a basic hiring fee of £15 plus £8·50 per hour after that.

    Cheap 'n Cheerful don't charge any basic fee, but their rental charges are £11·50 per hour.

    a From which company should I hire it ? (*Explain*).

    b It actually took 7 hours to move all my stuff.

    Would I have been better hiring it from the other company ? (*Explain*).

Comparing Data

13. Find the range of these numbers :- 74, 18, 45, 14, 78, 6, 27, 2, 7.

14. Determine the mode for these amounts :-

    £11, £10, £10, £12, £10, £11, £10, £11, £14, £14, £11, £11, £14.

15. Find the median temperature :-

    3°C, -6°C, 0°C, 6°C, -9°C, 4°C, 8°C, -20°C, 3°C, 1°C.

16. Calculate the mean weight in kilograms :-

    115 kg, 35 kg, 45 kg, 60 kg, 90 kg, 95 kg, 26 kg, 54 kg.

17. Shown is the number of pounds two women lost each week when on a strict diet.

Joan	2	3	2	2	2	5	3	2	6
Abby	0	3	3	2	1	3	3	1	2

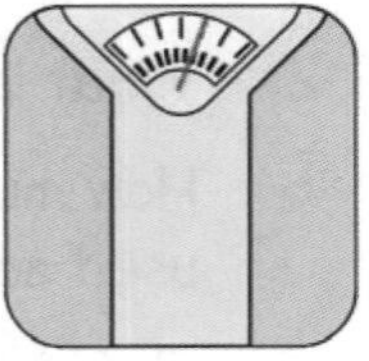

a Write down the modal number of pounds lost for each woman.

b Give a reason why it is unfair to say one woman lost more than the other woman by comparing them using the mode. What other "average" is better ? *Explain.*

Graphs & Charts

18. Use the table below to construct a Comparative Line Graph to show the sales of vacuum cleaners in 2 shops last week.

	Mon	Tue	Wed	Thu	Fri
Brown's	4	6	2	10	8
Timson	2	4	12	9	10

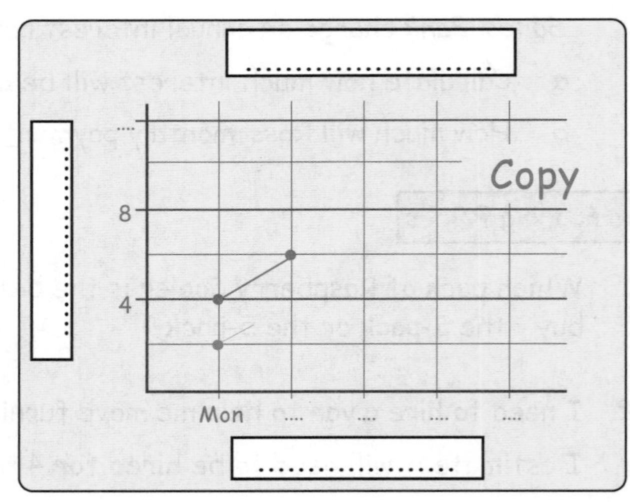

19. A group of people were asked to name their favourite Scottish female news presenter.

Here are the results :-

- 35% Jackie Bird
- 30% Sally Magnuson
- 20% Kirsty Walk
- the rest chose Shereen Nanjiani.

Copy (or trace) the blank pie chart and complete it showing the above information.

20. George went online to find the prices of baby monitors for his new grandson.

He found 20 sites which had a monitor he could afford and was in stock.

Here are the prices he found :-

£33	£48	£54	£80	£70	£60	£80	£68	£54	£67
£60	£76	£33	£54	£65	£70	£43	£82	£60	£54

a Construct an ordered stem-and-leaf diagram, including a key.

b What is the modal price of the monitors ?

c Determine the median price.

21. State whether there is a correlation between each of the following pairs of data :-

a The number of hours you practice swimming and the time it takes you to swim a length.

b The age and the shoe size of a child.

c The number of people picking strawberries in a field and the time it takes to pick all the strawberries.

d The month of the year and the sales of guitars.

22. Eight people counted the number of silver coins in their pocket and the total value of the coins in pence.

Their results are recorded in the table below.

No. of Coins	2	13	7	10	0	8	12	4
Total value (p)	40	170	70	150	0	110	140	40

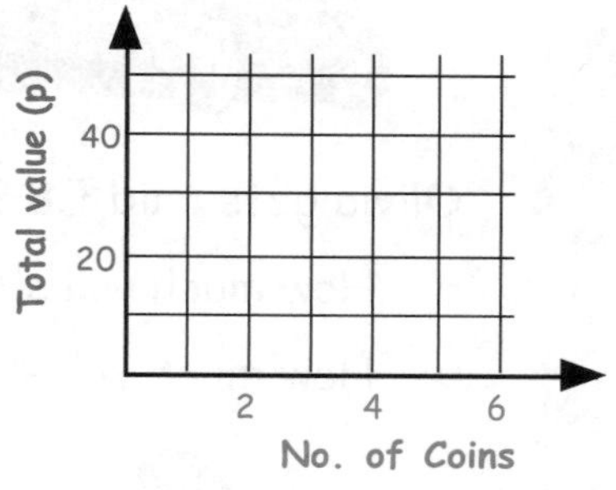

a Construct a scattergraph from this table.

b Draw a line of best fit on your scattergraph.

c Use your line to estimate the approximate value of a pocket holding 6 coins.

Probability & Chance

23. What is the probability someone was born in a month that ended with the letter "y" ?

24. Of the 320 Ryanjet flights out of Edinburgh, 240 of them left on time.

a What is the probability the next flight I catch will be delayed ?

b How many of my 72 business trips with Ryanjet were likely to have been delayed ?

25. This 6 sided dice has 2 red faces, 1 blue face and 3 yellow faces.

In a game, you are offered odds of 7 to 2 of rolling a red face.

In the long run, are you likely to come out winning or losing money if you bet on red, given these odds ?

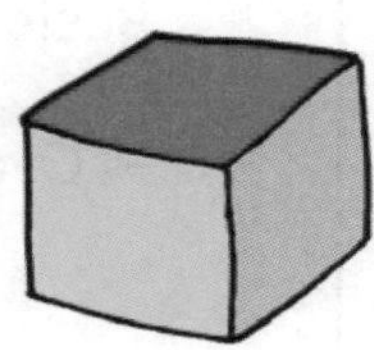

Income

Revision of National 4 Lifeskills

1. a Ed is paid £10·76 per hour. How much will he receive for a 40 hour week ?

   b Ted is paid £641·70 for 45 hours work. Find his hourly rate.

   c Pila earns £317·10 per week. What are her yearly earnings ?

   d Gio earns £21 429·20 a year. How much does he earn weekly ?

   e Simon is paid £36 048 per annum. What is his monthly pay ?

2. William is paid £22 200 per annum as a mortgage advisor.

   He is to receive a 6% pay rise.

   a How much will William earn after his pay rise ?

   b His wife Wendy is paid £25 400 per annum.

   She has to take a 4% pay decrease.

   Who now earns more, and by how much ?

3. Des earns 9% commission on all car sales.

   How much will Des get on £42 800 sales ?

4. Olivia gets paid £8·90 per hour as a secretary.

   a How much will she be paid for 12 hours at *double time* ?

   b How much will she get for 7 hours at *time and a half* ?

5. Ian's gross monthly pay is £1664·10.

   His deductions total £395·87.

   Find his *net* (*take-home*) pay.

6. Copy and complete the pay slip below to find the total pay.

Han Solo		*Payroll Number 009701*		*Date w/e 06/02/15*
Basic Rate = £12·80		*Overtime Rate = (1·5 x ....)*	=	£ ......
Basic Pay	=	40 x £12·80	=	£
+ Overtime Pay	=	6 x £..........	=	£
		Total Pay	=	£

Income

Wages & Salaries

There are many terms involving income that you should already be familiar with :-

Salary, Overtime, Bonus, Commission, Superannuation, Income Tax, etc...

Your teacher may remind you or discuss some of these terms with you.

Payment for work done by you is called your **pay**, your **wage** or your **salary**.

An **income** is generally regarded as a weekly, monthly or yearly (**annual**) salary.

Overtime is extra work above your normal number of hours.

It is usually paid at a **higher rate** of pay :-

Time and a Half	-	1·5 × the normal rate
Double Time	-	2 × the normal rate
Treble Time	-	3 × the normal rate

Exercise 1

1. Calculate the **weekly** wages for :-
   - a Ali - £9 per hour - works 40 hrs.
   - b Lee - £8·25/hour - works 38 hrs.
   - c Cal - £10·66/hour - works 52 hrs.
   - d Pam - £12·68/hour - works 44·5 hrs.

2. Calculate these **annual** salaries :-
   - a Gregor earns £380 per week.
   - b Natalie earns £824 per week.
   - c Calum earns £1325 per month.
   - d Russell earns £2376 per month.

3. Calculate each person's monthly salary :-
   - a Scott earns £19 800 annually.
   - b Zoe earns £36 000 per year.
   - c Lyle earns £42 586·56 per annum (yearly).

4. Calculate each person's weekly wage :-
   - a Stephen earns £29 265·60 annually.
   - b Ryan earns £38 012·52 yearly.
   - c Ross earns £50 445·20 per annum.

5. Pam is a secretary.
   Calculate her weekly wage.

   Secretary
   8·30 am - 5 pm (Mon to Fri)
   £8·42 per hour.

6. Calculate these weekly wages :-

a

Joiner's Assistant
9 am - 6 pm (Mon to Fri)
£7·20 per hour.

b

Architect
9 am - 4 pm (Mon to Sat)
£24·60 per hour.

7. Calculate the annual salaries for the joiner and the architect in question 6.

8. Josh earns £7 an hour as a plumber's mate. He also gets paid double time on a Saturday.

a Last week, Josh worked 38 hours (Mon-Fri).

How much did Josh earn ?

b Last Saturday, Josh worked for 6 hours.

How much did he earn last Saturday ?

c How much did he earn last week in total ?

9.

Mark earns £9·50 an hour as a labourer.

He gets paid time and a half on a Saturday and treble time on a Sunday.

His working times are as shown.

Calculate his total weekly wage.

9 am to 4 pm (Mon - Fri),
5 hours on Saturday and
4 hours on Sunday.

10. Amy works 36 hours a week as a fitness instructor. She earns £8·84 per hour.

She worked 4 hours on Friday night at time and a half and 3 hours on Saturday at double time.

a How much did Amy earn that week ?

b What would be her annual wage if these were her usual working times every week ?

11.

Mon-Fri from 9 am to 3 pm
Thursday night 8 pm to 4 am
Saturday from 11 am to 6 pm.

Sam earns £8·80 per hour at the supermarket.

He gets time and a half for weekends and double time for night shift work.

Calculate Sam's weekly wage.

12. Andrew earns the same hourly rate as Sam.

He starts work (Mon-Fri) at 9 am and also works the same hours as Sam does on a Thursday night and on a Saturday.

Andrew earns £475·20 a week.

What time must he finish work on a weekday ?

13. Claudia earned £244·80 for 12 hours overtime as a cleaner.

She *thought* she was being paid double time but *actually* only got paid at time and a half.

How much less did she get than she expected ?

Commission is usually paid as a **percentage** of the amount of sales.

Example :- Sean is paid 5% commission on £1800 worth of door to door cleaning equipment he sold.

Commission = 5% of £1800

= 0·05 x 1800

= £90

14. a Last month Stevie sold £24 600 worth of second hand cars.

How much commission (5%) did he earn ?

b Bronte earns 6% commission on all her sales.

How much commission would she earn on £32 000 worth of sales ?

c Kimmi earns 12·5% commission.

How much would she earn on £4400 sales ?

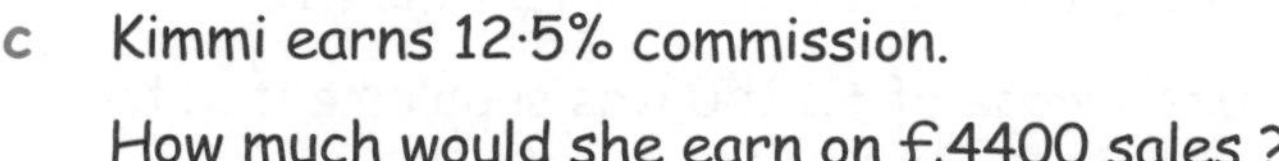

15.

Laura has a basic wage of £12 000 **p.a.** (***p.a.** is short for per annum*).

She also earns 8% commission, but this time it is only awarded on any sales over £10 000.

Last year, Laura sold £35 000 worth of clothes.

a What commission did she earn last year ?

b What were her total earnings last year ?

16. Lyndsay has a basic wage of £16 000 per year.

She sold £120 000 worth of window shutters and she earned 4·5% commission, based only on those sales over £50 000.

How much did Lyndsay earn in total ?

17. Two adverts for salespeople are as shown.

A good salesperson would be expected to sell £30 000 worth of cars each month.

With which company would a salesperson earn more (*based on £30 000 sales*) ?

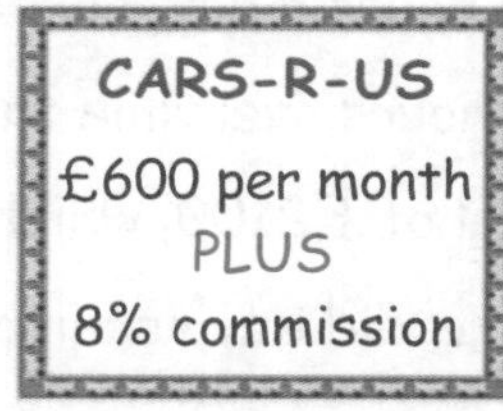

CELLCARS
£800 per month
PLUS
7% commission

18. Craig is paid £7·90 an hour basic rate as a computer salesman, working 9 am to 3 pm, Monday to Friday.

He also works 10 am - 6 pm on a Saturday for which he is paid at time and a half.

Craig also earns 3% commission on all sales, and last week Craig sold £9300 worth of goods.

What was his total wage last week ?

19. A sales company pays commission as shown in the table :-

a Calculate the commission on sales of :-

(i) £12 800 (ii) £33 480

(iii) £41 942 (iv) £25 000.

b Paula earned £3000 in commission.

What must her total sales have been worth ?

Total Sales	Commission
£5000 - £15 000	3·25%
£15 001 - £25 000	5·5%
over £25 000	7·5%

20. 

Alison earned £1514 in total last month.

Her basic wage of £1250 was supplemented by a percentage commission on all sales.

Last month her total sales were £17 600.

What percentage commission did Alison get ?

21. A company has an earnings pay scale as shown in the table.

Jay is on a grade 3 pay scale.

Jay worked 40 hours last week.

Jill is on a pay grade 2.

What is the minimum whole number of hours she would have had to work if she is to earn just more than Jay ?

Pay Scale	pay/hour
1	£7·45
2	£8·30
3	£9·70
4	£12·65

22. Ray earns £12·50 per hour as an editorial consultant.

He worked for six hours a day, five days a week for 4 weeks.

He also earned 16 hours overtime that month at time and a half.

Ray was paid a total of £2100, which included a bonus.

How much of a bonus did Ray receive ?

Gross Pay, Deductions and Net Pay

Gross pay is the amount that an employer pays you.

Deductions are taken from your gross pay and include things like :-

Superannuation - a type of extra pension for when you retire.

National Insurance - (N.I.) to pay for loss of earnings if you are sick/unemployed.

Income Tax - tax paid to the government to pay for education, health, transport, etc.

Net pay is the amount that you *take home* after deductions have been made.

Net Pay = Gross Pay − Deductions

Exercise 2

1. 

Sara works in an office and has a gross pay of £2640 per month.

Her total **annual** deductions are £3765.

Calculate her monthly net (*take-home*) pay.

2. Calculate each annual net pay :-

	Name	Gross Pay	Deductions
a	Steph	£18 000 p.a.	£3270 p.a.
b	Bianca	£24 500 p.a.	£4010 p.a.
c	Daniel	£2125 *per month*	£477 *per month*

3. Harry works in the same office as Sara and has a gross pay of £27 626 per annum.

He pays £5240 in deductions.

a Calculate his annual net pay.

b What is Harry's weekly take home pay ?

4.

Superannuation	: £920
National Insurance (N.I.)	: £1200
Income Tax	: £1152

Jack has an annual salary of £15 200.

He has to pay the deductions shown.

a Calculate Jack's total deductions.

b Calculate his annual net pay.

5. Ethan is paid £640 a week.

His weekly deductions are as shown.

Calculate Ethan's weekly net pay.

Income Tax	: £91
Nat. Ins. (N.I.)	: £76
Superannuation	: 5% of gross wage

6. a Will has a monthly net wage of £2460. His monthly deductions are £786.
Calculate his monthly gross wage.

b Frank has an annual net pay of £34 000. His deductions are £8275 per annum.
Calculate Frank's gross pay.

7. Ivan worked a 40 hour week as a blacksmith, earning a gross pay of £420.
As well as this, he worked 8 hours overtime, paid at **time and a half**.
Last week, he paid £36·30 Income Tax, £42·40 N.I. and 5% Superannuation.
Calculate his take home pay for last week.
(*You will need to calculate his basic rate of pay first*).

8. 

Alicia is the Managing Director of her own company and last year had a gross pay of £86 000.

Her take-home net pay was £59 765.

She paid £6840 towards her superannuation and paid £5320 in N.I. contributions.

What must she have paid in Income Tax last year ?

9. Shown are three different salary slips.
Calculate the net pay for Mr Jones, Ms Smith and Norman Bates.

a

Name	N.I. No.	Emp. No.	Week
Mr Jones	QP42127	003402	14
Basic Pay	**Overtime**	**Bonus**	**Gross P**
£410·00	47·40	£00·00	£.........
Nat. Ins	**Inc.Tax**	**Pension**	**Deduct**
£47·82	£54·82	£14·05	£.........
		Net Pay	**£ ......**

b

Name	N.I. No.	Emp. No.	Week
Ms Smith	QV08987	010087	35
Basic Pay	**Overtime**	**Bonus**	**Gross P**
£650·00	142·90	£300	£.........
Nat. Ins	**Inc.Tax**	**Pension**	**Deduct**
£101·52	£121·19	£33·04	£.........
		Net Pay	**£ ......**

c

IGLIS ENGINEERING

Name :- Norman Bates   Works No. :- 43870   Week No :- 16

Income	*Basic* -	£506·10	*O/Time* -	£65·50	*Bonus* -	£45·00	Total -	£..........
Deducts	*I.Tax* -	£122·73	*Superan* -	£32·80	*Nat Ins* -	£34·44	Total -	£..........
							Net Pay	£........

10. Study the pay slip shown below and hence find the amount of Superannuation paid.

IGLIS ENGINEERING								
Name :- Norma Desmond			Works No. :- 41704			Week No :- 16		
Income	Basic -	£806·10	O/Time -	£35·50	Bonus -	£145·00	Total -	£..........
Deducts	I.Tax -	£136·76	Superan -	£????	Nat Ins -	£74·10	Total -	£..........
						Net Pay		£737·08

11. Derek works for 40 hours happily each week as a traffic warden, earning £8·65 per hour.

Each week he pays £33·76 in income tax and £11·43 in National Insurance.

Calculate Derek's weekly net pay.

12. 

Alex works for 36 hours a week as a handyman in a children's home, and earns £8·70 per hour.

Each week he pays £31·87 Income Tax and £9·04 National Insurance contributions.

Calculate his take-home pay.

13. Sally earns £11·75 per hour in telesales and last week worked 44 hours.

She paid £54·65 in Income Tax, £14·12 in National Insurance and paid 4% of her gross wage into her pension.

Calculate her take home pay.

14. A mathematics lecturer pays the following monthly deductions :-

Income tax	£379·60,
Superannuation	£282·51,
National Insurance	£237·89.

The lecturer's take home pay for the month is £2100.

Calculate what percentage his deductions are of his gross pay.

15. Ella has a take home pay of £39 880 per annum as the Personnel Manager of an IT company.

She pays 6% of her gross pay towards superannuation, which comes to £3480.

Her NI payments are £4640.

Her only other deduction is for Income Tax.

Calculate her Income Tax payment.

Income Tax & Allowances — Income Tax

The Inland Revenue - This is the official name for the department you pay your taxes to.

The Inland Revenue do not calculate your income tax bill purely on your gross income.

Instead, they give you **allowances** and **relief** on part of your income - and other factors are taken into consideration such as :-

- Are you employed or self-employed ?
- What assets or liabilities do you have ?
- Expense accounts,
- Capital Gains, the list goes on.....

These allowances are **taken off** your income before it is taxed.

Income **less than** £31785 is taxed at a standard rate of **20%**. *

Example :-

Mr Greig has an **income** of £18 400.

He has a £7140 **tax allowance**.

How much tax will he pay ?

Taxable income is 18 400 - 7140 = £11 260

Tax = 20% of £11 260 = £2252

Total Income Tax due is **£2252**.

* These figures are for 2015 and will possibly change with time.

Exercise 3

1. Mr Fleming earns £23 650.
   He has a tax allowance of £8014.
   Calculate his income tax. Copy and complete :-

   Taxable income is 23 650 - 8014 = £.....
   20% of £............ = £ ....
   Total Income Tax due is £ ....

2. 

   Mr Bond works in IT and earns £28 400.
   He has a tax allowance of £10 566.
   Calculate how much income tax he is due to pay.

3. Jim, the office boy, has an annual salary of £17 000.
   He has a £9520 tax allowance.
   Calculate his income tax bill.

4. Calculate the income tax due, at 20%, on each of the following :-
   a Mr Dahl earns £19 780 per annum. He has a tax allowance of £4108.
   b Matilda earns £2200 each month. She has a monthly tax allowance of £345.
   c Charlie has a tax allowance of £97·60 on his weekly wage of £568.

5. Ken earns £31 640 per annum selling jet ski equipment.

He has a personal Tax Allowance of £9740.

Ken pays 20% tax.

a Calculate his tax bill.

b Ken also pays monthly N.I. contributions of £501·05 and 6% Superan. on his gross pay.

Calculate his net annual take home pay.

6. Peter has a Tax Allowance of £8764 on his £29 760 gross annual salary.

He pays 20% tax on his taxable income.

His other deductions include N.I. - £176·86 a month and a pension of £30 per week.

Calculate his **monthly** take home pay.

Income Tax calculation is actually much more complicated in real life.

It is a difficult and sometimes very confusing process.

The Inland Revenue determines your **Income Tax Due**, using the table below :-

(*correct as from April 2015*).

Rates of Tax :-

- first £31 785 of taxable income 20%
- £31 786 to £150 000 of taxable income 40%
- all remaining taxable income over £150 000 45%

Example:- Mr Bishop earns £68 400.

He has a £12 560 tax allowance.

Taxable income 68 400 - 12 560	=	£55 840
20% of **£31 785**	=	£6357
40% of £24 055	=	£9622
Total Income Tax due :-		
(£6357 + £9622)	=	**£15 979**

7. Calculate the income tax due on each **taxable income** below :-

a Mr Kenobi - £29 780

b Ms. Leia - £32 000

c Mr Yoda - £51 360

d Mr Solo - £$\frac{1}{4}$ million.

8. "*Jabba*" earned two point five million pounds as a singer last year and had a taxable allowance of £12 560.

Calculate how much income tax she had to pay.

9. Mr Ford owns his own joinery firm and has a taxable income of £142 400.

He completed his income tax form and sent off a cheque for £40 603.

Did he pay the correct amount ? *Explain.*

Income

Finance/Statistics Assessment 1

1. a Greg earns £21 618 per annum. Calculate his monthly wage.

   b Karen earns £11·68 per hour. She works 40 hours per week.

   Calculate her annual wage.

   c Dez earns £14·10 per hour. He works a five day week, 9 am to 4 pm.

   On a Tuesday night, he works three hours overtime at time and a half and he works 6 hours on a Saturday, at double time.

   Calculate Dez's weekly wage.

2. Kalia earned £141 commission on her £3000 sales.

   What is her commission, as a percentage of her sales ?

3. Andy's annual deductions are £4321.

   His net income is £28 451.

   a Calculate Andy's gross pay.

   b Calculate his total deductions as a percentage of his gross pay.

4. Ravi has an annual income of £24 752.

   He has a tax allowance of £9046.

   Calculate what his income tax will be, at a rate of 20%.

5. If Lee worked a basic 40 hour week, he would earn £502.

   Last week, on top of this, he also worked 5 hours overtime at treble time.

   Last week he paid £46·20 Income Tax, £51·10 National Insurance and Superannuation of 6%, based on his total gross pay.

   Calculate his take home pay for the week.

6. Ed earns £18 650 per annum as a consultant.

   He also has a salary from France of €9750 p.a.

   He gets an exchange rate of £1 = €1·30.

   His total income is taxed at 20% in the UK and he has an overall tax allowance of £9760.

   Calculate his total tax bill.

Money Matters

Revision of National 4 Lifeskills

1. Find each of the following :-

   a 25% of £640 b 37% of €1000 c $17\frac{1}{2}$% of £80

   d $\frac{1}{2}$ of £6531 e $\frac{2}{3}$ of \$33 f $\frac{5}{9}$ of €1350.

2. Sally buys a new outfit costing £126·80.
   She is awarded a 15% discount for using her store card.
   She gives the assistant five £20 notes and a £10 note.
   How much change should she receive ?

3. Two shops are selling the same computer.

Compushop

LapTopShop

Which of the deals works out cheaper ?

4. *CheapHols* had a flight to Tenerife for £245.
   There is then a price increase of 10%.
   Hols-R-Us has the same flight at £300.
   They are giving a 12·5% discount.
   Which company would you choose ? *Explain.*

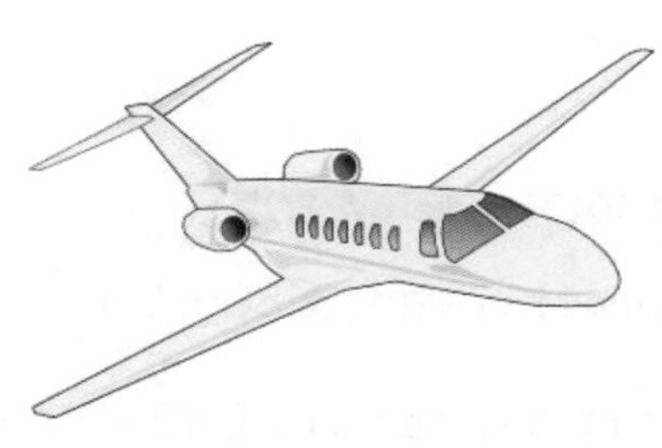

5. *ChocoFantastic* sell two different sizes of luxury chocolate.
   A 400 g box costs £4·20 and a 500 g box costs £5·20.
   Which is the better deal ? *Explain.*

6. a Li gets an exchange rate of £1 to 190 Japanese Yen.
   How many Yen will Li get for £460 ?

   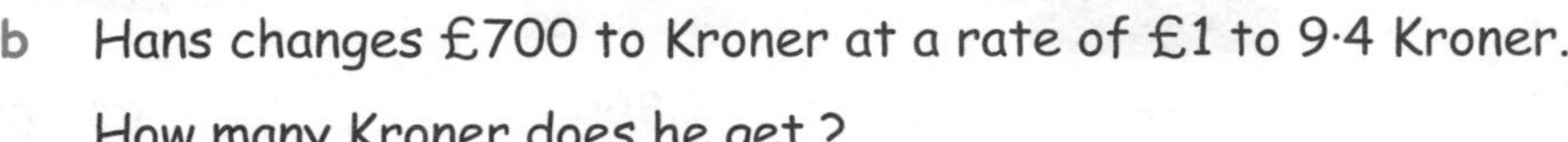

   b Hans changes £700 to Kroner at a rate of £1 to 9·4 Kroner.
   How many Kroner does he get ?

Money Matters

VAT (Value Added Tax)

The government raises some money by charging VAT (*Value Added Tax*).

Most items that you purchase and services that you use are charged VAT (*usually at 20%*).

However, some items like domestic heating, are charged at only 5%.

Items like medicines and school books are zero-rated (0% VAT).

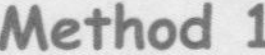

Example :- A 3D - DVD costs £18·80 plus VAT.

How much does the DVD cost in total ?

Method 1

VAT is 20% of £18·80

= 0·2 x 18·80

= £3·76

Total Cost is = (£18·80 + £3·76)

= £22·56

(or £18 · 80 ÷ 5. Remember 20% = $\frac{1}{5}$)

Method 2 Can you see why ?

Total cost is 120% of £18·80

= 1·2 x 18·80

= £22·56

Exercise 1

1. Find the total cost for each item (*using the standard VAT rate of 20%*).
   - a A DVD costing £16 + VAT.
   - b A carpet costing £80 + VAT.
   - c A fridge costing £275 + VAT.
   - d A computer game at £45 + VAT.
   - e A laptop costing £760 + VAT.
   - f A car costing £3120 + VAT.

2. Find the final cost of each item after adding VAT, (*at 20%*) :-

a

£16·80

b

£200

c

£860

d

£72 500

3. Copy and complete each bill :-

a

Dino's Cafe

Drinks.............	£ 8·60
Food	£23·40
Subtotal	....
VAT (20%)........	....
Total cost	....

b

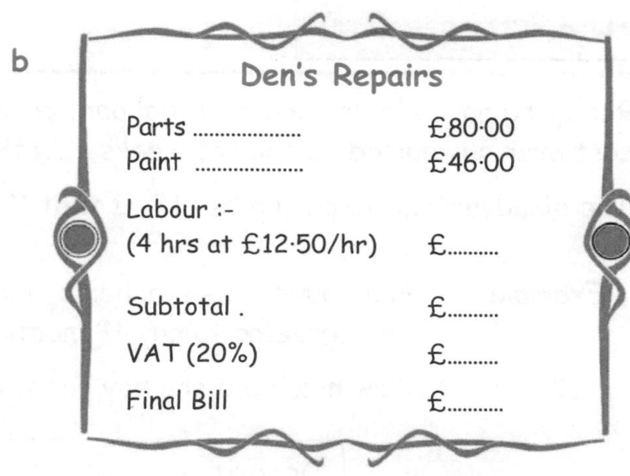

Den's Repairs

Parts	£80·00
Paint	£46·00
Labour :- (4 hrs at £12·50/hr)	£..........
Subtotal .	£..........
VAT (20%)	£..........
Final Bill	£...........

4. Another car is repaired at Den's Garage.

   The parts cost £147·40 and the mechanic spent 4 hours charging £22·25 per hour.

   The garage bill also includes 20% VAT.

   Create a bill and show the total charge for the repairs.

5. a James paid £2500 + VAT to a garden landscaper.

   How much would he have saved if VAT had been charged at 17·5% instead of 20% ?

   b Phil uses 350 units of gas at 3·4 pence per unit.

   The gas company also added a £36·10 service charge.

   Find the total bill including VAT at 5%.

6. A tractor is valued at £44 800 + 20% VAT.

   A 15% discount is to be given to a customer.

   The customer wants the discount taken off before the VAT is added.

   The tractor company want to give the discount after VAT has been added.

   Is there any difference to the final price ? (*Explain*).

7. Jason has estimated his plumber's bill to be under £150.

   The plumber's bill is as follows (*VAT at 20% is still to be included*) :-

4 m of plastic pipe at £6·50/m
5 knuckle joints at £11·20 each
Labour (3·5 hours at £15/hr)

   Was Jason correct in his estimate ? *Explain.*

Hire Purchase (HP)

Receiving goods by making an initial part payment, (**deposit**), and paying the remaining cost over a required number of weeks, months or years, is called **Hire Purchase** (H.P.).

The disadvantage to paying by H.P. is that the goods tend to be a little more expensive.

Example :- Anne buys a dishwasher by making a £30 deposit, and agreeing to pay 12 monthly instalments of £45.

How much did she pay for the dishwasher in total ?

Deposit	£30
Payments (12 x £45)	£540
Total price	**£570**

Exercise 2

1. Frank bought a new bed, paying an initial £50 deposit.

   He then made 18 monthly payments of £12·60.

   How much did he pay in total ?

2. Find the total price paid for each item :-

   a Fridge - £60 deposit, 12 payments of £35.

   b Suite - £800 deposit, 24 payments of £126.

   c TV - £50 deposit, 18 payments of £22·75.

   d Hi-Fi - £45 deposit, 36 payments of £1·25.

3. a Aisha bought a new carpet, costing £1124 in total.

   She paid a deposit of £80 followed by 12 equal monthly instalments.

   How much was each monthly instalment ?

   b Binnie paid a total of £789 for a new oven.

   She made a deposit followed by 18 monthly payments of £35·50.

   How much of a deposit did Binnie pay ?

4. It cost Kurt £680 for a cinema surround system.

   He paid a **10% deposit**, then made 12 equal monthly payments.

   How much was each payment ?

5. Celia paid £1460 for a bathroom suite.

She made a 20% deposit, followed by 40 equal payments.

How much was each payment ?

6. 

A motorised go-cart has a cash price of £250.

It could also be bought on Hire Purchase by making a deposit of 15% and 12 equal payments of £19·75.

How much cheaper is it to pay by cash ?

7. Three companies offer different rates of payments for a £3000 conservatory.

Calculate the total price for each company, and state which is the dearest.

	Deposit	Equal payments
CheapCons	£400	12 at £265 each
Cons-R-Us	10%	18 at £185 each
ConservCo	12·5%	16 at £195 each

8. 

Alan's new pool table ended up costing him £560.

He paid a deposit and made 24 payments of £17·50.

a Calculate the deposit he paid.

b Express the deposit as a percentage of the cost price.

9. The cash price of a motorcycle was £4000.

Ken made a 20% deposit, followed by 32 equal monthly payments.

Afterwards, he discovered he had paid 20% more than the cost price.

How much was each payment ?

10. Dennis has a £550 budget for his greenhouse project.

The company he has chosen to erect the greenhouse gave quotes as shown in the table.

These prices do not include the 20% VAT.

Size	Base		Panelling	
	Concrete	Turf	Glass	Perspex
Large	£450	£350	£125	£ 98
Medium	£360	£300	£100	£ 78
Small	£260	£200	£ 95	£ 70

a Explain why Dennis cannot afford a large greenhouse with a turf base and glass panelling.

b Will Dennis have enough to buy a Medium sized greenhouse with concrete base and perspex panelling, including a £20 payment for insurance ?

(*Remember the VAT*).

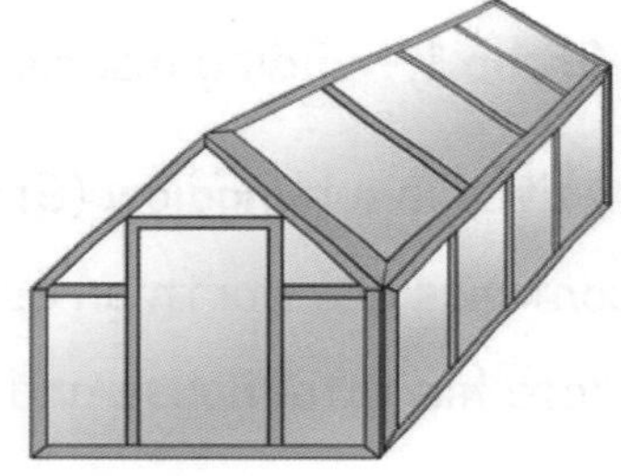

Insurance

Paying a sum of money, to cover you in case an unfortunate event might happen, is called **insurance**.

For example, a fire, a theft or a breakage.

Life insurance is usually referred to as **assurance**.

Payments to insurance or assurance companies vary, depending on many different factors.

The tables shown below give examples of the type of payments.

House and Contents insurance

(Monthly premiums per £10 000)

Group	Building Ins.	Contents Ins.
1	£1·90	£5·90
2	£2·80	£6·20
3	£3·25	£8·00

These groupings depend on the area you live in, how likely you are to be burgled etc.

Life Assurance

25 year term policy - monthly premiums
(for every £100 000 insured)

Age		Non-smoker	Smoker
Male	*Female*		
16-24	16-31	£6·10	£11·40
25	32	£6·50	£11·60
26	33	£6·65	£11·80
27	34	£6·80	£12·50
28	35	£7·10	£12·70
29	36	£7·40	£12·90
30	37	£7·70	£13·80
31	38	£8·20	£14·50

Exercise 3

Use the tables above to answer each question.

1. Keri lives in a Group 2 house.

   She insures its **contents** for £30 000.

   Copy and complete to find her monthly payments :-

   For £10 000 *premium* = £6·20
   For £30 000 *premium* = £6·20 x 3 = ...

2. Calculate each monthly premium :-

   a Group 3, **contents** insurance cover for £40 000.

   b Group 1, **building** insurance cover for £70 000.

3. Harry lives in a bungalow (Group 2), worth £150 000.

   His contents are worth an estimated £40 000.

   Calculate his total house and contents insurance premium.

4. Find the house and contents insurance premium for a :-
   - a £160 000 Group 2 house; contents £45 000.
   - b £215 000 Group 1 house; contents £57 000.

5. Jeremy pays a £17·10 monthly premium for his Group 1 house insurance.

   How much is his house worth ?

6. Each person below takes out a 25 year life assurance policy for £100 000.

   Find the monthly premiums (*payments*) for each person :-
   - a Bob, 22 year old, non-smoker.
   - b Alice, 30 year old, smoker.
   - c Sally, 37 year old non-smoker
   - d Simon, 29 year old, smoker.

7. a Brad, a 28 year old, smokes, and takes out life assurance for £300 000.

   What is his monthly premium ?

   b Paula is a 30 year old who has never smoked.

   She takes out a £200 000 policy.

   How much is her annual premium ?

Profit & Loss

If you buy a car for £7800 and sell it for £6500 you are said to have "made a **LOSS** of £1300".

FOR SALE
Clapped out Renoir Muggan. Unknown number of previous owners. 250 000 miles on the clock. Missing sun-roof. Needs some attention.
£6500 o.n.o.
01234 556677

If you buy a flat for £64 000 and sell it for £77 000 you are said to have "made a **PROFIT** of £13 000".

Profit	=	Selling Price – Buying Price	(*if selling price is greater than buying price*).
Loss	=	Buying Price – Selling Price	(*if buying price is greater than selling price*).

Exercise 4

1. Write down for each of the following the *profit* or *loss* made, and by how much :-
   - a Bought £140 - Sold for £175
   - b Bought £87 - Sold £76
   - c Bought £2164 - Sold £1176
   - d Bought £154·80 - Sold £156·90
   - e Bought £2010 - Sold £1150
   - f Bought £45 800 - Sold £60 000.

2. Janet bought an exercise bike for £420 and a rowing machine for £395.

One year later, she sold the bike for £365 and the rowing machine for £375.

How much of a loss did she make altogether ?

3. 

IMABIKESHOP bought twenty bikes for £4900.

They sold half of the bikes at a 30% profit and the other half in a sale at a 5% loss.

a What was the overall profit made ?

b What was the percentage profit from the original cost price ?

4. "*Ties-R-Us*" in Edinburgh bought a box of 6 identical ties for £49·50.

The ties were all sold, making a profit of 40% on each tie.

How much would a customer pay for one of the ties ?

5. A rope manufacturer recorded the following profit/loss statement :-

2012 - Profit £400 000	2013 - Profit 24% down on last year
2014 - Profit 40% down on 2013	2015 - Loss of half a million pounds.

What is the company's total Profit/Loss for these 4 years ?

6. 

Fran buys 400 shares in a Middle East oil company for £1100.

A month later, she decides to sell the shares at £2·45 each.

She also has to pay her broker 2·5% commission for the sale.

Calculate whether she will make a profit or loss, and of how much ?

7. A farmer organises a car boot sale on his land and charges stall holders 12·5% of their takings.

Since he has no overheads, he should make 100% profit on all he charges.

Jimmy's car lot took in a total of £120.

Jenny's lot took two thirds more than Jimmy's but she told the farmer she had only sold 75% of Jimmy's.

a How much profit did the farmer make from Jimmy and Jenny ?

b How much did Jenny cheat the farmer out of ?

Foreign Currency

You have already learned how to change from British Pounds to another currency (**by multiplying**) and changing back to British Pounds (**by dividing**).

Here, we are going to look at converting between different currencies.

British Pound (June 2015)	£1 =
Euros	1·37
American Dollars ($)	1·53
Chinese Yuan	9·48
Indian Rupees	97·71
Australian Dollars	1·97
Norwegian Kroner	11·99
Swiss Francs	1·43

Example :- Convert $100 to Euros.

Step 1 Convert $100 to £s first by ÷ 1·53

=> $100 = 100 ÷ 1·53 = £65·36

Step 2 Then convert £65·36 to €s by x 1·37

=> £65·36 = 65·36 x 1·37 = **€89 · 54**.

Exercise 5

1. If you were an American, you may wish to form a table similar to the one above, but this time for converting $1 to each currency in the table.

   This would give a new conversion table.

American Dollar (June 2015)	$1 =
British Pounds (£)	....
Euros	....
Chinese Yuan	....
Indian Rupees	....
Australian Dollars	....
Norwegian Kroner	....
Swiss Francs	....

   a Use the fact that £1 = $1·53 to convert backward. i.e. Find $1 = £(1 ÷ 1·53) = £ ......

   b To convert dollars to euros, copy and complete this calculation and enter your currency rate in your table.

   1·53 dollars = 1·37 euros

   => 1 dollar = 1·37 ÷ 1·53 = €.....

   c Similarly, calculate how many Chinese Yuan you get to the dollar.

   e Find the exchange rate from American Dollars to each of the other currencies and copy and complete the table. (*Give each answer to 2 decimal places*).

2. Sandy lives in Texas. He flies to Scotland and brings $800 with him which he converts to pounds at the airport.

   Use your new table to find out how much he gets, in £s.

3. 

   Jessica is flying from New York to Rome for some cosmetic surgery, costing €2300.

   She takes $2500 with her in cash to pay for the operation.

   Has she taken enough ? If not, how many more euros must she withdraw from the ATM in Rome to make up the difference ?

4. 

Betsy lives in California and is coming to Europe to visit some relatives in London, Paris and Copenhagen.

She converts \$600 into pounds, \$450 into euros and \$400 into Norwegian Kroner before she leaves.

How much of each currency will she receive ?

5. Krauss is German. He is going on holiday to Australia and converts €2000 to Australian dollars at the bank.

Use the method shown in the example at the top of the previous page to work out how many dollars Krauss will get.

6. 

Dustin converts \$3000 to euros at a rate of \$1 = €0·90.

He then decides to fly on to Beijing and converts these euros to Chinese Yuan at a rate of €1 = 6·90 Yuan.

Back home in the States, Dustin could have converted his \$3000 directly to Yuan at a rate of \$1 = 6·35.

Would this have given a better deal, and if so, how many extra Chinese Yuan would Dustin have got ?

7. Pierre, in Paris, was checking the price of a new Renoire Morven Estate car on various websites in different countries.

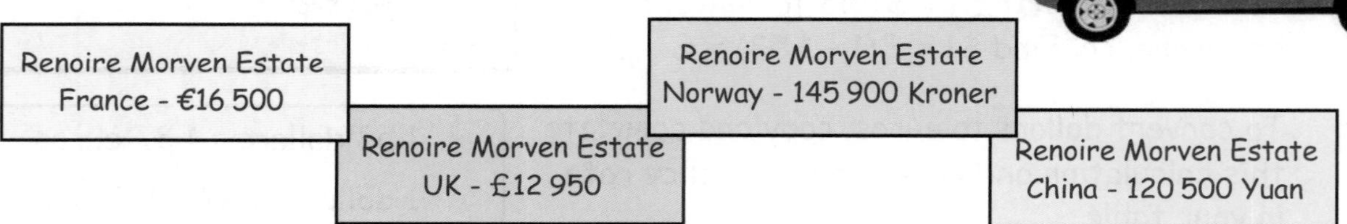

Rank the prices in order (in euros), starting with the cheapest.

8. This graph shows the value of the euro against the pound on the first of each month.

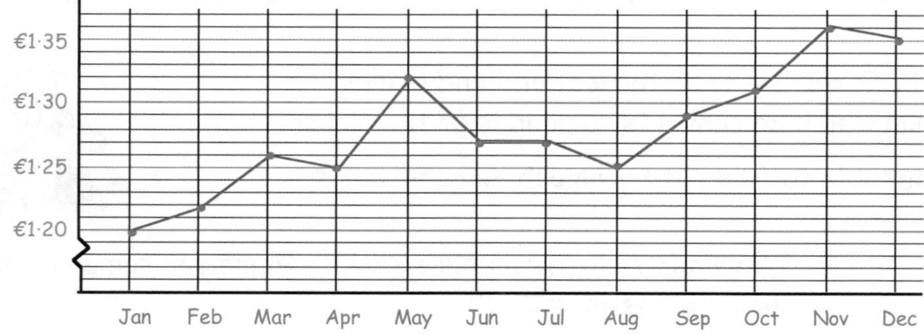

a What was £1 worth in euros on the 1st of :- (i) March (ii) October ?

b During which month did the pound rise by the greatest value against the euro ?

8. c I exchanged £400 on April 1st to Euros.

How many more euros would I have got if I had waited until the 1st of May ?

d What was the general "trend" in the exchange rate during that year ?

9. Robert is looking to buy a small yacht and he considers buying from a company in the south of France.

He can buy the yacht from an English company for £12 500.

The same yacht can be bought from a company in Marseille for €14 250. This appeared a better deal, but Robert discovered that he would have to pay a customs duty of 17% on the boat, and transporting it back to the UK would cost another €550.

Which of the two was the better deal ? (*Explain with working*).

£1 = €1.35

10. On the way to Australia, I found that the exchange rate was £1 = $1·95 (AUD).

On the way home, I found I had $450 left and the rate for exchanging back had gone up to £1 = $2·05.

Financially, was this a better or worse rate for me ? (*Explain*).

11. Terry is an industrial chemist and sees three potential new jobs - one in England, one in Sweden and one in the States.

British Pound	£1 =
Euro	1·38
American Dollar ($)	1·58
Swedish Krona	12·68

Chemical Industries Inc.
(Gothenburg City)
600 000 Kronor* per annum

* plural of Krona

Boston Pharmaceuticals Ltd
(Boston USA)
$39 000 for a
6 month Contract

UK Chemicals Incorporated
Birmingham UK
£3750 per month

a Which is the best offer, financially ? Back up your answer with calculations.

b Why might Terry decide, in terms of money, not to take this job ?

12. This conversion table allows us to convert easily between the six currencies shown.

For example, €1 is worth 6·95 Yuan.

a How many Indian Rupees are there to the Dollar ?

b How many Rupees for $250 ?

c Convert :-

(i) £16 to Pesos (ii) €400 to Dollars

(iii) 650 Pesos to Yuan (iv) 5000 Rupees to £s.

	£1 UK	€1 Europe	$1 USA	1 Peso Mexico	1 Yuan China
€1 Europe	1·37				
$1 USA	1·54	1·12			
1 Peso Mexico	23·91	17·45	15·53		
1 Yuan China	9·52	6·95	6·18	0·40	
1 Rupee India	98·40	71·82	63·90	4·12	10·34

* correct as of June 2015

Simple Interest Revision

There are many different types of bank accounts -

savings, current, high interest, etc.....

Banks generally use percentages to indicate what their interest rates are at any time.

Try to find out about all the different types of bank accounts available.

Exercise 6

1. There are two main reasons why, if you were to come into a sum of money, you should put it in a bank (or building society). Write down the reasons.

2. Dave and Dee put their combined savings of £4000 into "*SCOTTIE BANK*" (APR 3%).

   How much **interest** would they receive after 1 year ? (*3% of £4000*).

3. Calculate how much each of these savings would be worth in total at the end of 1 year :-

   a Sandy invested £12 000. Annual Interest Rate = 4% p.a.

   b Nadia invested £800. Annual Interest Rate = 2% p.a.

   c Stephen invested £3200. Annual Interest Rate = 3·5% p.a.

   d Ari invested £27 400. Annual Interest Rate = 5·5% p.a.

4. Kara had £7000 and decided to invest it with *Banka Building Society*.

   a What rate of interest should she expect (2·4%, 2·8% or 3·1%) ?

   b Calculate how much interest Kara would receive after 1 year.

BANKA BUILDING SOCIETY

"The more you bank - The higher the rate"

up to £1000	-	2·4%
£1000 - £10 000	-	2·8%
over £10 000	-	3·1%

5. For each of the following, the investment is given, along with the accrued interest at the end of 1 year in each person's account.

   Calculate what rate of interest each received, (*to 3 significant figures where necessary*).

   a Fran - £2000 - (£111 interest) b Jo - £400 - (£10·48 interest)

   c Harry - £11 400 - (£512·18 int.) d Jia - £4800 - (£235·87 int.)

6. Who got the highest interest rate in question 5 ?

Compound Interest

You have already met the idea of **simple interest** and **compound interest** in Chapter 3.

Remember, in **compound interest** questions, you calculate the interest in year 1, add it on, then calculate the interest for the 2nd year based on this new total.

You repeat this process for year 3, then year 4 etc.

This exercise will remind you how to set down your working and extend into likely exam type questions.

Exercise 7

1. Ailsa invests £600 in the *Scotia Bank*.

   Their annual rate is 4%.

   Calculate the compound interest that builds up in the account.

   Copy and complete the question shown opposite :-

1st Year Balance		£600·00
1st Year Interest = 4% of £600·00	=	£24·00
2nd Year Balance = £600·00 + £24·00	=	£624·00
2nd Year Interest = 4% of £624·00	=	£.....·.....
3rd Year Balance = £624·00 + £.....·....	=	£.....·.....
3rd Year Interest = 4% of £.....·.....	=	£.....·.....
=> Final Balance = £.....·..... + £.....·....	=	£.....·.....
=> **Total Interest** = £.....·... - £600·00	=	£.....·.....

2. Bonnie and Clyde invested £4800 in their building society account and left it there for two years.

   The annual interest rate was 3·5%.

   Calculate the compound interest in their account over 2 years.

3. Mr Jenkins was advised to invest his £18 000 life savings in a special High Interest Savings Account, but he had to agree not to touch it for 3 years.

   The interest rates for the 3 year period were 4·5%, 5% and 5·3% respectively.

   a Calculate the value of his savings at the end of each year.

   b What was the total interest that had accrued on his account ?

   c Express this as a percentage of his original investment.

   d Would Mr Jenkins have been better to invest in a fixed rate account with 5% interest ? *Explain.*

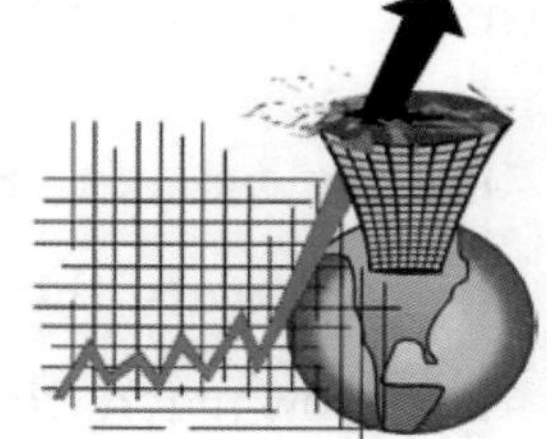

4. Which of the following would give a better return on investing £10 000 for 3 years :-

   TrustBank - A fixed interest rate of 3·6% each year.

   Bundabank - A rate of 2·5% in year one, 3·9% in year two and 4·4% in year three ?

Borrowing Money

Individuals and small to large companies sometimes need to borrow money.

This borrowing can take the form of a bank loan or credit or store card.

Example :- Zara needs to borrow £5000 to pay for a luxury holiday.

She has two options :-

a *Smart Bank* will charge her 18·9% if she repays it monthly over 1 year.

b *Sunny Personal Loans* will charge her £1104 per month over 6 months.

Which of the two will mean she pays less interest ?

Solution :-

a *Smart* - 18·9% of £5000 = 18·9 ÷ 100 x 5000 = **£945** total interest

Monthly payments = (£5000 + £945) ÷ 12 = **£495·42**.

b *Sunny* - Total payment over 6 months = 6 x £1004 = **£6024**.

Total interest due = £6024 - £5000 = **£1024**.

Discuss :-

- which is obviously the better deal ?
- why someone might have to take out a *Sunny Personal Loan* ?

Exercise 8

Scotia Bank has different APRs (Annual Percentage Rates).

The more you borrow, the lower the interest rate.

Loan	under £500	£500-£1000	£1000-£2000	£2000-£5000	over £5000
APR (1 year)	11·6%	9·2%	8·4%	6·5%	4·9%

1. Fred wants to borrow £4000 for 1 year to landscape his garden.
   a What is the APR Fred would expect to be charged ?
   b Calculate the added interest and the total amount payable.
   c If Fred sets up a standing order to pay the loan, what will his monthly payments be ?

2. Carole wishes to borrow £650 over one year to pay for her dentist's bill.
   a Calculate the added interest she must pay and the total amount payable.
   b How much will Carole's monthly payments be ?

3. Craig and Cara need to borrow £1800 for a new kitchen in their flat.
   They have a budget of £150 per month for the 12 repayments.
   Have they budgeted correctly ? Explain.

4. 

Olive needs a short term loan from *Scotia* of £2500.

She wishes to pay it back within 6 months.

a How much interest would this be for 1 year ?

b How much for 6 months and what would the amount payable be ?

c What would each of her six monthly payments work out at ?

5. The Smiths want to borrow £8000 to buy a new car.

Scotia offers them two different loan options :-

Scotia Bank Rates	Annual Interest Rate	Loan term
Loan payment 1st option	9·5%	12 months
Loan payment 2nd option	8·6%	6 months

a Calculate the monthly repayments for both the 1st and the 2nd options.

b Which option do you think they might choose and explain your reasoning ?

c A third option is to use a credit card at an APR of 1·25% per month.

Explain why they would be best NOT to consider this option.

6. Graeme borrows £900 from *Scotia Bank* to pay for a holiday.

The annual rate is 9·2% and he hopes to pay it back over 1 year.

He reckons he can afford £75 per month at most from his pay.

Will he be able to stay within his budget with his monthly payments ?

7. Gazza uses £3000 on his credit card for which the bank charges a **compound** interestrate of 2·5% **monthly** on money owed.

He moved house and forgot about it.

Six months later, the credit card company contacted him and he had to take out a one year bank loan at APR 7·8%, to just cover his debt.

How much were his monthly payments to the bank ?

8. Rhea needs to borrow £4000 to buy a car.

She has three options to consider.

Option 1	A garage will charge £210 a month for 2 years.
Option 2	A bank will charge the £4000 plus 17·5% interest over 18 months.
Option 3	A building society will charge £4000 plus 12·5% interest over 1 year.

a What is her cheapest monthly payment option ?

b What is her cheapest option overall ?

c Which option would you choose ? Explain your choice.

Money Matters

Finance/Statistics Assessment 2

1. Find the total cost of each item, using VAT at 20% :-

   a A suit costing £350 + VAT

   b A caravan costing £24 000 + VAT.

2. An electrician's bill is as shown :-

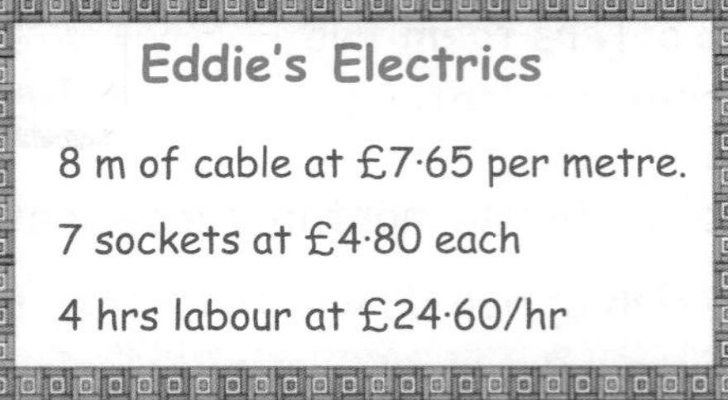

Eddie's Electrics

8 m of cable at £7·65 per metre.

7 sockets at £4·80 each

4 hrs labour at £24·60/hr

The customer has paid his bill, but has forgotten to add on the 20% VAT.

How much does the customer still have to pay ?

3. Find the total price of a suite, when a customer makes a £40 deposit, followed by 12 payments of £64 each.

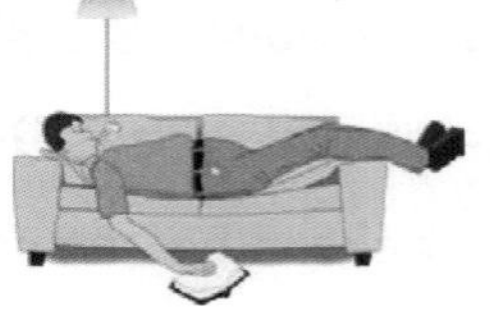

4. 

   Quinten paid a total of £1450 for his new computer.

   He made a 20% deposit followed by 20 equal payments.

   How much was each payment ?

5. Kath insures her house and contents with *A-Sure*.

   She pays monthly :-

   £1·76 for every £10 000 worth of contents

   £4·90 for every £50 000 worth of building.

   Her contents are worth £45 000 and the building is worth £150 000.

   How much is her total monthly insurance premium for house and contents ?

6. Harry bought 200 toy vintage cars at £16·75 each.

   He then spent 15% of the cost price restoring them.

   A year later, he auctioned the whole collection for £6000.

   Harry wanted to make a profit of at least 50%.

   Did he achieve his minimum profit ?

7. a Gina gets an exchange rate of £1 to $1·64.

   How many dollars will she receive for £640 ?

7. b Josh exchanged £350 for Albanian Lek at a rate of £1 = 191·76 Lek.

He estimated he would get 67 000 (± 100) Lek.

Was his estimate correct ? *Explain.*

Albanian Flag

c Isla exchanged £365 for €485·45.

What was her exchange rate ?

8. Calculate how much these savings would be worth :-

a Sandy invested £4600 for one year at an APR of 3%.

b Sean put £8760 in an account for **four months** at an APR of 3·2%.

9

a Sam invested £3200 in a building society which gave a return of 2·9% interest annually, (*compounded*).

How much will he have in his account after 3 years ?

b After leaving £640 in her account for 2 years, Ella got a return of 3% p.a. compound interest on her investment.

How much interest did she get back ?

10. Grace is buying a new kitchen, priced at £4800.

She considers the three options below :-

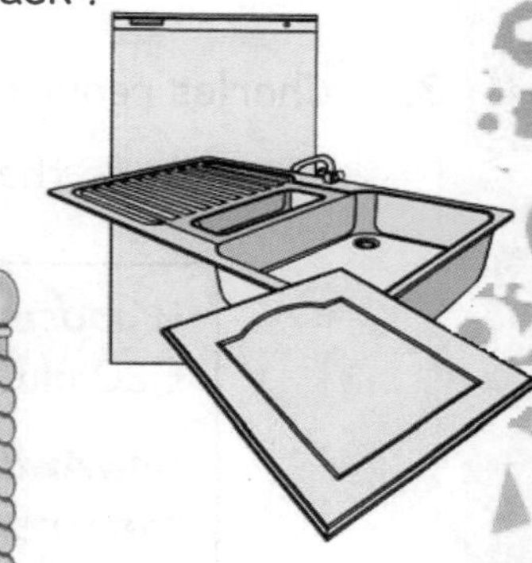

A Bank loan charging an APR of 9·8% over one year.

B Finance company charging 7·6% p.a. as long as the loan is paid in 6 monthly instalments.

C Kitchen Store Card giving a 5% discount and then charging an APR of 13·5% over one year.

Which has the lowest monthly payments and which is cheaper overall ? *Explain.*

11. Eric has two savings accounts, one in the UK and one in Germany.

His UK account has £4600 and gives an APR of 3·6%.

His German account has €6400 and gives an APR of 3·2%.

(*Eric can get an exchange rate of £1 to €1·20*).

Which bank will yield more compound interest after 2 years, and how much more ?

Best Deals

Revision of Best Deals

1. *Killemall Weedkiller* comes in 2 sizes.

   The 400 ml bottle costs £7·40 and the
   1·5 litre plastic container costs £25·50.

   a How much does it cost per 100 ml for the bottle ?

   b How much does it cost per 100 ml for the container ?

   c Which is better value ? (*Explain*).

2. Which pack of *Pot Noodles* is the best buy - the 4-pack, the 6-pack or the 10-pack ?

£2·40

£3·48

£5·70

3. Charles requires to hire a chain saw to cut down dead fir trees in his back garden.

   He reckons that he will need it for 6 hours.

   Woodcutters charge a basic hiring fee of £20 plus £12 per hour after that.

   SawAway don't charge any basic fee, but their rental charge is £15·50 per hour.

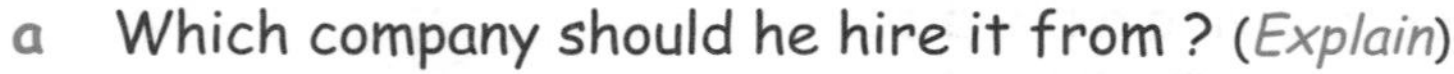

   a Which company should he hire it from ? (*Explain*).

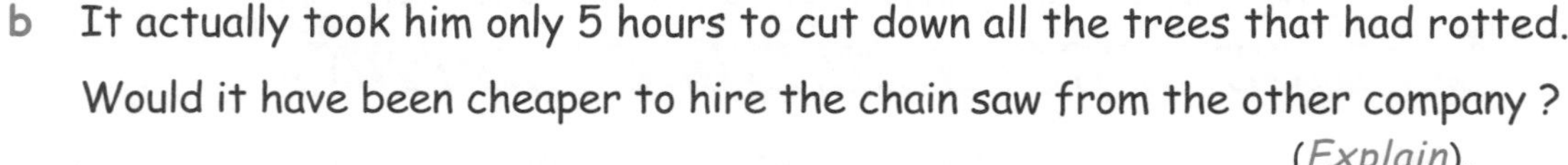

   b It actually took him only 5 hours to cut down all the trees that had rotted.

   Would it have been cheaper to hire the chain saw from the other company ? (*Explain*).

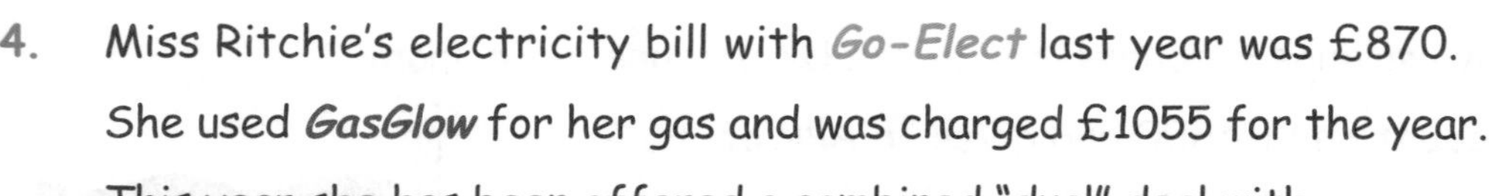

4. Miss Ritchie's electricity bill with *Go-Elect* last year was £870.

   She used ***GasGlow*** for her gas and was charged £1055 for the year.

   This year she has been offered a combined "dual" deal with ***ElectroGas***, with her total bill for both gas and electricity estimated to be £155 per month.

   Should Miss Ritchie sign up with ***ElectroGas*** for the oncoming year ? (*Explain*).

Best Deals

Managing Your Money - Finding the Best Deal

When running a home, most people have to work to a budget.

When shopping, money can be saved by finding the **best buys** for individual items.

Example :-

Puss Puss cat food comes in three sizes.

- A 300 gram tin costs £1·89.
- A 550 gram tin costs £3·52.
- A 1 kg gram tub costs £5·79.

By calculating the cost of **100 grams** of food for each size of tin, decide which is the **best deal**.

Cost of small tin per 100 g :-

£1·89 ÷ 3 = £0·63.

Cost of medium tin per 100 g :-

£3·52 ÷ 5·5 = £0·64.

Cost of large tub per 100 g :-

£5·79 ÷ 10 = £0·579.

Best Deal is the large 1 kg tub.

The 550 g tin is the dearest.

Exercise 1

1. Three hotels ordered the same make of pork chops from different supermarkets.

   - *Park Hotel* paid *Murrysons* £31·50 for 7 kg of chops.
   - *River Hotel* paid *Tespo* £43·70 for 10 kg.
   - *Duke Hotel* paid *Wainbrose* £57·50 for 12·5 kg.

   Which hotel got the best deal ? *Explain.*

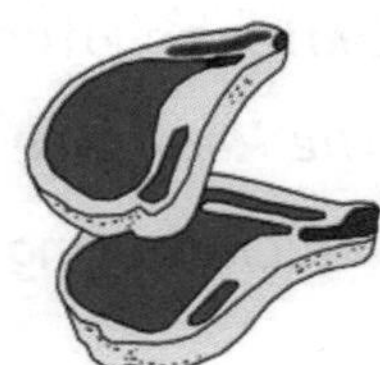

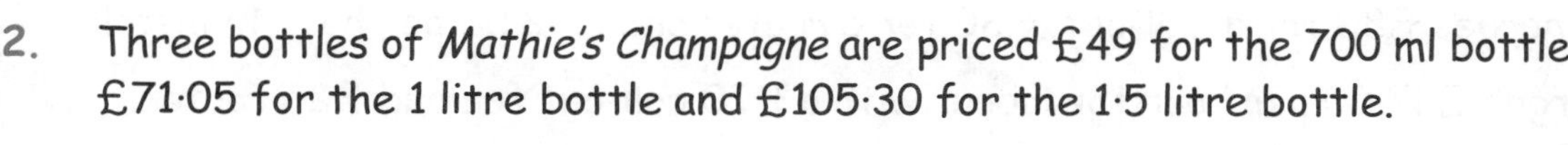

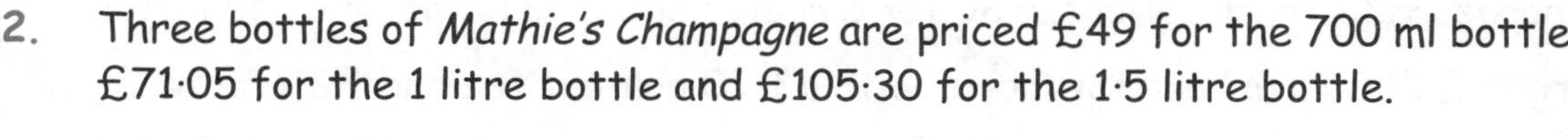

2. Three bottles of *Mathie's Champagne* are priced £49 for the 700 ml bottle, £71·05 for the 1 litre bottle and £105·30 for the 1·5 litre bottle.

   Which size of bottle gives the best value ? *Explain.*

3. Mr Robson the gardener is buying plants to put in his clients' gardens.

   He sees the following prices in different garden centres :-

   - *McCall Nurseries* are selling packs of 4 for £4·60.
   - *Doddies* are selling packs of 6 for £7·38.
   - *The Rose Garden* sells packs of 20 for £22·50.

   Assuming that all plants are in good condition and that he requires 60 plants :-

   a Where should he go for his plants ?

   b *McCall Nurseries* offer him - "buy 3 of their packs for £12". Should he reconsider ?

4. A tailor buys buttons in bulk. The following prices are the best online at the moment :-

- Box of 1000 from *Boutons* - £15·50.
- Pack of 2500 from *Button Hole* - £38.
- Box of 4000 from *Button.com* - £60·60.

Which company is offering the best online deal ? Explain.

5. *Canary Island Holidays* are promoting these 3 special offers (per couple) :-

- Tenerife Hotel - from Edinburgh - 7 nights, all inclusive, flights, free bus transfer - £1624.
- Lanzarote Palace - from Glasgow - 10 nights, all inclusive, flights, free taxi transfer - £2300.
- Hotel Gran Canaria - from Edinburgh - 11 nights, all inclusive, flights, free bus transfer - £2559·70.

The Henrys from Paisley don't care how long the holiday lasts - they simply want the best deal.

Suggest at least 3 reasons (including the price) why they should choose Lanzarote Palace.

6. *JR Roofing* charge a rate of £35 per hour and have a £40 call-out fee.

Slaters have a £25 call-out charge and a rate of £31·50 per hour.

The Roof Man has a £10 call-out fee and a rate of £58·20 per hour.

JR Roofing quoted Miss Thomas for a four hour job to repair her roof.

Slaters quoted five hours to do the same job.

The Roof Man said he could do the job in three hours.

Which roofing company gave the lowest quote and by how much ?

7. Mr Ralston needs a new phone line set up, and a new router.

RG Media charges £80 for a call-out, £30 for a router and £42·50 per hour to install.

Stirgin charges £47·50 per hour for labour with a £70 call-out fee and £25 router.

Sunbox charges £30 for a call-out, £40 per hour for labour and £75 for a router.

The job is scheduled to take 2 hours.

a What would be Mr Ralston's cheapest option ?

b If the work was to run into a third hour, would this option still be the cheapest ?

8. *DMS* have 3 hire purchase options on offer for this 3-seater sofa bed.

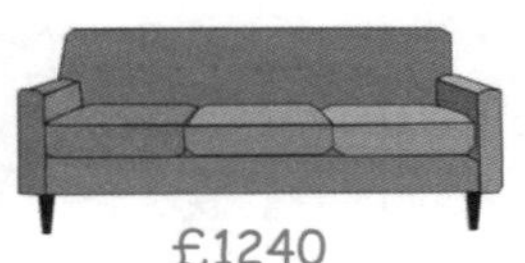

£1240

- Pay a deposit of 15% and make 12 payments of £88·50.
- Pay no deposit and pay it up with 24 payments at £52·50.
- Pay a deposit of 12·5% and pay it over 3 years at £32 per month.

Which method works out cheapest ?

9. Alfie is looking for the best currency exchange rate to change his Euros to £'s.

- *Xchange* give a rate of 1·32 Euros to the £.
- *Money House* offer 1·30 Euros to the £.
- *Foreign Exchange* will give you 1·295 Euros for your £, but they charge a 1% handling fee.

If Alfie has 265 Euros to exchange, how much less would he get by choosing the dearest, rather than the cheapest exchange company, to the nearest ten pence ?

10. Farmer Wylde is taking out an £18 500 loan to buy another tractor.

Three different companies offer him the interest rates shown :-

a Which company should he use ? (*Explain*).

b Calculate the greatest amount of interest he will have to pay for his loan.

c How much will he save by taking the best rate rather than the 2nd best rate ?

LoanHere	-	12·5% interest
Pay-for-It	-	14% interest
Loans-On-Us	-	15·5% interest

11. Des looks online to upgrade his gardening equipment. He finds the following prices :-

Retailer	Storage Box	Lawnmower	Strimmer	Hand Tools	Hedge Cutter
Q&B	£140	£140	£25	£60	£105
Housebase	£145	£150	£30	£55	£85
B&R	£135	£190	£35	£40	£130
Dubbies	£140	£175	£25	£80	£135
QWC	£125	£160	£30	£45	£90
GardenQuip	£130	£190	£20	£50	£115

a Des wants to buy one of each item and is happy to buy them from different retailers.

Calculate the minimum cost for his new gardening equipment.

b

Des can't afford to pay for all of them at once.

He contacts the retailers and only one of them, GardenQuip, can come up with a finance package for him.

They ask for a deposit of 15% of their total cash price, followed by 12 payments of £37·50.

If he agrees to this package, how much more will it cost him overall than the minimum cost he found in part a ?

Best Deals

Finance/Statistics Assessment 3

1. These wooden troughs come in 3 sizes.

   The small 50 litre trough costs £10·95;
   the 75 litre one costs £17·20
   and the 100 litre trough costs £21·50.

   Which one gives the best value per litre ?

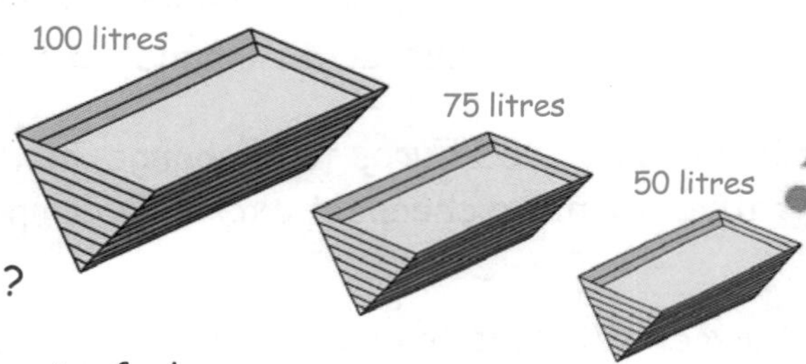

2. Anthony is having his front garden lawn re-turfed.

   - *LawnLay* charges £5·80 per m^2, as well as a charge of £8·50 for the fertiliser.
   - *Turfy* charges £6·10 per m^2, but the fertiliser only costs £6·90.
   - *GreenGrass* charge £5·45 per m^2, but their fertilizer is costly at £21·29.

   Anthony's lawn has an area of 40 square metres.

   Which company offers the best deal for his size of lawn ?

3. Simon is looking at 3 different mobile phone providers' tariffs.

4 Mobile	*£18·50 per month*	*200 min free - then 10p/min*	*300 free texts then 10p/text*
Movaphone	*£26 per month*	*400 mins free - then 8p/min*	*100 free texts then 9p/text*
T3	*£39·50 per month*	*350 mins free - then 5p/min*	*free texting.*

   Last month's statement indicated that he used 430 minutes of calls and 280 texts.

   a Work out which option is best for Simon by calculating what it would have cost him last month with these 3 providers.

   b Simon decided to take out a contract with 4 Mobile.

   This month, he has used 500 mins and 350 texts.

   Would he have been better off with another provider ?

4. Mr & Mrs Murray want to put £8000 into a savings account for 1 year.

   They looked at various bank interest rates and decided to invest in one of these three banks :-

Bank	Interest Rates	Tax
Inverdale	1·9% + a bonus* of 0·4%	20%
Tayport	2·2%	20%
Portlet	1·8%	free
*bonus given for no withdrawals		

   a Calculate the net interest on their money for each bank.

   b Advise the Murrays as to which bank(s) they should use, using your calculations to justify your advice.

Budgeting

Revision of Budgeting

1. Sue sets up a standing order and pays £45 per month into a special account to help pay for a holiday in Tenerife.

   She does this for 9 months, at which time she has to pay for the trip.

   If the holiday costs £625, how much extra does Sue need to add to her savings to pay for the holiday fully ?

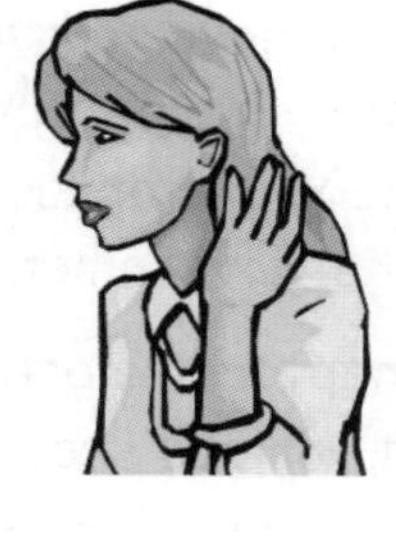

2. Sue works as a receptionist for a large Media Company.

   Her hourly rate of pay is £9·15 and last month she worked a total of 160 hours.

   Her payslip showed deductions of £287·00.

   As well as this, Sue works 5 hours on each of four Friday evenings in a restaurant, where the hourly rate is £7·75, with no tax.

   a Calculate Sue's total net income for last month.

   She rents a flat and estimates her outgoings each month.

Rent - £370	Car Loan - £105	Electricity - £155
Food - £160	Petrol - £80	Mobile - £37·50
Entertainment - £150	Holiday £45	Cigarettes - £160

   Whatever she has left, Sue puts into her savings account.

   b How much can Sue save during the month ?

   c What could she cut down on to help with her savings ?

3. Sue reckons her flat needs a makeover.

   She decides to borrow £900 to have it decorated and to help purchase a new suite.

   She takes the loan out over 1 year and the bank charges her 12% for the loan.

   a Calculate the overall cost.

   b Calculate her monthly repayments.

   c Can Sue afford the payments if she does not cut back on her other expenses listed in question 2 ?

Budgeting

Budgeting

Most people have to **budget** their money, whether it is someone at school with possibly a part time job, a student at college staying in a flat, a family where one or more might be working (or not), or the Local Authority or even the Government itself.

In this chapter, we are going to study various aspects of budgeting, by looking at various scenarios that Eve, a single mum, finds herself in.

Exercise 1

1. Eve's friend Jim is saving £25 a week to buy a new bike costing £595, in time for his cycling holiday in 18 weeks.

   a Will he have managed to save enough for the bike ?

   b How much more will he need to add to his savings ?

2. Eve herself saves £7·50 every week for 12 weeks to buy a pair of red shoes costing £125.

   For how many more weeks will she need to save ?

3. Eve's sister Sophie saves £20 a week for an outfit costing £196.

   Sophie's partner Dan saves £35 per week for a £225 suit.

   Who will be able to buy their item first and by how many weeks ?

4. Jim's mate Eric saves £85 every month, hoping to buy a HD TV set costing £675.

   a For how many months will he need to save to be able to afford the TV set ?

   b After 3 months, he notices a sale, where the TV is reduced by 20%.

   For how many more months will he have to save ?

5. Eric works 5 days a week and has budgeted a maximum of £60 per week from his pay.

   £40 is for his train fares to and from work, and he wants to spend £5 a day on his lunch.

   a What is wrong with his calculations ?

   b What should he do to correct this ?

Managing a Budget Scenario 1 - Monthly Budgeting

Eve is a single mother of two young boys Alfie & Finn, and she is concerned about managing her finances properly. She works part time in an office and receives benefits from the government to help her look after her children, but she has a lot of expenses each month. She decides to set up a monthly budget so that she knows how much money she is spending.

Exercise 2

1. Eve has listed her income and expenditure. Some of these are weekly - others are monthly.

Council Tax	£55 per month	Gas	£80 per month
Wages	£750 per month	Food	£320 per month
Electricity	£45 per month	Rent	£350 per month
Child benefit	£33·50 per week	Fuel	£70 per month
Child Tax Credit	£113·50 per week	Working Tax Credit	£68 per week
Car Loan	£108 per month	Car Ins	£51 per month
Credit card	£100 per month	TV Licence	£15 per month
Clothing & Shoes	£80 per month	Mobile Phone top-up	£60 per month

Can you calculate the following monthly amounts to assist Eve ? (*Use 1 month = 4 weeks*)

a Child Benefit per month –

b Child Tax Credit per month –

c Working Tax Credit per month -

2. Draw up a planner, similar to that shown below, and transfer the information from the table above onto the appropriate side on the Income/Expenditure list.

3. By subtracting her expenditure from her income, Eve calculates how much money she has left each month. How much does she have ?

Make up and fill in a Budget Planning sheet like this.

Monthly Budget Planner Sheet for Eve Jones	
INCOME	EXPENDITURE
Over/Under Spend (Income – Expenditure)	£ ....

4. Eve has both fixed and variable amount expenses.

   List her fixed amount expenses.

5. Eve takes her car to the garage for an MOT and she gets a bill for £220 for repairs needed to be carried out.

   How much money will Eve have left this month once the bill is paid ?

6. Eve currently works 21 hours a week, but her manager asks if she could increase her hours to 28 hours per week. This would mean her pay would go up to £1000 per month, but her working tax credit would decrease to £150 per month.

   What affect would this have on her budget ? Should she increase her hours ?

7. Look at Eve's income and expenditure, what other changes could effect her budget ?

Managing a Budget Scenario 2 - Savings Accounts

Eve has been carefully budgeting for some months and wants to begin saving for her family's future. She can only afford to save a small amount each month, but she hopes to be able to save more in 6 months when her credit card bill is paid off. She decides to visit her local bank to get some advice.

Exercise 3

1. Eve has £100 savings at the end of June 2015, and decides she can afford to save £50 per month from then and £120 per month once her credit card is paid off in 6 months time.

   a After a year, how much money would Eve have in her savings ?

   b The bank manager asks Eve how much access she needs to her savings. What does this mean ?

2. Eve wants to be able to take her money out in the event of an emergency, so the bank manager shows her what savings accounts are available.

Unmistakable SAVINGS — FLEXIBLESAVER

1·5% variable interest per year	£1·00 only to open the account
Unlimited withdrawals	Card Account

Special Instructions :- Account holder must be 16+ years

Unmistakable SAVINGS — MIGHTYMONTHLY

2·5% variable interest per year	£100 needed to open the account
Unlimited withdrawals	Passbook Account

Special Instructions :- £100 minimum balance £20-£1000 to be paid monthly

Unmistakable SAVINGS — ISASAVER ACCOUNT

4% fixed interest for 3 years	£500 needed to open the account
NO withdrawals	Online Account

Special Instructions :- Tax Free Savings Acc Holder must be 16+ years

   a Which of the savings accounts do you think would be the most suitable for Eve ?

   b State your reasons for choosing that account, pointing out why this is a better choice than either of the other two accounts ?

3. Eve opens a *MIGHTYMONTHLY* account with her £100 at the start of July 2015 and finds that interest is paid on the account after 6 months and after 1 year. (i.e. every 6 months).

   a If she pays in £50 per month from 1st July for the first 6 months, then £120 per month for the next 6 months, what will the balance in her account be at the end of :-

   (i) December 2015 (ii) May 2016 ?

   b Eve is disappointed to find that if she wishes to close her account, then the amount of interest she would receive would be slightly less than she expected.

   Can you suggest a possible reason for this ?

4. Here is the page showing Eve's savings in her passbook.

She increases the amount she pays into her account to £120 per month from 1st January 2016.

Write up the entries in the passbook to show how much Eve has in her account just after interest is added on the 30th June 2016.

	Paid In	New Balance
31/12/15	-	£405·00
01/01/16	£120·00	£525·00
01/02/16	£120·00	£6
01/03/16		

5. At the end of the year, Eve decides to transfer £800 of her savings into a new account which will earn her a better rate of interest.

   a Into which of the 3 accounts should Eve transfer her money ?

   b List differences between this new account and her existing account.

6. The interest in this account is calculated at the end of each year and is **compounded**.

   If Eve leaves her £800 in this account for the 3 years, how much will her savings in this account be worth at the end of that 3 year period ?

7. Alfie opens an account to save his pocket money. The bank's YoungSaver account pays 6·5% per year with an annual 0·75% bonus paid if a minimum of £20 is paid into the account each month. Interest is credited to the account at the end of December.

   a Alfie pays in half of his £50 monthly allowance on the 1st of each month from 1st July 2015 to 1st December 2015. How much is in Alfie's account on 2nd December ?

   b Does Alfie qualify for the interest bonus ?

   c How much will he have in his account at the end of December once interest is added ?

8. Eve inherits £2500 from her great aunt and decides to save the money towards the boys' university fees. She doesn't want to have access to the money until the boys start university and she wants the best savings interest rate for the money.

   The best rates Eve could find are listed opposite :-

Name of Company	Type of Account	Int Rate
Initial Savings Bank	3 year fixed bond	3·75% pa
BAC Bank PLC	5 year fixed bond	4·5% pa
Thrifty Credit Union	10 year fixed bond	6·0% pa

   a How much interest would Eve receive from each of the above accounts after 12 months ?

   b Assuming the interest is compounded on each of the accounts, how much would Eve's money be worth at the end of each bond ?

   c Alfie is 11 years old at present and will go to university when he is 18 years old.

   Which bond do you think that Eve should put her money in ? Why do you think this ?

   d What are the reasons that Eve might consider splitting the money and opening 2 separate accounts ?

Managing a Budget Scenario 3 - Credit & Borrowing

Eve's sister, Sophie, and her partner Dan have a new baby girl called Alice. They need a bigger car, but Sophie is on maternity leave so her income is reduced. Dan has worked out a budget based on their monthly combined income & expenditure to see how much money they can afford to pay for a car loan.

Exercise 4

1. Dan calculates that their income is £1860 per month and their current expenditure totals £1684 per month.

   How much do they have left to spend on their monthly car loan repayments ?

2. Dan & Sophie have a meeting at their bank to arrange a car loan for £7500.

   The loan APR is 6·2% and the loan can be repaid over a 2 year, 3 year or 5 year term.

   a Calculate how much interest Dan and Sophie would pay over each loan term.

   b What choice do Dan and Sophie have, in as far as taking out the £7500 loan ?

B.A.C BANK PLC.

£7500 @ 6·2% over 24 months	£332·51 per month
£7500 @ 6·2% over 36 months	£228·27 per month
£7500 @ 6·2% over 60 months	£145·10 per month

3.

Sophie and Dan drive their new car to the retail park.

In her favourite store, *Bambino*, Sophie is offered a store card when she goes to pay for her shopping.

If she completes an application form and uses it to pay for her shopping, she will get "15% discount off today's purchases".

   a She completes the application for the store card. How much does it actually end up costing for her goods, totalling £119·95, in her shopping basket ?

   b To repay the money spent on the store card, Sophie must either pay back £5 per month or 3% of the outstanding balance - whichever is the greater amount.

   How much are Sophie's monthly repayments ?

   c Sophie is sent a monthly statement to show the amount outstanding on the store card.

   After 12 monthly repayments, her store card statement showed that the balance outstanding was £74·80. If she decided to pay this off straight away, how much extra would it have cost her altogether by this time than if she had not taken out the card ?

   d It takes Sophie 35 months to eventually clear the balance on her store card.

   How much will her purchases actually end up costing her ?

4. Sophie really needs a new food mixer to use for her bread making business.

   It is very expensive at £399·95, but comes with lots of accessories.

   In her *Shopper's Paradise* catalogue she can pay for the food mixer at £3·44 per week. (£14·90 per month).

   a It will take Sophie 130 weeks to pay off the food mixer.

     How much will the food mixer end up costing Sophie ?

   b Was this a sensible choice for Sophie to make ? What could she have done instead ?

5. How much money are Sophie & Dan now paying out in total per month, including the car loan, the store card and *Shopper's Paradise* expenditure ?

6. What impact will this have on their original budget ?

7. The delivery company Dan works for is not doing well and he has been forced to reduce his working hours for this month.

   This means that the family income is reduced to £1674 for the month.

   a Express this reduction as a %age of their previous income.

   b (i) What does this mean for the family's budget ?

     (ii) What is their monthly deficit ?

8. Dan sees an advert for *QuickPound* Pay-Day Loan Company on the TV.

   According to the advert, he will get the money quickly and he thinks this would be a potential solution to their financial problems.

QuickPound Pay-Day Loan			
Representative APR	Loan Amount	Maximum Term	Repayment per £1
1270% APR	£50 to £1000	3 months	£1·24 over 30 days

   Dan borrows the exact amount needed to cover his month's deficit. (i.e. - £175).

   a What monthly interest rate is being charged for the *QuickPound* loan ?

   b How much would he be charged for this loan at the end of the 30 day period ?

   c Assuming that Dan gets paid his full wage next month, along with his annual bonus of £150, can they afford to pay the loan back within the 30 days, in addition to their existing outgoings ?

9. What alternative solutions to the *QuickPound* loan do Dan & Sophie have to cover the shortfall in their budget ?

10. Reviewing Dan & Sophie's actions - where do you think they made their mistake ?
    (***note*** *:- Handing the baby back is definitely not an option !*)

Budgeting

Finance/Statistics Assessment 4

1. Charlie starts saving 8 weeks before his sister's wedding.

   He hopes to give her £300 as a wedding present.

   He saves £1 in week one, £2 in week two, £4 in week three, £8 in week four and so on right up to week of the wedding.

   Will he have saved enough, or if not, how much more must he add ?

2. Charlie's sister, Nicola works in *Tara's* as a shoe sales assistant.

   Her hourly rate of pay is £9·75 and in June she worked a total of 144 hours.

   Her payslip showed deductions of £225·50.

   As well as this, she helped out 6 hours on each of four Sundays in June at a children's nursery, where the hourly rate was £7·20, with no tax.

   a Calculate Nicola's total net income for the month of June.

   Nicola rents a flat and estimates her outgoings for June as follows :-.

Rent - £380	Car Loan - £105	Electricity - £115	Food - £240
Petrol - £90	Mobile - £37·30	Entertainment - £240	Savings - ?????

   Whatever she has left, Nicola puts into her savings account.

   b How much can she save in June ?

   c What could she cut down on to help with her savings ?

3. Nicola's bill for her wedding dress was just over £1000.

   She had borrowed £1200 for 1 year to pay for this and the bank charged her 4% for the loan.

   a Calculate the overall amount payable and her monthly repayments.

   b Will Nicola have enough funds left in June to meet the monthly payment.

4. She decides that from June to January, she will cut her spending each month on entertainment by a quarter.

   a Assuming her monthly income remains the same from June to January, how much will she have in her savings by January ?

   b For her honeymoon, Nicola changed £400 of her savings to euros at an exchange rate of £1 = €1·35. How many euros will she have to spend ?

Statistical Calculations

Revision of National 4 Lifeskills

1. Find the range of these numbers :- 136, 80, 107, 76, 140, 68, 89, 64, 69.

2. Determine the mode for these weights (grams) :-

   12 g, 11 g, 11 g, 13 g, 11 g, 12 g, 11 g, 12 g, 15 g, 15 g, 12 g, 12 g.

3. Find the median temperature :-

   3°C, –6°C, 0°C, 6°C, –8°C, 4°C, 8°C, –20°C, 3°C, 1°C.

4. Calculate the mean length, in centimetres :-

   250 cm, 150 cm, 160 cm, 179 cm, 205 cm, 210 cm, 141 cm, 169 cm.

5. Here are the number of points scored by a rugby team in its five matches :-

   46 28 41 40 28

   a Find the mode and the median.

   b Which one - the mode or the median, gives a better idea of the team's scoring performance ?

6. 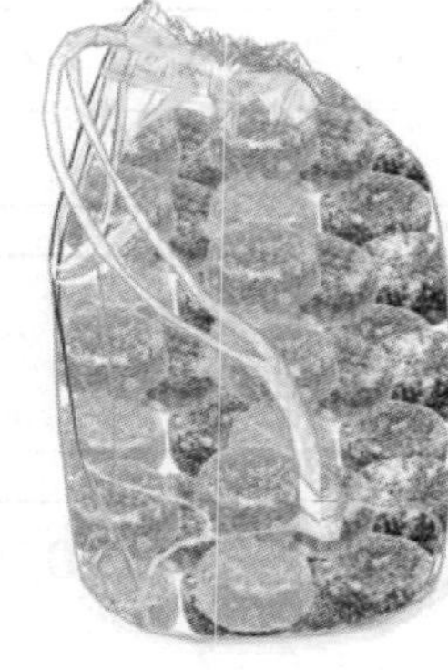

   mean number
   26 per packet

   The contents of ten packets of gums are examined.

   The packets have the following number of gums :-

   24, 28, 22, 27, 23, 26, 25, 23, 28, 24.

   a Why is the manufacturer's claim wrong ?

   b An eleventh packet is examined.

   How many gums would need to be in that packet in order for the manufacturer's claim to then be considered to be correct ?

7. Shown is the number of cans of diet cola consumed by two girls over a 9 week period.

Claire	5	7	5	5	5	8	6	5	8
Joyce	2	6	6	7	4	4	6	6	4

   a Write down the modal number of cans drank by each girl.

   b Give a reason why it is unfair to compare what they drank by using the mode.

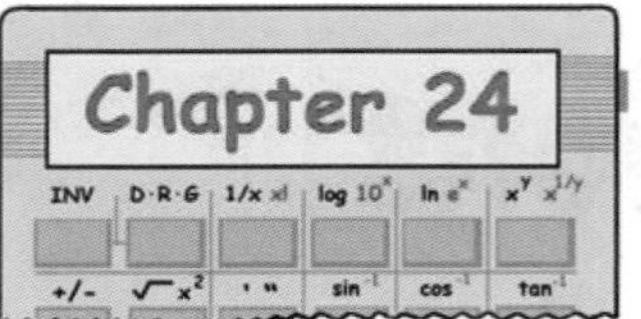

Statistical Calculations

Statistics - a Definition

Statistics is the branch of Mathematics which analyses information and data gleaned from surveys, questionnaires or reports. Its purpose is to present this information in a more understandable form, either graphically or in some numeric format.

"Average" and "Spread"

Imagine we had a set of numbers to analyse - for example, the ages of those on a Sunday School trip to the beach.

2, 6, 6, 7, 7, 7, 7, 8, 8, 8, 10, 10, 11, 13, 40.

There are basically two "numerical" aspects you might wish to look at.

- The Average age - this is a measure of where the "centre" of the group lies.
- The Spread of ages - this gives you an idea of what "range" of ages there are.

Averages - Mean, Median and Mode

Revision of National 4 - Lifeskills

You have already learned how to calculate an average of a set of values - namely, the mean.

You should also know of two further measures of average, called the median and the mode.

Mean - "Add" all the data together and "divide" by the number of pieces of data.

$$\frac{2 + 6 + 6 + 7 + \quad .... + 13 + 40}{15} = 10$$

Median - The "middle" number, (*as long as the numbers are in "order"*).

2, 6, 6, 7, 7, 7, 7, 8, 8, 8, 10, 10, 11, 13, 40.
median = 8

Mode - The number that occurs "most".

2, 6, 6, 7, 7, 7, 7, 8, 8, 8, 10, 10, 11, 13, 40.
mode = 7

Exercise 1

1. Calculate the mean for each set of data :-
   - a 2, 3, 4, 5, 6, 7, 8, 9, 10
   - b 8, 9, 12, 13, 13, 18, 22, 25
   - c 0·3, 0·5, 0·6, 0·7, 0·8, 0·9, 1·1
   - d 3, −7, 12, −14, −5, 2, −14, −5, −3, −9.

2. Find the median for each set of data :- (*Remember to put the numbers in order first*)
   - a 6, 9, 5, 3, 2, 7, 3, 10, 8
   - b 41, 51, 44, 16, 57, 39, 45
   - c 2·7, 3·3, 2·4, 3·5, 2·1, 2·8, 3·3
   - d 122, 133, 76, 184, 155, 130, 168.

Median If there is not a single middle number, take the **mean of the middle two numbers.**

Example :- For 2, 2, 4, 5, 6, 7, 8, 10

The **median** is (5 + 6) ÷ 2 = **5·5.**

3. Find the median for each of the following :-

a 14, 21, 17, 18, 22, 17

b 0·6, 0·7, 0·1, 1·0, 1·6, 0·9, 0·2, 0·3

c −6, −6, −3, −1, 1, 3, 5, 10

d 2, $2\frac{1}{2}$, $2\frac{1}{2}$, $4\frac{1}{2}$, $5\frac{1}{2}$, $5\frac{1}{2}$, $5\frac{1}{2}$, 7.

4. Find the mode for each set of data :-

a 2, 3, 4, 5, 6, 7, 8, 8, 9

b 1·4, 1·8, 2·0, 1·1, 1·8, 5·7, 1·8

c 1131, 1210, 1113, 1124, 1021, 1120, 1124

d $\frac{3}{4}$, $\frac{1}{4}$, $\frac{2}{3}$, $\frac{1}{2}$, $\frac{3}{4}$, $\frac{4}{5}$, $\frac{1}{4}$, $\frac{3}{4}$.

A Measure of Spread - The Range

The **Range** is a mathematical tool used to measure how widely spread a set of numbers are.

=> **Range = Highest score − Lowest score**

Example :- For the set of numbers :- 3, 3, 4, 6, 7, 7, 8, 11, 13, 13.

=> **Range** = 13 − 3 = **10**

5. Look at this data set :- **5, 7, 2, 9, 10, 2, 3, 4, 57**

a Find the range.

b Find the mean, median and mode.

c Which average is best suited here ?

d Explain why you think the other two averages are less suitable.

6. Calculate the mean, median, mode and range for each set of data below :-

a 2, 3, 3, 3, 5, 9, 17

b 6·7, 3·3, 5·4, 5·4, 6·1, 5·4, 4·8

c 65, 65, 63, 64, 67, 66, 67, 67

d −5, −2, 7, 15, −8, −5, 0, 7, −5, 6.

7. The weights of six women are shown :-

45 kg, 55 kg, 68 kg, 45 kg, 52 kg, 54 kg.

a Find the range of their weights.

b Calculate the mode and median weights.

c Choose which is the better average of the two and explain why.

8. Rory buys 10 Easter Eggs.

The number of chocolates in each is listed here :-

8,	7,	9,	6 ,	8,
7,	8,	11,	5 ,	9

a Calculate the mean, median and mode.

b How many eggs contain less than the mean number of chocolates ?

9. a Calculate the mean and the range of the first ten prime numbers.

b Calculate the mean and the range of the first ten square numbers.

10. The heights of six boys are shown opposite.

Bob says, " the average height is 1·23 m."

Bill says, " the average height is 1·57 m."

Ben says, " the average height is 1·47 m"

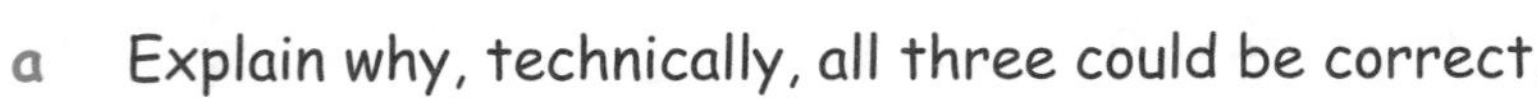

a Explain why, technically, all three could be correct.

b Which of the three would be least likely to be used ?

11. 

The mean weight of two tyres is 12 kilograms.

If one of the tyres weighs 13·5 kg, what must the weight of the other tyre be ?

12. The mean age of five children is 13 years old.

Four of the children's ages are 10, 10, 12 and 16.

What is the age of the fifth child ?

13. In an ice skating competition, there are six judges.

Each judge gives a skater a raw score out of 10 and each skate has a difficulty rating.

The following rules are also applied :-

- discard the lowest score
- work out the mean of the other five
- multiply the mean by 5 and divide by 8
- multiply this value by the difficulty rating and round to one decimal place.

Skater	Difficulty	Judges Raw Scores					
Tordill	3·1	9·0	9·5	9·0	8·5	7·5	8·0
Vean	3·4	7·5	7·5	7·0	8·5	7·5	8·0

The table shows the judges' raw scores for two skaters.

a In this round, Tordill's final score is 17·1.

Is this higher or lower than Vean's final score ?

b Vean will win the competition if he achieves a final score of 17·2 in his last skate.

If he maintains his mean score from part a, what is the minimum level of difficulty Vean would need to win the competition ?

The Semi-Interquartile Range - A new Measure of Spread

Shown below are the ages of the group on a Sunday School trip we looked at earlier.

2, 6, 6, 7, 7, 7, 7, 8, 8, 8, 10, 10, 11, 13, 40.

If we use the only measure of spread we have - the range - there is a slight problem.

Range = Highest - Lowest = 40 - 2 = 38.

- Can you see that most of the children are aged 6 to 13 ?
- The Sunday School teacher is aged 40 and has her 2-year old son with her.
- A range of 37 gives a false impression of "how widely spread" the actual ages are.
- The range only concentrates on the two "end" ages and disregards all other ages.

We need a new measure of spread which takes into account more numbers in the distribution.

Such a measure of spread exists - the semi-interquartile range, which we will study soon.

The Quartiles of a Set of Numbers

The Median is the value that splits a distribution of ordered numbers into two equal bits.

2, 6, 6, 7, 7, 7, 7, (8), 8, 8, 10, 10, 11, 13, 40.

← 7 values → median ← 7 values →

The Quartiles are 3 values that split a distribution of ordered numbers into 4 equal bits.

Can you see that, for the above group of ages :-

the lower quartile (Q_1) = 7, the middle quartile (Q_2) = 8, the upper quartile (Q_3) = 10 ?

* the middle quartile (Q_2) is just another name for the median.

The quartiles must split up a distribution of ordered numbers in such a way that there is an equal number of values in each of the 4 "quarters" of the distribution.

Quartiles - continued

Example :- Find the quartiles for the set :- 2, 3, 3, 4, 5, 5, 9, 10, 10, 10, 11, 12, 15, 17, 17, 19, 20.

Step 1 There are 17 values in the question.

This means that the **median** must be the 9th value. => median = **10**.

2, 3, 3, 4, 5, 5, 9, 10, (10), 10, 11, 12, 15, 17, 17, 19, 20.

Step 2 This now leaves 8 values in each half of the distribution.

2, 3, 3, 4, 5, 5, 9, 10, 10, 10, 11, 12, 15, 17, 17, 19, 20.

4 values | 4 values | 4 values | 4 values

Q_1 = 4·5 Q_2 = 10 Q_3 = 16

The **middle** of the **LEFT** set is between the 4th and 5th value => $Q_1 = \frac{4 + 5}{2} = 4 \cdot 5$.

The **middle** of the **RIGHT** set is between the 4th and 5th value => $Q_3 = \frac{15 + 17}{2} = 16$.

Exercise 2

1. a Copy these 11 numbers. *(You should try to space them fairly widely and fairly evenly)*

   8, 8, 9, 10, 10, 11, 11, 11, 12, 13, 14.

   b Circle the **middle** value - the **median**.

   c How many numbers are there to the left of the median - and how many to its right ?

   d Find the middle of the left set of numbers - the **lower quartile** - Q_1.

   e Find the middle of the right set of numbers - the **upper quartile** - Q_3.

2. Find the **median** (**middle quartile**), the **lower quartile** and the **upper quartile** for each :-

   a 1, 3, 4, 7, 7, 9, 13.

   b 3·2, 3·5, 3·6, 3·8, 3·8, 4·0, 4·4, 4·4, 4·7, 5·3, 5·4, 5·9.

   c 34, 31, 25, 35, 35, 23, 23, 40, 37, 27, 21, 29, 39.

3. Mrs Jones weighs the 63 children in Primary 7 and writes them all down in order.

   Their weights, (in kg), are :- 34, 34, 35, 36, 36, 36, 37, ..., 50, 50, 51.

   a Of the 63, which child's weight should be given as the **median** weight. (*30th, 31st, 32nd..*)

   b Which of the children's weights gives the **lower quartile** and which gives the **upper** ?

The Semi-Interquartile Range

Let us look again at the example on the ages of the group on a Sunday School trip.

2, 6, 6, 7, 7, 7, 7, 8, 8, 8, 10, 10, 11, 13, 40.

We found the **quartiles** and these are shown below :-

2, 6, 6, (7), 7, 7, 7, (8), 8, 8, 10, (10), 11, 13, 40.

lower quartile Q_1 — median — upper quartile Q_3

Range :- You learned previously that the **range** was a simple measure of spread.

Range = highest - lowest = 40 - 2 = 38 (but this gave too "**big**" an answer).

If we now find the **difference** => **upper quartile - lower quartile**, and **halve** this answer,

we end up with a new measure of spread, called the **semi-interquartile range**. (S.I.Q.R.)*

$$\text{*Semi-Interquartile Range} = \frac{\text{Upper Quartile} - \text{Lower Quartile}}{2}$$

$$\text{S.I.Q.R} = \frac{Q_3 - Q_1}{2} = \frac{10 - 7}{2} = 1 \cdot 5$$

* In many instances, this measure of spread is preferable to the range. It does not simply rely on the two end values, the "highest" and "lowest" - rather, it takes into account more of the numbers in the distribution.

Exercise 3

1. Calculate the median and lower and upper quartiles for each set of values.

   Calculate the **inter-quartile range** and hence the **semi-interquartile range** of each.

   a 13, 13, 15, 19, 23, 23, 24, 26, 27.

   b 2·4, 2·6, 2·9, 2·9, 3·1, 3·1, 3·3, 3·6, 3·6, 3·8, 4·1, 4·1, 4·5, 4·7, 4·9, 5·0.

   c 101, 108, 109, 112, 112, 115, 120, 121, 125, 131, 131, 134, 135, 138, 140.

2. A group of 25 third year pupils was asked to say how many cousins they had.

   3, 1, 4, 2, 3, 4, 5, 2, 2, 4, 5, 1, 0, 6, 8, 2, 4, 4, 6, 2, 3, 1, 0, 9, 6.

   a Rearrange them in order, starting with the lowest.

   b Calculate the mean, median and modal value.

   c Determine both the range and the S.I.Q.R.

3. A shoe shop assistant took a note of the sizes of a popular make of trainers that were sold in her shop last week.

   Calculate the range and the S.I.Q.R. and say why the S.I.Q.R. would be a better spread indicator of the shoe sizes sold last week, than the range.

   1, 4, 4, $4\frac{1}{2}$, 5, 5, 5, $5\frac{1}{2}$, $5\frac{1}{2}$, 6, 6, 6, $6\frac{1}{2}$, $6\frac{1}{2}$, 10.

Boxplots - 5 Point Diagrams

Let us look once more at the ages of the group on the Sunday School trip.

2, 6, 6, 7, 7, 7, 7, 8, 8, 8, 10, 10, 11, 13, 40.

We found that Q_1 = 7, Q_3 = 10, the **median** = 8, the **lowest** value is 2 and the **highest** is 40.

This can be represented on a **boxplot** (*or 5-point summary*) as shown below.

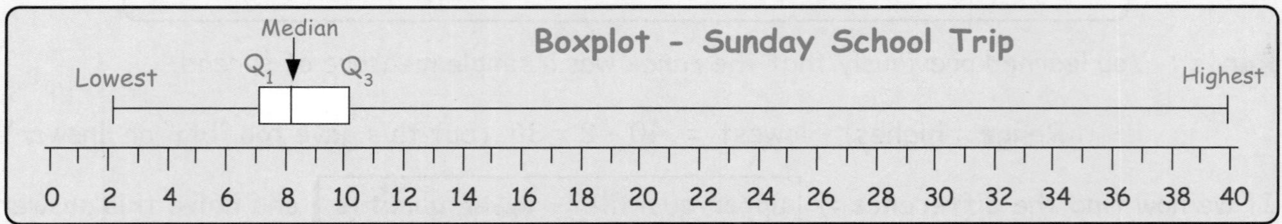

Boxplots are very useful diagrams, particularly when you wish to compare 2 or more sets of values. They are also sometimes referred to as **box-whisker** diagrams for obvious reasons.

Exercise 4

1. James rolled two die, (*plural of dice*), 12 times, and noted the total score each time.

   3, 5, 6, 7, 7, 7, 8, 9, 9, 10, 10, 12.

   a Calculate the median as well as the upper and lower quartiles.

   b Copy this scale and draw a neat **boxplot** to represent the above scores.

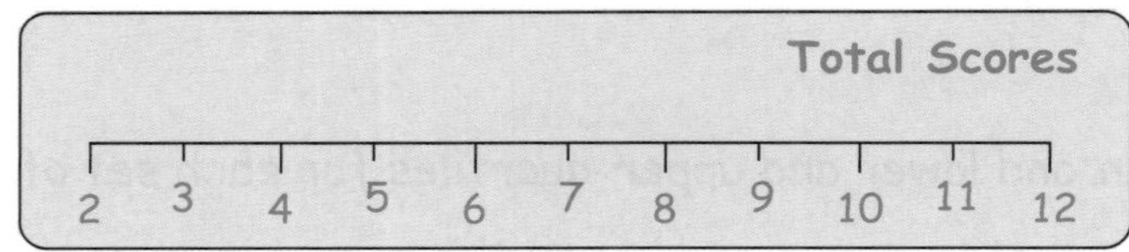

2. A group of pupils took part in a sunflower growing competition and they all planted their sunflower seed at the same time.

   Eight weeks later, the heights of the plants were measured (*to the nearest 5 cm*).

35, 35, 40, 40, 40, 50, 50, 55, 60, 70, 85, 85, 95, 105.

   a Calculate the values of the three quartiles, Q_1, Q_2 and Q_3.

   b Use a suitable scale to show the above heights on a neatly drawn labelled boxplot.

3. The weights, (*in kilograms*), of the luggage of the 15 passengers boarding a plane bound for the Orkneys was recorded.

   15, 18, 14, 22, 19, 18, 14, 25, 24, 18, 10, 13, 21, 18, 24.

   a Arrange them in order, smallest first, and calculate the median and the quartiles.

   b Draw and label a boxplot showing these weights. (*Choose a suitable scale*).

4. *Osiris* claim that their light bulbs last longer than *Awlbright's* bulbs. A sample of each was tested. *Osiris'* sample is shown below (*in months*).

8, 9, 10, 10, 12, 14, 14, 14, 15, 15, 17, 17, 18.

A boxplot was created to represent *Awlbright's* sample and is shown below.

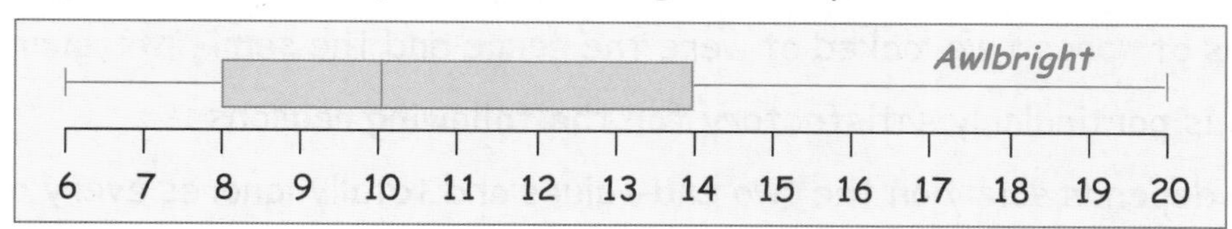

a Find the median and the quartiles for the sample of *Awlbright's* light-bulb lifetime.

b Calculate the median and the quartiles for the sample of *Osiris'* light-bulb lifetime.

c Make a neat copy of the above boxplot, and on the same graph, draw the boxplot above the *Awlbright's* boxplot, showing the *Osiris'* bulbs.

d Write a couple of sentences comparing the two samples.

5. A group of men and a group of women in a local gym, decided to hold a competition. They counted how many pull-ups each person could do in a two minute period.

men	7	9	9	11	13	13	15	15	18	18	20	25
women	5	5	6	7	7	10	12	12	14	14	15	17

a Calculate the medians and quartiles for both the men and the women.

b Draw a neat labelled composite boxplot diagram to show how the two groups fared.

c Write a couple of sentences comparing the male competitors with the women.

6. Both *Flyjet* and *Airbee* fly daily from Edinburgh to London Stanstead. The flight is supposed to take 1 hour.

Over the course of one week in June, the flight times of every *Flyjet* and *Airbee* plane from Edinburgh to Stanstead were recorded, in minutes.

Flyjet ...	55	57	61	63	66	66	67	70	70	72	72	75	75	77	80
Airbee ...	61	61	61	62	63	65	65	65	66	66	68	68	68		

a Draw a neat labelled composite boxplot diagram to show the above flight times.

b Make a statement comparing each company's flight times from Edinburgh to London.

7. Three men hit 15 golf balls on a driving range, each using a number 6 iron. The boxplot diagram shows the distances (in metres) they hit their golf balls.

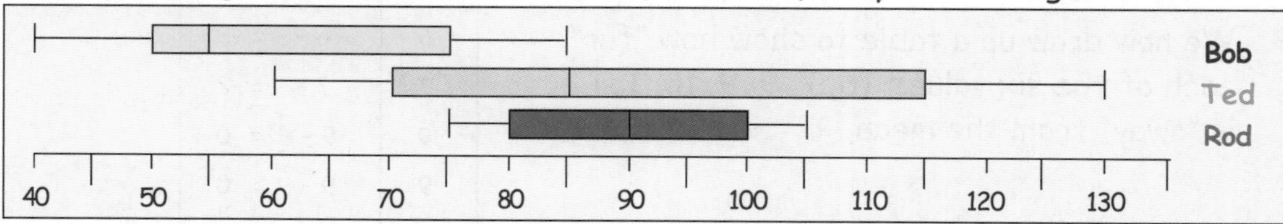

Write a few sentences comparing the three men's driving skills, mentioning their median scores, the spread of their shots, who was likely to be the novice, who was most erratic and who was most consistent.

Standard Deviation - a Better Measure of Spread

Let us take a final look at the ages of the group on the Sunday School outing.

2, 6, 6, 7, 7, 7, 7, 8, 8, 8, 10, 10, 11, 13, 40.

The two measures of **spread** we looked at were the **range** and the **semi-interquartile range**.

Neither of them is particularly satisfactory for the following reasons :-

- the **range** depends solely on the two end-values and totally ignores every other value.
- the **S.I.Q.R.** totally disregards the two end-values.

We require a new measure of spread that takes into account **all** the numbers in the distribution, not just the end-values or the quartiles.

This new measure is called the **Standard Deviation**.

Definition :- For a set of values (e.g. the ages of the group above), the **standard deviation** is a measure of how "far away", on average, each of the values is, from the **mean**.

Let us explain exactly what we mean, by following through a simpler example :-

Example :- Six pea-pods were opened and the number of peas in each was noted.

6, 7, 9, 9, 10, 13.

Calculate the **mean** and the **standard deviation**.

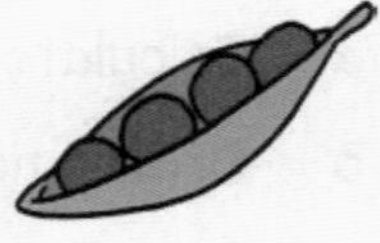

Step 1 Calculate the **mean** first.

A new notation :- If we think of any of the variables, (*the values*), as x's, then the **mean** = (the sum of all the x's) ÷ (the number of values).

We have a **mathematical** way of expressing this, namely :-

$$\bar{x} = \frac{\sum x}{n}$$ where $\bar{x}$, (reads as "x bar"), is the **mean**.

and $\sum x$ means the "**sum of all the x's**".

and n is the **number** of values used.

In our example, $\bar{x} = \frac{\sum x}{n} = \frac{6+7+9+9+10+13}{6} = \frac{54}{6} = 9.$ the **mean**.

Step 2 We now draw up a table to show how "far" each of the six values, (6, 7, 9, 9, 10, 13), is "away" from the mean, $\bar{x} = 9$.

x	$(x - \bar{x})$
6	6 - 9 = -3
7	7 - 9 = -2
9	9 - 9 = 0
9	9 - 9 = 0
10	10 - 9 = 1
13	13 - 9 = 4

cont'd ......

x	$(x-\bar{x})$	$(x-\bar{x})^2$
6	-3	$(-3)^2 = 9$
7	-2	$(-2)^2 = 4$
9	0	$(0)^2 = 0$
9	0	$(0)^2 = 0$
10	1	$(1)^2 = 1$
13	4	$(4)^2 = 16$

To find the "**average**" of these $(x - \bar{x})$'s, we should really add them together, then divide by 6.

A problem :- if we add $(-3) + (-2) + 0 + 0 + 1 + 4 \rightarrow$ we get 0 !
(This is because they all "cancel" each other out).

A "neat" trick :- If we "**square**" these 6 values ((-3), (-2), 0, 0, 1, 4), all the negative signs disappear.

=> we add on an extra column showing $(x - \bar{x})^2$'s.

Step 3 Now find the "**average**" of the numbers in this column. $(9 + 4 + 0 + 0 + 1 + 16) \div 6 = 5$.

We can use our new notation => $\textbf{average} = \dfrac{\sum(x-\bar{x})^2}{n} = \dfrac{30}{6} = 5.$ the **average** is 5

Step 4 But remember - these 6 numbers, (9, 4, 0, 0, 1, 16), were the **squares** of the $(x - \bar{x})$'s.

=> As a final step, we find the **square root** of this "average", (the 5) => $\sqrt{5}$.

How far away the values are from the mean, we call the **standard deviation**.

We have a special formula for it :-

$$\textbf{standard deviation} = \sqrt{\frac{\sum(x-\bar{x})^2}{n}}$$

* this is not exactly the correct formula, but we'll explain this later.

=> In our example, we have $s.d. = \sqrt{\dfrac{\sum(x-\bar{x})^2}{n}} = \sqrt{\dfrac{30}{6}} = \sqrt{5} = 2 \cdot 236.$

* The important thing about this measure of **spread** is that it takes into account every one of the six numbers, and gives a "feel" for how far, on average, each value is from the middle of the distribution, (the **mean**).
The **lower** the standard deviation is, the more **tightly grouped** is the set of values.

Exercise 5

1. Shown below are the number of touchdowns, made by the Cincinnati Crawlers in their last 5 matches.

2, 3, 9, 6, 5.

Copy the following and calculate the **mean** and the **standard deviation**.

a **mean** = $\bar{x} = \dfrac{\sum x}{n} = \dfrac{2+3+9+6+5}{5} =$ .....

b **standard deviation** - see table ....

$s.d. = \sqrt{\dfrac{\sum(x-\bar{x})^2}{n}} = \sqrt{\dfrac{.....}{5}} = \sqrt{...} = ...$

x	$(x-\bar{x})$	$(x-\bar{x})^2$
2	2 - 5 = -3	$(-3)^2 = 9$
3	3 - 5 = -2	....
9	....	....
6	....	....
5	....	....

$\sum(x-\bar{x})^2 =$

2. The first sentence James read in his new book had eight words in it.

The number of letters in each word was :- 1, 3, 4, 8, 5, 1, 7, 3.

Calculate the mean number of letters per word and the standard deviation.

Copy and complete the following :-

a mean = $\bar{x} = \frac{\sum x}{n} = \frac{1+3+4+8+.....}{.....} = ...$

b standard deviation - see table ....

$s.d. = \sqrt{\frac{\sum(x-\bar{x})^2}{n}} = \sqrt{\frac{.....}{.....}} = \sqrt{...} = ...$

You may use "*s.d.*", or "*s*" or "σ" to represent the term "standard deviation".

x	$(x-\bar{x})$	$(x-\bar{x})^2$
1	1 - 4 = -3	$(-3)^2 = 9$
3	....	....
4	....	....
8	....	....
5	....	....
1	....	....
7	....	....
3	....	....

$\sum(x-\bar{x})^2 =$

Standard Deviation - the Real Formula

Statisticians discovered that they could get a better idea of the spread of a distribution of values by altering the formula for the standard deviation slightly.

They decided it worked better using $(n-1)$* rather than just n.

The formula for the standard deviation became :-

$$s.d. = \sqrt{\frac{\sum(x-\bar{x})^2}{(n-1)}}$$

* the reason for this is too complicated to explain at this stage !

** From now on, use the new formula for standard deviation using (n – 1) rather than n.*

3. The weights of the first four letters George weighed in his post office one morning, were :- 30 grams, 41 grams, 48 grams, 29 grams.

   a Calculate the mean weight, in grams.

   b Draw up a table and use the formula, $s.d. = \sqrt{\frac{\sum(x-\bar{x})^2}{n-1}}$ to calculate the standard deviation.

4. The school bus should arrive at Bromley Primary every day at 3.30 prompt.

The head teacher noted how many minutes late the driver was last week – 6 mins, 15 mins, 8 mins, 2 mins, 9 mins.

Calculate the mean number of minutes late and the standard deviation of the times.

5. The Edinburgh Annual Paper Airplane Making contest was held in June.

The distances travelled by the planes of the last 8 competitors were :-

22 m, 35 m, 26 m, 28 m, 30 m, 24 m, 36 m, 23 m.

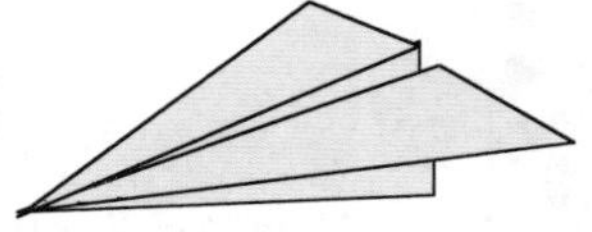

a Calculate the mean distance travelled by the 8 planes.

b Draw up a table and use it, along with the formula, to calculate the standard deviation of the distances travelled.

6. On a field trip, Susan collects 7 worms and measures their lengths.

6·1 cm, 4·1 cm, 9·2 cm, 9·1 cm, 8·1 cm, 12·0 cm, 7·4 cm.

Calculate the standard deviation.

7. Two men were playing a "friendly" game of darts.

The scores, for each of their first six darts, are shown below.

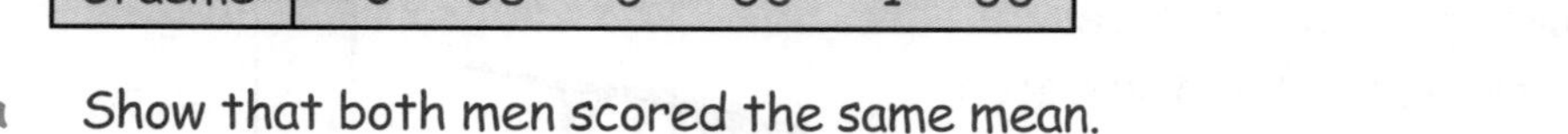

Donald	18	22	17	20	15	16
Graeme	3	38	6	30	1	30

a Show that both men scored the same mean.

b Draw 2 separate tables and calculate the standard deviation of both men's scores.

c Comment on what the two different standard deviations tell you about the scores.

Standard Deviation - an Alternative Formula Optional

If the **mean** is an "awkward" decimal, the calculations in your standard deviation tables become difficult to work with. In this situation, a **rearrangement** of the standard deviation formula can be used.

$$s = \sqrt{\frac{\sum x^2 - (\sum x)^2 / n}{(n-1)}}$$

Example :- Calculate the mean and standard deviation for the numbers :- 3, 5, 2, 9, 1, 8.

mean :- $\bar{x} = \frac{\sum x}{n} = \frac{28}{6} = 4 \cdot 6666\ldots$

s.d. :- $s = \sqrt{\frac{\sum x^2 - (\sum x)^2 / n}{(n-1)}}$

$s = \sqrt{\frac{184 - 28^2 / 6}{5}} = \sqrt{\frac{53 \cdot 33..}{5}} = \sqrt{10 \cdot 6....} = \mathbf{3 \cdot 27}$

x	x^2
3	9
5	25
2	4
9	81
1	1
8	64
$\sum x = 28$	$\sum x^2 = 184$

8. Use the new formula to calculate the mean and the standard deviation of the following :-

a 4, 12, 9, 6.

b 45, 32, 37, 34, 40, 27.

c 6·2, 7·3, 9·1, 5·7, 11·4.

d 115, 130, 122, 129, 130, 133, 136.

9. Re-calculate the standard deviation for the set of numbers :- 4, 12, 9, 6, (**Qu 8a**), using the "real" formula given on page 242, and check it gives the same value.

Statistical Calculations

Finance/Statistics Assessment 5

1. Mrs Addison works for the Consumer Research Council and as part of her job, she investigates the price of half a litre of milk at various outlets.

   The costs she found were :-

   32p, 34p, 34p, 35p, 36p, 37p, 40p, 43p, 47p.

   a Find the median cost of half a litre of milk.

   b Find the lower and upper quartiles, and make a neat clearly labelled boxplot.

2. A keen tomato grower tried two different fertilizers on two of his batches of tomato plants.

   The boxplot shown opposite indicates the heights (in centimetres) of the batch treated with *Growmore* fertilizer.

   120
   105
   GROWMORE SAMPLE
   96
   93
   90

   a State the upper and lower quartiles for the distribution of plant heights.

   The graph below shows the boxplot representing the sample treated by *Heighten* fertiliser.

   The range of heights for this sample was 40 centimetres and the semi-interquartile range was 11 centimetres.

   b Calculate the values represented by A and B.

   c Make any two valid comments on the success of the fertilizers.

3. 6 brand new *Mini's* were tested by pouring exactly 1 gallon of petrol into their tanks and carefully measuring how far they travelled before the cars came to a halt. The distances, in miles, were :-

   42, 43, 45, 49, 50, 53.

   a Calculate the mean number of miles to the gallon.

   b Calculate the standard deviation, to 2 decimal places.

   Six brand new *Maxi* cars were also tested. Their mean was 40 miles to the gallon, with a standard deviation of 3.

   c Make two valid comparisons between the two makes of car.

Scattergraphs

Revision of Scattergraphs

1. The scattergraph shows the ages and waist sizes (*in inches*) of a group of men.

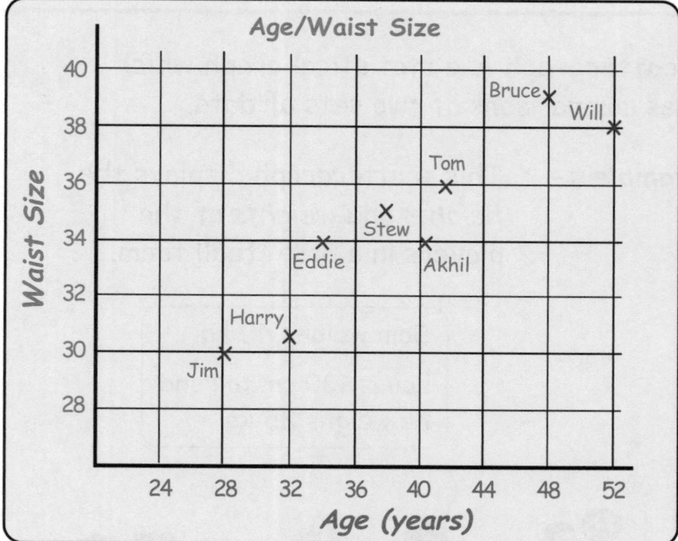

   a Who :-

      (i) is the youngest

      (ii) is the oldest

      (iii) has the biggest waist ?

   b Is there a connection between age and waist size ?

   c What would you estimate the waist size of Brian to be if he is 44 years old ?

2. State whether there is a connection between each of the following pairs :-
(*If there is a connection, state whether it is (strongly or weakly) positive or negative*).

   a The number of hours you spend revising for a test and your score in the test.

   b The weight and the age of a child.

   c The collar size of a person and the colour of his/her eyes.

   d The amount of rain falling and the number of people out for a walk.

3. Eight boys sat a Maths exam and a German exam.
Their results are recorded in the table below.

Maths	15	40	75	60	25	65	75	40
German	85	60	35	50	70	40	45	70

   a Construct a scattergraph from this table.

   b What is the general connection between a boy's Maths mark and his German mark ?

   c Estimate the German mark of a 9th boy who scored 50 in his Maths exam.

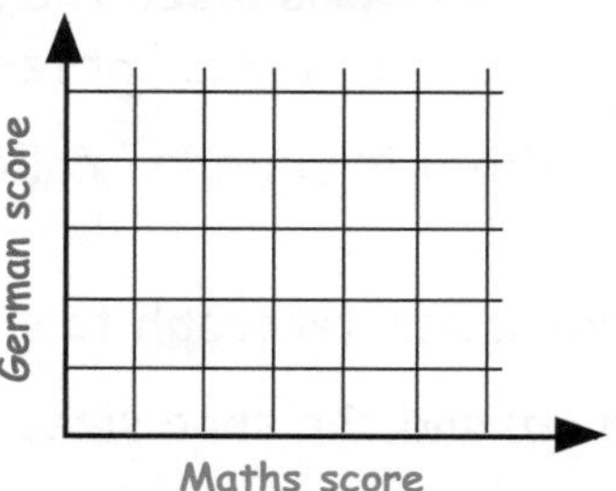

Scattergraphs

Scattergraphs

A **Scattergraph** is a statistical graph which makes comparisons of two sets of data.

Example :- This scattergraph displays the *heights* and *weights* of the players in a basketball team.

Sam weighs 40 kg.

Lou is 130 cm tall and he weighs 25 kg.

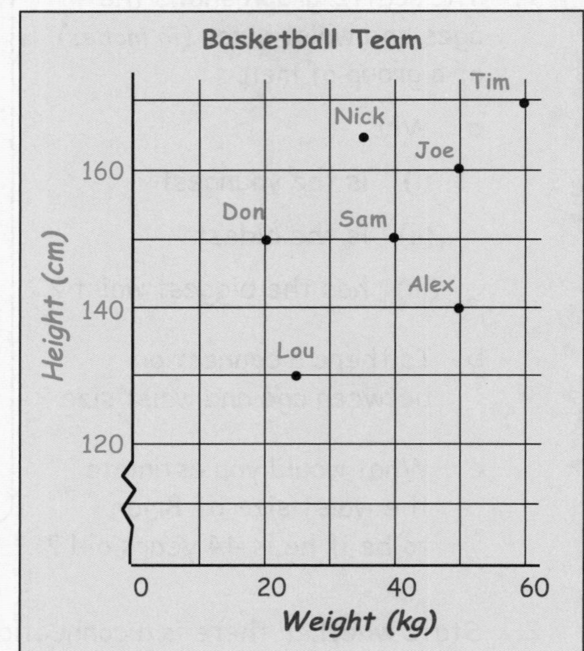

Exercise 1

1. From the scattergraph above, write down the height and weight of each player.

2. The scattergraph opposite shows the ages and weights of several children.

   a Who is the :-

   (i) youngest (ii) lightest

   (iii) oldest (iv) heaviest child ?

   b Write down the age and weight of each child.

   c Child "*x*" is older than Ali, younger than Pat and is lighter than Shaz.

   What is child "*x*" called ?

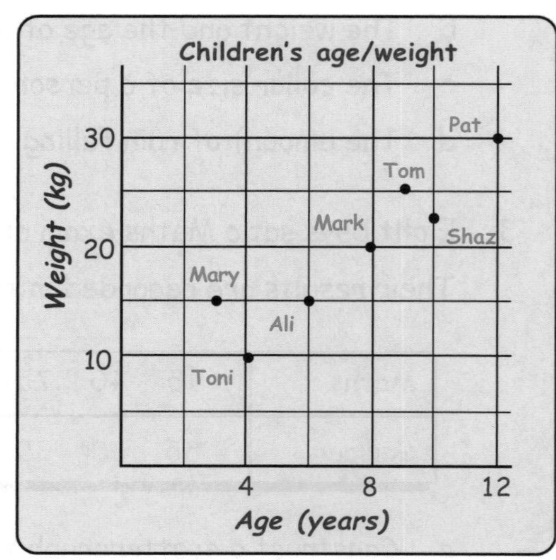

3. Draw a scattergraph to show the weights (*in kg*) and the shoe sizes of a group of pupils.

	Mat	Bill	Fred	Jan	Tam
Weight	20	15	30	25	35
Shoe size	4	3	6	6	9

4. a For both (i) and (ii) below, construct a scattergraph to represent each set of data.

(i)	May	Zak	Jack	Tippi	Guy
Height cm	120	115	130	145	135
Weight kg	40	30	60	76	70

(ii)	Jan	Feb	Mar	April	May
Car Sales	25	20	30	55	45
Profit (£1000's)	30	20	35	60	50

b Sandy's height and weight lie exactly halfway between Tippi's and Guy's.

How tall and how heavy is Sandy ?

Sandy

c In June, the profit on car sales was £32 500.

Estimate how many cars were sold in June.

5. a Construct a scattergraph from the English and Maths grades of these ten pupils.

Name	Eng	Maths	Name	Eng	Maths
Tom	1	2	Neil	3	3
Dick	1	3	Iain	2	3
Bill	2	4	Jack	2	2
Jerry	3	4	Ewan	6	6
Nick	6	7	Bob	4	5

b What is the general connection between the English grades and the Maths grades, remembering for example, that a grade 1 is better than a grade 2 ?

6. a Draw a scattergraph, plotting the number of hours Mr Thomson has his central heating on each day compared with the average outside daily temperature on each day.

No. Hours	1	2	4	5	7	8	8	9	10	11	12
Temp. °C	22	18	14	12	10	9	8	6	4	2	0

b What do you think the temperature is when Mr Thomson leaves his heating on for nine and a half hours ?

c How many hours should he have the heating on if the outside temperature is 20°C?

d Is there a connection between the number of hours he has the heating on and the daily temperature ? Describe this connection in words.

Scattergraphs - Correlation

In this *example*, we look back at the Maths and English Grades for 10 pupils.

Name	Eng	Maths	Name	Eng	Maths
Tom	1	2	Neil	3	3
Dick	1	3	Iain	2	3
Bill	2	4	Jack	2	2
Jerry	3	4	Ewan	6	6
Nick	6	7	Bob	4	5

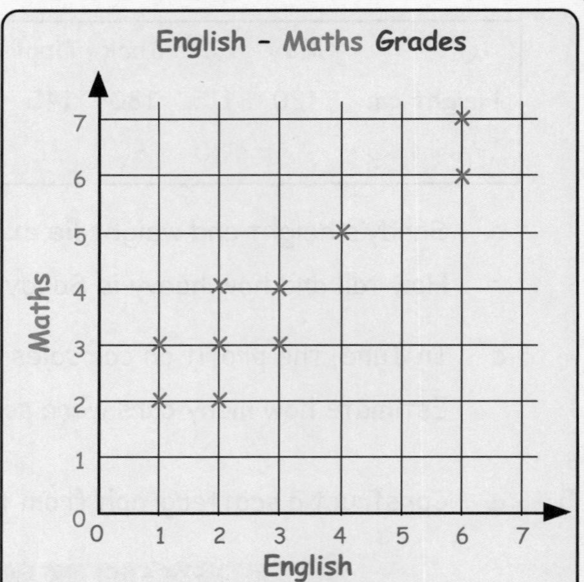

Each pair of grades is plotted on a **Scattergraph**.

Can you see there is a **fairly strong connection** between the two sets of grades ?

If two sets of values are so strongly connected that it is possible to make a fairly accurate estimate of one of the values, knowing the other, we say there is a strong **correlation** between the two sets of values.

Can you see that this is the case - there is indeed a fairly strong **positive correlation** between the Maths and the English Grades ?

(*Positive because the grouping of pairs of values is "sloping upwards" from left to right*).

Line of Best Fit

The correlation in this example is good enough to allow us to draw a "**Line of Best Fit**" through the group.

Though the line is only an "estimate", it should :-

- go through as many points as possible
- split up the group so there are roughly as many points above the line as there are below it.

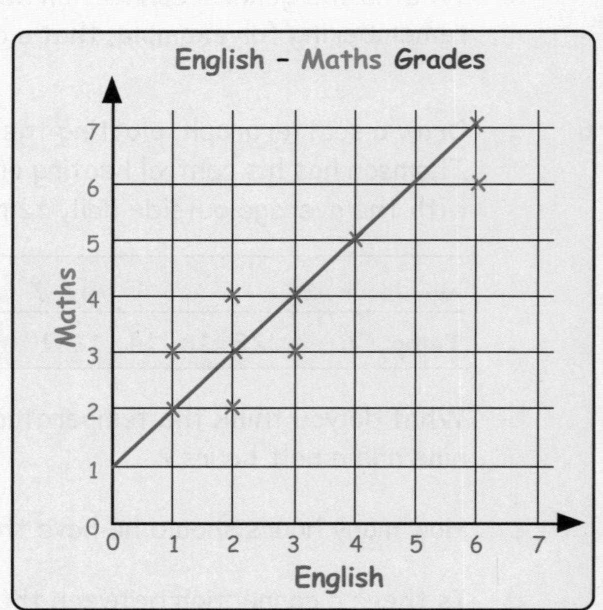

Shown is a good estimate for a **Line of Best Fit**.

We can use the line to make further estimates.

An eleventh child, Harry, is known to have scored a **5** in English. A fair estimate for his Maths grade would be a **6**.

Exercise 2

1. This scattergraph shows the ages and the shoe sizes of several children.

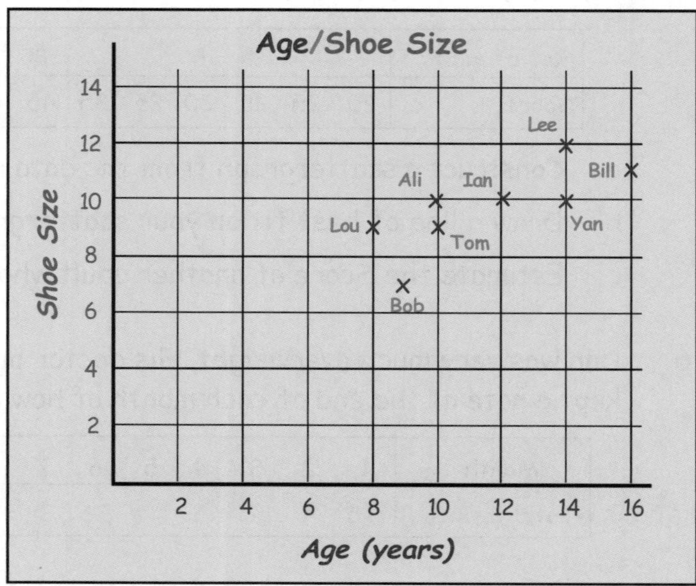

   a Which of the children :-
      (i) is the youngest
      (ii) has the smallest shoe size
      (iii) is the oldest
      (iv) takes the largest shoe size ?
   b Is there a strong correlation, a weak correlation or no correlation at all ?
   c Copy the scattergraph and draw in, by eye, the line of best fit.
   d Estimate the shoe size for Stephen, aged 6.

2.

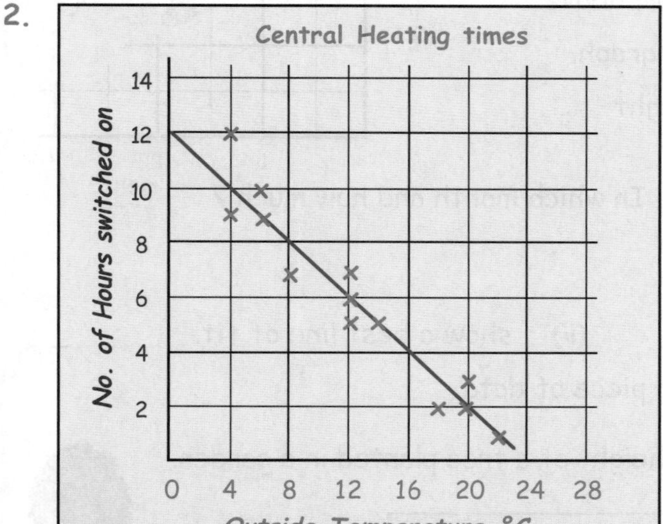

This scattergraph shows the number of hours a lady had her central heating on each day, plotted against the average daily outside temperature that day.

This graph shows a **strong negative correlation** since all the points lie roughly on a straight line going **downwards** from left to right.

The line of best fit is also shown.

Use your line to estimate how many hours she would expect to run her central heating for, if the average outside temperature one day was 16°C.

3. Write down whether you think there will be a correlation between these pairs :-
(*If there is a correlation, say whether it is positive or negative*).
   a the temperature and the sales of ice-cream in June.
   b the temperature and the number of people on a beach each day.
   c the hours that the sun is shining and the sale of umbrellas.
   d the ages of a group of children and the number of coins in their pockets.

4. Write down 2 of your own examples of pairs of measurements where there would be :-
   a a positive correlation b a negative correlation c no correlation between the pairs.

5. Shown are the number of hourly visits a group of adults attended judo classes, along with their Scores in their end-of-season assessment.

The results are shown in the table below.

No. of visits	2	3	4	5	6	7	8	10	11	12	13
Score	20	25	25	30	25	35	45	40	40	45	45

a Construct a scattergraph from the data recorded.

b Draw a line of best fit on your scattergraph.

c Estimate the Score of another adult who came 9 times for judo lessons.

6. Dan was very much overweight. His doctor put him on a strict diet in January and Dan kept a note at the end of each month of how much weight he had lost, in total.

Month	1	2	3	4	5	6	7	8	9	10	11	12
Total loss (kg)	3·5	4	4	5	5·5	5·5	7	8	6·5	8	9	9

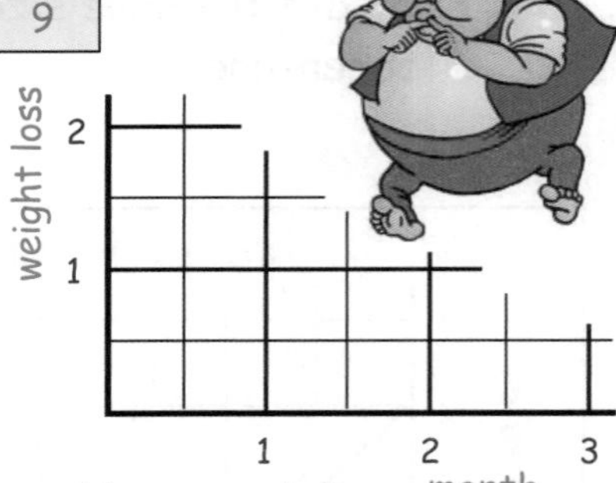

a Draw up a set of axes as shown and plot the 12 pairs of pieces of data from the table above.

b Draw a line of best fit on your scattergraph.

c Estimate what his total weight loss might be after 15 months.

d Dan actually gained weight at one point. In which month and how much ?

7. For each set of data below :-

(i) construct a scattergraph. (ii) show a best line of fit.

(iii) use your line to estimate the missing piece of data.

a The data below shows the age and the height of a tree planted in a garden.

age (years)	1	2	3	4	5	6	7	8	9	10
height (m)	4	5	6	10	10	14	16	16	?	21

b The data shows the number of rats still alive in a store after poison was put down.

week	1	2	3	4	5	6	7	8	9	10	11	12
no. of rats	65	60	65	50	50	45	?	40	45	30	25	25

c A group of eight pupils compared their French and English marks in two tests.

French	10	35	60	24	56	17	42	49
English	23	57	88	40	85	33	62	?

Scattergraphs

Finance/Statistics Assessment 6

1. A researcher noted the length and weight of each banana in a bunch.

   a Is there a correlation between the lengths and the weights of the bananas ?

   b One of the bananas was 20 cm long.

   How heavy was it ?

   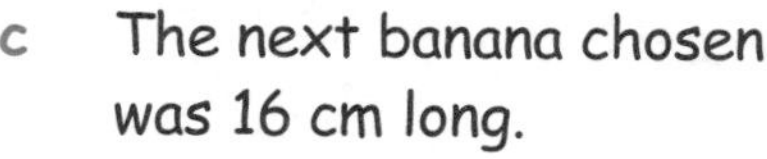

   c The next banana chosen was 16 cm long.

   Estimate its weight, in grams.

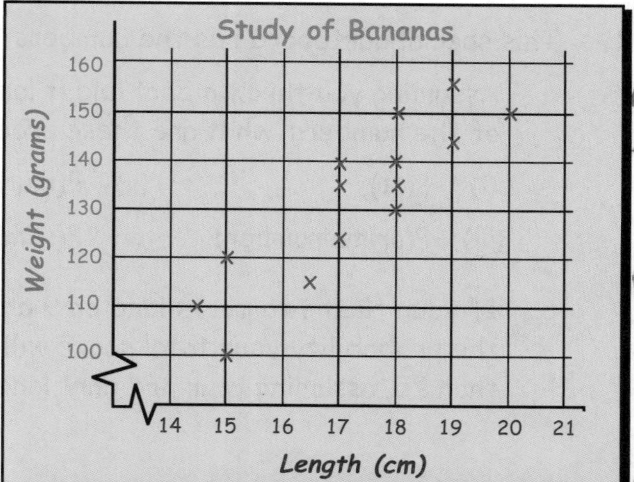

2. The ages and weights of a group of young people are recorded in the table.

Age	10	10	11	12	13	14	15	16	16	17	18	19
Weight (kg)	30	20	30	35	45	35	45	60	50	75	65	?

   a Construct a scattergraph to represent this information.

   b Write a sentence to explain the correlation in this example.

   c Draw a Line of Best Fit on your scattergraph.

   d Estimate, using your line, the weight of the 19 year old.

3. A farmer checked out ten of his 10 kg sacks of potatoes.

   He noted the average diameter of each potato, (in cm), in a sack and the number of potatoes in that sack.

Diam (cm)	4	15	7	13	16	10	18	6	20	5
No. in sack	50	23	38	28	26	37	22	43	15	44

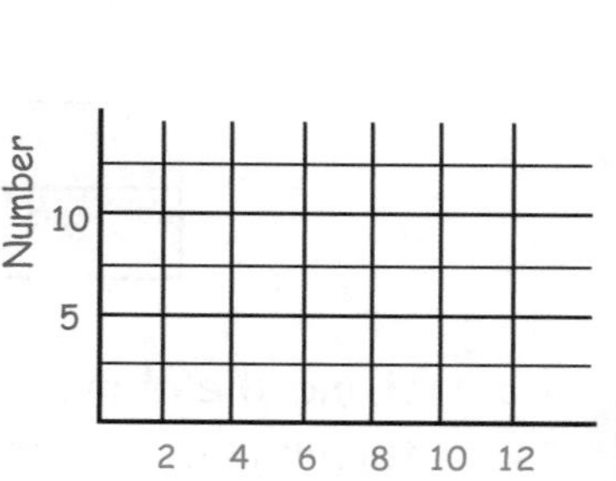

   a Construct a scattergraph to represent this information.

   b Write a sentence to explain the correlation here.

   c Draw a Line of Best Fit on your scattergraph.

   d Estimate, using your line, the number of potatoes you might find in a 10 kg sack if the average diameter of each potato is 9 centimetres.

Statistical Risk

Revision of Probability & Chance

1. This special dartboard has the numbers 1 to 12 on it.

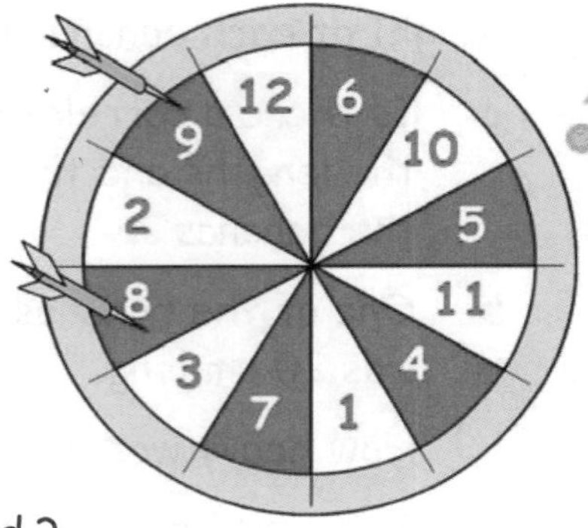

   a Assuming you throw a dart and it lands on one of the numbers, what are these probabilities :-

   (i) P(11) (ii) P(multiple of 3)

   (iii) P(prime number) (iv) P(number > 2) ?

   b If your first two darts land on 9 and 8, what's the probability your total score will be greater than 25, assuming your 3rd dart lands on the board ?

2. At a tombola stall, 500 raffle tickets are sold.

   a If you buy ten tickets, what are your chances of having a winning ticket ?

   b There are 30 prizes at the tombola stall. Have you a greater than or less than evens chance of winning one of the prizes ?

3. 

   At the end of a night out with his mates, Gerry states, "The chance of me getting up and going to work tomorrow is about 0·05".

   What <u>percentage</u> chance does Gerry think he has of not making it to work ?

4. To decide if this spinner is "biased", (i.e. does not randomly stop showing each colour an equal number of times), Debbie spins it 120 times and records the colours.

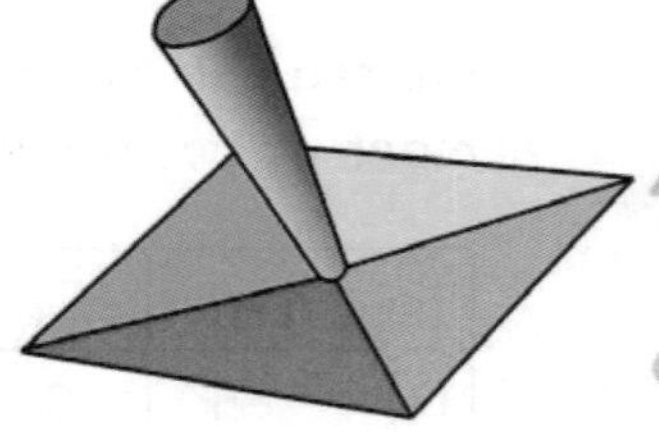

red	green	yellow	bl
48	30	18	

   a Using the above table, calculate the probability of each colour turning up and simplify each fraction as far as possible.

   b Does the spinner appear to be unbiased ?

   c If she spun it 300 times, how many times might she expect blue to turn up ?

Statistical Risk

Probability and Expected Frequency

Remember :- The PROBABILITY of something happening simply means the FRACTION of times it would happen "in the long run".

Probability is a fraction or decimal and can only take values from 0 to 1.

Examples :- The probability of tomorrow being Wednesday if today is Monday is **0**.

The probability of throwing a number less than 4 on a 6-sided dice is **0·5**.

The probability you will get wet if you fall in a pond is **1**.

EXPECTED FREQUENCY is simply the number of times an event should happen, based on the statistical chance of it actually happening.

Example :- The probability of being dealt a heart in cards is 1 in 4, or P(heart) = $\frac{1}{4}$.

If I shuffle a pack, choose a card, return it, shuffle the pack and choose again 60 times, how many times might I expect to draw a heart ?

Solution :- The expected number of hearts :- $E(\text{heart}) = P(\text{heart}) \times 60 = \frac{1}{4} \times 60 = 15$.

Exercise 1

1. The dial on this 12 sided spinner is spun.

   a What is the probability that when spun, it stops showing 7 ?

   We say the chances of it showing a 7 is 1 in ......

   b Does this mean that if we spin the dial 12 times it will stop at 7 exactly 1 time ?

   c Explain your answer.

   d How many times might you "roughly" expect a 7 to show, $E(7)$, if you rolled it :-

   (i) 60 times (ii) 600 times (iii) 12 000 000 times ?

2. The weatherman says "the chance of it raining in April on any day is 1 in 5".

   a On how many days in April might you realistically expect rain ?

   b If it rained on 8 days would you be justified in calling the so called weather expert "rubbish" ?

   c If not, explain why not.

3. In an assembly line, where plastic buckets are produced, the probability of a faulty handle occurring has been worked out at 0·005.

   a How many of last week's production of 40 000 buckets might be expected to have a faulty handle ? (i.e. *E*(faulty)).

   b The cost of producing a bucket is 45p and they sell for £1·15 each.

   Last month, the company produced 120 000 buckets and sold all those that were not faulty. Faulty ones were scrapped.

   How much profit did the company make ?

4. During a flu epidemic in a small town with 8500 inhabitants, it is reckoned that the chances of catching the virus during the first week is 0·02.

   a How many of the inhabitants are expected to catch the flu ?

   During the 2nd and 3rd weeks the chances of those unaffected catching the flu drop to 0·015 and 0·01 respectively.

   b How many of the 8500 are likely to have been unaffected by the end of the 3 week period ?

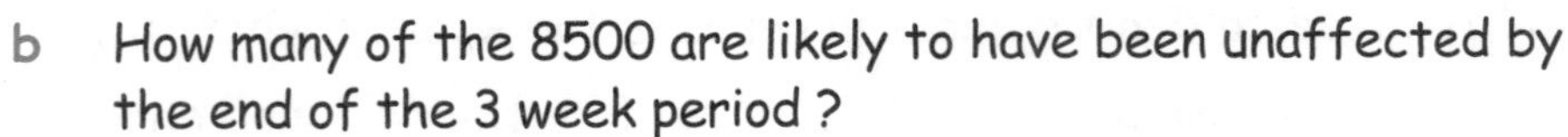

5. 

Crime statistics for two towns, Longsmuir and Tensville, show that the probability that a resident's house will be broken into during the 5 year period from 2010 to 2015 is given by :-

Prob(Longsmuir) = 0·018. Prob(Tensville) = 0·022.

There are 15 000 houses in Longsmuir and 13 500 in Tensville.

Which town had more burglaries during that period, and how many more ?

6. In 2015, there were approximately 2 750 000 people licensed to drive in Scotland.

   There were 8986 reported car accidents during that year.

   a Calculate, to 3 decimal places, the probability of a driver having a car accident during the year 2015.

   b Use this to calculate how many accidents there are likely to have been in each city with the following numbers of drivers :-

   (i) Glasgow (312 000) (ii) Edinburgh (260 000) (iii) Aberdeen (115 000).

   c Why, by just using the general statistic, can we not rely too much on these figures ?

A **probability tree diagram** is a pictorial way of showing combinations of events, where the probability of each individual event is known.

If • the probability of event A happening is 0·6

and • the probability of event B happening is 0·3

=> the probability of event A happening, then event B happening is :- **0·6 x 0·3 = 0·18.**

note :- you multiply the probabilities

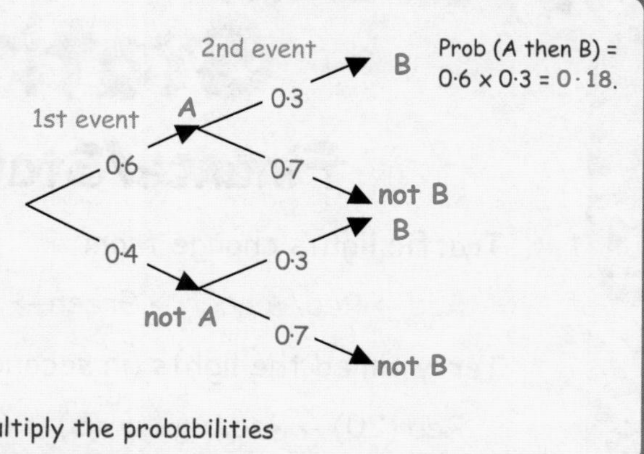

7. a Use the above probability tree diagram to calculate the following probabilities :-

   (i) Prob(A then not B) (ii) Prob(not A then B) (iii) Prob(neither A nor B).

   b If you add all 4 answers together, what do you get ? Can you explain why ?

8. This 3-sided spinner is spun and the coin tossed.

   a What is :- (i) P(Blue) (ii) P(Head) ? (*Give as fractions*).

   b Copy the tree diagram and fill in the missing probabilities :-

   c What are the following :-

   (i) P(red & head)

   (ii) P(red & tail)

   (iii) P(blue & head)

   (iv) P(blue & tail) ?

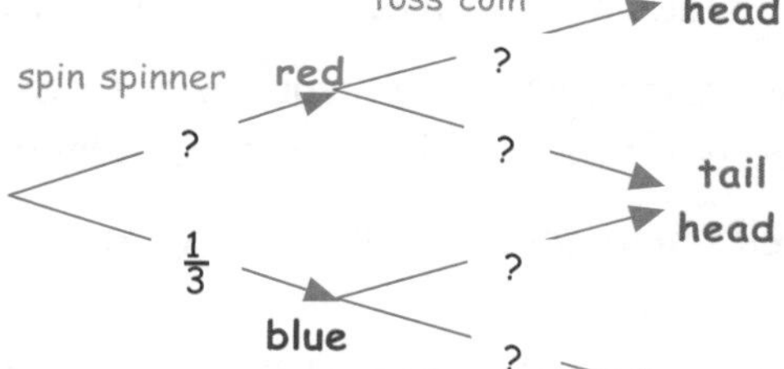

9. a It rained on 6 days in April. What is the probability it rained on any particular day, as a decimal ?

   b Copy and complete the tree diagram showing the probability it will rain or not rain on any 3 consecutive days.

   c What is the probability it was dry on day 1, day 2 **and** day 3 ?

   d What is the probability that it rained on **at least one** of these 3 days ?

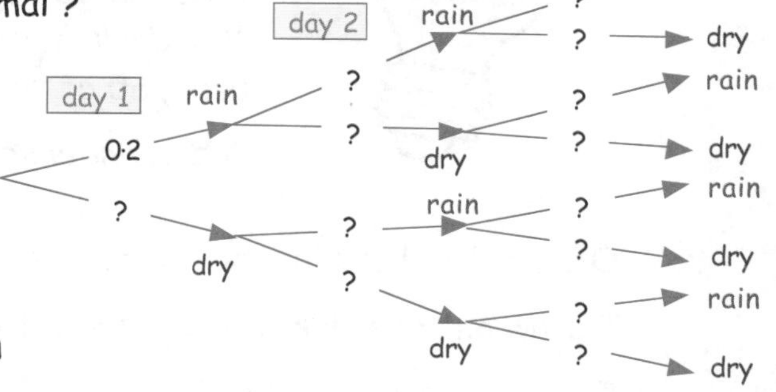

10. The dials on each of these 2 discs are spun.

   a Draw up a probability tree diagram to show all the combinations arising from spinning the dials.

   b What is the probability the first dial lands on red and the second green ?

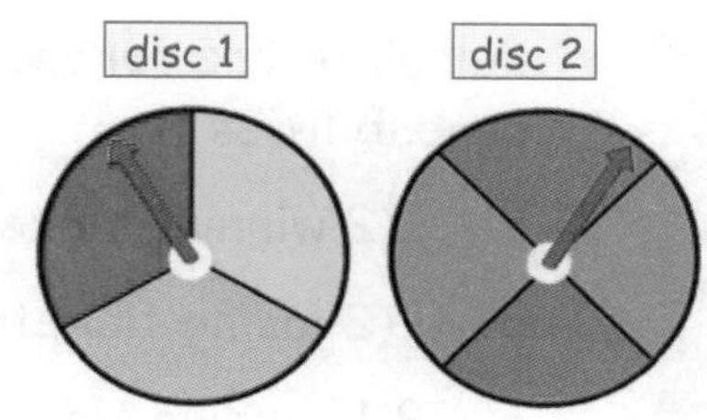

Statistical Risk

Finance/Statistics Assessment 7

1. Traffic lights change from

   Red -> Red/Amber -> Green -> Amber -> then back to Red.

   Terry timed the lights (in seconds) and found the following :-

   Red (20) -> Red/Amber (5) -> Green (15) -> Amber (10)

   If I arrive at the lights, what is the probability :-

   a the lights will be at red ? b the lights will not be showing green ?

2. The probability of snow falling on any particular day in January, February or March in 2015, was 0·111.

   On how many days during that 3 month spell was it likely to snow ?

3. Two people are gambling using this 10 sided dice.

   Three of the sides are painted yellow and seven are red.

   One man says to the other "If you always bet on yellow, I will offer you odds of 3 to 1 (double your money + original stake) on winning".

   Should the 2nd man accept this bet ? (*Explain your answer*).

4. *Wonderlight* claim that the chance of one of their bulbs failing within 5000 hours of use is less than 0·002.

   A new large department store bought and began to use *Wonderlight* bulbs. They discover that of the 23 000 bulbs used, 65 of them failed in under 5000 hours worth of use.

   Did *Wonderlight's* claim live up to expectations ?

5. Of the 8 tickets in a box, 3 of them are winning tickets.

   I draw out one ticket, keep it and then draw out a 2nd ticket.

   This is represented by the probability tree opposite :-

   Calculate the following probabilities :-

   a P(2 winning tickets)

   b P(2 losing tickets)

   c P(1 winning ticket).

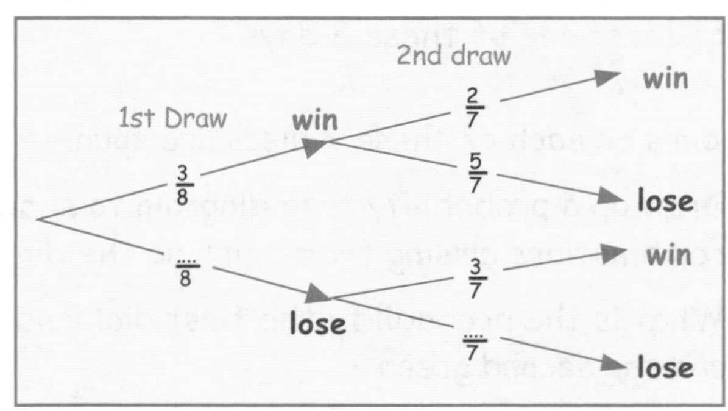

Unit Assessment

Finance & Statistics

Assessment Tasks

This investigation follows a young couple, Pauline and James, buying a ground floor flat and renovating it.

Investigation 1. Buying within Budget.

The first thing Pauline and James decide to do is buy a new bathroom suite from *Vincent Roma Bathrooms*.

There are various styles and optional extras to add.

Make	Basic Kit	Shower unit	Gold Fittings	Installation*
Barnaby	£895	£125	£85	£350
Regal	£1255	£185	£125	£350
Delooks	£1495	£140	£125	£525
Adelaide	£1975	£585	£475	£500
Premiere	£2125	£650	£295	£650

VAT at 20% is added on to the total, except the installation*, which already includes VAT.

Pauline and James decide to buy from *Vincent Roma Bathrooms* and they have a budget of £4000.

a Explain why they cannot afford to buy the Premiere Suite with all the extras, including installation.

Use calculations to justify your answer. (4)

b What is the most expensive suite Pauline and James can afford to buy with all the extras and the installation ?

Use calculations to justify your answer. (3)

Investigation 2. Insuring the Flat's Contents.

Most people insure their house and contents against fire or structural damage.

ScotElec offer insurance covering any problems with gas, electricity, white goods and plumbing for a 2 year period, and this would cost them £350.

ScotElec also guarantee repairs would be completed within 24 hours.

This probability tree diagram shows statistically the chances of there being a problem with gas, electricity, white goods or plumbing during the first 2 years of a contract being taken out.

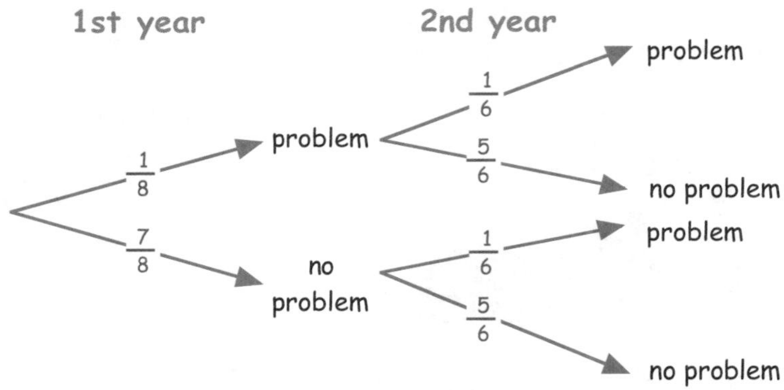

a Use the tree diagram to work out the probability that :-

(i) there will be a problem each year within the 2 year period

(ii) there will be no problems during that time

(iii) only 1 problem will occur during those 2 years. (4)

b James' friend Billy, who works for *ScotElec* says that from experience, most electricity, gas, white goods or plumbing problems would cost around £250 to repair if they had to get someone in to do the job.

Use your answers to part a to give advice to Pauline and James, regarding taking out this insurance policy from *ScotElec*. (1)

Investigation 3. Electricity Usage.

Pauline deals with household bills. She checks and pays her electricity bills monthly.

Her meter is the old style and the readings from 1st November to 1st December are shown in the two dials below :-

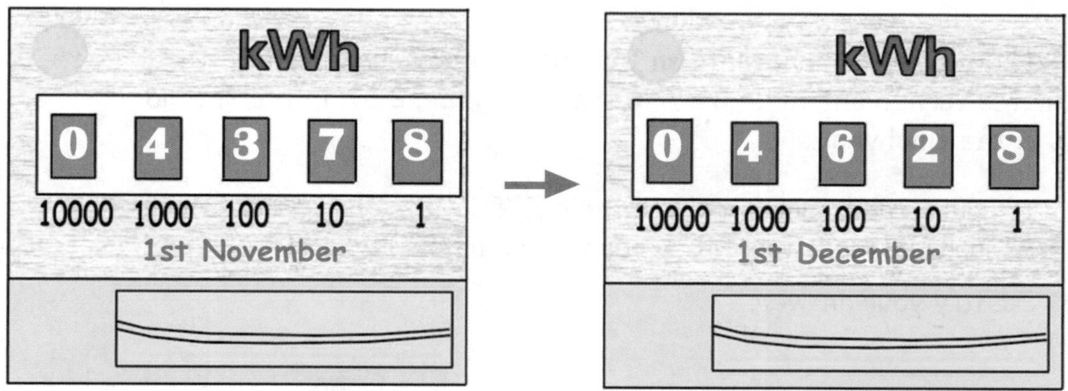

a How many units (kWh) of electricity were used during November ? **(1)**

b The electricity company charges 19·5p per kWh of electricity used as well as a monthly maintenance charge of £5·75.

On top of this, VAT (at 5%) is added.

Calculate Pauline and James' electricity bill for that 1 month period. **(2)**

c Pauline noted the number of units (kWh) she used over a 6 month period.

Here are her readings :- 250 285 310 302 245 192.

For the above 6 readings, calculate :-

(i) the mean (ii) the standard deviation. **(4)**

d During the other 6 months, Pauline found that the mean was 158 and the standard deviation was 24·3.

Compare the mean and standard deviation of the two different 6 month periods, and say why you think there is such a variation in the results. **(2)**

Investigation 4. Interest, Loans and Hire Purchase.

When they got married 3 years ago, Pauline and James were given money from friends and family amounting to £7500.

They invested it in a fixed rate 3 year High Interest Rate Bond, with a compound interest rate of 2·8%, the interest being paid into their account annually.

They could have put the money into an Instant Access Account where the interest rates turned out to be 3·2% in the first year, 2·5% in the second and 2·7% in the final year.

a If Pauline and James had put their £7500 into the Instant Access Account instead, would they have ended up better off ?

Justify your answer. **(6)**

Pauline and James decide to install a new kitchen from *McTaggarts* in their flat, costing £4500.

They cannot use their £7500 savings without invoking a penalty, so they look at 3 ways of paying for the new kitchen.

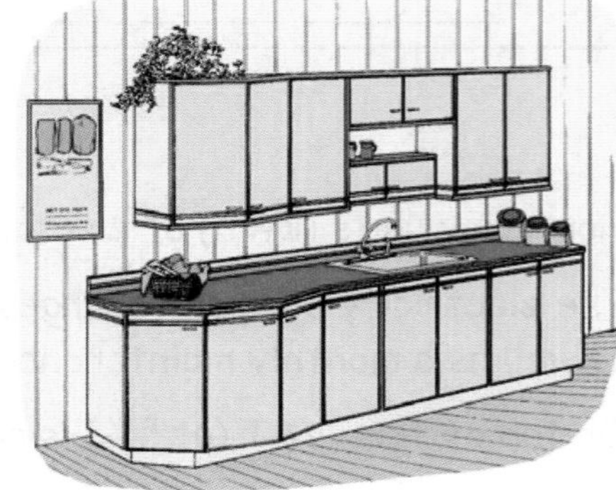

McTaggarts offer a Hire Purchase deal and ask for a 20% deposit, followed by monthly repayments of £185 over 2 years.

Their local bank offers a loan of the £4500, charging 7% p.a. compound interest, over 2 years.

They could use <u>two</u> Credit Unions as follows :-

- Take out a loan of £2500 from the first, where the they are charged 8·5% p.a. compound interest over a 2 year period.
- Take out a loan from the second of £2000 for 1 year, where the interest rate this time is only 6·5% p.a.

b Which of these deals works out at the cheapest overall and which provides the lowest monthly payments ?

Use your calculations to justify your answer. **(7)**

Investigation 5. Planning a Break.

Pauline and James are going on a short break in 6 weeks time and they both feel they need to lose some weight.

They both go on a diet and weigh themselves each morning over a 3 week period.

Their weights are shown in the back to back stem-and-leaf diagram below. (7)

weight (kg)

James		Pauline
	59	0 1 1 3 4 5 7 9
	60	1 2 2 2 3 5 8
	61	0 0 1 2 2 4
	62	
	63	
9 8 7 7	**64**	
9 7 5 5 3 0	**65**	
9 8 5 5 3	**66**	
9 4 2 0	**67**	
1 0	**68**	
$n = 21$		$n = 21$

	60	1	means 60·1 kilograms
7	**64**		means 64·7 kilograms

a Calculate :- (i) Pauline's mean weight,

(ii) Pauline's median weight,

(iii) Pauline's range of weights,

during that 3 week spell. (3)

b During the final 3 weeks before their holiday, Pauline found her mean weight had dropped to 57·6 kg, and her range of weights was 1·8 kg.

James' mean for the first 3 weeks was 66·2 kg with a range of 3·4 kg, and during the final 3 weeks his mean was 64·9 kg with a range of 2·9 kg

Comment on how Pauline's weight changed from the first three weeks to the last three weeks compared to that of James. (1)

When they were considering where to go, James began to make a note of how far away various towns and cities were from Edinburgh, and the price Ryanjet were charging for a return flight there.

From Edinburgh to	distance miles	Cost £'s
Manchester	180	67
Newcastle	90	42
Wick	170	60
Aberdeen	100	46
Carlisle	70	38
Nottingham	220	77
Skye	160	63
Birmingham	250	79
Isle of Man	120	50

c (i) Plot an appropriate graph to show the cost (in £s) against the distance flown (miles), using squared paper and the suggested scale shown. **(2)**

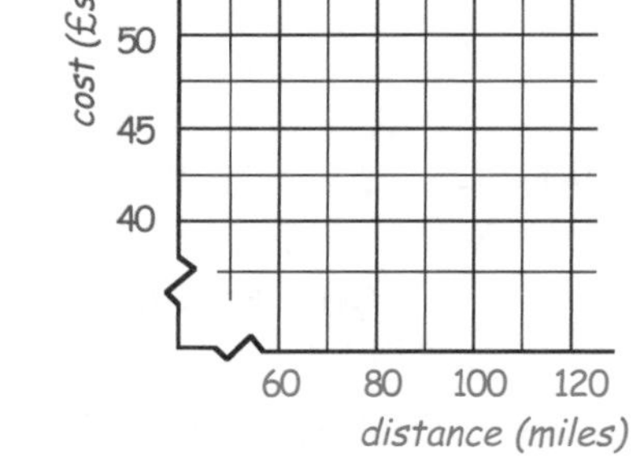

(ii) 1 mile is approximately 1·6 kilometres.

If the Ryanjet plane flies at an average speed of 450 km/hr, how long would the flight to Birmingham take in minutes, to the nearest minute ? **(4)**

(iii) Draw in, by eye, a Line of Best Fit and use it to estimate the cost of flying to Leeds, which is 150 miles from Edinburgh. **(1)**

(iv) Pauline and James decide to fly to Dublin, 210 miles away.

On top of their flights, they pay an airport tax of 8% and book in two suitcases at £20 each.

Estimate the overall cost of their flight. **(3)**

National 5 Lifeskills
Paper 1

50 minutes

Marks

1. Andi arrives at Glasgow International Airport at 0740.

   Her flight takes off in 1 hour and 50 minutes.

   The flight time to Cancun is 11 hours.

   Cancun is 6 hours behind British time.

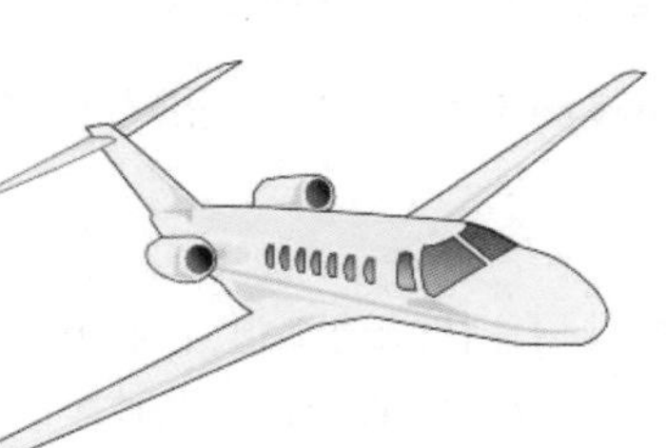

   a At what time (local time) does the flight arrive in Cancun ? (2)

   b Glasgow to Cancun is 7680 kilometres.

   Calculate the average speed of the aircraft, giving your answer to two significant figures. (2)

2. *Lucette Donatelli* ice cream company use a large wooden factory logo.

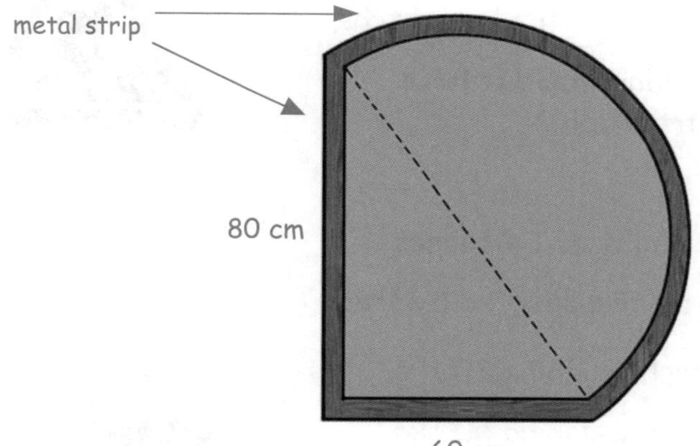

   The logo consists of a right angled triangle and a semi-circle.

   There is a metal strip running along the logo's perimeter.

   Calculate the length of the metal strip. (3)

3. Tia, Lee and Ron each monitor how many hours sleep they get.

   During the month of June,
   - Tia slept for 190 hours
   - Lee slept for $\frac{5}{12}$ of the month
   - The number of hours Ron slept worked out at the mean number of hours slept by both Tina and Lee.

   How many hours sleep did they all get in total ? (2)

4. Erich exchanges £800 into Euros at a rate of £1 to €1·20.

He spends on average €90 per day on his 7 day trip to Germany.

Before returning, he then spends half his remaining money on presents.

Does he have enough money left to afford the £120 flight home ? (2)

5. At a funfair stall, a game consists of throwing a ball onto a table with a series of trays, coloured red, blue and green.

The chance of landing on red is 0·4.

The chance of landing on blue is one in four.

To win the game, your ball must end up in a green tray.

What is the probability you will win when you throw one ball ? (1)

6. It took 10 men 20 hours to dig a 12 metre long ditch.

Working at the same rate, how long would it have taken 8 men to dig that 12 metre ditch ? (2)

7. A truck can carry a maximum weight of 1·4 tonnes.

The following 16 boxes are to be transported by truck :-

8 type A crates - each weighing 200 kg
4 type B crates - each weighing 500 kg
2 type C crates - each weighing 350 kg
1 type D crate - weighing 600 kg
1 type E crate - weighing 700 kg.

Copy and use the table to show how all the boxes can be transported in 4 trips, without exceeding the maximum weight on any trip. (2)

Trip	Type of Crate
1	
2	
3	
4	

8. Tony's gross pay last year was £24 000.

His taxable allowance worked out at 15% of his gross pay.

a Calculate Tony's taxable income. (2)

b Calculate the tax he paid, at a tax rate of 20%. (1)

Tony also paid £2280 in National Insurance and £1440 into his pension scheme last year.

c Calculate his net pay for the year. (1)

9. Carrie buys a new car for £18 000.

She has two optional ways of paying for it :-

Option 1 :-	Pay a deposit of 15% and make 12 monthly payments of £1350.
Option 2 :-	Pay no deposit followed by 24 monthly payments of £800.

Which option works out cheaper, and by how much ? (2)

10. To change a temperature from degrees Celsius (°C) to degrees Fahrenheit (°F), you would use the formula :-

$$F = 32 + \frac{9C}{5}.$$

Find numerically, the ratio of 60 degrees Celsius to its Fahrenheit value, expressing your ratio in its simplest form. (2)

11.

The gradient of a wheelchair ramp is 3 in 10.

The ramp has a horizontal distance of 43 metres.

Calculate the height of the ramp. (1)

[End of Question Paper 1]

National 5 Lifeskills
Paper 2

1 Hour 40 minutes | Marks

1. The scores taken by 6 golfers in a medal competition last Saturday were :-

72, 76, 76, 78, 81, 103.

a Calculate the mean, the mode and the range of scores. (3)

b Calculate the median and the semi-interquartile range of the scores. (2)

c Calculate the standard deviation of the scores. (3)

d Comment on which of the 3 averages, mean, median and mode and which measure of spread, the range, semi-interquartile range or standard deviation are most appropriate here. (1)

Total Score (9)

2. During the war in the African desert, a tank took part in an operation to rescue a pilot whose plane had crashed.

The maximum speed of the tank was 30 miles per hour.

The tank commander set off from base camp before dawn at 0430 on a bearing of 035° for 24 minutes, before turning to a new bearing of 170° for a further 1 hour and 6 minutes till he reached the pilot.

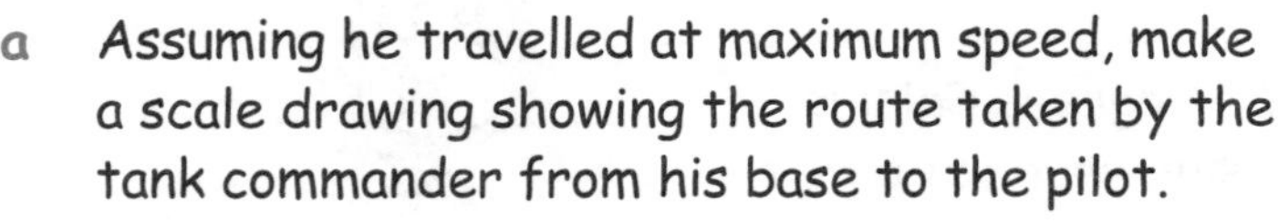

a Assuming he travelled at maximum speed, make a scale drawing showing the route taken by the tank commander from his base to the pilot.

Use a scale of 1 cm : 2 miles. (3)

b Use your scale drawing to work out the bearing the commander will have to take and the distance he will have to travel in order to return the pilot directly to base. (2)

c Dawn was known to break at 0655 that day.

Will the tank be able to make it safely back to camp under the cover of darkness before dawn comes ? (3)

Total Score (8)

Marks

3. A new game is devised called 15-pin bowling, similar to 10-pin bowling, but is played over 5 frames and has the following rules :-

- In each frame, you have possibly 2 shots at rolling the ball.
- If you get a "Maximum" (*15 pins down with first ball*), the frame is over for you, but you get to add on to the 15, the total scored with your next 2 balls.
- If you get an "Extra" (15 pins down but using both balls), you also get to add on to this the score with your next 1 ball.
- If you get an "Open", (like 8, then 4), you simply add the two.

a Here are Jed and Lucy's scores for the first 2 frames :-

		Jed	Lucy
Frame 1	Ball 1	7	9
	Ball 2	4	6
Frame 2	Ball 1	14	5
	Ball 2	0	1

Who is winning by the end of frame 2, and by how much ? (2)

b Here are Jed and Lucy's scores for frames 3 and 4 :-

		Jed	Lucy
Frame 3	Ball 1	15	5
	Ball 2	-	10
Frame 4	Ball 1	4	6
	Ball 2	5	.....

What would Lucy require to score with her 2nd ball in the 4th frame to end up with the same total score as Jed ? (2)

cont'd

Marks

3\. c • The last rule of the game states that if in the final (5th) frame, you score a "Maximum", then you get to roll 2 more, balls and the total for these 2 balls counts double.

If you get "Extra" in the 5th Frame, you get to roll 1 more ball and this score is doubled and added to your total.

15-pin

Here are Jed and Lucy's scores for the game with Jed still to roll his 2nd ball in frame 5 :-

		Jed	Lucy
Frame 1	Ball 1	7	9
	Ball 2	4	6
Frame 2	Ball 1	14	5
	Ball 2	0	1
Frame 3	Ball 1	15	5
	Ball 2	-	10
Frame 4	Ball 1	4	6
	Ball 2	5	2
Frame 5	Ball 1	11	15
	Ball 2		-
Extra	Ball 1		9
	Ball 2		5

Can Jed beat Lucy ? (*Explain your answer*). (3)

Total Score (7)

4\. The top of a cocktail glass is in the shape of a cone.

The diameter of the top is 12 centimetres and the length of the sloping side is also 12 centimetres.

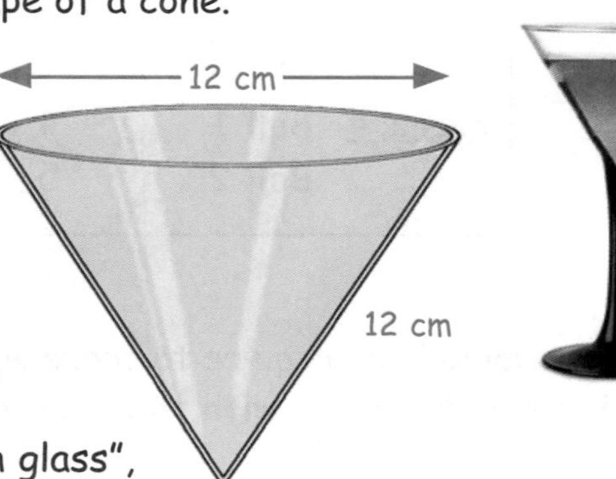

A barman makes up 3 litres of a champagne cocktail for a wedding toast.

If he is told to "three quarter fill each glass", how many glasses will he be able to make up with his cocktail mix ? (4)

Total Score (4)

Marks

5\. When Louise came into some money, she decided to buy a flat, do it up, then rent it out for 5 years, before re-selling it.

The flat cost Louise £85 000 which included rewiring it and installing a new bathroom.

Louise managed to rent it out to a young couple who were happy to pay £475 per month in rent, with a 5 year lease.

a Louise found she had to pay 20% tax on the income from the flat. How much was Louise left with at the end of the lease period ? (3)

b Louise had estimated, from studying flat prices, that the flat would increase in value by about 5% per year in each of the first 2 years, then 8% for each of the last three years.

When she did sell it at the end of the lease period, she got £105 000.

How did this compare with Louise's estimation ? (4)

c How much profit, **altogether**, did Louise make on the flat ? (2)

Total Score (9)

6. Joe lives in Glasgow. He has just received an invitation to his brother's wedding in Paris.

Current exchange rate is £1 = €1·25

He looks at 3 ways of getting to the wedding.

Car :- Joe considers driving the 480 miles to Dover, getting the car ferry to Calais, then driving 180 miles to Paris.

- Petrol in the UK is £1·20 per litre; in France it is €1·50 per litre and he knows he can get 12 miles to the litre.
- The return ferry crossing with car costs £35.
- He would need to stay overnight at Dover where bed and breakfast would cost him £30. On the way home, he would leave early and drive without staying overnight.

Train :-

- The train from Glasgow to London Euston costs £89 return.
- An overnight stay at a London hotel is £55.
- The Eurostar from London to Paris is €60 for a return.
- Would not need a hotel stop on the way home.

Flight :-

- The *Scottish Airways* return flight from Glasgow to Charles de Gaul (CGD) in Paris costs £170 + 5% tax and this includes a suitcase.

  The return train journey from CGD to the centre of Paris is another €15.
- *Ryanjet* only charge £95 for a return flight + 5% tax but they charge an additional £25 each way for a suitcase.

  The flight goes to Beauvais which is 100 km North of Paris, takes 90 minutes to travel by coach to Paris and costs €50 return.

a Work out the cost of Joe's trip if he goes by car. (3)

b How much cheaper would it be if he chooses to go by train ? (3)

c Which of the two journeys by plane is the cheaper ? (3)

d Say which of the above <u>you</u> would choose, and give a valid reason. (1)

Total Score (10)

7. The Scotts got *Sortit Landscape Garden Company* in to redesign their garden.

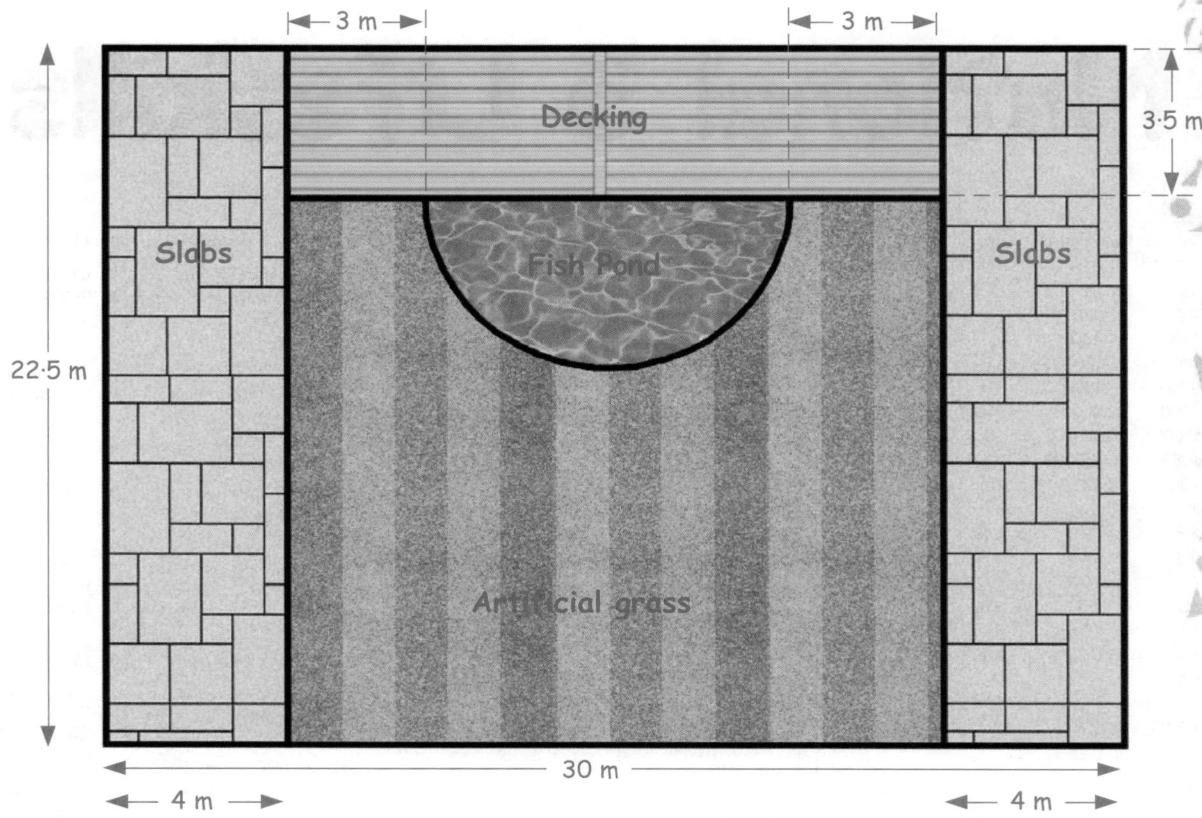

Decking :- Bought in packs of 5 square metres and priced at £75 per pack.

Artificial grass :- Calculate the area, add on 10% and round **up** to the nearest square metre. The cost of the grass is £8·50 per m^2.

Slabs :- Add 10% to the area for wastage. Slabs cost £13·50 per m^2.

Fish Pond :- Material costs are £875.

Extras :- Sand, cement etc. £65.

a Calculate the total cost for all the above materials. **(4)**

b *Sortit* worked out that they had put 180 man hours in at a rate of £11·75 per hour to build the new garden. Calculate the labour cost. **(1)**

c VAT at 20% is to be added on to the whole bill, but the owner of *Sortit* told the Scotts that if they paid half the bill cash, they would only charge VAT on the remaining half.

Assuming they did this, calculate the bill for the whole garden. **(3)**

Total Score (8)

[End of Question Paper 2]

answers to National 5 Lifeskills

Answers to Revision A Chapter (page 1)

1. a 46 b 84
2. a 150 b 970
3. a 1300 b 4000
4. a 18000 b 126000
5. a 9000 b 100000
6. a 8000 b 500 c 8000
7. a 1500 b 404000 c 6002000
8. a 1080 b 150600 c 1050000
9. a 230 b 225 c 156
10. 620
11. a 3·6 b 39·9 c 20·8 d 0·7
12. a 6·38 b 23·40 c 0·87 d 0·10
13. a 6·39 b 20·88 c 12·16 d 23·91
14. a 60·3 b 7·5 c 8·82 d 1·59
15. a 67 b 20·5 c 80·7
d 6·91 e 0·0835 f 1·03
16. 13·57
17. a 18·7 cm b 0·13 m c 60·45 km
18. a £7·05 b £705
19. a $^{67}/_{100}$ b 0·67
20. a $^{4}/_{5}$ b $^{7}/_{20}$ c $^{6}/_{25}$
21. a 0·35,35% b 0·76,76% c 0·875, 87·5%
22. 85%
23. a £33 b £4·20 c £28 d £200
24. a £120 b £360
25. a 9·6 b 54·4 acres
26. £3328
27. £36 and £2436
28. $^{6}/_{10}$,$^{9}/_{15}$
29. a $^{2}/_{3}$ b $^{4}/_{5}$ c $^{1}/_{7}$
30. a 36 g b 70p
31. a 1700 b 126 kg
32. 15 lambs
33. a $^{1}/_{4}$ b $^{3}/_{5}$ c $^{3}/_{20}$
34. a £26 b £7·50 c 96p
d 25p e £13 f £120
35. 540 times
36. 12 mph
37. 2 hr 30 mins
38. 1815 -> 1915 France time
39. 26 square centimetres
40. a 198 cm^2 b 144 mm^2 c 1·5 m^2
41. a 60 mm b 31·2 cm c 86 m
42. a -16°C b -15°C
43. a +£1170 b +£62·21
44. a 3°C b -27°C c -17°C
45. 356°C
46. a -5 b 6 c -20 d -11
e -13 f -100 g -15 h -160
47. a -3 b -300
48. 3 : 9 = 1 : 3
49. a 3 : 4 b 5 : 9 c 1 : 3 d 2 : 1
e 3 : 5 f 8 : 9 g 3 : 2 h 1 : 4
50. 8
51. 45
52. £4·25
53. 14 mins 10 secs
54. 1200 cm^3
55. 8 cm
56. a 5·5 L b 0·95 L c 0·04 L
57. a 5800 ml b 65 ml c 3250 ml
58. a 105000 cm^3 b 105000 ml
c 105 Litres d 30 mins
59. a $^{1}/_{12}$ b $^{1}/_{2}$ c $^{11}/_{12}$ d $^{7}/_{12}$
60. a $^{1}/_{6}$ b $^{13}/_{18}$ c $^{8}/_{9}$
61. a $^{1}/_{4}$ b $^{2}/_{11}$
62. a 7000 b 2500 c 2500 d $^{1}/_{5}$
63. a 1700 b 4 h 15 m
c (i) 30000 (ii) 15000 d 1830-1845
e 2015-2030 f 2045
64. a Mowing b $^{1}/_{4}$ c (i) 16 hr (ii) 32 hr
65. a (i) 1 (ii) 3 b 46, 48, 50, 52 c $^{1}/_{4}$
66. There should be a downwards spread since the more you practice, the lower your time for the race will generally be.
67. a (i) Avondale's (ii) Surefit (iii) McClutchie's
b £19

Answers to Chapter 1 (page 9)

Chapter 1 Revision Exercise - page 9

1. a 4 b 7 c 21 d 63
e 17 f 103 g 245 h 208
2. a 50 b 70 c 10 d 210
e 320 f 1000 g 8010 h 1010
3. a 100 b 500 c 100 d 800
e 4700 f 6300 g 1400 h 10000
4. a 2000 b 8000 c 6000 d 13000
e 82000 f 111000 g 225000 h 110000
5. a 200 b 2000 c 20000 d 300000
6. a 400 b 700 c 20000
d 3 e 15 f 300
7. a 730 b 1600 c 21000
d 1250 e 30000 f 450000
g 11010 h 80100 i 610000
8. a 4 b 8 c 6
d 57 e 62 f 35
g 7500 h 398 i 120
9. a 560 b 480 c 540 d 2250
e 5760 f 13500 g 164800 h 4500
i 2800 j 4800 k 10000 l 9000
m 70000 n 75000
10. a 21 b 8 c 9 d 90
e 430 f 330 g 610 h 44
i 33 j 8 k 43 l 77
m 81 n 520
11. 30000
12. a 13500 b 14000
13. 220
14. 985
15. a 345 b 350

Chapter 1 Exercise 1 - page 11

1. a £1627716 b £135643
2. a Wills by 1606 votes b 93000
3. 48880
4. £115251
5. £170
6. a £11 900 million b £11 350 million
7. £18 612 000
8. £98 000 000
9. 350 000
10. 193 670 368
11. £21864
12. €75·50
13. a 240 b 480 c 6850
d 6400 e 445 f 1100
g 1 h 380 i 71926

Chapter 1 Exercise 2 - page 13

1. a -3°C b 4°C c -14°C d -26°C
2. a -£20 b -£120
3. a overdrawn by £340 b +£783
4. a 14°C b 6°C c -10°C d 3°C
e 6°C f -25°C g -19°C h -32°C
5. a -21°C b -12°C c -510 ft
d 985 yrs e 30340ft f 75°C
6. a -4 b -4 c -6 d 3
e -10 f -14 g -14 h -30
i 0 j -210 k -77 l -31
m 5 n -110 o -200 p -38
q 30 r 1500 s -1250 t -41
7. a 6 b 9 c 0
d -2 e 0 f -10
g -1 h -17 i -100

Answers to Chapter 2 (page 16)

Chapter 2 Revision Exercise - page 16/17

1. 3·6
2. a 8·2 b 9·9 c 32·1 d 0·8
e 158·9 f 62·7 g 70·2 h 100·0
3. a 7·18 b 11·71 c 0·88 d 9·93
e 0·09 f 16·56 g 0·10 h 100·00
4. a 7·77 b 15·34 c 42·12 d 50·88
e 10·13 f 22·94 g 143·58 h 210·988
i 49·8 j 5·3 k 7·12 l 1·58
m 0·0628 n 340·2 o 4·05 p 860
5. a 89·1 b 611·4 c 23·4
d 73·11 e 0·7109 f 0·63
g 1401·4 h 0·729 i 0·000007
6. a 13·4 b 2·81 c 0·16 d 0·54
7. a 7·5 cm b 0·82 m c 5·8 km
d 400000 e 18000mm f 1000000 mm
8. a 35·74 kg b 28·63 kg
9. a 19·4 kg b 3 trips
10. a 105000g b 105 kg c 0·105 tonne

Chapter 2 Exercise 1 - page 18

1. a 7·29 b 14·55 c 20·18

2. a 6·34 b 36·05 c 10·30 d 1·01
3. a 1·285 b 2·973 c 5·329
d 6·186 e 9·922 f 8·040
4. It should be 7·0
5. a 6·88 b 11·0 c 5·988
d 12·65 e 11·00 f 9·99
g 0·06 h 317·146 i 2·0000

Chapter 2 Exercise 2 - page 19

1. a 70 b 700 c 6000 d 60000
e 4000 f 3000 g 8 h 0·05
i 0·5 j 0·01 k 0·0006 l 40
2. a 610 b 5100 c 31000 d 650000
e 47 f 37 g 9·3 h 0·12
i 0·59 j 0·0066 k 0·045 l 100
3. a 7650 b 55100 c 99800 d 345000
e 8·23 f 77·9 g 0·534 h 0·877
i 0·00154 j 0·0107 k 0·0557 l 0·100
4. a 48 kg b 46·3 L
5. a 73 kg b 4000 ml

Chapter 2 Exercise 3 - page 20

1. a 29·64 b 86·07 c 49·27
d 12·69 e 24·99 f 154·82
g 34·83 h 29·07 i 12·262
2. a 86·96 b 76·09 c 95·84
d 7·43 e 5·87 f 5·42
g 2·35 h 7·21 i 30·751
j 1456·29 k 21·12 l 39·648
m 7·5 n 3·75 o 12·75

Chapter 2 Exercise 4 - page 21

1. a 84·1 b 312·9 c 851 d 790
e 41 f 3180·1 g 87 h 1010
2. a 0·58 b 0·421 c 3·57 d 0·357
e 4·71 f 0·03001 g 0·0181 h 0·003
3. 11·5 L b 1150 L
4. a 0·14 m 140 mm

Chapter 2 Exercise 5 - page 22

1. a 84·6
b 59·1 c 6050 d 184·8
e 32040 f 620 g 540
h 684 i 701·4 j 2·85
2. a 9·12
b 0·73 c 0·042 d 1·6
e 0·0421 f 0·00048 g 0·202
h 0·61701 i 0·10001 j 0·009
3. a 842 kg b 25260 kg
4. a 0·0133 m b 13·3 mm

Chapter 2 Exercise 6 - page 23

1. a 14·3 hrs b 4·8 hrs
2. a 49·63 secs b 1·20 secs
3. a 700 secs b Charlie by 9·6 secs
4. a USA by 17·9 secs b 31 secs
5. a 90·9 secs b 11000 times

Answers to Chapter 3 (page 25)

Chapter 3 Revision Exercise - page 25/26

1. a $\frac{47}{100}$ b 0·47
2. a $\frac{9}{100}$ b 0·09
3. a $\frac{3}{20}$ b $\frac{13}{50}$ c $\frac{21}{25}$
d $\frac{1}{4}$ e $\frac{2}{25}$ f $\frac{7}{10}$
4. a 0·45, 45% b 0·04, 4%
c 0·12, 12% d 0·875, 87·5%
e 0·325, 32·5% f 0·8125, 81·25%
5. 72·5%
6. 60%
7. a £4·80 b 50p c £23·10 d £54
e £174 f £70 g £920 h £4·50
i 80p j £48 k £10 l £12·50
m £180 n £90
8. a 171 b 209
9. a £117 b £273
10. £31·50 11. £486
12. £643·50
13. 23 mph
14. £46·75
15. 9·6 cm
16. 15p more

Chapter 3 Exercise 1 - page 27

1. $\frac{1}{2}, \frac{1}{4}, \frac{3}{4}, \frac{1}{3}, \frac{2}{3}, \frac{1}{5}, \frac{2}{5}, \frac{3}{5}, \frac{4}{5}, \frac{1}{10}, \frac{3}{10}, \frac{7}{10}, \frac{9}{10}$
2. a £4·20 b £301 c 52p
d 56p e £153 f £21
g £13·50 h £32·40 i £1800
j £21350 k £364 l 2p
m £100 n 54p o £2
3. 72
4. a 24 b 18 c 30
5. a $\frac{9}{25}$, 0·36 b $\frac{13}{20}$, 0·65
c $\frac{21}{100}$, 0·21 d $\frac{37}{50}$, 0·74
e $\frac{22}{25}$, 0·88 f $\frac{3}{50}$, 0·06
g $\frac{1}{8}$, 0·125 h $\frac{1}{40}$, 0·025
6. a £4·50
b £8·40 b £19 d £97·20
e £18·24 f £1660 g £7·60
h £2·38 i 27p j £22·50
7. 138 mm
8. £1624
9. £220
10. a £26·40 b £2426·40

Chapter 3 Exercise 2 - page 29

1. a 6% b 40% c 28% d 72%
e 35% f 95% g 84% h 37·5%
i 24% j 87·5% k 62·5% l 75%
m 25% n 50%
2. a 90% b 38% c 62·5%
d 15% e 75%
3. a 60% b 40%
4. 22·2%
5. a 77·1% b 97·6% c 8·8%
6. a 50%, 60%, 90%, 60%, 50%, 100%,
65%, 85%, 83%, 76%
b see graph
c 71·9% d Generally improving
7. 50
8. a £30 b 20%
9. a £4 b $33\frac{1}{3}$%

Chapter 3 Exercise 3 - page 31

1. £185·45
2. £35·61
3. £28529·15
4. £6503·88
5. a £55·36 b £195·07 c £28·49 d £251·56
6. a (i) £8480 (ii) £8988·80 b 4 years
7. a £41000, £42230, £43581·36, £45542·52
b £5542·52 c 13·86%
8. A - £5624·32, B - £5623·80 - A a little better

Chapter 3 Exercise 4 - page 33

1. £260
2. a £337·50 b £253·13 c £189·84
3. £102600
4. 19934 ft
5. £30000 -> £36000 -> £28800. No !
6. a £182·70 b £185·44 c £193·91
7. a (i) 3% (ii) 3·6% b £94·32
c (i) £166400 (ii) £177562 (iii) £195884

Answers to Chapter 4 (page 36)

Chapter 4 Revision Exercise - page 36/37

1. a $\frac{2}{3}$ b $\frac{3}{4}$ c $\frac{5}{7}$ d $\frac{4}{5}$
e $\frac{3}{4}$ f $\frac{5}{9}$ g $\frac{4}{9}$ h $\frac{5}{8}$
2. a $\frac{1}{3}$ b $\frac{1}{4}$ c $\frac{2}{7}$ d $\frac{1}{5}$
e $\frac{1}{4}$ f $\frac{4}{9}$ g $\frac{5}{9}$ h $\frac{3}{8}$
3. a $\frac{2}{6}, \frac{3}{9}$ b $\frac{4}{10}, \frac{6}{15}$ c $\frac{14}{22}, \frac{21}{33}$ d $\frac{10}{6}, \frac{15}{9}$
4. a $\frac{4}{5}$ b $\frac{3}{4}$ c $\frac{2}{3}$ d $\frac{1}{3}$
e $\frac{4}{5}$ f $\frac{1}{2}$ g $\frac{1}{3}$ h $\frac{2}{3}$
5. a 35 mm b 16 kg c 201 mm d 28 kg
e 153 L f 3355 cm g £3500 h 608 m
6. a 120 b £800 c $\frac{1}{2} + \frac{1}{3} + \frac{1}{4} = \frac{13}{12}$ X
7. a $\frac{1}{100}$ b $\frac{1}{4}$ c $\frac{1}{10}$
d $\frac{3}{4}$ e $\frac{2}{5}$ f $\frac{1}{8}$
8. a £87 b 40p c 16 kg
d 112 mm e £15 f 50p
g £8 h £1·20 i £4
j £3·36 k £6·72 l £400
9. 0·098, 0·125 ($\frac{25}{200}$), 0·130 (13%),
0·200 ($\frac{1}{5}$), 0·300 (0·3), 0·333 ($\frac{1}{3}$)
10. a £102 b £33·90
11. a 35% b Jill £250000, Jane £300000,
June 100000, Janet £350000

Chapter 4 Exercise 1 - page 38

1. a $8\frac{1}{3}$ b $4\frac{5}{8}$ c $2\frac{5}{6}$
2. a $5\frac{2}{3}$ b $7\frac{3}{4}$ c $7\frac{1}{5}$ d $10\frac{1}{9}$
e $8\frac{6}{7}$ f $8\frac{1}{8}$ g $8\frac{5}{8}$ h $7\frac{3}{10}$
i $3\frac{1}{2}$ j $8\frac{2}{11}$ k $11\frac{1}{2}$ l $12\frac{1}{6}$
3. a $6\frac{5}{7}$ L b $2\frac{1}{6}$ m c $35714\frac{2}{7}$ gallons
d $827\frac{7}{9}$ L e (i) $274\frac{2}{5}$ m (ii) $158\frac{4}{5}$ m
4. $7\frac{1}{2}$
5. a $6\frac{2}{5}$ b $21\frac{1}{2}$ c $4\frac{1}{2}$ d $6\frac{2}{3}$
e $1\frac{23}{50}$ f $8\frac{1}{2}$ g $2\frac{1}{2}$ h $11\frac{1}{2}$
6. a 3 b 12 c 2
d 14 e $4\frac{2}{3} = \frac{14}{3}$
7. a 20 b 3 c 23 d $5\frac{3}{4} = \frac{23}{4}$
8. a $\frac{93}{10}$ b $\frac{21}{8}$ c $\frac{100}{9}$
9. a $\frac{36}{5}$ b $\frac{38}{3}$ c $\frac{77}{5}$ d $\frac{407}{10}$
10. a $\frac{5}{2}$ b $\frac{16}{5}$ c $\frac{32}{3}$ d $\frac{87}{5}$
e $\frac{10}{7}$ f $\frac{89}{9}$ g $\frac{1009}{10}$ h $\frac{1219}{20}$
11. a 2 b 12 c 11
12. a 5 b 6 c 17 d 39

Chapter 4 Exercise 2 - page 41

1. a $\frac{3}{5}$ b $\frac{5}{9}$ c $\frac{3}{5}$ d $\frac{3}{4}$
2. a $\frac{3}{7}$ b $\frac{5}{9}$ c $\frac{4}{9}$ d $1\frac{1}{2}$
e $\frac{1}{6}$ f $1\frac{5}{6}$ g 1 h $\frac{1}{2}$
3. a $3\frac{2}{3}$ b $3\frac{1}{5}$ c $6\frac{2}{7}$ d 10
4. a $1\frac{2}{5}$ kg b $\frac{1}{5}$ m c $2\frac{4}{5}$ L

Chapter 4 Exercise 3 - page 42

1. a $1\frac{1}{12}$ b $\frac{2}{15}$ c $\frac{1}{8}$ d $1\frac{11}{21}$
2. a $\frac{13}{15}$ b $\frac{1}{4}$ c $1\frac{7}{24}$ d $1\frac{3}{10}$
e $\frac{1}{2}$ f $\frac{1}{12}$ g $1\frac{1}{12}$ h 0

Chapter 4 Exercise 4 - page 42

1. a $\frac{1}{15}$ b $\frac{2}{9}$ c $\frac{7}{12}$ d $\frac{1}{16}$
2. a $\frac{1}{8}$ b $\frac{1}{40}$ c $\frac{2}{15}$ d $\frac{5}{14}$
e $\frac{9}{14}$ f $\frac{3}{16}$ g $\frac{2}{5}$ h $\frac{1}{5}$

Answers to Chapter 5 (page 44)

Chapter 5 Revision Exercise - page 44/45

1. a (i) 1 hr 5 min (ii) 1 hr 40 min (iii) 6 hr 50 min
   b (i) 6.00 pm (ii) 7.40 pm
2. 105 miles
3. 2 hours
4. 860 mph
5. 4 metres per hour
6. $2^1/_2$ hours
7. 68 km/hr
8. 27 miles
9. 1 hour 15 minutes
10. 15500 km
11. a $1^1/_2$ hrs b 15 mins
12. 2030
13. 15 metres
14. 4 metres per second

Chapter 5 Exercise 1 - page 46

1. a 60 km/hr b 2 hours
   c 140 miles d 60 km/hr
   e 180 metres f 2 hrs 45 mins
2. 300 miles
3. 12 km/hr
4. 4 hours
5. 90 km
6. 40 mph
7. 4 hrs 15 mins
8. 2 hrs 45 mins
9. 5250 miles
10. a 2 mph b 4 mph faster

Chapter 5 Exercise 2 - page 48

1. a 0·3 hr b 0·1 hr c 0·8 hr d 0·4 hr
   e 0·9 hr f 0·35 hr g 0·65 hr
2. a 0·17 hr b 0·33 hr c 0·28 hr
   d 0·87 hr e 0·83 hr f 1·17 hr
3. a 1·8 hr b 2·6 hr c 3·85 hr
   d 4·95 hr e 6·2 hr f 5·1 hr
4. 32 miles
5. a 9 miles b 8 km c 17·5 miles
   d 200 km e 4 miles
6. Pat 14 km, Drew 10 km - Pat by 4 km
7. 360 miles
8. a 224 miles b 46 km
9. 100 mph
10. a 65 mph b 460 mph c 36 km/hr
    d 70 mph e 950 mph

Chapter 5 Exercise 3 - page 50

1. a 48 mins b 51 mins c 42 mins
   d 24 mins e 40 mins f 36 mins
2. 4 hr 54 mins
3. a 6 hrs 12 mins b 1 hr 30 mins
   c 3 hrs 39 mins d 4 hrs 48 mins
   e 2 hrs 51 mins f 7 hrs 42 mins
   g 2 hrs 40 mins h 1 hr 50 mins
   i 2 hrs 35 mins j 3 hrs 55 mins
4. a 2 hrs 45 mins b 4 hrs 36 mins
   c 6 hrs 20 mins
5. a 3·3 hrs b 3 hrs 18 mins
6. a 1·2 hrs b 1 hour 12 mins
7. a 32 hrs 18 mins b 20 mins
   c 21 mins d 1 hr $7^1/_2$ mins
8. a 2 hrs 15 mins b 2 hrs
   c 6 hrs 45 mins
9. a 7 m/sec, 420 m/min, 25200 m/hr
   b 25·2 km/hr

Answers to Chapter 6 (page 53)

Chapter 6 Revision Exercise - page 53

1. a 220 mm² b 64 cm² c 31·5 m²
   d 168 cm² e 22·09 m² d 8464 cm²
2. a 64 mm b 32 cm c 25 m
   d 62 cm e 18·8 m f 368 cm
3. 62 cm²
4. 15 cm
5. 6·5 cm
6. a 88 cm² b 65 m² c 33·6 m²
   d 250 cm² e 18 mm² f 7 cm²

Chapter 6 Exercise 1 - page 54

1. a 27 cm b 42 cm c 33 m
   d 34 m e 45·8 cm f 575 mm
2. 20 cm
3. a 24·8 m b £108
4. 28·26 cm
5. a 31·4 cm b 47·1 cm c 75·36 cm
6. a 157 cm b 81·64 mm c 150·72 cm
7. 43·96 cm
8. a 62·8 cm b 15·7 m
9. a 4·2 m b 6·594 m c 10·794 m

Chapter 6 Exercise 2 - page 56

1. a 105 cm² b 42·5 cm²
   c 110·25 cm² d 72 cm²
   e 105 cm² f 750 mm²
   g 66 m² h 92 cm²
   i 110 cm²

Chapter 6 Exercise 3 - page 57

1. 28·26 cm²
2. a 78·5 cm² b 31400 mm²
   c 113·04 m²
3. 452·16 cm²
4. 226·9 cm² and 3·14 m²
5. a 3215 cm² b 4·52 m²
   c 0·196 m² / 1963 cm² d 615 cm²
6. a 1444 cm² b 1133·54 cm² c 310·46 cm²
7. 2150 cm²
8. 16·08 m²
9. £22·08

Chapter 6 Exercise 4 - page 59

1. a 264 cm² b 70 cm² c 334 cm²
2. a 1600 cm² b 280 cm² c 1880 cm²
3. a 296 cm² b 215 cm² c 303 cm²
   d 624 cm²
4. 126 cm² + 105 cm² = 231 cm²
5. a 3025 mm² b 60 m² c 255 cm²
6. a 94·99 cm² b 146·2 cm² c 71·7 cm²

Answers to Chapter 7 (page 62)

Chapter 7 Revision Exercise - page 62/63

1. a 24 : 18 b 4 : 3
2. a 72 : 160 b 9 : 20
3. a 1 : 8 b 5 : 1 c 3 : 8 d 4 : 1
   e 7 : 9 f 17 : 53 g 3 : 4 h 3 : 4
   i 1 : 4000 j 3 : 4 k 3 : 1 l 101 : 1
   m 3 : 10 n 1 : 4 0 1 : 30 p 1 : 4
4. 30
5. a 220 b 260
6. 70
7. a 12p b £6 c £7 d £40
   e £51 f £5·70 g £1·20 h £51·83
8. a 96 kg b 4·2 m c 40·5 kg d 105 m
9. a £9·10 b £36·40
10. a 52 secs b 10 litres
11. 7·5 kg
12. 5 litres
13. <u>Gary</u> - 8 km/hr, Gareth - 9 km/hr, Gio - 8·5 km/hr

Chapter 7 Exercise 1 - page 64

1. a 18 b 24 c 35
2. a 30 b 63
3. a 90 b 12 c 217
4. a £400 b £205 c £768
5. a Very dark purple b Light purple
   c Mid purple d Dark purple
   e Very light purple
6. a 40 b 80 c 36
7. a 26 b £12·30
8. a 15 b 88 c 132 d 50
9. 200

Chapter 7 Exercise 2 - page 66

1. £100 and £250
2. a £2000 & £8000 b £45 & £75
   c £400 & £480 d £2200 & £1800
   e £26 & £24 f £115 & £135
   g £500 & £1500 & £1000
   h £200000 & £300000 & £500000
3. a £120000 4. 600

Chapter 7 Exercise 3 - page 67

1. a £4·70 b £23·50
2. a 9 kg b 63 kg
3. €84
4. 9000 square centimetres
5. a 4800 b 2160
6. a £8·90 b 36 kg c £25 d 75p
7. £168
8. 37·8 metres
9. £25·50
10. 2700 miles
11. a Yes b No c No d Yes
12. a £6 b £45 c £208
13. £108

Chapter 7 Exercise 4 - page 69

1. 15 hours
2. 9·6 hrs (9 hrs 36 mins)
3. 126 km/hr
4. 5 days
5. 2 weeks longer (5 weeks)
6. 20 more men (80 altogether)
7. 40 km/hr
8. a No (direct) b No (direct)
   c Yes (for a short time) d Yes
9. a 48 b 10 minutes quicker
10. 3 days longer 11. 10 men
12. 4·5 minutes
13. Boiling an egg - 2 people take same time as 1.

Answers to Chapter 8 (page 72)

Chapter 8 Revision Exercise - page 72/73

1. a 40 cm³ b 24 cm³ c 16 cm³ d 56 cm³
2. a 160 cm³ b 2040 cm³ c 1000 cm³
   d 1980 cm³ e 900 cm³ f 40000 cm³
3. 5 cm 4. a 30 cm b 15 cm
5. a 4 L b 90 L c 0·1 L
   d 0·75 L e 0·008 L f 0·0001 L
6. a 5000 ml b 4100 ml c 100000 ml
   d 800 ml e 7 ml f 1·5 ml
7. 2·5 litres
8. a 140000 cm³ b 140000 ml
   c 140 litres d 28 minutes

Chapter 8 Exercise 1 - page 74

1. 240 cm^3
2. 240 cm^3
3. 3 cm
4. a 20000 cm^3 b 20000 ml c 20 litres
5. a 504000 cm^3 b 1·2 hours or 72 minutes

Chapter 8 Exercise 2 - page 75

1. 200 cm^3
2. 216 cm^3
3. 1240 cm^3
4. 7 cm
5. 15 cm
6. 5 cm
7. a 24 cm^2 b 360 cm^3
8. 270 cm^3
9. a 40 cm^2 b 720 cm^3
10. 8·5 cm

Chapter 8 Exercise 3 - page 77

1. 1130·4 cm^3
2. a 4 cm b 703·36 cm^3
3. 1st = 339·12 cm^3, 2nd = 381·51 cm^3 => 1st
4. a 423900 cm^3 b 423·9 litres
5. 850π cm^3
6. a 28260 ml b 56 full tins
7. a 24000 cm^3 b 2486·88 cm^3
   c 10 times (9·65 times)
8. a 12560 cm^3 b 12·56 litres
9. a 1·96 cm^3 b 39·25 grams c £981·25
10. a 78500 cm^3 b 78·5 litres
11. 0·99 m^3
12. 29000 cm^3
13. 10 cm
14. 20 cm
15. a 31400 ml b 40 cm
16. 3·6 cm
17. a 350 m^3 b 7 hours

Chapter 8 Exercise 4 - page 80

1. a 4000 ml b 15 L c 70000 ml
   d 0·9 L e 4 L f 2500 ml
   g 70 ml h 0·025 L i 4250 ml
2. a 800 cm^3 b 0·8 Litres
3. 48 Litres
4. a 13564·8 cm^3 b 13·56 L c 18·84 cm

Answers to Chapter 9 (page 82)

Chapter 9 Revision Exercise - page 82/84

1. a 200 b 125 c 25
   d 50 e red 100 f 900
2. a 20% b 10% c 30% d 15%
   e 5% f 3000 g 10000
3. a (i) 280 (ii) 320 b 3 c Feb (400)
   d (i) May (ii) 40 e April to May
4. a Food - Power - Transport - Clothes
   b $^{1}/_{4}$ c £60 d £135 e £300
5. a The older you get the less sleep you need
   b 13·5 hrs c 10 year olds
   d 1 year olds
   e level off to about 6-7 hours sleep per night
6. a (i) 1 (ii) 2 (iii) 3 b 6 c 20
   d 8 mph - possibly a tractor ?
7. a (i) £7·50 (ii) £13·50 (iii) £14 (iv) £18
   b £9·50 + £16·50 + £12·50 = £38·50

Chapter 9 Exercise 1 - page 85

1. a (i) orange (ii) grapes
   b 7 c 14 d 3
2. a 8 b 14 c 23 d 5
3. a 70 b 5 c Marigolds
   d 15 e A & Q by 15
4. a 20% b 20% c no d Lib Dem
5. various representations - see graph
6. a 20 b 24
   c Greys sold 130, Clarks sold 86 - NOT true
7. a £1·30 b £1·30 c week 5 d 10p
8. a (i) 3°C (ii) -2°C b 15th and 16th
   c In both cities there was a general dip around the 6th and the 12th, rising later in the month. For the majority of the time Glasgow was 3-4 degrees above Aberdeen throughout the month.
   d Glasgow' mean 3·1°C, Aberdeen's mean 0·9°C
9. a (i) 11 (ii) 10 b male 59 c woman
   d 45 - a man & woman
   e male - 35·8, female - 29 Male by 6·8 years
10. a (i) 43 mins (ii) 38 mins
    b appears to be an improvement c 9 mins
    d pr - 57·75 mins, race - 52·25 mins
    an improvement on average by 5·5 minutes.
11. a

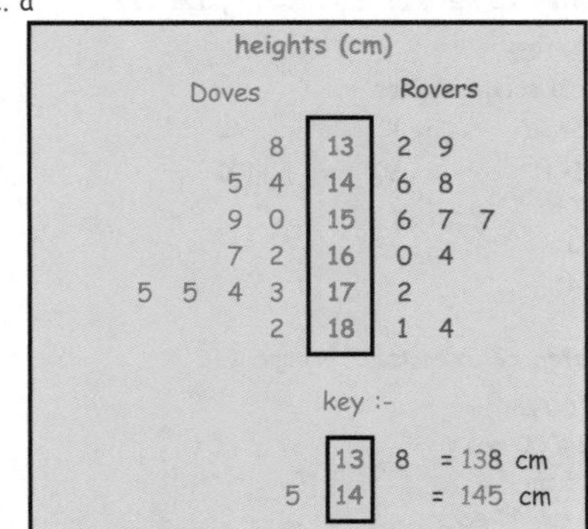

    b Doves generally a bit taller
    c Doves - 158 cm, Rovers - 162 cm (Rovers)

Chapter 9 Exercise 2 - page 89

1. a (i) $^{2}/_{5}$ (ii) $^{1}/_{10}$ (iii) $^{1}/_{5}$ (iv) $^{3}/_{10}$
   b Burgers, soup, pizza, salad
2. a (i) 40% (ii) 30% (iii) 20%
   b (i) 60 (ii) 270
3. a (i) 25% (ii) 40% (iii) 15% (iv) 20%
   b (i) 125 (ii) 100
4. a

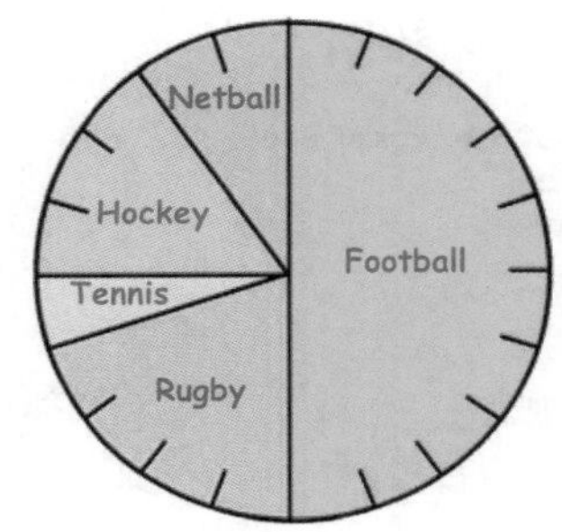

5 - 7 See piecharts

8. a see piechart b McCann c 2400

Chapter 9 Exercise 3 - page 91

1. a (i) Mary (ii) Toni (iii) Pat (iv) Pat
   b Mary (3, 15 kg) Toni (4, 10 kg)
   Ali (6, 15 kg) Mark (8, 20 kg)
   Tom (9, 25 kg) Shaz (10, 22 kg)
   Pat (12, 30 kg)
   c Mark
3. a 7 hrs b yes c neg d 4 hrs
4. a yes b 64 g c about 58 g
5. a strong +ve correlation between temp & sales
   b 40-45 c 20 d about 25°C
6. a b +ve correlation c 50-55

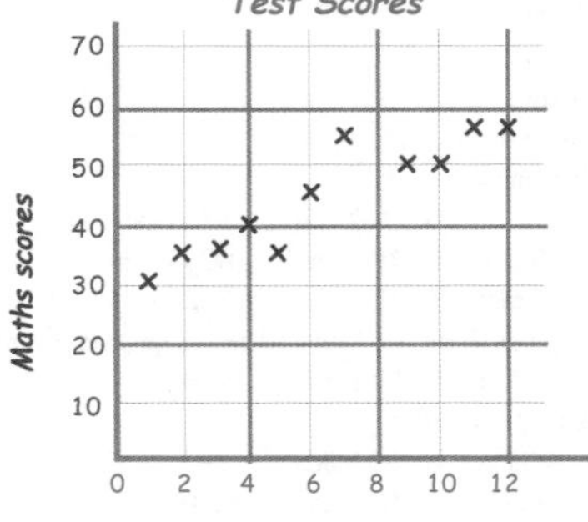

Chapter 9 Exercise 4 - page 93

1. a €135 b €207 c Barcelona
   d Berlin (€358) is the dearest
2. a Coke-Cola b 43%
   c 27% d 65% to 35% (240)
3. a 14°C b 20°F c 73·25 mm

Answers to Chapter 10 (page 96)

Chapter 10 Revision Exercise - page 96

1. A - evens, B - certain, C - impossible
   D - highly unlikely, E - poorer than evens
2. a $^{1}/_{100}$ b $^{1}/_{2}$ c $^{99}/_{100}$ d $^{51}/_{100}$
3. a $^{1}/_{12}$ b 0 c $^{1}/_{2}$
   d $^{1}/_{3}$ e $^{11}/_{12}$
4. $^{8}/_{9}$ = 0·888., $^{6}/_{7}$ = 0·857, $^{10}/_{12}$ = 0·833 =>United

Chapter 10 Exercise 1 - page 97

1. $^{27}/_{69}$ = $^{9}/_{23}$
2. a $^{1}/_{2}$ b $^{1}/_{12}$ c $^{1}/_{4}$ d $^{1}/_{2}$
3. a 1-2 times b 0 c 10
4. a (1,1),(1,2), (1,3), (1,4), (1,5), (2,1), 2,2)..(5,5)
   b (i) $^{1}/_{25}$ (ii) $^{1}/_{25}$ (iii) $^{3}/_{25}$ (iv) 0
5. a $^{14}/_{30}$ = $^{7}/_{15}$ b 560, 120, 240, 200, 80
6. a 24 b (i) $^{1}/_{2}$ (ii) $^{1}/_{6}$ (iii) $^{1}/_{24}$
7. WW - 5·5, SS - 5·3, BB - 5·8.. Berwick Bears
8. a $^{1}/_{200}$ b $^{1}/_{1000}$ c $^{1}/_{10}$ d $^{1}/_{100}$
9. 204
10. a 0·92 b 168
11. a 12 b at least £145 per fete
12. C (or possibly D)
13. Graph 2
14.

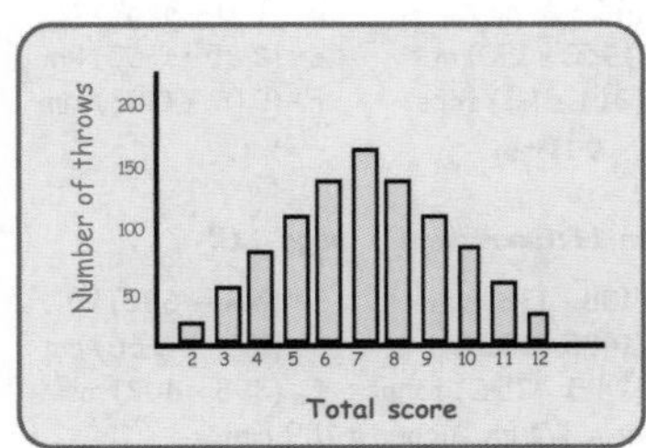

15. a 120 b Prob = 0·015 - slow it down
16. a $^{1}/_{5}$ b $^{2}/_{15}$ c $^{11}/_{15}$ d 1

Answers to Revision B Chapter (page 104)

1. a $^{60}/_{180}$ b $^{1}/_{3}$
2. Left = 2, right = 3·25 => Right ladder safe

3. 0·38, $^3/_8$, $^7/_{20}$, 30%
4. a 36 cm b 30 m c 220 mm
5. 30 cm
6. 145 mm
7. 94 cm
8. 234 cm²
9. 6500 mm²
10. a 192 cm² b 320 cm² c 575 cm²
11. a 63 cm² b 180 cm² c 8000 mm²
12. a 78·5 m² b 1256 cm² c 2826 cm²
13. shape with edges 1 cm, 10 cm, 6 cm and 3 cm
14. a 13·5 cm b 18 cm c 50 mm
15. 42 metres
16. a 4·5 cm b 90 miles
17. a 140 cm³ b 180 cm³ c 500 m³
18. 2·5 cm
19. a 360000 cm³ b 360000 ml c 360 litres
20. a 230 cm³ b 340 cm³
21. a 27 cm² b 216 cm³
22. 471 cm³
23. a 12·5 cm b 84·9 mm
24. a 120 cm b 6000 cm³
25. 94 cm
26. a 0953 b Gatsburgh (1927) c 23 mins
    d (i) 34 m (ii) 55 m (iii) 16 m (iv) 1 hr 4 m
27. 8.10 am (0810) next day
28. 1 hr 30 mins
29. a 36 b 75 c 20
30. 12
31. a see drawing b 6·4 cm c 32 m
32. 135°
33. a 025° b 160° c 305°
34. a (86 - 94) km b (222 - 232) g
    c (90 - 150) volts d (1850 - 2350) pounds
    e (6·6 - 7·8) litres f (0·28 - 0·32) cl
35. (8 ± 0·75) ounces
36. a (45 ± 5) mm b (120 ± 3) g
    c (4800 ± 400) m d (3·95 ± 0·05) hrs
    e (36·8 ± 0·3) secs f (0·04 ± 0·03) km
37. a 44 b 14080
38. 32 strips = 32 ÷ 3 = 10·66... => 11 rolls needed
39. a 64 m² x £28 = £1792
    b (0·2 x 16) + $^1/_2$(2·5 + 1·5)x6 = 15·2 m².

Answers to Chapter 11 (page 111)

Chapter 11 Revision Exercise - page 111

1. a 83 m b 76 m
2. a 46 m - 54 m b 207 - 223 g
   c 225 amp - 255 amp d 1350 mile - 1650 miles
   e 6·8 mg - 7·6 mg f 0·85 kg - 0·95 kg
3. a 92p b £1·18
4. a Yes b No c Yes d Yes
5. (65 ± 7) mph
6. a (45 ± 5) ml b (170 ± 5) g
   c (1950 ± 150) m d (2·35 ± 0·05) km
   e (21·1 ± 1·3) secs f (0·07 ± 0·03) mm
7. (9·1 ± 9·1) mm

Chapter 11 Exercise 1 - page 112

1. a (108 - 132) mm b (570 - 630) kg
   c (1485 - 1515) m d (0·54 - 0·66) cm
   e (24·5 - 25·5) tonnes f (398 - 402) ml
2. lower = 171 cm, upper = 189 cm
3. 39·2°C to 40·8°C
4. 80·5 poundals down to 59·5 poundals
5. 57·75 kg
6. 112·7 cm to 117·3 cm
7. a yes b yes c no d yes
8. a yes b yes c no d yes
9. a (60 ± 6) secs b 60 mins (± 10%)

Chapter 11 Exercise 2 - page 114

1. For large distances like the length of a football pitch, 1 cm compared with 100 metres is about 0·01% of an error. With say a 1 metre window from, 1 cm is a much bigger relative error being 1% which is 100 x more critical than 1st example.
2. range is 44·2 to 45·0. Scale reads 44·9. Is ok
3. $7^5/_8$ to $7^7/_8$
4. 8 x 13·53 = 108·24 mm so space of 108·25 mm is ok
5. 47·20 + 46·89 + 47·96 + 45·72 = 187·77 secs
6. least = 2·5 x 25 = 62·5m, most = 2·5 x 35 = 87·5m
7. At best, 209 hours, at worse, 256 hours
8. Fastest = 9·64 m/sec, slowest = 9·59 m/sec
9. a Min vol = 293 cm³, Max vol = 307 cm³
   b Max weight = 307 x 8·05 = 2471 grams
10. Least vol = 2887·5 ml, Greatest vol = 3062·5 ml
11. a no loss b €144000 c €375000

Answers to Chapter 12 (page 117)

Chapter 12 Revision Exercise - page 117

1. £41·51
2. 201 square inches
3. a 36 b 12 c $^1/_4$
   d 11 e 60 f 100
4. £30
5. 13
6. 14

Chapter 12 Exercise 1 - page 118

1. 200 km/hr
2. 24000 cm³
3. 15 cm
4. 1 min 40 secs
5. £153·99 b postage & packing
6. 11 cm
7. 30°C
8. 20 miles
9. 78·5 cm²
10. £57·50
11. 8·5 m
12. 11 pounds

Chapter 12 Exercise 2 - page 120

1. a 75 b 60 c 2000 d 18
   e 0 f 63 g 102 h 4
   i 7 j $^9/_{20}$ k $3^1/_3$
2. 18·8
3. a £1900 b loss of £380 c 5
4. 20410 cm³
5. 180 cm³
6. 9
7. 10°C
8. 11
9. 56·52 cm³
10. 19·5
11. 15·2
12. 59°F
13. 5
14. 150 km
15. 15

Chapter 12 Exercise 3 - page 123

1. a $^3/_4$ b 5
2. 6
3. 6250 cm²
4. 12
5. 20 cm²
6. a 7 cm b 5 cm

Answers to Chapter 13 (page 125)

Chapter 13 Revision Exercise - page 125

1. a 15 metres
   b see rectangle 3 cm by 20 cm
2. See drawing measuring 4 cm by 6·5 cm
3. a 045° b 100° c 295°
4. see drawings
5. 225°
6. a/b rectangle 9 cm by 12 cm
   c 15 cm d 60 metres

Chapter 13 Exercise 1 - page 126

1. a see drawing b 5·7 cm d 17·1 ft
2. a see drawing b 6 cm d 12 m
3. a see drawing b 31 m
4 a (i) see drawing (ii) 21 m
  b (i) see drawing (ii) 72·8 m (73 m)
  c (i) see drawing (ii) 468 m (470 m)
  d (i) see drawing (ii) 2500 feet
5. a see drawing b 55 m
6. a see drawing b 19·3 m
7. a see drawing b 14·4 km
8. a 3 km b see drawing c 17·6 km

Chapter 13 Exercise 2 - page 129

1. a 040° b 110° c 145°
2. a 250° b 270° c 330°
3. a b 87 miles

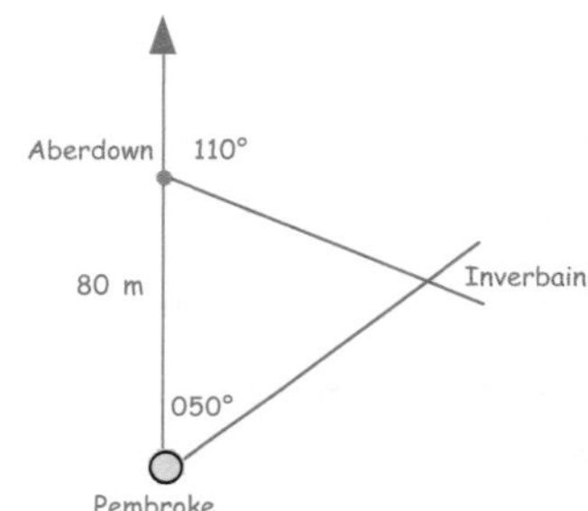

   c min = 2 hrs 29 mins, max = 3 hrs 29 mins
4. a see drawing b 060°
5. a see drawing b 9·3 cm
   c 744 km d 448 km/hr
6. a see drawing b 288° (286° - 290°)
   c 34·7 km d 3 hrs 28 mins
7. a see drawing b 880 km c 316°
8. a see drawing b 160 km
   c quickest - 41·7 mins, slowest - 56·5 mins
9. a see drawing b 200 km c 25 km/hr

Answers to Chapter 14 (page 133)

Chapter 14 Revision Exercise - page 133

1. a 1500 b 0800 c 1919 d 1145
2. a 1.30 pm b 10.15 pm c 1.05 am d 12.01 am
3. a 2 hrs 30 mins b 5 hrs 15 mins
   c 10 hrs 0 mins d 8 hrs 45 mins
   e 3 hrs 30 mins f 6 hrs 40 mins
   g 1 hrs 15 mins h 10 hrs 45 mins
4. a 3 hrs b 100 mile c 70 mph d 20 m
5. a 120 mile b 30 min c 300 km/hr
6. 9.20 pm UK time
7. a Mary - 1 hr 15 min - NO
   b 1 hr 40 mins

Chapter 14 Exercise 1 - page 134

1. a 0·1 hr b 0·2 hr c 0·4 hr
   d 0·6 hr e 0·15 hr f 0·55 hr
   g 0·9 hr h 0·45 hr i 0·6666.. hr
2. a 0·33 hr b 0·02 hr c 0·98 hr d 0·42 hr
   e 0·32 hr f 0·18 hr g 1·17 hr h 3·42 hr
3. a 3·75 hrs b 2·6 hrs c 1·4 hrs
   d 5·55 hrs e 2·92 hrs f 10·13 hrs
   g 19·47 hrs h 30·17 hrs i 100·05 hrs
4. 18 km
5. a 40 km b 12·5 miles c 3 m d 66 km
6. Sally - 48 km, Simon - 50 km => Simon by 2 km
7. 54 km
8. a 8533 m b 17 m c 12·6 km d 11·25 km
9. 5 km/hr
10. a 30 mph b 80 km/hr c 12000 mph
    d 100 km/hr e 6 km/hr f 3 mph
    g 56000 mph h 5·5 mph i 2·05 m/min

Chapter 14 Exercise 2 - page 136

1. a 24 mins b 18 mins c 33 mins
   d 6 mins e 54 mins f 40 mins
2. 4 hrs 12 mins
3. a 2 hrs 18 mins b 5 hrs 27 mins
   c 14 hrs 15 mins d 0 hrs 45 mins
   e 8 hrs 24 mins f 7 hrs 40 mins
   g 9 hrs 54 mins h 2 hrs 50 mins
   i 15 hrs 42 mins
4. a 3·8 hrs b 3 hrs 48 mins
5. a 2·75 hrs b 2 hrs 45 mins
6. a 1 hrs 27 mins b 0 hrs 36 mins
   c 4 hrs 40 mins d 0 hrs 16 $^1/_2$ mins
7. a 24 mins b 18 mins c 1 hr 33 mins
8. a 5 m/sec b 18 km/hr
9. a 72 km/hr b 180 km/hr
   c 1440 km/hr d 45 km/hr
10. van 50·4 km/hr is slightly faster
11. Cat - 90 km/hr, Greyhound - 60 km/hr
    Horse - 72 km/hr => Big Cat is fastest
12. 41·9 km

Chapter 14 Exercise 3 - page 138

1. 2330
2. a 37·58 km/hr
   b 9·90 secs => 0·32 secs slower than Bolt
3. 6 km
4. 45 mins + 1 hr = 1 hr 45 mins -> 9·45 pm
5. a 16 hrs 12 mins b No. 0015 in morning
   c 16 hrs 12 mins + 1 hr 45 mins + 50 mins
   + 1 hr 25 mins + 1 hr 35 mins = 21 hrs 47 mins
   => 2225 + 21 hrs 47 mins = 2012 + 2 hrs
   => arrives at 2212 the next night.
6. a 30 km/hr b 40 km/hr
7. 64 cm
8. a 64 hrs 45 mins b 0445 on Thursday
   c 450 mph
9. 1·65 km
10. 4 hours 41 minutes and 20 seconds
11. 8.34 am
12. a Rabbit - 5 m/sec, fox - 6·66.... m/sec
    Rabbit time = 16 secs, Fox time = 18 secs
    Rabbit makes it with 2 seconds to spare
    b Need to cover the 120 m in 16 secs or less
    => fox needs to run at at least = 7·5 m/sec
    => fox needs to run a 27 m/sec or greater
13. a 340 ÷ 50 = 6 hrs 48 mins
    12.20 + 6 hrs 48 mins = 1908 which is before the latest time of 7.10 pm. => YES
    b Speed = 60 mph => time = 5 hrs 40 mins
    latest arrival time = 10.40 pm
    latest leaving time = 5 pm
14. a 1 hour 18 minutes 36 seconds
    b 10000 ÷ (3·14 x 0·8) = 3981 approx
    c 16·22 km/hr
15. 2 237 760 km

Answers to Chapter 15 (page 143)

Chapter 15 Revision Exercise - page 143

1. a 9 b 1 c 10 d 7·42
2. a 13 cm b 20 cm
3. a 24 cm b 5·66 cm
4. 16·1 m
5. 450 cm

Chapter 15 Exercise 1 - page 144

1. 54 cm²
2. 21·66 cm
3. a 89·3 cm b 341·6 cm²
4. 17
5. a 84 cm² b 48 cm
6. a 10·3 cm b 31·9 cm c 53·4 cm²
7. a 36 m b £495
8. 61·9 km
9. 21·5 m
10. a 13500 cm²
    b 15300 cm² => 135 : 153 = 45 : 51 = 15 : 17
11. 1·755 m²
12. If it is a RAT, $10^2 + 15^2$ should = 20^2 It doesn't
13. Max dist = $\sqrt{(8{\cdot}8^2 + 5{\cdot}5^2)} + 8{\cdot}8 + 5{\cdot}5 = 24{\cdot}7$ km. OK
14. 21·3 metres
15. 10·606 km = 10606 metres

Answers to Chapter 16 (page 149)

Chapter 16 Revision Exercise - page 149

1. a $^{120}/_{300}$ b $^2/_5$
2. a $^1/_{10}$ b $^1/_{11}$ c Viscount
3. 0·06
4. $^{2·5}/_{5·2}$ = 0·48 which is ok.
5. Roof = 0·7, porch = 0·15 => Roof steeper by 0·55

Chapter 16 Exercise 1 - page 150

1. a 6·44 m b grad = 0·14 => just safe
2. a 104 cm b 0·706 c Yes, - just
3. a Ramp 1 - 0·22, Ramp 2 - 0·28 b Ramp 2
4. a 3·66 m b No since gradient = 1·69 (> 1·5)
5. a grad = 0·064 which is less than 0·065. => ok
   b 25·05 metres
6. a grad = 0·045 => is less than minimum of 0·05
   Tell pilot to rise by to least 180 metres
   b 3603 metres => 51·5 seconds
7. a grad = 0·35. OK. b 18·0 metres
8. a 2·21 to 2·99 b grad = 2·9 => ok
9. a Yes since *h* = 600 mm b Yes, grad = 1 in 15
10. a grad = 65/76 = 0·86 - unsafe
    b 474 metres approximately

Answers to Chapter 17 (page 154)

Chapter 17 Revision Exercise - page 154

1. a 120 cm² b 34 m² c 880 mm²
2. a 2900 cm² b 875 mm²
3. a 120 cm² b 625 cm² c 247 cm²
   d 168 cm² e 600 cm² f 1050 mm²
   g 250 cm² h 201 cm² i 706·5 mm²

Chapter 17 Exercise 1 - page 156

1. 28·26 cm²
2. a 50·2 cm² b 380 cm² c 133 cm²
3. a 633 mm² b 491 cm² c 0·785 m²
4. a 113 cm² b 19·6 m² c 1260 mm²
5. a 91·6 cm² b 13·8 cm²
   c 3420 mm² d 0·196 m²

Chapter 17 Exercise 2 - page 157

1. a 100·5 cm² b 39·25 mm² c 7·60 m²
2. a 63·6 cm² b 314 cm² d 0·50 m²
3. a 92·1 cm² b 178·3 cm²
   c 144·6 cm² d 89·6 cm²
4. 8478 cm²
5. 55·04 cm²
6. a 530 mm² b 35·3 m²
7. D = 30 cm, Vol = 10800 cm³
8. a 165·6 m² b Area to paint = 331·2 m²
   => cost = 17 x £19·95 = £339·15
9. Min area = 415 cm² , Max area = 491 cm²
10. A = 68 m² , B = 68·25 m² , C = 68·13 m² => B
11. a 90·28 m² b 90 x £1·80 + £105 = £267
12. Triangle height = 10·4 cm => Area = 62·4 cm²
    Circle area = 200·96 cm² =>
    Triangle, as a %age of circle = 31·5% => Yes - ok

Answers to Chapter 18 (page 161)

Chapter 18 Revision Exercise - page 161

1. 66
2. a 7 rolls b £199
3. a 96 b 800
4. 16·625 m²
5. £9975 - Yes

Chapter 18 Exercise 1 - page 162

1. a 16 b 800 c 120
2. a 60 b 1000 c 5060
3. 600
4. 7500
5. a 500 b 45 x 500 = 22500
6. a 135 b A (32) B (30) => A
7. a 140 b 2·45 m³ c Yes 150 crates
8. 5 385 600 dolls

Chapter 18 Exercise 2 - page 165

1. a right tips down b balanced
   c right tips down
2. a 24 b 24 c 8 d 8
3. a 384 b 96 c 8 d 512
4. 10100
5. £14 000
6. a C b C c B d B
7. Roughly :-

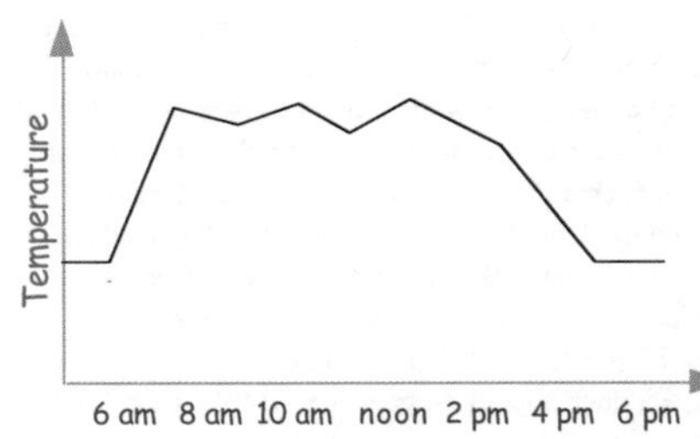

8. a Fill 3 L and pour into 5 L
   Fill 3 L again and pour till 5 L is full
   You are left with 1 L in the 3 L containers
   b Fill 5 L and pour 3 L into 3 L container
   Empty 3 L
   Pour remaining 2 L from 5 L into 3 L
   Fill 5 L again
   Pour 1 L into 3 L till it is full
   You are left with 4 L in 5 L container

9. a

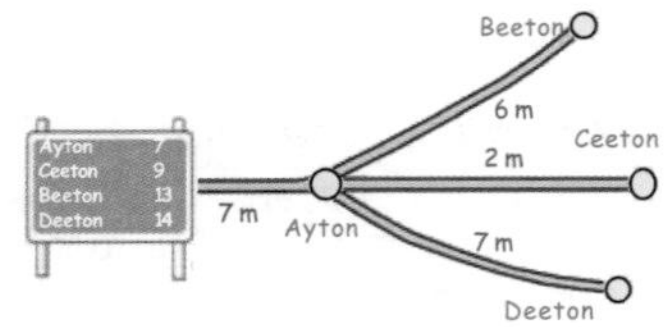

b

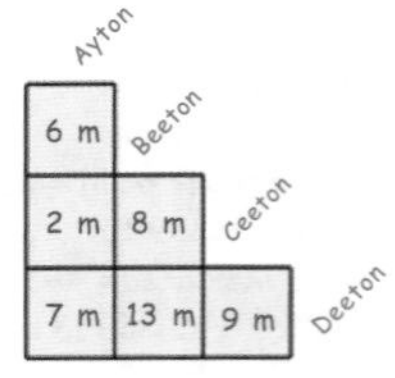

10. 95
11. Various answers

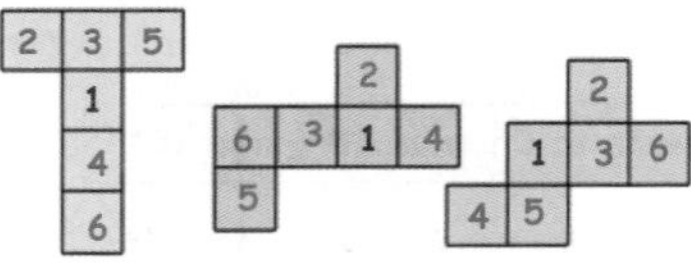

12. a £720 b £920 c £7000
13. Fence => 17 sections = £314·50
    Turf => 72·26 m^2 => 73 x 22 = £1606
    Total = £314·50 + £1606 + £650 = £2570·50
    Add on VAT => £2570·50 + £514·10 = £3084·60
14. Diam = 9·22 cm => Area = 45·73 cm^2
15. a $1/4$ b $1/4$ c $1/2$
16. a $1/8$ b $3/8$ c $3/4$
17. a see diagram b (i) $1/36$ (ii) $1/12$
18. a 216 possibilities b (i) $1/216$ (ii) $5/108$

Chapter 18 Exercise 3 - page 168

1. Jenna - Create database then tidy office which will take her (4 hrs 30 mins)
   Jemma can File folders, restock and do inventory which takes (3 hrs 45 mins)
   So all can be done in 4 hrs 30 mins
2. 4 hrs 46 mins 30 seconds
3. Potatoes 8:03 -> Carrots 8:18 -> Steak 8:19
   Sauce 8:21 -> Brocolli 8:22 -> Salad 8:27
4. Green circle (3) => red ellipse (3) => wait (3) mins till green dries => red triangle (3) => blue square (3) => blue rectangle (3) => then wait (4) mins till it dries = 22 minutes
5. Level ground (3 hr) => build frame for concrete (3 hrs) => pour concrete (30 mins) => Build g'house frame while concrete is setting (8 hrs) => secure to concrete (15 mins) = Place glass in frame (2 hrs) =. Total = 16 hrs 45 mins
6. paint (1 hr 30 mins) => replant (1 hr) => Mow lawn (15 mins) => part edge lawn (15 mins) => paint again (1 hr 30 mins) => finish edging (30 mins) => total time 5 hours
   Gardner should be paid 5 x £12·85 = £64·25

Answers to Chapter 19 (page 173)

Chapter 19 Revision Exercise - page 173

1. 900 cm^3
2. 5 cm
3. a 5000 cm^3 b 5000 ml c yes - 1·11 gals
4. 1360 cm^3
5. a 30 cm^2 b 330 cm^3
6. No - only 5·652 litres
7. a 11 cm b 5 cm

Chapter 19 Exercise 1 - page 174

1. 35 cm^3
2. 110 cm^3
3. 380 cm^3
4. a 225 cm^2 b 1500 cm^3
5. big - 864 cm^3 small - 500 cm^3 => 364 cm^3
6. a 4 cm b 12 cm^2 c 40 cm^3
7. 314 cm^3
8. a 25·12 cm^3 b 603 cm^3 c 159 cm^3
9. a 314 cm^2 b 15 cm
10. 9770 kg (approx) or 9·77 tonnes
11. a 2035 cm^3 b just over 2 litres (2·035)
12. a 1130·4 cm^3 b 565·2 cm^3
    c total vol of shape = 1695·6 cm^3
    total vol of cube = 1728 cm^3
    yes, with 32·4 cm^3 left over

Chapter 19 Exercise 2 - page 177

1. 7235 cm^3
2. 14130 cm^3
3. 33493 mm^3
4. 10·3 inches ^{3}
5. a pupil's answer b 4186·66 cm^3
   c 523·33 cm^3 d ... 8 x .....
6. 7065 cm^3
7. a 3617 cm^3 b yes
8. cone = 2198 cm^3 , cuboid = 2200 cm^3
   hemisphere 2093 cm^3
   cuboid holds most and hemisphere least
9. a 1210 cm^3 b 268 cm^3 c 2·21 cm

Chapter 19 Exercise 3 - page 179

1. 264938 cm^3 + 110391 cm^3 = 375329 cm^3
2. 12208 cm^3 + 16956 cm^3 = 29164 cm^3
3. 0·08 m^3 + 0·864 m^3 = 0·944 m^3 x 2 = 1·888 m^3
4. a 502·4 cm^3 b 13990 cm^3
5. 3956·4 cm^3 + 565·2 cm^3 = 4521·6 cm^3
6. 3000 mm^3
7. 1·59 m^3 (1590000 cm^3)
8. V = 602618 cm^3 = 602·6 litres
   needs a further 352·6 litres
9. a 602·88 cm^3 b 348·54 cm^3 which
   is <u>more</u> than half (301·44 cm^3).
10. 10·0 cm
11. a 340·17 cm^3 b 2·89 cm
12. a 123·5 cm^3 b 963·3 grams
13. 5367 cm^3

Answers to Revision C Chapter (page 186)

1. a £377·28 b £9·75
   c £16237 d £427·50
   e £1562·50
2. a £32960 b Abigail - £33587·50
   Abigail earns £2627·50
3. £384
4. a £194 b £101·85
5. a 17160 F b 24450 R c £80 d £120
6. €462
7. £25·20
8. Int = £42 + £84 = £126 => could have got £174
9. a 1·25% b (i) £607·50 (ii) £2430
10. a £87 b £107·25
11. 3 pack - 78p/bot, 5 pack - 76p/bot => 5 pack
12. a Van Man - £49 Cheap/Cheerful - £46 (✓)
    b Van Man - £74·50 Cheap/Cheerful - £80·50
    Better to go with Van Man
13. 76
14. £11
15. 2°C
16. 65 kg
17. a Joan - mode = 2, Abby - mode = 3
    b If you look at mean, Abby - 2, Joan 3 (✓)
18.

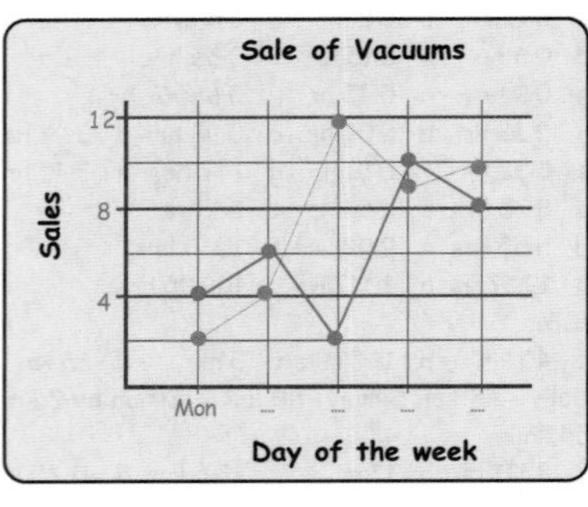

19.

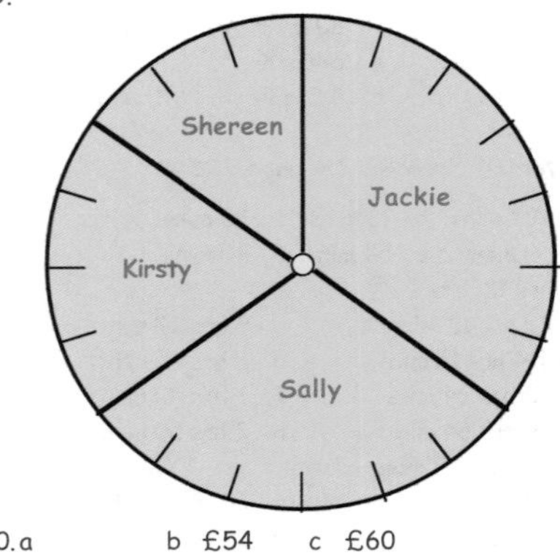

20. a b £54 c £60

3	3 3
4	3 8
5	4 4 4 4
6	0 0 0 5 7 8
7	0 0 6
8	0 0 2

4 | 3 means £43

21. a Correlation (neg) b correlation (pos)
    c Correlation (neg) d none
22. a graph b see line c 80p

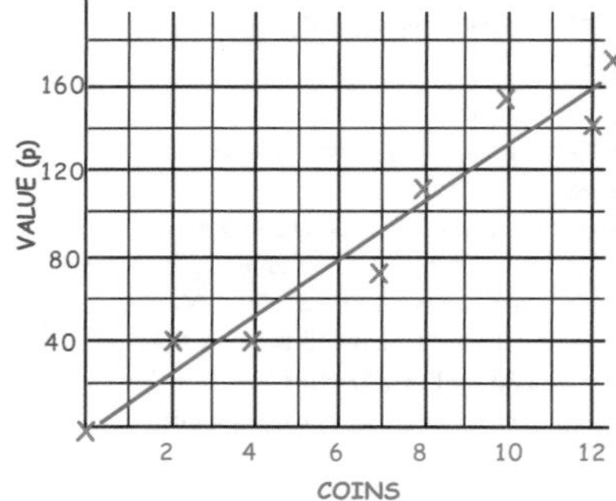

23. $1/3$
24. a $1/4$ b 18
25. P(red) = $1/3$ => (1 in 3) chance of winning
    but you get (3·5 to 1) odds => win in long run.

Answers to Chapter 20 (page 190)

Chapter 20 Revision Exercise - page 190

1. a £430·40 b £14·26 c £16489·20
   d £412·10 e £3004
2. a £23532 b £24384 => Wendy by £852
3. £3852
4. a £213·60 b £93·45
5. £1268·23
6. £19·20 => £512 + £115·20 = £627·20

Chapter 20 Exercise 1 - page 191

1. a £360 b £313·50 c £554·32 d £564·26
2. a £19760 b £42848 c £15900 d £28512
3. a £1650 b £3000 c £3548·88
4. a £562·80 b £731·01 c £970·10
5. £357·85
6. a £324 b £1033·20
7. a £16848 b £53726·40
8. a £266 b £84 c £350
9. £517·75
10. a £424·32 b £22064·64
11. £497·20
12. 2.30 pm
13. £81·60
14. a £1230 b £1920 c £550
15. a £2000 b £14000
16. £19150
17. CARS-R-US => £3000 (✓), CELLCARS => £2900
18. £610·80
19. a (i) £416 (ii) £2511 (iii) £3145·65 (iv) £1375
    b £40000
20. 1·5%
21. 47 hours
22. £300

Chapter 20 Exercise 2 - page 195

1. £2326·25
2. a £14730 b £20490 c £19776
3. a £22386 b £430·50
4. a £3272 b £11928
5. £441
6. a £3246 b £42275
7. £440
8. £14075
9. a £340·71 b £837·15 c £426·63
10. £38·66
11. £300·81
12. £272·29
13. £427·55
14. 30%
15. £10000

Chapter 20 Exercise 3 - page 198

1. £3127·20
2. £3566·80
3. £1496
4. a £3134·40 b £371 c £94·08
5. a £4380 b £24860·55
6. £1823·21
7. a £5956 b £6443 c £14187 d £98643
8. £1105491
9. No - Still owes £10000

Answers to Chapter 21 (page 201)

Chapter 21 Revision Exercise - page 201

1. a £160 b £370 c £14
   d £3265·50 e ¢22 f €750
2. £2·22
3. Compushop £440 (✓), LapTopShop £450
4. Cheaphols £269·50, Hols-R-Us £262·50 (✓)
5. 400 g => £1·05/100 g, 500 g => £1·04/100 g (✓)
6. a 87400 Yen b 6580 Kroner

Chapter 21 Exercise 1 - page 202

1. a £19·20 b £96 c £330
   d £54 e £912 f £3744
2. a £20·16 b £240 c £1032 d £87000
3. a £32 => £6·40 => £38·40
   b £176 => £35·20 => £211·20
4. £283·68
5. a £62·50 b £50·40
6. discount before VAT => £45696
   discount after VAT => £45696 the same
7. £161·40 => No

Chapter 21 Exercise 2 - page 204

1. £276·80
2. a £480 b £3824 c £459·50 d £90
3. a £87 b £150
4. £51
5. £29·20
6. £24·50
7. Cheapcons -£3580 Con-R-Us - £3630
   ConservC0 - £3495 (✓)
8. a £140 b 25%
9. £125
10. a Turf + glass = £475 + 20% = £570 - too dear
    b Med = £360 + £78 = £438 + 20% = £525·60
    plus £20 insurance = £545·60 - YES

Chapter 21 Exercise 3 - page 206

1. £18·60 per month
2. a £32 b £13·30
3. £42 + £24·80 = £66·80
4. a £72·70 b £74·48
5. £90000
6. a £6·10 b £11·40 c £7·70 d £12·90
7. a £38·10 b £12·20

Chapter 21 Exercise 4 - page 207

1. a Profit of £35 b Loss of £11
   c Loss of £988 d Profit of £2·10
   e Loss of £860 f Profit of £14200
2. £75
3. a £612·50 b 12·5%
4. £11·55
5. £386400
6. Loss of £144·50
7. a Jimmy - £15, Jenny - £11·25 => £26·25
   b £25 - £11·25 = £13·75

Chapter 21 Exercise 5 - page 209

1. a £0·65 b €0·90 c 6·20 Yuan
   d 63·86 Ruppees, 1·29 Aus Dollars
   7·84 Kroner 0·93 Swiss Francs

American Dollar (June 2015)	$1 =
British Pound (£)	£0·65
Euro	€0·90
Chinese Yuan	6·20
Indian Rupee	63·86
Australian Dollar	1·29
Norwegian Krone	7·84
Swiss Franc	0·93

2. £520
3. No - needs to take out another €50
4. £390, €405 and 3136 Kroner
5. 1 euro = 1·97 ÷ 1·37 = 1·44 Aus dollars
   => €2000 = 2875·91 Aus dollars
6. €2700 => 18630 Yuan
   $3000 => 19050 Yuan, Yes better by 420 Yuan
7. France (€16500) - Norway (€16671) -
   China (€17414) - UK (€17741) approximately
8. a (i) €1·26 (ii) €1·31 b April
   c €28 d generally rising in value
9. Cost in England = €16875
   France = €14250 + €2422·50 + €550 = 17222·50
   Buying from England is a better deal
10. Worse => at $1·95 I get £230·77
    at $2·05, I get £219·51
11. a Sweden = £47319/yr , USA = £49367/yr
    UK = £45000/yr => America has best offer
    b It is only a 6 months contract. No guarantee
12. a 63·90 b 15795 Rupees
    c (i) 382·56 (ii) $448 (iii) 260 (iv) £50·81

Chapter 21 Exercise 6 - page 212

1. Safety and to gain some Interest
2. £120
3. a £12480 b £816 c £3312 d £28907
4. a 2·8% b £196
5. a 5·55% b 2·62% c 4·49% d 4·91%
6. Fran

Chapter 21 Exercise 7 - page 213

1. £74·92
2. £341·88
3. a £18810, £19750·50, £20797·28
   b £2797·28 c 15·54%
   d Yes - would end up with £2837·25 instead
4. Trustbank - Interest = £1119·35 (✓)
   Bundabank - Interest = £1118·34

Chapter 21 Exercise 8 - page 214

1. a 6·5% b £260 & £4260 c £355
2. a £59·80 b £59·15
3. Total payable = £1951·20 ÷ 12 = £162·60 - NO
4. a Int for 1 yr = £162·50,
   b Int/6 mths = £81·25 = > tot due = £2581·25
   c Payments = £430·21 per month
5. a 1st Option => £730/month for 12 months
   2nd option => 1390·67/month for 6 months
   b Depends on their finances. Option 2 is more expensive per month but loan is paid off quicker
   c Much more expensive at over 15% per year
6. Amount to pay back = £982·480 ÷ 12 = £81·90
   No - his £75 maximum is not enough.
7. $1{\cdot}025^{6}$ = 1·1597 x £3000 = £3479·08 owed.
   Int = 7·8% added on => now owes £3750·45
   Has to make 12 monthly payments of £312·54
8. Option 1 => 24 x £210 = £5040 ÷ 12 = £420
   Option 2 => 4000 x 1·175 = £4700 ÷ 18 = £261·11
   Option 3 => 4000 x 1·125 = £4500 ÷ 12 = £375
   a Lowest monthly payment comes from Opt 2
   b Overall cheapest is Option 3
   c Possibly Option 2. Dearer than Option 3 but monthly payments, though over 18 mths, are less and this may suit her budget better.

Answers to Chapter 22 (page 218)

Chapter 22 Revision Exercise - page 218

1. a £1·85 b £1·70 c Container (✓)
2. 4 pack - 60p, 6 pack - 58p, 10 pack - 57p (✓)
3. a Woodcutters - £92 (✓) , SawAway - £93
   b Yes by £2·50
4. Combined price is £1860, Individual = £1925
   She is better changing and will save £65

Chapter 22 Exercise 1 - page 219

1. Park = £4·50/kg, River = £4·37/kg
   Duke = £4·60/kg River got better deal
2. £7·00/100 ml, £7·10(5)/100 ml, £7·02/100 ml
   The 700 ml bottle worked out cheapest
3. a McCall - £1·15, Doddies - £1·23,
   Rose Garden - £1·12(5) => Rose garden best
   b Yes - works out at £1 each
4. Boutons - £1·55/100 Button Hole - £1·52/100
   Button.com - £1·51(5)/100 => Button.com is best
5. Tenerife Hotel - £232/night
   Lanzarote Palace - £230/night
   Hotel Gran Canaria - £232·70/night
   Cheapest, taxi transfer, closer to Glasgow A'port
6. JR Roofing - £180 Slaters - £182·50
   Roof Man - £184·60 => JR Roofing is cheapest

7. a RG Media - £195 Stirgin - £190
   Sunbox - £185 => Sunbox is best deal
   c Yes since they have the cheapest rate/hr
8. 12 months - £1248 24 months - £1260
   36 months - £1307 => 12 months is cheapest
9. Xchange - £200·76 Money House -£203·85
   For Ex - £202·59 => Money House best by £3·09
10. a Loan Hire - cheapest rate
    b £2867·50 c £277·50
11. a £125 + £140 + £20 + £40 + £85 = £410
    b Cost = £525·75 => £115·75 dearer

Answers to Chapter 23 (page 223)

Chapter 23 Revision Exercise - page 223

1. £220
2. a £1177 + £155 = £1332
   b Savings = £1332 - £1262·50 = £69·50
   c various (cigarettes !)
3. a £1008 b £84 c No

Chapter 23 Exercise 1 - page 224

1. a No b £145
2. 5 more weeks
3. Sophie - 10 weeks, Dan - 7 weeks
   Dan will reach his target first by 3 weeks
4. a 8 months b 4 months
5. a short of £5 b £4/day for lunch

Chapter 23 Exercise 2 - page 225

1. a £134 b £454 c £272
2.

Monthly Budget Planner Sheet for Eve Jones	
INCOME	EXPENDITURE
£750	£55
£134	£45
£454	£108
£272	£100
	£80
	£80
	£320
	£350
	£70
	£51
	£15
	£60
Total = £1610	Total = £1334
~~Over/~~ Under Spend (Income - Expenditure)	£ £516

3. £276
4. Council Tax, Electricity, Car Loan, Credit Card, Gas, Rent, Car Insurance, TV Licence (Answer may vary)
5. £56
6. +£100 per month => Yes, if she has the time
7. Varous answers => need children's school clothes, gas during winter period higher etc

Chapter 23 Exercise 3 - page 226

1. a £1120 b If you guarantee not to touch your savings during the years, you may get a higher rate of interest.
2. a Mighty Monthly
   b She has £100 so investing in this account gives her 2·5% instead of 1·5%
3. a (i) £400 savings => £405
   (ii) £405 + £720 = £1125 => £1139·06
   b Interest is taxed
4. £645->£765->£885 ->£1005->£1125->£1139·06
5. a ISASAVER b Gives 4% interest, it is tax free, but she needs to leave it for 3 years or she may face a penalty charge.
6. £899·89
7. a £150 b yes c £155·44
8. a Initial Savings - £93·75
   BAC - £112·50
   Thrifty - £150
   b Initial Savings - £2791·93
   BAC - £3115·45
   Thrifty - £4477·11
   c BAC Bank Ltd - Thrifty Credit need 10 years but Alfie going to Uni in 7 years time
   d Could put half (£1250) in BAC account and other half in Thrifty which gives higher rate She might not need all her savings right away when Alfie goes to Uni. + Finn may go to Uni.

Chapter 23 Exercise 4 - page 228

1. £176
2. a 24 months - £480·24
   36 months - £717·72
   60 months - £1206
   b They must take it out over 60 months as they only have £176 left each month
3. a £101·96 b £5 c £14·85
   d £175 - £101·96 => £73·04 extra
4. a £447·20
   b possibly - she could have saved up instead or taken a short term bank loan.
5. £1684 + £145·10 + £5 + £14·90 = £1849
6. Much tighter with only £11 left each month
7. a 10% b (i) overdrawn (ii) £175
8. a 24% b 1·75 x £124 = £217
   c No - Income = £1860 + £150 = £2010
   Expenditure = £1849 + £217 = £2067.
   Still short by £57
9. Bank loan might have been possible with cheaper interest rate
10. Various depending on their need for a car or not - possibly a cheaper food processor etc. - Discuss

Answers to Chapter 24 (page 231)

Chapter 24 Revision Exercise - page 231

1. 76
2. 12 g
3. 2°C
4. 183 cm
5. a mode = 28, median = 40
   b median - gives a better feel for the "middle"
6. a mean is only 25 b 36
7. a Claire - 5, Joyce - 6
   b Mode makes it look like Joyce drank more but if you use the means of 6 for Claire and 5 for Joyce, it shows Claire drank more

Chapter 24 Exercise 1 - page 232

1. a 6 b 15 c 0·7 d -4
2. a 6 b 44 c 2·8 d 133
3. a 17·5 b 0·65 c 0 d 5
4. a 8 b 1·8 c 1124 d $^3/_4$
5. a 55 b mean- 11, median - 5, mode - 2
   c median - gives better picture of "middle" and disregards 57 and the 2's
6. a mean - 6, median - 3,
   mode - 3, range - 15
   b mean - 5·3, median - 5·4,
   mode - 5·4, range - 3·4
   c mean - 65·5, median - 65·5,
   mode - 67, range - 4
   d mean - 1, median - -1,
   mode - -5, range - 23
7. a 23 kg b mode - 45 kg, median - 53 kg
   c median gives better sense of the "middle"
8. a mean - 7·8, median - 8, mode - 8 b 4
9. a mean - 12·9, range - 27
   b mean - 38·5, range - 99
10. a mean = 1·47, mode = 1·23, Median = 1·57
    so all 3 could be deemed to be correct
    b the 1·23 gives no idea of the "middle"
11. 10·5 kg
12. 17
13. a Vean - 16·6 - Higher
    b 3·6

Chapter 24 Exercise 2 - page 236

1. a/b median = 11 c 5
   d Q1 = 9 d Q3 = 12
2. a Q1 = 3, Median = 7, Q3 = 9
   b Q1 = 3·7, Median = 4·2, Q3 = 5·0
   c Q1 = 24, Median = 31, Q3 = 36
3. a 32nd b Q1 = 16th and Q3 = 48th

Chapter 24 Exercise 3 - page 238

1. a Q1 = 14, Med = 23, Q3 = 25 =>
   Quartile Range = 11, SIQR = 5·5
   b Q1 = 3·0, Med = 3·6, Q3 = 4·3 =>
   Quartile Range = 1·3, SIQR = 0·65
   c Q1 = 112, Med = 121, Q3 = 134 =>
   Quartile Range = 22, SIQR = 11
2. a 0, 0, 1, 1, 1, 2, 2, 2, 2, 2, 3, 3, 3, 4, 4, 4, 4, 4, 5, 5, 6, 6, 6, 8, 9
   b mean = 3·48, median = 3, modes = 2 and 4
   c range = 9, SIQR = 1·5
3. range 9, SIQR = $^3/_4$ => shows a much narrower spread of values when the 1 and 10 are discarded

Chapter 24 Exercise 4 - page 239

1. a Q1 = 6·5, Med = 7·5, Q3 = 9·5 b

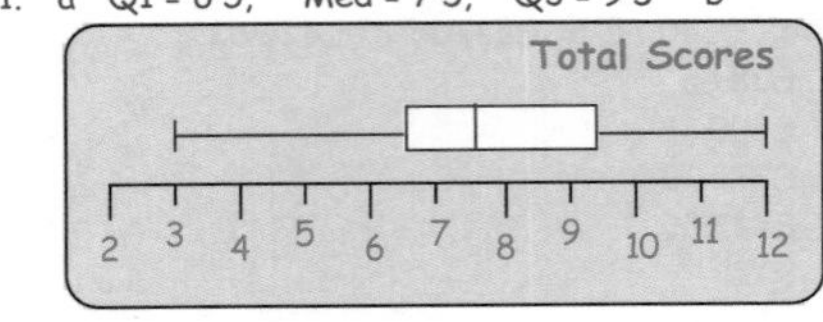

2. a Q1 = 40, Med = 52·5, Q3 = 85 b

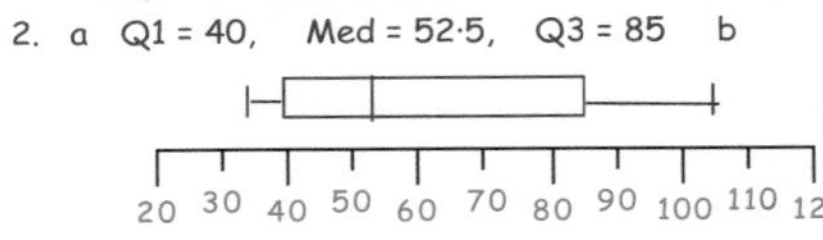

3. a Q1 = 14, Med = 18, Q3 = 22 b

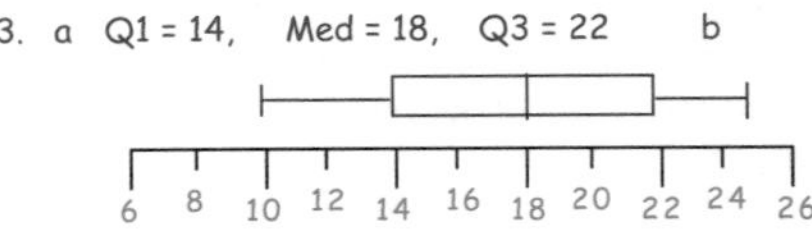

4. a Q1 = 8, Med = 10, Q3 = 14
   b Q1 = 10, Med = 14, Q3 = 16 c

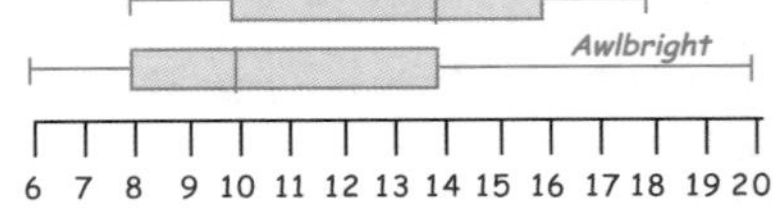

   d Osiris' bulbs on average appear to last longer and looking at the range, they are more consistent
5. a men Q1 = 10, Med = 14, Q3 = 18
   women Q1 = 6·5, Med = 11, Q3 = 14
   b

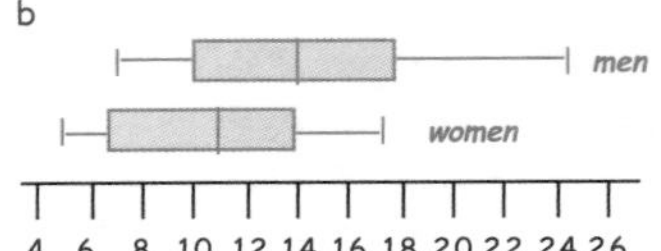

   c women weaker but more consistent
6. a Flyjet Q1 = 63, Med = 70, Q3 = 75
   Airbee Q1 = 61·5, Med = 65, Q3 = 67

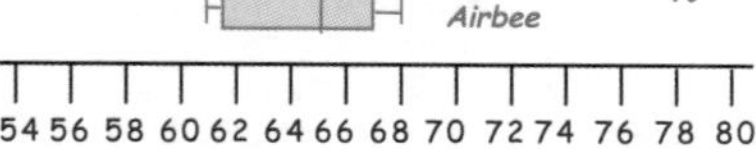

b Airbee have the better flying times and are more consistent with the (SIQ) range

7. Rod's average distance of 90 (median) appears to be the best with Bob's 55 yards the worse. Rod also seems the more consistent with a SIQR of 10 yards , compared to Ted's 22·5 and Bob's 12·5. Bob appears to be the novice, Ted most erratic and Rod the more consistent

Chapter 24 Exercise 5 - page 241

1. a mean = 5 b SD = 2·45
2. a mean = 4 b SD = 2·39
3. a mean = 37 grams b SD = 9·13 grams
4. a mean = 8 minutes b SD = 4·74 minutes
5. a mean = 28 m b SD = 5·32 m
6. mean = 8·0 cm, SD = 2·51 cm
7. a mean of both is 18
   b SD for Donald = 2·61, SD for Graeme = 16·4
   c Donald is the more consistent, but Graeme managed to get some very high (and some very low) scores.
8. a mean = 7·75 SD = 3·5
   b mean = 35·83 SD = 6·31
   c mean = 7·94 SD = 2·33
   d mean = 127·86 SD = 7·10
9. all answers the same.

Answers to Chapter 25 (page 245)

Chapter 25 Revision Exercise - page 245

1. a (i) Jim (ii) Will (iii) Bruce
   b yes - strong positive c about 37 inches
2. a strong positive b positive
   c no connection d negative
3. a

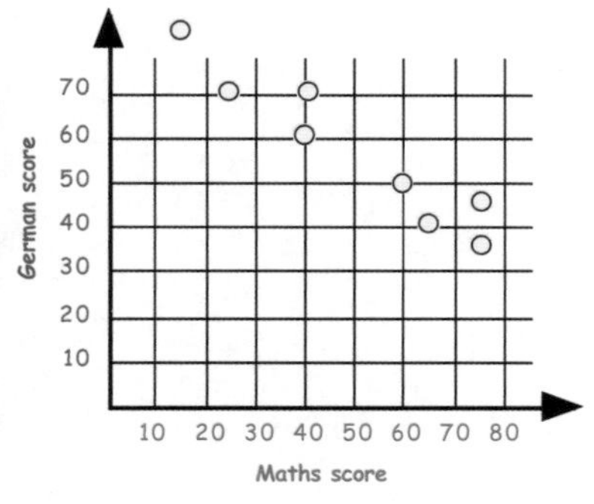

b the higher Maths mark => the lower German

c 55-60

Chapter 25 Exercise 1 - page 246

1. Lou (25 kg, 130 cm) Don (20 kg, 150 cm)
   Sam (40 kg, 150 cm) Alex (50 kg, 140 cm)
   Nick (35 kg, 165 cm) Joe (50 kg, 160 cm)
   Tim (60 kg, 170 cm)
2. a (i) Mary (ii) Toni (iii) Pat (iv) Pat
   b Mary (3, 15 kg) Toni (4, 10 kg)
   Ali (6, 15 kg) Mark (8, 20 kg)
   Tom (9, 25 kg) Shaz (10, 23 kg)
   Pat (12, 30 kg)
   c Mark

3.

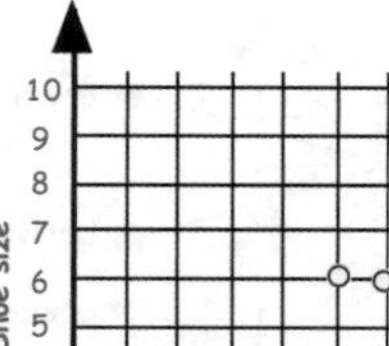
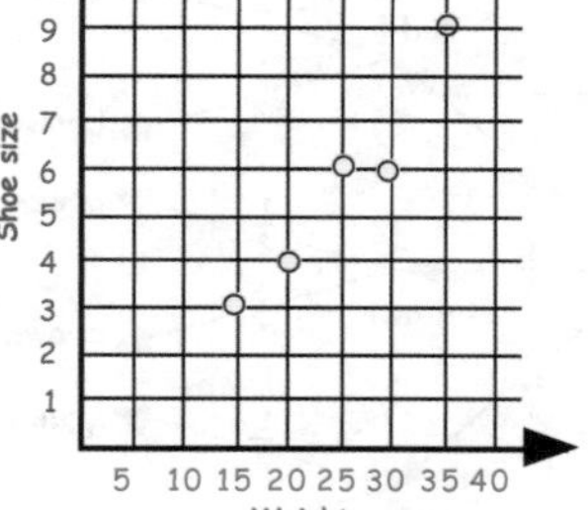

4. a (i) and (ii)

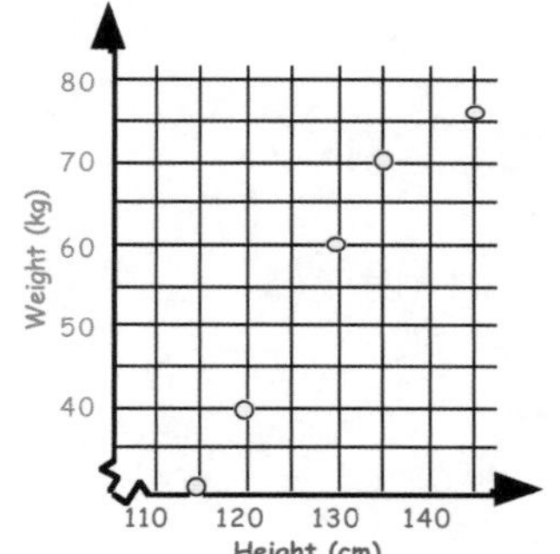

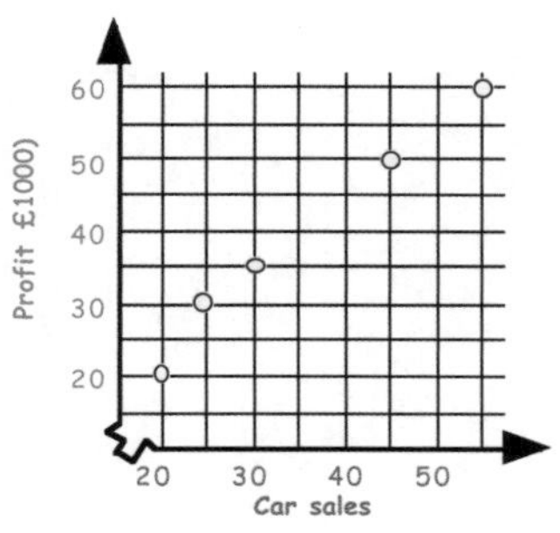

b 140 cm and 73 kg c 25 - 30

5. a b higher English -> higher maths

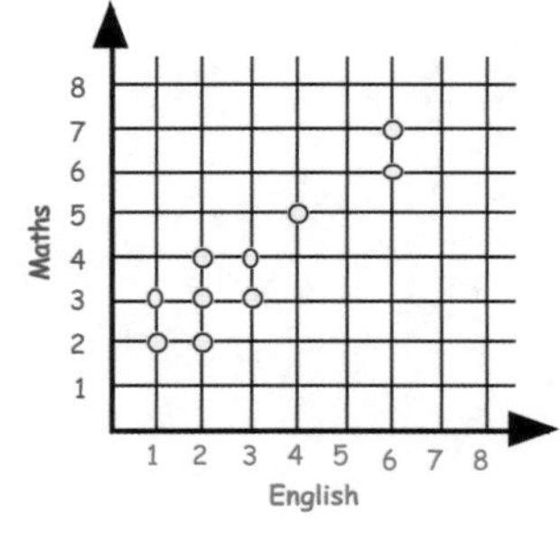

6 a b 5°C c 1·5 d yes (neg)

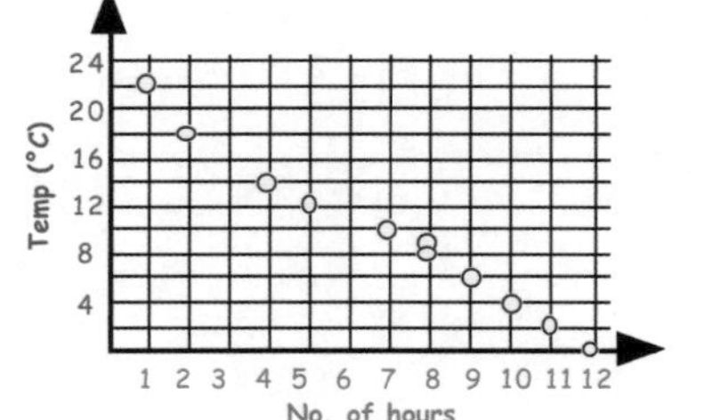

Chapter 25 Exercise 2- page 249

1. a (i) Lou (ii) Bob (iii) Bill (iv) Lee
   b yes c d 6

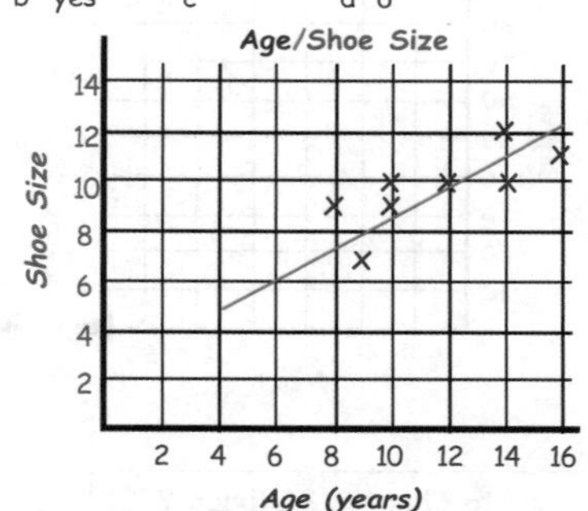

2. 4 hours
3. a yes (positive) b yes (positive)
   c yes (negative) d none
4. various
5. a/b c 45-50

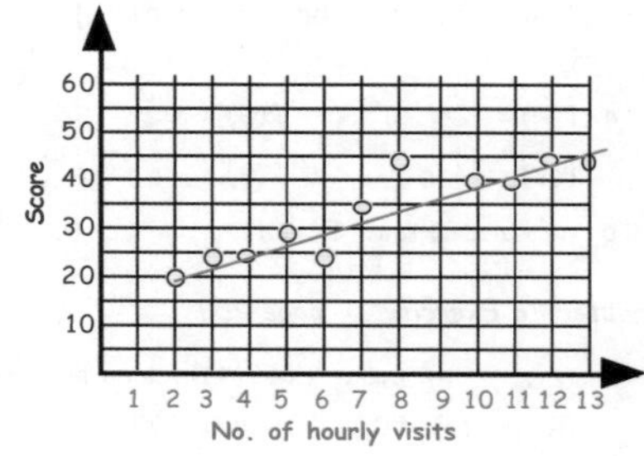

6. a/b c 11 kg d Month 9 & 1·5 kg

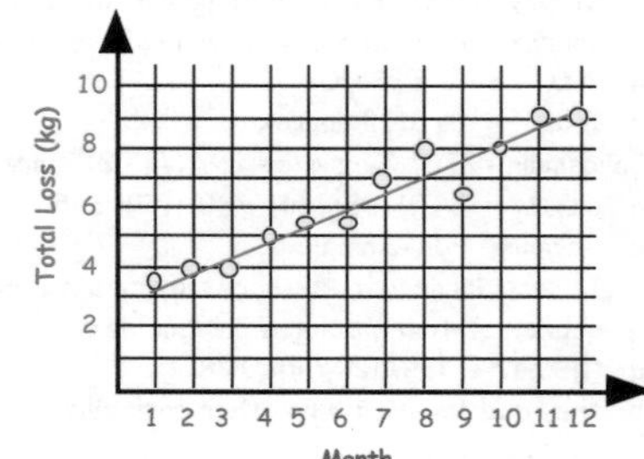

7. a (i)/(ii) (iii) 19 m

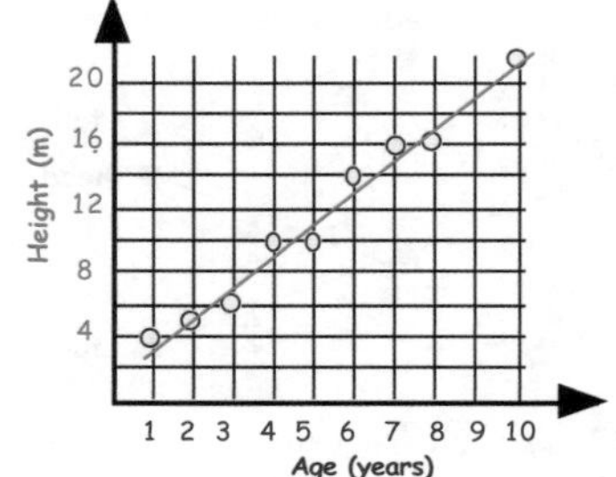

b (i)/(ii) (iii) 40 - 45

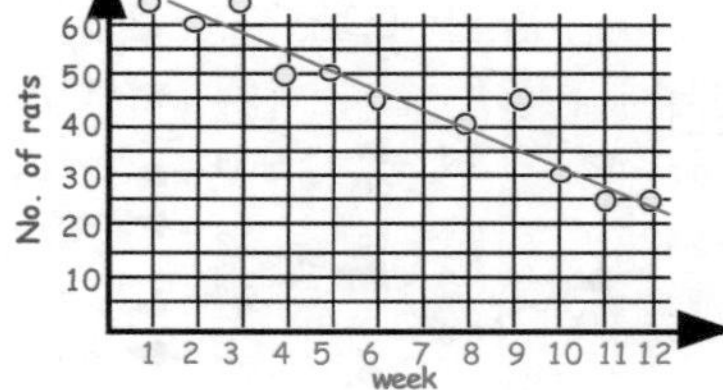

c (i)/(ii) (iii) 73

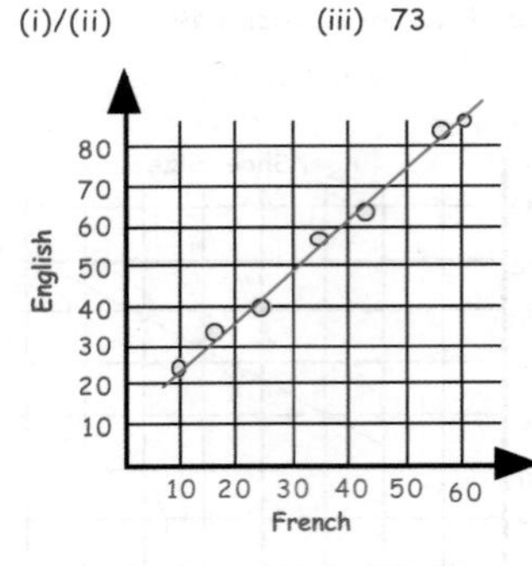

Chapter 26 Revision Exercise - page 252

1. a (i) $1/12$ (ii) $1/3$ (iii) $5/12$ (iv) $5/6$

   b $1/3$

2. a $1/50$ b $3/5$ (better than evens)
3. 95%
4. a P(R) = $2/5$ P(G) = $1/4$

   P(Y) = $3/20$ P(B) = $1/5$

   b no - biased towards red c 60

Chapter 26 Exercise 1 - page 253

1. a $1/12$ b no c in the long term only

   d (i) 5 (ii) 50 (iii) 1000000
2. a 6 b no

   c Statistics is not an accurate science.
   It only states that in the long run, in April approximately on 6 days it will rain.
3. a 200 b £83310
4. a 170 b 8123 approx
5. Longsmuir - 270, Tensville - 297 (√) - 27 more
6. a 0·003 b (i) 936 (ii) 780 (iii) 345

   c Various - For example :-
   In some larger cities, there may be a higher chance of there being a car accident
7. a (i) 0·42 (ii) 0·12 (iii) 0·28

   b they add to give 1=> no other possibility
8. a (i) $1/3$ (ii) $1/2$ b

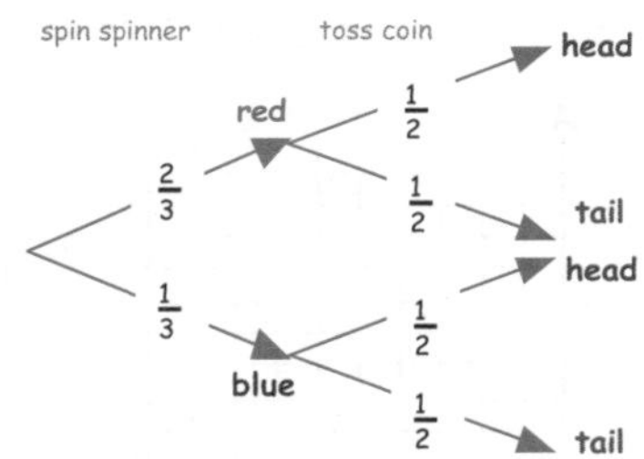

   c (i) $1/3$ (ii) $1/3$ (iii) $1/6$ (iv) $1/6$
9. a 0·2 b c 0·512 d 0·488

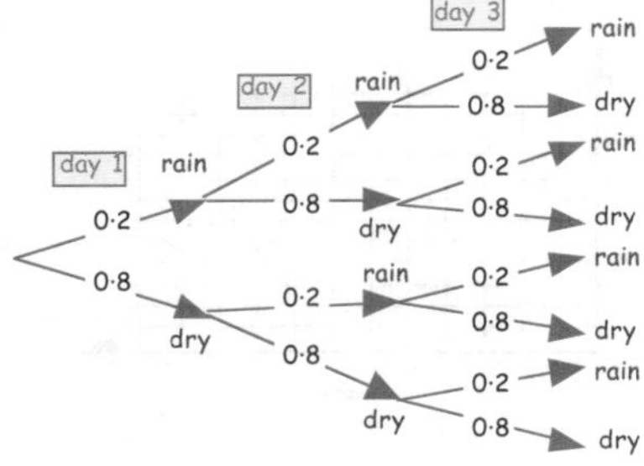

10. a b $1/6$

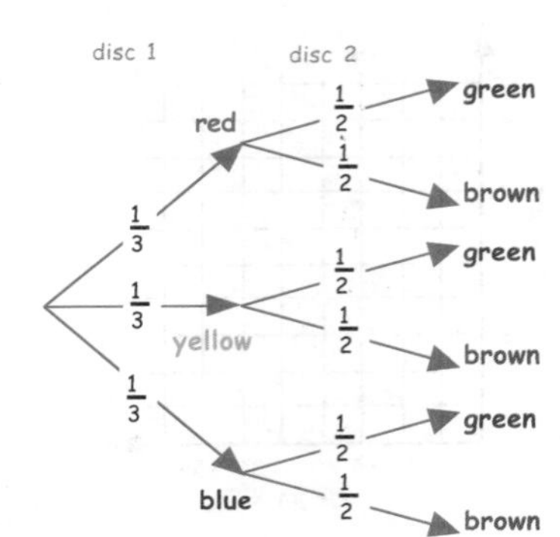

§